2nd Edition

CONCEPTS OF
CHEMICAL DEPENDENCY

2nd Edition

CONCEPTS OF
CHEMICAL DEPENDENCY

Harold E. Doweiko

Brooks/Cole Publishing Company
Pacific Grove, California

I(T)P ™ The trademark ITP is used under license.

 A CLAIREMONT BOOK

Brooks/Cole Publishing Company
A Division of Wadsworth, Inc.

Printed in the United States of America

10 9 8 7 6 5 4 3 2

Library of Congress Cataloging-in-Publication Data
Doweiko, Harold E., [date]
    Concepts of chemical dependency / Harold E. Doweiko. — 2nd ed.
        p.   cm.
    Includes bibliographical references and index.
    ISBN 0-534-19884-8
    1. Substance abuse. I. Title
    RC564.D68   1993   92-33225
    362.29—dc20   CIP

Sponsoring Editor: *Claire Verduin*
Editorial Associate: *Gay C. Bond*
Production Editor: *Kirk Bomont*
Manuscript Editor: *Ann Mirels*
Interior and Cover Design: *Roy R. Neuhaus*
Cover Photo: *Comstock Inc./Michael Stuckey*
Art Coordinator: *Lisa Torri*
Interior Illustration: *Graphic Arts*
Typesetting: *Kachina Typesetting, Inc.*
Cover Printing: *Phoenix Color Corporation*
Printing and Binding: *The Maple Press, Inc.*

To Jan, for everything

PREFACE

I n the three years since the first edition of *Concepts of Chemical Dependency* was published, a number of people have taken the time to let me know their feelings about the text. Their comments addressed both the writing style and the accuracy of the content. This thoughtful feedback was of considerable use to me in planning the current edition.

The need for a revised edition was clear, considering the dramatic changes we have witnessed in the field of substance abuse over the short span of three years. While evidence would suggest that the latest wave of drug abuse peaked in the mid-1980s, recent bumper crops of opium poppies, record supplies of heroin, and higher levels of purity for "street" heroin all point toward the possibility of a new wave of heroin abuse in the next few years.

A wealth of new information has been included in this edition to better prepare the reader for the drug world of the mid-1990s. For example, there is information on "ice," a smokable form of methamphetamine that only began to surface when the first edition went to press. There is an entirely new chapter on the abuse of anabolic steroids, as well as expanded sections on the impact of drug abuse on children and adolescents and on drug abuse during pregnancy.

Each chapter in the original manuscript was reviewed and revised as necessary in an effort to produce a totally up-to-date new edition. A new chapter exploring the relationship between crime and drug abuse was included in the current manuscript in response to requests from faculty and students for information about this complex topic. Chapter 16 on the medical model of addiction was completely rewritten to include research findings suggesting that the dopamine D_2 receptor gene is associated with alcoholism. Chapter 17 was also completely rewritten to include the latest reactions against the disease model of addiction, including research findings suggesting that the dopamine D_2 receptor gene is *not* associated with alcoholism.

Concepts of Chemical Dependency does not offer conclusions where none are possible; rather, contradictory theories and conclusions are presented "as is." Thus, the attempt was made to stimulate critical thinking on the part of the reader. It is my hope that students will be sufficiently challenged by conflicting evidence to undertake their own research projects, possibly uncovering critical new information that would shed new light on the problem of drug abuse.

Acknowledgments

Most certainly, I would like to thank my wife, Jan, for offering to read each chapter as it emerged (and reemerged) from my word processor. I would also like to thank the reviewers who read the manuscript, providing valuable suggestions and insights: Steve Baron, Santa Clara University; Floyd Grant, Rogers State College; Joe Herzstein, Trenton State College; and Linda L. Marshall, Mankato State University.

Harold E. Doweiko

Contents

Chapter 16
THE MEDICAL MODEL OF CHEMICAL ADDICTION
174

Chapter 17
ARE PEOPLE PREDESTINED TO BECOME ADDICTS?
190

Chapter 18
ADDICTION AS A DISEASE OF THE HUMAN SPIRIT
203

Chapter 26

THE PROCESS OF INTERVENTION

304

Chapter 27

THE TREATMENT OF CHEMICAL DEPENDENCY 315

Chapter 28

TREATMENT FORMATS FOR CHEMICAL DEPENDENCY REHABILITATION

332

Chapter 1

FOUNDATIONS

In the era before the introduction of antibiotics, syphilis was called the "Great Imposter." Shortly after an individual was infected, the spirochete *treponema pallidum* would invade any of the various body organs. When symptoms began to appear, they would vary widely depending on the age, sex, and race of the individual; the particular part of the body most heavily involved in the infectious process; and the current stage of the infection.

Diagnosis of syphilis was difficult, often requiring an element of detective work on the part of the physician. During the initial stages, syphilis would frequently leave little or no outward sign of infection. In many advanced cases, it mimicked the symptoms of other diseases, adding to the difficulty of diagnosis. When left untreated, between 5% and 10% of those persons infected went on to develop an organic brain syndrome known as *general paresis* (Hutchinson & Hook, 1990; Sagar & McGuire, 1991).

Although modern antibiotics have brought syphilis under control, there is a lesson to be learned from the early struggle against this disease; namely, to understand the actual cause of observed symptoms, one must look beneath the surface. In many cases, syphilis was able to masquerade as something else. Unless the physician had actively ruled out syphilis, valuable time might have been spent treating the patient for the wrong condition.

Chemical dependency, in all of its forms, is very much like syphilis in this sense. It, too, can express itself in different ways according to a given set of factors. These include the specific drug in question; the length of time the person has been addicted; the person's overall health; and his or her financial, social, and emotional resources. Consider the case of two amphetamine addicts—one is independently wealthy; the other, unemployed. Although their patterns of addiction will differ, both are equally addicted to amphetamines.

When confronted with a new case, many professionals are unlikely to probe beneath the surface problem of depression, suicidal tendencies, spouse abuse, or the sudden onset of hallucinations, in an effort to find out whether or not the person is using chemicals. Professionals who have worked in the field of chemical dependency for any length of time often share stories of addicts who managed to keep their addiction hidden for months, if not years, while in therapy for other "problems."

Substance abuse tends to hide behind a wall of various problems that are, in fact, complications resulting from the drug use itself. In this sense, the addictive disorders are "imposters." And, unfortunately, many mental health professions have adopted a head-in-the-sand philosophy that ignores various signs that addiction may exist in troubled families, or that addiction may be involved in cases of depression or in a range of other human problems.

In recent years, however, there has been a growing awareness that many of the problems encountered by human service and health care professionals are either caused by, or at least complicated by, drug addiction of one form or another. In the past generation, as the drug abuse crisis has grown, professionals in a variety of fields have gained a new appreciation for the many faces of addiction. Although there is still much to be discovered about chemical dependency, many professionals are at last starting to accept the possibility that drug addiction is the greatest problem faced by society today.

In this chapter, we will explore some of the concepts and terms that one needs to know in order to discuss the problem of substance abuse and addiction. In the next chapter, issues surrounding the interrelationship between the abuse of a drug or drugs and the addiction to these same agents will be explored. Taken together, these two chapters should provide a firm foundation for understanding the basic issues of drug use and abuse.

SUBSTANCE ABUSE—A NEW PHENOMENON?

The answer to this question appears to be no. Historical evidence suggests that people have traditionally attempted to find ways to alter the normal state of consciousness using naturally occuring hallucinogenics, oxygen deprivation, and alcohol. Every society has taken the time to develop a set of rules governing the use of mood-altering chemicals. Obviously, such rules would not be needed if people had no access to psychoactive agents or if chemical use were not socially acceptable.

It thus appears that over the years people have taken full advantage of various biochemical methods to alter their perception of the universe (*Health News*, 1990). Surprisingly, the drive to alter consciousness by chemical means is found in many nonhuman animals, including elephants, bighorn sheep, and various members of the ape family.

Research findings suggest that a number of species will go out of their way to ingest plants "whose only attraction is a fast-acting buzz" (Engelman, 1989, p. 12 E). The tendency for animals to apparently go out of their way to ingest substances that have psychoactive properties would suggest a possible biological basis for the use of chemicals that alter the state of consciousness.

The Evolution of Social Rules Governing Chemical Use

Students in the field of substance abuse are often surprised to learn that *every* culture has sanctioned the use of selected psychoactive agents for its members under certain conditions. Over time, each social group has evolved a series of rules which not only specify when and where certain mood-altering agents may be used, but which also prohibit the use of other mood-altering chemicals. For example, in the Middle East the use of hashish is accepted, but there are strong religious sanctions against the use of alcohol.

At first, social rules that govern the use of mood-altering chemicals might seem rather strange. This is because drug-use standards evolve as a result of social, historical, religious, and legal forces over time, and the social rules that evolve in one era may or may not apply to the realities of life in another. One need only consider the social attitude toward marijuana use in the 1950s as opposed to the current set of standards to see how drug-use patterns might change over time.

Society's Current Drug-Use Standards: An Exercise in Schizophrenia?

As noted by Weil (1986), the consumption of alcohol has a long history in Western cultures despite the fact that, pharmacologically, alcohol is as much a "drug" as any other chemical substance. Indeed, alcohol has been used by so many people for such a long period of time that most people have stopped thinking of it as a drug. Weil goes on to observe that as a result of the process of cultural evolution, we are currently in something of a social paradox. We spend a great deal of time and money exploring why people use drugs, but only to understand why some people take certain drugs we disapprove of rather than those that are socially acceptable.

Within Western society, as in every society, the use of certain chemicals is acceptable, whereas the use of other chemical agents is forbidden. To an outside observer, current American social attitudes toward chemical use must seem somewhat schizophrenic. For example, consider the fact that within this culture

> alcohol is legal, but it is not legal to drive under the influence of alcohol or to sell it to children. Conversely, we speak about cocaine and the opiates as *il*legal, but in fact doctors can prescribe these drugs. (Nadelmann, Kleiman, & Earls, 1990, p. 44).

As a further example of how illogical society's standards have become, in certain parts of the United States the sale, possession, or use of alcohol might be legal on Saturday and illegal on Sunday. But, with the proper prescription signed by a physician, a person can purchase narcotics or cocaine for medicinal purposes any day of the week. Is it any wonder that the whole subject of substance use, abuse, and addiction is a rather confusing one?

CHEMICAL DEPENDENCY: A "DISEASE" WITH NOBODY TRAINED TO DIAGNOSE IT

The confusion surrounding substance use and abuse is not limited just to the general public. Within the medical community, there are those who argue that drug addiction is a "disease" and others who argue just as strongly that it is not a true "disease." No matter which position one adopts, modern medicine's response to the problem of substance use/abuse/addiction is no less confusing than that of society's.

For example, either directly or indirectly, alcoholism is *the* condition most frequently encountered by the physician in practice today (Beasley, 1987; Twerski, 1989). The other forms of substance abuse/addiction merely reinforce the fact that, either directly or indirectly, chemical dependency is *the* most common "disease" encountered by the modern physician.

Research has shown that 50% of the patients seen in emergency rooms are there either directly or indirectly because of chemical abuse (Evans & Sullivan, 1990). Further, either directly or indirectly, chemical abuse plays a role in one-third to one-half of those individuals seen for psychiatric emergencies (Evans & Sullivan, 1990; Galanter, Castaneda & Ferman, 1988). The economic cost of chemical abuse alone is more than two and a half times that of all other forms of mental illness combined (Group for the Advancement of Psychiatry, 1991).

According to Treadway (1987), one form of addiction or another is present in half the cases of those being seen for family/marital counseling. Unfortunately, therapists in these fields only rarely ask the proper questions to identify addicted individuals. Beasley (1987) points out that the medical treatment of alcoholism and drug addiction, combined with the various psychiatric consequences of these disorders, accounts for approximately 40% of hospital usage in this country. Despite these statistics, Peyser (1989) contends that

> we do not adequately teach about alcohol and drug abuse in our schools of medicine, social work, and psychology. Where it is taught, it is minimized as a second-class disorder. . . . The mental health profession in general ignores this major underrecognized and untreated mental health problem. (p. 221)

Both Galanter (1986) and Twerski (1989) support this assertion. Indeed, Twerski notes that in his medical school training he was taught about many rare and infrequently encountered diseases, but not one single hour of lecture was devoted to the addictions, in spite of the fact that they account for one-third of all hospital admissions. Further, although he was trained in psychiatry at a major university hospital, he states that "at no time was I exposed to any teaching about addictive diseases" (p. 37). His conclusion that psychiatric and psychologic training programs fail in this area is strongly supported by the Group for the Advancement of Psychiatry (1991).

Unfortunately, one result of this gap in the training of physicians, especially psychiatrists, is that many doctors are not able to recognize the early signs of such addictive disorders as alcoholism. Moreover, according to Rains (1990), many physicians consider alcoholism untreatable. And, as the Group for the Advancement of Psychiatry (1991) suggests, they are "often pessimistic about the efficacy of treatment" (p. 1295).

This diagnostic blindness is not limited to physicians. Only 504 of the approximately 68,000 psychologists who are members of the American Psychological Association identified substance abuse as their primary specialty; 789 listed it as their secondary specialty (Youngstrom, 1991). Obviously, the professional response to the problem of substance abuse has been far short of the need. In a very real sense, no matter whether or not substance abuse/addiction is a true "disease," the health care and mental health professions have not responded to it by training practitioners in how to recognize and treat the signs of this disorder.

In a study by Colquitt, Fielding, and Cronan (1987) reviewing the medical and legal consequences of 252 motor vehicle accidents, only slightly over half the injured admitted to a major New England hospital were examined for blood-alcohol level. Of the remainder, 84 individuals involved in the accidents were found to be legally intoxicated at the time of the accident. However, only 3 of them were ultimately arraigned for driving under the influence of alcohol, and there were no convictions.

The preceding study is important for two reasons. First it demonstrates that physicians are hesitant to look for alcoholism, even in cases where there is strong evidence that alcohol abuse exists (an alcohol-related automobile accident). Secondly, even when charges of drunk driving were filed, it was still difficult to get a conviction for this charge in court. Again, one is left with the impression that the mental health and health care professions have not responded to this problem with the attention it demands.

DEFINITIONS: "SUBSTANCE ABUSE," "SOCIAL USE," "DRUG OF CHOICE," AND "ADDICTION"

Chemical dependency has a terminology that is often confusing to the newcomer to the field. Occasionally, addicts themselves will use the ambiguity of this terminology as a defense. For example, there was the man who hotly denied being alcoholic, although the opinion of numerous human service professionals, as well as that of a judge, was somewhat different. This man defined himself as simply a "problem drinker."

When asked to define the difference between a problem drinker and an alcoholic, the man was unable to do so. He even went so far as to ask if he could have a couple of hours to think it over! This man was clearly demonstrating the addict's tendency to avoid admitting to his or her addiction.

Substance Abuse

The concept of *substance abuse* is simple. In essence, if an individual is using a chemical agent when there is no legitimate medical need to do so, or if the person is drinking in excess of accepted social standards, that person could be said to be abusing the drug (Schuckit, 1989). Thus, current social standards or accepted medical practice are used to classify the individual's chemical use as either appropriate or abusive.

Social Use

The so-called social use of a substance is defined by traditional social standards. By the term *social use*, we usually mean the rare or infrequent use of a drug in a social setting. Further, the individual will not use the drug in such a manner as to cause physical, social, financial, or legal problems. The use of the chemical is confined to a social setting, where its use is governed by social rules and regulations.

Alcohol is the chemical most frequently used in a social context—often, during get-togethers with family or friends. It is also used in some religious ceremonies. In some circles, marijuana is used in a social context.

Drug of Choice

In this era of poly-addiction, the concept of *drug of choice* is often difficult to explain. A person's drug of choice is just that: of all the possible drugs available—of all the drugs the person may have used over the years—*what specific drugs would **this** person use if given the choice?*

Many cocaine addicts will drink alcohol or use minor tranquilizers as a supplement to their cocaine or amphetamine use. They do this in order to take the edge off of the side effects of cocaine, commonly known as the "coke jitters." Frequently, these side effects are so uncomfortable that the individual must attempt to control them with tranquilizers, such as alcohol or the benzodiazepines. But use of these drugs is secondary to use of their primary drug of choice: cocaine.

Addiction

The term *addiction* refers to dependence on a chemical. Schuckit (1989) suggests that there are two aspects to physical dependence on a chemical: (1) an increasing tolerance to the drug's effects and (2) a withdrawal syndrome when the drug is discontinued.

As tolerance to a drug's effects increases, the individual requires higher and higher doses of the drug in order to achieve the same effect that he or she experienced the first time. Tolerance develops over a period of time, so the individual must use the drug on a continual basis for tolerance to build. Schuckit (1989) identifies two forms of tolerance to a drug: (1) metabolic tolerance and (2) pharmacodynamic tolerance.

Metabolic tolerance takes place when, after being continuously exposed to a drug for a period of time, the liver becomes more efficient at breaking down the chemical. Drugs are foreign to the body, and so the liver will try to break down (or metabolize) the chemical to prepare the way for elimination of that substance. If the liver is continuously exposed to a substance, the number of cells assigned to the task of breaking down that chemical for elimination will increase. This will result in a more rapid elimination of the chemical from the blood.

Pharmacodynamic tolerance is a term applied to the increasing insensitivity of the central nervous system to the drug's effects. When the cells of the central nervous system are continuously exposed to a chemical, they will often try to maintain normal function by making minute changes in their structure. These cells then become less sensitive to the effects of the chemical; hence, the person must increase the dosage of the drug to achieve the initial effect.

If a drug is abused for a long enough period of time, a characteristic *withdrawal syndrome* will result when the person stops taking the drug. The exact nature of the withdrawal syndrome will vary, depending on such factors as the class of the drug, the period of time that it has been abused, and the individual's state of health. But each group of drugs will produce certain physical symptoms when the person stops taking the drug.

The existence of a withdrawal syndrome is evidence that pharmacodynamic tolerance has developed. For, in a very real sense, the withdrawal syndrome is caused by the absence of the chemical that the central nervous system had previously adapted to. When the drug is removed, the central nervous system will go through a period of *re*adaptation as it learns to function normally with the drug no longer present. It is during this period that the individual will experience the physical signs of withdrawal.

Consider the case of alcohol, which is a central nervous system depressant. Alcohol functions very much like a chemical "brake" on the cells of the central nervous system, much like the brakes on your car. If you attempt to drive while the brakes are engaged, it might be possible to eventually force the car to go fast enough to meet the posted speed limits. But, if you were then to suddenly release the pressure on the brakes, the car would suddenly leap ahead because the brakes were no longer fighting the forward motion of the car. You would have to ease up on the gas pedal, so that the engine would slow down enough to keep you within the posted speed limit.

During that period of readjustment, in a sense the car is going through a withdrawal phase. Much the same thing happens in the body when an individual stops using drugs. The body must adjust to the absence of a chemical that previously it had learned would always be there. This withdrawal syndrome, like the presence of tolerance to the drug's effects, provides strong evidence that the individual is addicted to one or more chemicals.

WHAT DOES "ADDICTION" MEAN?

For many years, one of the basic strategies against drug use was to exaggerate the dangers associated with it. As Musto (1991) described it, there was almost an unwritten law that drugs had to be presented in such a negative light that nobody in his or her right mind would even consider experimenting with them. As a result, a certain degree of hysteria surrounding drug use has become part of our social structure. Because of this hysteria, people have lost sight of the fact that even use of chemicals such as cocaine or heroin does not automatically bring about the advanced, destructive forms of compulsive drug use usually thought of when these substances are mentioned.

This is not to deny that substance abuse/addiction has extracted a terrible cost from those within its grasp; moreover, it is not the goal of this text to advocate the use of chemicals. However, an open, honest examination of research findings indicates that only a small percentage of the population is actually addicted to chemicals.

Holloway (1991), for example, reported that only 5.5 million Americans (or about 2% of the current population of approximately 250 million) are addicted to illegal drugs. This estimate does not include those addicted to alcohol. Gazzaniga (1988) arrived at a different estimate, stating that perhaps 10% of the population "falls into addictive patterns with drugs" (p. 143). This would be approximately 25 million Americans based on a population estimate of 250 million. In either case, it does not appear that a majority of the population is actually addicted to drugs.

In addition to the tendency of the media to exaggerate the dangers associated with chemical abuse, there has been a disturbing trend to refer to larger and larger numbers of people as addicts. Many substance-abuse professionals now speak of "addiction" to food, sex, gambling, men, women, play, television, shopping, credit cards, making money, carbohydrates, and a host of other nondrugs and nondrug behaviors (Peele, 1989; Peele, Brodsky & Arnold, 1991). Unfortunately, this expanded definition of the term *addiction* appears to be expanding still further.

In this text, we will use the term *addiction* only with reference to the various drugs of abuse. Furthermore, we will use the criterion of a demonstrated withdrawal syndrome to indicate whether an individual actually is addicted to a chemical. As we will discuss in the next chapter, substance abuse often blends into addiction to that same chemical; thus, the terms *substance use, chemical dependency, substance abuse,* and *addiction* will often be used interchangeably in the text. But these terms will be applied only to the problem of drug addiction.

THE UNITY OF ADDICTIVE DISORDERS

Many years ago professionals would speak of alcoholism and drug addiction as if they were separate disorders. In the past generation there has been a growing trend for professionals to refer to the so-called addictive behaviors. According to Miller (1980), this term encompasses alcoholism, drug addiction, obesity, smoking, and compulsive gambling.[1]

[1]The problems of obesity and compulsive gambling are not within the scope of this text. However, the reader should be aware that some researchers believe that these compulsive behaviors are also forms of addiction.

All of the addictive disorders are characterized by what W. R. Miller (1980) describes as "some form of indulgence for short-term pleasure or satisfaction at the expense of longer-term adverse effects" (p. 4). The exact reason for this "indulgence," however, has not yet been discovered. But mental health professionals have long been aware that addiction to a single substance is becoming increasingly rare (Boodman, 1990). Indeed, fully 50% of those seeking treatment for alcoholism use other drugs of abuse on a regular basis (Schmitz et al., 1991). The implication of these findings is that if addicts find it so easy to switch chemicals, perhaps alcoholism and drug abuse are not separate conditions, but different manifestations of a single disease—addiction.

Franklin (1987) points out that addiction may express itself through the compulsive use of any number of different chemicals. Indeed, he suggests that, among the various drugs of abuse, there is almost a social stratification process at work. Alcoholism may be barely tolerated, however it is more socially acceptable to be hospitalized for an alcohol problem than for a narcotic dependency problem. Thus, although the underlying process of addiction is the same, the diagnosis of "addiction" assumes different meanings based on the degree to which use of the particular drug is socially acceptable.

Further, different social groups tend to gravitate toward different chemicals. "[For] many inner-city blacks . . . heroin was their history, their balm . . . and their master" while white heroin addicts were a minority (Franklin, 1987, p. 58). By contrast, barbiturates were widely used as sleeping pills by middle-class America, until replaced by Valium—the "opiate of the suburbs" (p. 57).

Whatever the actual percentage of Americans addicted to chemicals, it is becoming increasingly apparent that there are fewer and fewer differences between habitual use of illegal drugs and habitual use of socially approved chemicals, such as tobacco and alcohol. Rapidly accumulating evidence suggests a common foundation to *all* addictions. The final expression of addiction, however, might be molded by many different social, economic, physical, and psychological forces (Donovan, 1988).

Dole (1988) postulates that, ultimately, all disorders of behavior, including addictions, might be reduced to biochemical interactions, which only now are starting to be understood by science. Furthermore, Dole advanced the theory that one form of compulsive drug use, narcotic addiction, reflects a dysfunction of an unidentified subsystem in the brain. The implication of Dole's theory is that other forms of addiction also reflect dysfunction of certain biochemical systems within the brain that are yet to be discovered. While Dole's (1988) theory is appealing, if only because it offers a specific cause for the problem of drug abuse, the neurobioligial theory of substance abuse/addiction has been strongly challenged by other neurobiologists (Peele, Brodsky, & Arnold, 1991).

In a study of the psychodynamic foundation of addiction, Khantzian (1986) noted that all addictions seem to come about as a result of similar evolutionary forces. He suggests that addicts turn to drugs in order to regulate their emotional state. In an earlier paper, Khantzian (1985) suggests that the specific drug an individual comes to obsessively use is selected "on the basis of personality organization and ego impairments" (p. 1260). This psychodynamic viewpoint holds that an addict turns to a chemical in order to control internal feeling states. The drug of choice is the one that will offer the greatest subjective relief.

The fact that addicts, as a general rule, use the same psychological defense mechanisms may be taken as further evidence of the unitary nature of addictive disorders. Addicts, no matter what the exact nature of their specific addiction, all struggle to defend, as well as to control, their individual addiction. They engage in many of the same behaviors while addicted, and often use many of the same drugs.

Alcoholics, for example, may use amphetamines or cocaine to help them fight off the sedating effects of alcohol, so that they can drink more. At the same time, amphetamine or cocaine addicts may use alcohol to fight the overstimulation that often accompanies amphetamine or cocaine abuse.

The common nature of addictive disorders is also reflected in the similarities in the self-help programs of Alcoholics Anonymous (A.A.), Narcotics Anonymous (N.A.), and Cocaine Anonymous (C.A.). With few exceptions, all three programs use the same concepts and language to help addicts come to terms with their addiction. This commonality notwithstanding, much of the research on addiction to date has addressed only the isolated addiction to alcohol. While a great deal of attention has been drawn to problems involving other drugs in the past decade, the fruits of these research efforts will not be apparent for many years.

SUMMARY

In this chapter we discussed substance abuse from a historical perspective, including the evolution of drug-use rules and standards. We then presented evidence to support the view that, until recently, substance abuse/addiction has been a neglected problem among health care and mental health professions.

In a section on "definitions," we explored key concepts, including social use, drug of choice, and addiction. We concluded the chapter with the suggestion that there is but one addictive disorder, which may express itself through the use of a variety of chemical agents.

Chapter 2

THE SCOPE OF CHEMICAL ABUSE AND ADDICTION

In the last chapter we introduced the basic terminology of the field of substance abuse. We are now prepared to explore the scope of the drug-abuse/addiction problem in the United States. We will also briefly discuss some of the issues that face the professional in making an accurate diagnosis of chemical dependency.

THE CONTINUUM OF ADDICTION

It is not uncommon in this day and age to hear health care and mental health professionals use the terms *drug abuse* and *drug dependency* inter-changeably—as if they meant the same thing. In fact, there is a subtle difference between substance abuse and dependency. The abuse of a chemical and addiction to that chemical are different aspects of a single problem: the use of artificial chemicals to modify an individual's emotions. But, there are those who confuse the abuse of a chemical with the more serious problem of addiction to that chemical.

Of course, substance abuse in itself is serious enough. Nobody would deny the great potential for harm in the misuse of chemicals for personal pleasure. The point being made here is that chemical addiction is *not* simply an either/or condition. There are a variety of different chemical-use patterns, of which the habitual, compulsive use of a drug that denotes addiction is an extreme.

Unfortunately, because of society's attitudes and prejudices, there are few clear-cut lines between experimental drug use, the "social" use of a chemical, the abuse of that same chemical, and chemical dependency (*Health News*, 1990). Even in the case of alcohol, which is humankind's oldest drug, professionals often disagree over what constitutes alcohol abuse or the more serious condition of alcoholism (Washton, 1990).

Substance abuse can follow one of many different patterns. According to Peele, Brodsky, and Arnold (1991), "[addiction] is not an all-or-nothing thing, but a continuum from moderate excess to severe compulsion" (p. 133). Brower, Blow, Young, and Hill (1991) agree, noting that "severity of drug dependence may be considered a continuum" (p. 761). This continuum of

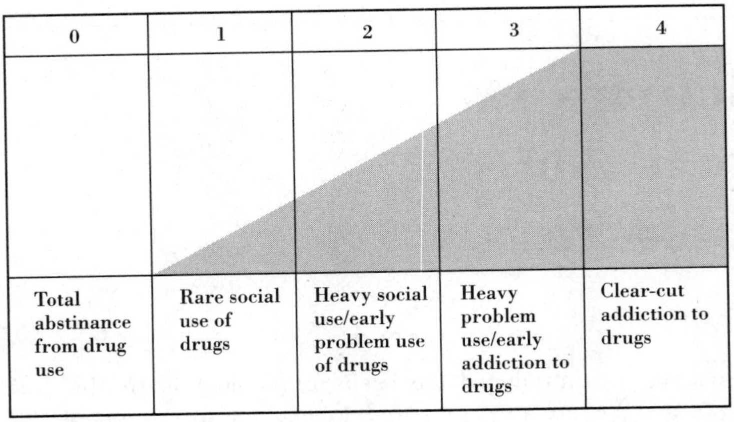

0	1	2	3	4
Total abstinance from drug use	Rare social use of drugs	Heavy social use/early problem use of drugs	Heavy problem use/early addiction to drugs	Clear-cut addiction to drugs

FIGURE 2-1   The drug-use continuum.

drug use ranges from total abstinence from all chemical use, to rare (or, for want of a better word, "social") use of drugs, to heavy use, and ultimately to addiction to chemicals (see Figure 2-1).

Thus, any given individual might be classified as (a) abstaining from all drugs, (b) using one or more drugs on a social basis, (c) abusing one or more drugs on an episodic basis, (d) abusing one or more drugs on a continual basis, or (e) being addicted to a drug or drugs—or, perhaps, the individual might fall somewhere between categories.

As with any continuum, movement back and forth from one stage to another is possible. In his research on alcoholism, Vaillant (1983) found considerable fluctuation in alcohol consumption over the course of the lifetime of any given individual. For example, rather than progressing smoothly from occasional social drinking to alcohol addiction, a rare social drinker might go through a period of frequent abusive drinking following the breakup of an engagement, after which he or she might return to the occasional social use of alcohol.

The continuum is a useful construct because it allows for the classification of chemical use of various intensities and patterns. Rather than thinking in terms of whether a person is or is not addicted to chemicals, the clinician is able to determine where on the continuum of drug use a particular individual might fall. The different stages of chemical use on this continuum are as follows:

Level 0: Total abstinence   The individual abstains from any and all recreational alcohol or chemical use.

Level 1: Rare social use   The individual will rarely use alcohol or chemicals for recreational purposes, but is able to drink or use chemicals without the typical problems associated with the more serious levels of alcohol or drug use.

Level 2: Heavy social use/early problem drug use   The individual is likely to be seen as an "abusive" or "problem" drinker, or as a person whose chemical use is clearly above the norm for his or her social group. At this point on the continuum, the possible onset of various combinations of social, legal, financial, occupational, and personal problems associated with chemical use might become apparent, although no problems have surfaced as yet. Thus, the individual is in a "grey area." Friends or relatives may be concerned, but the individual still has not encountered the type of problems that are the hallmark of a serious substance-abuse problem.

Level 3: Heavy problem use/early addiction   The person's alcohol or chemical use has now reached the point where there clearly is a problem. Indeed, the person may have become addicted to chemicals, although he or she may argue the point. For some of the drugs of abuse, medical complications associated with addiction now arise. Also at this phase, the individual will demonstrate classic withdrawal symptoms when unable to continue the use of drugs. The addict will also experience various combinations of ongoing social, legal, financial, occupational, and personal problems.

Level 4: Clear-cut addiction to drugs   At this point on the continuum, the person demonstrates the classic addiction syndrome. Multiple social, legal, financial, occupational, and personal problems become increasingly worse. The person also will demonstrate various medical complications associated with chemical abuse and may be near death as a result of chronic addiction. This individual is clearly addicted beyond any shadow of a doubt in the mind of an outside observer. It should be noted, however, that the addicted individual may try to rationalize away or deny problems associated with his or her alcohol or drug use even at this late stage. More than one elderly alcoholic, for example, has tried to explain away an abnormal liver function as being the aftermath of a childhood illness.

Admittedly, this classification system, like all others, is imperfect. The criteria used to determine the various levels are arbitary and subject to debate. As stated by Vaillant (1983), "the variety of alcohol related problems, not any unique criterion, [is what] captures what clinicians really mean when they label a person alcoholic" (p. 42). Which is to say that it is *a constellation of various symptoms, rather than the existence of any single symptom, that identifies the existence of alcoholism* or any other drug dependency.

However, as will be outlined below, even in the case of such drugs of abuse as the narcotic family of drugs, or cocaine, significant percentages of those who use these drugs—even if they do so on a regular basis—*are not necessarily addicted*. Thus, one should keep in mind when reviewing "The Scope of Chemical Dependency," below, that substance use falls on a continuum.

THE SCOPE OF CHEMICAL DEPENDENCY

Over the years, there have been many estimates of how serious the drug-addiction problem is in the United States. J. Franklin (1987), for example, concluded that when statistics on alcoholism, addiction to illegal drugs, and addiction to prescription drugs like Valium were combined, it would appear that "perhaps one in every five Americans was hopelessly addicted to something—and another one or two were steady users (p. 59).

If we accept the estimate of 20% of the U.S. population as being addicted, then (assuming a national population of 250 million) this means that *approximately 50 million Americans are addicted to chemicals, while another 50 million are steady users.* Fortunately, other estimates do not suggest a problem of this magnitude.

In a study of lifetime prevalence rates of various forms of mental illness in the United States (including alcohol and substance-abuse disorders), Regier et al. (1990) estimate that 2.8% of the population would meet diagnostic criteria for either alcohol abuse or dependence at any given point in time. Another 1.3% of the population would meet diagnostic criteria for drug abuse or dependence. These researchers also conclude that, over the course of their lives, approximately 13.5% of the population will meet the criteria for either alcohol abuse or dependence. Another 6.1% will meet the criteria for substance abuse or dependence.

With a U.S. population of approximately 250 million, the estimates just noted mean that at any given time 7 million Americans would meet the diagnostic criteria for alcohol abuse or dependence, while another 2.35 million would qualify for a diagnosis of drug abuse or dependence. Furthermore, over the course of their lifetimes, some 33.8 million Americans will either abuse or become addicted to alcohol. And approximately 15 million will have either a drug-abuse or dependency problem at some point in their lives.

In the journal *Psychotherapy Today* (1991) approximately 6.4% of the population was reported to have been using illicit drugs in 1990. This translates to about 16 million Americans, based on an estimated population of 250 million. This estimate was significantly lower than the 12.1% thought to have been using illicit drugs in 1983. Both the estimates of *Psychotherapy Today* and those of Regier et al. (1990) are significantly lower than J. Franklin's (1987) estimate of 20% of the population being addicted.

Estimates of Addiction or Abuse: A Breakdown by Substance

Alcohol addiction   Only a small minority of those who drink are thought to be addicted, with estimates for adults running from approximately 6 million (Ellis, McInerney, DiGiuseppe, & Yeager, 1988) to 10 million (Bays, 1990) to perhaps as many as 12 million (L. Siegel, 1989). This number does not include another estimated 1 million children and adolescents (Ellis et al., 1990) to 3 million (Turbo, 1989) who are also thought to be addicted to alcohol. According to Kaplan and Sadock (1988), about 13 million Americans, including children and adolescents, are thought to be alcoholics.

Narcotics addiction   On hearing "drugs of abuse," people frequently think of narcotics first. In 1988, Kaplan and Sadock suggested that there were perhaps 400,000 to 600,000 narcotics addicts living in the United States—approximately half living in New York City alone. According to Bays (1990) about 500,000 Americans are addicted to heroin, but the *Mayo Clinic Health Letter* (1989) estimates between 500,000 and 750,000 heroin addicts in the United States.

A significant percentage of those addicted to narcotics are women. Peluso and Peluso (1988) estimate that perhaps as many as 100,000 of the known heroin addicts are women, while Kaplan and Sadock (1988) give a ratio of three male narcotics addicts for every female. Given their estimate of 400,000 to 600,000 narcotics addicts, then Kaplan and Sadock's (1988) estimate would mean that between 100,000 and 150,000 American women are addicted to narcotics.

Cocaine addiction   Cocaine remains a popular drug of abuse, with a significant potential for addiction. Musto (1991), for example, estimates that between 3% and 20% of those who use cocaine will eventually become addicted.

In 1988, Peluso and Peluso reported 2 million cocaine addicts in the United States. Two years later, it was reported that 1 million Americans were addicted (Hause, 1990). Still, the problem is serious—and it is not limited to adults. It has been estimated that approximately 600,000 adolescents between the ages of 12 and 17 are addicted to "crack" cocaine (Gelman, Underwood, King, Hager, & Gordon, 1990).

Marijuana abuse   We use the term *abuse* rather than *addiction* with respect to marijuana because it is not yet clear whether one can become "addicted" to marijuana in the traditional sense of the word. The possibility of an individual going through withdrawal symptoms as a result of chronic marijuana use will be discussed in more detail in Chapter 9.

According to the U.S. Department of Health and Human Services, marijuana is currently the most commonly abused drug in the United States. It is the fourth most commonly abused chemical in Canada, after caffeine, alcohol, and tobacco (*Health News*, 1990). More than 66 million Americans have used marijuana at some point in their lives: Approximately 21 million used it at least once in 1990, and of this number, 3.3 million used it on a daily basis (Department of Health and Human Service, 1990). Thus, of those Americans who used marijuana in 1990, only 16% used it daily.

Hallucinogenic abuse   As with marijuana, there are questions as to whether or not one may become addicted to hallucinogenics. For this reason, we speak of hallucinogenic abuse rather than addiction. Perhaps as many as one-fifth of Americans under the age of 25 have used hallucinogenics at one time or another (Kaplan & Sadock, 1990). However, use of these drugs is quite rare, and of those young adults who have used them, Kaplan and Sadock estimate that only 1% or 2% will have done so in the past 30 days.

Tobacco abuse   Tobacco is a special drug. Like alcohol, in it is legally sold to adults. Unfortunately, tobacco products are also readily obtained by adolescents, who make up a significant proportion of those who use tobacco. It has been quite difficult to obtain accurate estimates of how many Americans continue to smoke. According to Henningfield and Nemeth-Coslett (1988), approximately 50 million Americans smoke cigarettes and another 10 million use "smokeless" tobacco products, such as chewing tobacco. These figures are quite close to the estimate of 54 million Americans who smoke provided by the Department of Health and Human Services (1990).

THE HIDDEN PROBLEM OF SUBSTANCE ABUSE

From the figures presented in the preceding section, it is clear that significant numbers of Americans are drug users. It should be noted, however, that the information provided thus far is on the scope of chemical *dependency*. Fortunately, not every person who uses a given drug of abuse, even if he or she does so repeatedly, will ultimately become addicted to that substance.

Indeed, it has been suggested that only a small percentage of drug users will ultimately become addicted to chemicals (Peele et al., 1991). In 1990, the Department of Health and Human Services concluded that although almost 13 million Americans over the age of 12 had used illicit chemicals in 1989, many of those individuals were *abusers* of chemicals, not addicts.

Estimates of the scope of alcohol abuse   It has been estimated that perhaps as many as 100 million Americans use alcohol at least occasionally (Ellis et al., 1988; L. Siegel, 1989), but that only 10–13 million are addicted (Kaplan & Sadock, 1988). According to D. W. Goodwin (1989), about 140 million Americans drink at least occasionally and perhaps 25 million might be classified as "heavy" drinkers. The rest of the drinking population would fall at levels 1 and 2 of the drug-use continuum introduced earlier in the chapter.

The Department of Health and Human Services (1990) estimated that 103 million Americans age 12 or older drink alcohol at least occasionally. Of this number, it was estimated that about 42 million Americans drink alcohol at least once a week. This means that 61 million Americans drink alcohol less often than once a week, suggesting that the majority of those who drink do so infrequently.

Estimates of the scope of cocaine abuse   Only a small percentage of those who use cocaine are actually addicted to it. Estimates range from 1 user in 6 (Peele et al., 1991) to 1 in 12 (Peluso & Peluso, 1988). According to the

Department of Health and Human Services (1990), of the 6.2 million Americans who were thought to have used cocaine in the preceding year, only 660,000 used the drug once a week or more often.

Estimates of the number of Americans who use cocaine on a regular basis range from between 4 and 5 million people (Kaplan & Sadock, 1988) to upwards of 24 million people (Peluso & Peluso, 1988), depending on how the word "regular" is defined. According to Peele et al. (1991), there are 300,000 daily users of cocaine in the United States. L. Siegel (1989) estimates between 500,00 and 750,000 daily users.

Thus, we are left with a diagnostic dilemma. Exactly how many people are *abusing* cocaine, and, how many are *addicted* to this drug? It is extremely difficult to answer this question because most cocaine users take great pains to hide the fact. However, the data we do have suggest that between 6 and 12 times as many people are abusing cocaine as are addicted to it.

Estimates of the scope of narcotics abuse   It is also quite difficult to estimate how many people use narcotics without ever becoming addicted to this family of drugs. Jenike (1989) estimates that perhaps only half of those who abuse narcotics go on to become addicted to them. The American Academy of Family Physicians (1989) estimates that 2 million Americans use narcotics occasionally, in addition to the 500,000 who are addicted. This gives a 4:1 ratio of abusers to addicts. If one were to classify those who do abuse narcotics without becoming addicted on the drug-use continuum, they would fall at levels 1 and 2.

What these figures indicate, besides the staggering numbers of people who are addicted to chemicals in the United States, is that a significant percentage of the population engages in recreational drug use without becoming addicted to a drug of choice.[1] Perhaps as many as 72 million Americans (*Minneapolis Star-Tribune*, 1989a) admit to having used an illicit drug other than alcohol at least once. Most certainly, the research to date does not suggest that all of these people (some 29% of the population) are addicted to drugs. As mentioned earlier, Regier et al. 1990) estimate that only about 6% of the population will ever meet the diagnostic criteria for drug abuse/dependence.

It should come as no surprise that there is a significant amount of recreational drug use going on in the United States that is not reflected in statistics on addiction. After all, large numbers of Americans drink alcohol at least occasionally, but never go on to become addicted to it. The social upheaval in the 1960s and 1970s, which saw large numbers of people using marijuana—often on a daily basis—only to set their drug use aside in order to pursue careers or other goals, also should have led us to expect that many people can use chemicals without necessarily becoming addicted.

On the brighter side of the coin, however, there is evidence that casual drug use may have peaked in the early to mid 1980s and that the total number

---

[1]Unfortunately, it is not possible to determine in advance who will be able to use chemicals without becoming addicted and who will not. If only for this reason, experimental drug use should be discouraged.

of casual drug users may have started to decline (Draper & Haga, 1989; Gold, 1990; *Mayo Clinic Health Letter*, 1989). For example, the Drug Abuse Warning Network (DAWN) noted that, in 1990, "only" 365,708 drug-related cases were treated in hospital emergency rooms, a 14% reduction over the 426,000 drug-related emergency-room visits reported for 1989 (*Alcoholism & Drug Abuse Week*, 1991a). Thus, it would appear that there is indeed a reduction in the total number of casual drug users.

Limitations of Current Research

Surprisingly, much of what we think we know about addiction may be faulty information for any of the following reasons:

1. Much of the research on substance abuse is based on a distorted sample of people: those who are in treatment for substance-abuse problems (Gazzaniga, 1988). Virtually nothing is known about those people who use chemicals on a social basis, never become addicted, and who never enter treatment programs for their drug use. These people, who are known as "chippers," make up a subpopulation of drug users for which there are no statistics.

2. There are those people who are able to afford private treatment for their substance-abuse problems. Individuals who use the services of clinicians in private practice or in private treatment centers are rarely included in research studies on substance abuse.

3. As professionals in the field know, many of those who abuse or become addicted to chemicals will stop without professional intervention (Gazzaniga, 1988; *Mayo Clinic Health Letter*, 1989; Peele, 1985, 1989; Tucker & Sobell, 1992). Indeed, the *Mayo Clinic Health Letter* (1989), in reviewing a recent Department of Health and Human Services survey of drug use in the United States, concluded that "despite the widespread availability of drugs and their addictive qualities, millions of Americans who once used them regularly appear now to have given them up" (p. 2). These individuals only rarely are included in research studies on substance abuse.

Many Vietnam veterans, for example, became addicted to drugs during the war. But apparently large numbers of them stopped their use of chemicals without professional intervention. Of 1,400 American soldiers who tested positive for drugs upon their return from Vietnam in 1971, only one-third, or 495 men, were still using chemicals 8 months later (Gazzaniga, 1988). Jenike (1989) pointed out that up to 40% of the U.S. enlisted men who served in Vietnam had abused heroin at one time or another, but that only 5% of the men continued to abuse narcotics after their return home.

4. As stated previously, much of what we think we know about substance abuse is based on research carried out on those in treatment for drug addiction. Unfortunately, much of this research has failed to dif-

ferentiate between *abusers* of a chemical and those who are *addicted* (Peele, 1985). This is an important distinction. Not everybody who uses a chemical for even extended periods of time is necessarily addicted to it, even in the case of heroin! But, for a number of reasons, many people who are only heavy abusers of chemicals are in treatment for their "addiction."

5. Residents of drug-rehabilitation programs are assumed to be representative of the general population, or at least that part of the population addicted to chemicals. However, those who are in treatment for drug problems, even if they all are actually addicted, are not a random sample of the addicted population. As described by Gazzaniga (1988),

> they are a subculture that cannot easily give up their addictions. Yet it is the patients from these centers who make up most of the studies about addiction and about how hard it is to kick the drug habit. (p. 143)

Thus, much of what we think we know about addiction is based upon a grossly distorted sample population. It is not the purpose of this text to deny that large numbers of people abuse drugs, or that such drug abuse carries with it a terrible cost in personal suffering. It is also not the purpose of this text to deny that many people are harmed by drug abuse. Admittedly, people become addicted to chemicals. Our purpose in this section is simply to make the reader aware of the shortcomings of the current body of research on substance abuse.

The available literature on the subject of drug addiction is extremely limited in other ways, as well. One limitation is that only a small portion addresses forms of addiction other than alcoholism. An even smaller proportion deals with the impact of chemicals on women (Peluso & Peluso, 1988). Griffin, Weiss, Mirin and Lang (1989), in exploring differences between male and female cocaine abusers, state that "the drug abuse literature has paid relatively little attention to women" (p. 122). That is, it has simply failed to differentiate between male and female drug addicts.

As for children and adolescents, virtually no research has been done on their drug abuse or addiction. Newcomb and Bentler (1989) state that there is virtually no information on chemical use in the first decade of life, and that research into adolescent chemical use is scanty at best. Mikkelsen (1985) agrees with this assessment, citing a "relative paucity of investigations" (p. 6).

THE COST OF CHEMICAL ABUSE AND ADDICTION

Substance-abuse policy, as we noted in the last chapter, often does not seem to make sense. For example, consider the contrast between marijuana and tobacco. Jenike (1989) estimated that 60% of the U.S. population (150 million people) have tried marijuana at least once. Between 10 million Americans (Kaplan & Sadock, 1988) and 20 million Americans (Jenike, 1989; L. Siegel, 1989). use this drug on a regular basis.

Three times this number of people (or about 60 million people) are thought to smoke tobacco products (cigarettes or cigars) on a regular basis. The social quandry lies in the fact that the legal use of tobacco resulted in 434,000 deaths just for the year 1988 (Associated Press, 1991a), while to date there has not been a single death attributed to marijuana use alone, although marijuana is an illegal drug (L. Siegel, 1989).

The Cost of Alcohol Abuse

It has been estimated that alcohol-related traffic accidents, alcohol-related household accidents, and alcohol-related diseases, such as cirrhosis of the liver and heart disease, together are responsible for 98,000 deaths each year in the United States (Beasley, 1987). Some estimates have been even higher; for example, L. Siegel (1989) estimates that 100,000 Americans die each year from alcohol-related diseases. Yet alcohol is a *legal* drug.

In 1990 alcoholism alone cost the United States in excess of $136 billion in both direct medical costs and indirect costs, such as lost work productivity (Anderson, 1990). For example, alcohol-induced brain damage is second only to Alzheimer's disease as a known cause of mental deterioration in adults (Beasley, 1987). Between 15% and 30% of the beds in U.S. nursing homes are occupied by individuals who have a history of chronic alcoholism (Schuckit, 1989). Many of these nursing home beds are supported, at least in part, by public funds, making this another indirect cost of alcohol abuse. Finally, it has been estimated that 65 of every 100 U.S. citizens will be involved in an alcohol-related auto accident at some point in their lives (Beasley, 1987).

It has been reported that between 30% and 40% of homeless Americans are alcohol abusers, while 10% to 15% abuse drugs (Caslyn & Morse, 1991; McCarty, Argeriou, Huebner, & Lubran, 1991). Some estimates of the yearly cost of providing social service support (Housing, medical treatment, food, and so forth) to this population might be as high as $23,000 per client (Whitman, Friedman, & Thomas, 1990). When one considers the number of homeless Americans, these figures amount to a massive investment of social support dollars that also must be included in the cost that addiction extracts from U.S. resources.

The Cost of Substance Abuse

In addition to the cost of alcohol abuse/addiction to society, drug abuse is thought to cost an additional $33 billion each year in lost productivity (Nolan, 1990). Estimates of the amount of money Americans spent on drugs in any given year range from $40 billion (Associated Press, 1991c) to $41 billion (*Alcoholism and Drug Abuse Week*, 1991b) to a high of $150 billion (Collier, 1989). Nor was all of this money spent by the hardened addict. A significant proportion of this money was spent by the casual, nonaddicted, recreational drug user.

Substance abuse and victims of crime   There is a known relationship between chemical abuse in one form or another and having been victimized, both sexually and nonsexually. Burnam et al. (1989) found that substance abuse or dependency in women was one common result of having been sexually assaulted at some time in their lives. According to Kilpatrick (1990), women who were victims of some form of violent crime were three to six times as likely to have alcohol/drug problems as women who were never victimized.

Walker, Bonner, and Kaufman (1988) state that both alcohol and drug addiction frequently play a part in the physical abuse of children. Alcohol abuse is also associated with spouse abuse. For example, Gondolf and Foster (1991) reported that 39% of their sample of 218 male veterans in an alcohol treatment program said they had assaulted their wives or partners at least once during the previous year. One-fifth of these men said that the assault was severe.

Beasley (1987) points to an even stronger relationship between alcohol abuse and family violence. He contends that alcohol abuse is involved in approximately 50% of all cases of spouse abuse and 38% of all cases of child abuse. Chasnoff (1988) reports that alcohol and/or drug abuse was involved in 64% of all child-abuse cases in New York City. As stated by Bays (1990), "at least 675,000 children each year are seriously mistreated by an alcoholic or drug-abusing caretaker" (p. 881). While there is some disagreement as to the exact nature of the relationship between alcohol and/or drug abuse and family violence, there is no doubt that there is a strong connection between these two social problems.

Alcohol or drug use may not be a causative factor in child or spouse abuse. However, as noted by Gelles and Straus (1988), alcohol or drug use is more likely to be present in a home where physical abuse takes place because such families tend to demonstrate a number of antisocial behaviors. In other words, such families suffer from multiple problems, of which chemical use and physical abuse are only two of the more visable examples.

Substance abuse and suicide   There is a known association between substance abuse and suicide. Approximately one-quarter of the successful suicides in any given year are alcoholics (Hyman, 1988). Furthermore, upwards of 60% of suicide attempts either directly or indirectly may be traced to alcoholism (Beasley, 1987). Although there is no way to determine the role of drug abuse/addiction in suicide, certain classes of drugs, specifically the amphetamines and cocaine, are known to cause suicidal depression following prolonged use.

Substance abuse and intimacy dysfunctions   According to Gold (1988), chemical abuse can result in various forms of sexual dysfunction, including changes in the individual's ability to achieve a stage of sexual excitement, orgasm, and resolution following sexual activity. Gold also reports that drug abuse can result in various forms of performance dysfunction, as well as interfere with the individual's ability to enjoy sexual relations. Furthermore, the use of alcohol, benzodiazepines, and similar agents can result in impotence in the male and decreased vaginal secretions in the female.

THE STATE OF THE ART: UNANSWERED QUESTIONS, UNCERTAIN ANSWERS

As the reader has by now discovered, there is much confusion in the professional community over the problems of substance abuse/addiction. Even in the case of alcoholism, which is perhaps the most common of the drug addictions, there is an element of confusion, or uncertainty, over what constitutes the essential elements (Helzer, 1987). Some even question whether alcoholism is really a disease (Dreiger, 1986).

How Do the Mass Media Influence the Development of New Drug Trends?

One of the most serious of the unanswered questions facing mental health and substance abuse professionals is whether the media have exerted a positive or negative influence in combating problems of substance abuse/addiction. Because it is illegal to import or to use a wide variety of drugs, activities surrounding these drugs become "newsworthy."

It has been suggested by some that media reports of the dangers inherent in the use of certain drugs have actually contributed to the aura surrounding inhalant abuse (Brecher, 1972) and use of a new form of amphetamine known as "ice" (Cotton, 1990). The media often report on how to use a particular drug and describe the effects the drug will have. Huge profits earned by those who sell drugs are often cited. The charge has been that the media have served not to make chemical use unattractive, but rather to make drugs seem more attractive to many who otherwise might not have been motivated to try them.

The Duch experiment in dealing with the drug problem (see Chapter 31, "Drugs and Crime") supports the theory that when legal sanctions against drug use are removed, they actually become *less* attractive to the average individual, with the result that casual drug use declines. The Dutch approach substance abuse not from the perspective of a legal problem, but from a public health perspective. The point to remember is that there is a great deal of evidence suggesting that media reports actually contribute to the problem of substance abuse in the United States by lending an aura of mystery and "charm" to the illegal street drug world. Whose side is the media on? would seem to be a valid question.

What Constitutes a Valid Diagnosis of Chemical Dependency?

Another unanswered question is how to distinguish between casual use of a given chemical, problem use of that same chemical, and addiction to the chemical. As to what establishes whether alcoholism is an issue, Vaillant (1983) suggests that "often it is not who is drinking by *who is watching*" (p. 22, italics added). Peele (1985) concurs, noting that "what is defined as alcoholism at any time or place is a social convention" (p. 35). Which is to say that the society in which the individual is living will define what is problematic alcohol or drug use.

Are there valid diagnostic signs of drug addiction that are not simply matters of social convention? Lewis, Dana, and Blevens (1988) argue that presently the diagnosis of chemical dependency remains difficult, and in the final analysis may be considered a value judgment. Criteria such as the American Psychiatric Association's *DSM-III-R* may make the judgment easier, but even in rather advanced cases of drug abuse, the issue of whether or not the individual is addicted is not clear-cut.

For the moment, let's focus on the problem of alcoholism and its diagnosis. According to Greenblatt and Shader (1975), three elements must be present to arrive at a diagnosis of alcoholism: (1) a deterioration in the person's work performance, family relationships, and social behavior, which they term *a pathological psychosocial behavior pattern;* (2) *a classic drug-addiction process,* including withdrawal symptoms following abstinence from alcohol of sufficient severity for the person to try to avoid them by continued use of alcohol; and (3) *a medical disease,* such as cirrhosis of the liver, certain nutritional disorders, and certain forms of neurological damage, representing complications of alcoholism.

Greenblatt and Shader go on to point out that alcoholism is easy to recognize when all three elements are present. They note, however, that many "skid row" alcoholics who have been hospitalized many times for alcohol withdrawal symptoms such as the "DT's" may never develop any of the diseases associated with chronic alcoholism. Thus, conditions 1 and 2 are evident, but not condition 3.

The common experience of a heavy-drinking business executive whose drinking pattern never interferes with family or occupational performance, but who develops withdrawal symptoms when hospitalized for elective surgery (say for a hernia repair), illustrates how it is possible to demonstrate condition 2, but not 1 or 3, of Greenblatt and Shader's triad of symptoms.

Finally, although many "binge" drinkers may never become addicted to alcohol and may never develop any of the physical complications associated with alcoholism, many of them will ultimately suffer broken families and loss of employment as a result of their drinking. Here, we see condition 1, but not 2 or 3.

Using Greenblatt and Shader's criteria, then, even alcoholism, perhaps our best understood form of addiction, is not so easy to diagnose. In the final analysis, any diagnosis of chemical dependency is the opinion of a professional about another person's chemical use. The issue of assessing another individual's substance-use pattern will be discussed in a later chapter. The point being made here is that there is still much to be learned about how best to assess a person's chemical-use pattern and provide an accurate diagnosis.

SUMMARY

In this chapter we introduced the concept of a continuum of drug use. Following a review of research findings on the extent of the problem of the abuse of various drugs and addiction to different chemicals, we pointed out some of the shortcomings of current research.

We then turned our attention to the costs of alcohol and substance abuse, discussing them in both economic and social terms. In conclusion, unanswered questions about chemical use were raised, including the role of the media in combating the problems of substance abuse/addiction.

Chapter **3**

ALCOHOL AND
ITS ACUTE EFFECTS

Alcohol is humankind's oldest drug. It was a part of civilization thousands of years before the dawn of written history. Historians believe that early humans learned to ingest alcohol as a result of watching animals eat fermented fruits from the forest floor (R. Siegel, 1986). Once alcohol was "discovered," it quickly became part of human culture. Indeed, alcohol has become a yardstick by which cultural development may be measured. As Beasley (1987) notes:

> Virtually all cultures in time and place—whether hunter-gatherers or farmers; whether technologically advanced or primitive—share two universals: the development of a noodle and the discovery and use of the natural fermentation process. (p. 17)

It has even been suggested that early civilization came about in response to the need for a stable home base from which to ferment an early form of beer (Stone, 1991). Thus alcohol, which is also known as *ethanol*, or *ethyl alcohol*, is found in virtually every human culture, past and present. Other forms of alcohol that are not normally used for human consumption will not be considered in this chapter. It is enough to understand that ethyl alcohol has been with us for a long, long time.

A BRIEF HISTORY OF ALCOHOL

Mead, a form of beer made from fermented honey, was in common use some 10,000 years ago, around the year 8000 B.C. (Ray & Ksir, 1987). This form of beer was quite unlike modern beers, for its thick liquid was quite nutritious, providing necessary vitamins and amino acids to the diet of the drinker. Modern beer, by contrast, is very thin—almost anemic in comparison with mead. The earliest written records that detail how beer is made date back some 4,000 years, to approximately 1800 B.C. (Stone, 1991).

According to Ray and Ksir (1987), wine made from berries dates back to around 6400 B.C. Wine made from grapes has a shorter history, dating back to approximately 3500 B.C. (McGovern, cited in Wilford, 1991). While nobody knows how the practice of drinking wine first began, Youcha (1978) relates a

4,000-year-old Persian legend about the discovery of wine. According to this legend, a mythical Persian king, Jamshid, had vats of grapes stored in the basement of his palace. Jamshid loved grapes, and apparently wanted to store some away to enjoy during the cold winter months when grapes were out of season. However, after some time, he discovered that some of the vats had developed a sour liquid at the bottom. Thinking that this liquid was poison, he set the sour fluid aside for future use in palace politics.

The legend has it that a lady of the court was subject to headaches so severe that she decided to end her life. She opened the jar marked "poison" and expecting death, drank some of the fluid. Not only didn't she die, she found relief from her headaches and from time to time began to sneak into the storeroom to drink some of the mystical fluid. When the supply of fluid was exhausted our nameless heroine confessed her discovery to the king, who ordered that grapes be fermented and that the secret of wine be made known to his subjects.

Admittedly, this is only a legend. As we have noted, the process for making mead has been known for some 10,000 years, or since around the year 8000 B.C. The importance of alcohol to the developing civilizations of the Mediterranean Basin might be measured by the fact that both the Egyptian and Roman empires had a god or goddess of wine. Both beer and wine are also mentioned in Homer's *Iliad* and *Odyssey*, legends that date back thousands of years. It was not by accident that Ulysses helped the Cyclops become drunk before attempting his escape. Knowledge of alcohol's depressive effects on the central nervous system was well known long before Ulysses set sail for Troy.

HOW ALCOHOL IS PRODUCED

By whatever means, somehow people discovered that if you crush certain forms of fruit and allow them to stand for a period of time in a container, alcohol is produced. We now know that unseen microorganisms called *yeast*, which float in the air, settle on the crushed fruit and digest the sugars in the fruit in a chemical process called *fermentation*. The yeast breaks down the carbon, hydrogen, and oxygen atoms it finds in the sugar for food, and in the process recombines these atoms into ethyl alcohol and carbon dioxide.

Alcohol is actually a waste product of the process of fermentation. When the concentration of alcohol reaches about 15% it becomes toxic to the yeast, and fermentation stops. Thus, people were able to produce alcoholic beverages whose highest concentration of alcohol was about 15% since before the time of Babylon.

However, to obtain alcohol concentrations above the 15% limit imposed by the nature of yeast took several thousand years more. This is the process of *distillation*, which did not emerge until around the year A.D. 800, or just over 1,100 years ago. In the distillation process, the wine obtained from fermentation is heated, causing some of the alcohol content to boil off as a vapor, or steam. Alcohol boils at a much lower temperature than does water, so the steam that forms when wine is boiled contains more alcohol than water vapor.

When the steam is then collected and allowed to cool down, it forms a liquid again. This liquid contains a higher concentration of alcohol and a lower concentration of water than did the original wine. The vapor is collected in a special cooling coil. The higher-alcohol-content liquid that forms drips from the end of the coil into a container of some kind. This is the famous "still" of lore and legend.

In the *Iliad* and the *Odyssey*, Homer describes people drinking wine with meals. In some parts of the modern world, it is still the custom to drink wine with meals on a regular basis. In some cases, this may be because the local water supply cannot be trusted as fit to drink. For whatever reason, wine or beer has long been considered a natural part of lunch and supper.

Unfortunately, in the process of distillation, many of the vitamins and minerals that were in the original wine are lost. Where the original wine might have contributed *something* to the nutritional requirements of the individual, even this modest contribution is not gained in drinking distilled spirits. Further, when the body breaks down alcohol, it finds "empty calories." The body obtains carbohydrates from the alcohol, without the protein, vitamins, and minerals needed by the body. This may contribute to a state of vitamin depletion called *avitaminosis*, to be discussed in the following chapter.

The process of distillation was developed in Arabia, but within two centuries had spread to Europe. It is reported that by the year A.D. 1000, Italian wine-growers were distilling wine to produce various drinks with higher concentrations of alcohol, mixing the obtained distilled spirits with various herbs and spices. This mixture was then used for medicinal purposes. Indeed, distilled spirits were viewed as the ultimate in medicines in Europe, where they were called the *aqua vitae*, or "water of life" (Ray & Ksir, 1987).

The history of alcohol in Western society is marked by increasing use over time. Periodic efforts at control or regulation of alcohol use have been almost uniformly unsuccessful. (For a detailed discussion of this aspect of the history of alcohol, see Ray and Ksir [1987].)

ALCOHOL TODAY

Over the last 900 years since the development of the distillation process, various forms of fermented wines using various ingredients, different forms of beer, and distilled spirits combined with various flavorings have emerged. With the march of civilization, some degree of standardization has resulted in uniform definitions of various classes of alcohol, although there still exists some regional variation.

Today, most American beer has an alcohol content of about 4% to 5%. As a class, wine continues to be made by allowing fermentation to take place in vats containing various grapes or other fruits. Occasionally, the fermentation involves products other than grapes, such as the famous "rice wine" from Japan called *sake*. Wine tends to have an alcohol content of approximately 9% to 12%, and there are only minor variations in how different wines are made.

Another class of wines are known as "fortified" wines. These are produced by adding distilled wine to fermented wine to raise the total alcohol content to about 20%. This class contains the various brands of sherry, and port (Ray & Ksir, 1987). Finally, there are the "hard liquors"—the distilled spirits whose alcohol content may range from 20% to as high as 95% (in the case of "Everclear" and similar distilled spirits).

Beverages that contain alcohol are moderately popular drinks. It has been estimated that 103 million Americans over the age of 12 (or 41% of the population) consumed alcohol at least once in the preceding year. Of this number, 61 million Americans drank less than once a week, on the average, while the remainder consumed at least one alcoholic beverage per week (Department of Health and Human Services, 1990). Unfortunately, a percentage of those who consume alcohol do so to the point where it interferes with their physical health and their social well being. We will discuss this drinking population in more detail in the next chapter.

THE PHARMACOLOGY OF ALCOHOL

Alcohol itself is a small molecule and is usually introduced into the body by drinking a liquid. Actually, alcohol may also be introduced into the body intravenously, or even as a vapor, however these methods are extremely dangerous and are used by physicians only rarely.

As stated by Julien (1988), about 20% of the alcohol consumed is immediately absorbed through the stomach lining; the other 80% is absorbed into the body through the small intestine. However, Rose (1988) contends that when one drinks on an empty stomach, all of the alcohol passes into the bloodstream through the stomach lining; indeed, Rose points out that the first alcohol will appear in the bloodstream in as little as a minute.

The concentration of alcohol in any individual's blood is influenced by a number of factors. When alcohol is mixed with food, only about 20% of the alcohol is absorbed immediately. It was once thought that the speed at which the remaining 80% enters the bloodstream, and thus is detoxified by the liver, was determined by how quickly the stomach empties into the small intestine. That is to say it was once thought that, sooner or later, *all* of the alcohol that was ingested would be absorbed (Julien, 1988).

However, recent research (for example, Frezza et al., 1990) suggests that, for some drinkers, the process of alcohol metabolism begins in the gastrointestinal tract. In other words, the body begins to break down the alcohol even before it reaches the general circulation, at least for some drinkers! Frezza et al. found that people produce an enzyme in the gastrointestinal tract known as *gastric alcohol dehydrogenase*. This enzyme begins to break down alcohol in the stomach, even before it reaches the bloodstream. Measured levels of gastric alcohol dehydrogenase were highest in rare social drinkers and significantly lower in individuals who ingested alcohol on a regular basis. Further, it was found that men produced more of this enzyme that women, a finding that Frezza et al. concluded may explain why women often have higher blood alcohol levels than men after drinking a similar amount of alcohol.

Folk remedies for hangovers sometimes include advice on how to avoid them. One piece of advice is to take an aspirin *before* drinking, so that the aspirin is already in the system for the morning after. Surprisingly, research findings suggest that the use of aspirin an hour prior to drinking alcohol will decrease the effectiveness of gastric alcohol dehydrogenase. This will result in a higher blood alcohol level for the rare social drinker than had been intended (Roine, Gentry, Hernandez-Mundoz, Baraona, & Lieber, 1990).

Another factor that will influence the amount of alcohol in any individual's blood (the *blood alcohol level*, or *BAL*) is body size. Maguire (1990) reports that 2 drinks consumed within 1 hour will result in a BAL of 0.09% (slightly below legal intoxication in most states) for an individual who weighs 100 pounds. But, a 200-lb individual will have a measured BAL of only 0.04% after consuming the same amount of alcohol. Since men usually are bigger than women, this would seem to be another reason why men are able to consume more alcohol than women before becoming intoxicated.

Once in the blood, alcohol tends to rapidly pass into all body tissues, including those of the brain. Since alcohol may diffuse into muscle tissue and fat tissue, an obese or muscular person will normally have a slightly lower blood alcohol level than a leaner person after a given dose (Julien, 1988). About 95% of the alcohol that reaches the blood is metabolized by the liver before it is excreted, at about the rate of one-third ounce of pure alcohol per hour in the normal, healthy individual. The other 5% of the alcohol found in the bloodstream is excreted unchanged through the lungs and skin, or passed as urine (Schuckit, 1989).

Macguire (1990) offers the following rule of thumb for estimating the rate at which alcohol is metabolized: The body can detoxify about one mixed drink of 80-proof alcohol, or one can of beer, per hour. Unfortunately, the rate at which alcohol is metabolized by the liver is "relatively slow, constant, and independent of the amount ingested" (Julien, 1988, p. 66). Thus, if a person drinks at about the rate of one ounce of whiskey per hour, or one can of beer per hour, the BAL will stay relatively constant until the body is able to metabolize the alcohol ingested.

If a person consumes more than one ounce of whiskey or one can of beer per hour, the amount of alcohol in his or her bloodstream will increase. The effects of alcohol are similar to that of other drugs that act as depressants on the central nervous system. This class of drugs, called the *CNS depressants*, includes the barbiturates, the benzodiazepines, and the so-called minor tranquilizers. Indeed, Maguire (1990) likens alcohol's effects to those of the anesthetic ether.

So similar are the effects of the CNS depressants to alcohol that one class of drug potentiates the effects of the other. *Potentiation* is a process whereby one drug enhances or exaggerates the action of another, similar, drug. In many cases, the potentiation effect between alcohol and CNS depressants of one kind or another has resulted in accidental (or occasionally intentional) death by drug overdose.

Sometimes a person who has been drinking heavily will vomit, as the body attempts to rid itself of the alcohol. Vomiting, however, can be fatal if a person is unconscious. If the person happens to inhale any of the material being regurgitated, he or she might develop a condition known as *aspirative pneumonia*. This is a very real, albeit rarely discussed, danger of drinking.

THE EFFECTS OF NORMAL DOSES OF ALCOHOL FOR THE AVERAGE DRINKER

After the average drinker has had a couple of drinks, respiration initially speeds up and the blood vessels in the surface of the skin dilate. This causes the person to feel warm, but actually the body is losing heat more rapidly as the warm blood rushes to the skin from the deeper parts of the body. Because respiration and the heart rate are initially speeded up when a person begins to drink, people used to think that alcohol was a stimulant. Lingeman (1974) refers to the "pseudo-stimulant" effect of alcohol. We know now that alcohol is a CNS depressant as potent as the barbiturates, *not* a stimulant as was once thought.

Surprisingly, an individual's expectations play a role in how he or she interprets the effects of normal doses of alcohol (S. A. Brown, 1990). Drawing upon her previous research into the role of expectancies and alcohol use, S. A. Brown notes that "expectancies are closely linked to actual drinking practices of both adolescents and adults" (p. 17). Thus, individuals who drink will have their alcohol experience shaped not only by the pharmacological effects of alcohol but also by their expectations for what the alcohol will do.

According to S. A. Brown (1990), males are more likely than females to expect that alcohol will decrease their anxiety, enhance sexual arousal, and make them more aggressive. Females are more likely to anticipate pleasurable changes from moderate drinking. Such expectations for the effects of alcohol are common and tend to reinforce the tendency to drink (S. A. Brown, 1990; Critchlow, 1986).

In a study of the expectations for alcohol by adolescents who abuse alcohol and those who do not, Brown, Creamer, and Stetson (1987) found that adolescents who abuse alcohol are more likely to anticipate a positive experience when they drink, whereas those who do not abuse alcohol are less likely to anticipate positive drinking experiences. This finding was attributed to the adolescents' home environment. Those who abused alcohol were more likely to come from a home where parents reported positive experiences with alcohol than the nonabusing adolescents.

Thus, at low to moderate dosage levels, one factor that influences the effect that alcohol has on the individual is the expectation the person has for the alcohol. Indeed, S. A. Brown (1990) concludes that at low to moderate dosage levels, an individual's expectations and subjective interpretation of alcohol's effects may be at least as important as the pharmacological effects of the alcohol consumed, if not more so.

It has long been known that alcohol has a *disinhibition effect* on individuals. This effect comes about as the alcohol starts to interfere with the normal function of the nerve cells in the cortex—the part of the brain most responsible for "higher" functions, such as abstract thinking, speech, and so forth. The cortex is also the part of the brain where much of our voluntary behavior is planned. As the alcohol interferes with normal nerve function, one tends to temporarily "forget" social inhibitions. Julien (1988) estimates that this disinhibition effect can be achieved after a person has ingested as little as 1 to 3 ounces of whiskey. Thus, the individual may be unable to accurately judge his or her ability to drive a car, contributing to alcohol-related accidents on the road.

In the normal individual, the effects of one or two drinks are interpreted as pleasant and relaxing. The individual might feel more confident or less tense. There seems to be a tendency for people to attribute *any* pleasant change to an alcoholic beverage, despite the alcohol's effects on the body (Critchlow, 1986). This again reflects the individual's expectations for the alcohol rather than its actual physiological effects.

THE EFFECTS OF ABOVE-NORMAL DOSES OF ALCOHOL FOR THE AVERAGE DRINKER

As we have noted, alcohol is a CNS depressant, which at high dosage levels is an anesthetic (Julien, 1988; Schuckit, 1989). Although many people fail to realize that one can die from an alcohol overdose, occasionally this does happen. The amount of alcohol in the blood necessary to bring about a state of unconsciousness is only a little less than the level necessary to bring about an alcohol overdose. Thus, when a person drinks to the point of losing consciousness, he or she might be dangerously close to overdosing on alcohol.

On a physiological level, alcohol's effects are virtually identical to those of the CNS depressants. CNS depressants can serve as sedatives, tranquilizers, hypnotic agents, or as anesthetics depending on the dose (Julien, 1988). At extremely high levels in the bloodstream, death may result from any of the CNS depressants. Indeed, for *all* drugs classified as CNS depressants, there is a progression from mild sedation to heavy sedation to coma and, ultimately, to death, as the bloodstream concentrations increase.

According to Ray and Ksir (1987), a BAL of 0.05% would result in lowered alertness, feelings of euphoria, a loss of inhibitions, and impairment of judgment. For someone who weighs 160 lbs or less, a BAL of 0.05% could be achieved after only 2 drinks (Maguire, 1990).

A 160-lb person who had consumed 4 drinks in an hour's time would have a BAL of 0.10% or higher and would be legally intoxicated in most states

(Maguire, 1990). A physical examination would reveal slowed reaction times and impaired ability to coordinate muscle actions (a condition called *ataxia*).

A person with a BAL of 0.15% could be expected to have serious difficulty reacting fast enough to avoid an accident while driving (Lingeman, 1974). With a BAL of 0.20%, the person most definitely would be intoxicated, with a marked ataxia (P. R. Matuschka, 1985). With a BAL of 0.25% the person would stagger around and have trouble interpreting sensory data (Ray & Ksir, 1987). The person with a BAL of 0.30% would be stuporous and, although conscious, would be likely to be unable to recall what happened to him or her in that state of intoxication (P. R. Matuschka, 1985).

At a 0.35% BAL, surgical anesthesia is achieved (P. R. Matuschka, 1985). According to Ray and Ksir (1987), without medical supervision and support, about 1% of those whose blood alcohol concentration is this high will die. Ray and Ksir also note that a BAL of 0.40% will result in about a 50% death rate from alcohol overdose without medical intervention. However, according to Schuckit (1989), a person who is tolerant to the effects of alcohol might still be conscious and able to talk with a BAL as high as 0.78%.

Segal and Sisson (1985) hold that the approximate lethal BAL in human beings is 0.5%, whereas Lingeman (1974) argues for a likely lethal BAL of somewhere between 0.5% and 0.8%. However, since a BAL of 0.35% or above may result in death, it is suggested that all cases of known or suspected alcohol overdose be immediately treated by a physician.

MEDICAL COMPLICATIONS OF ALCOHOL USE FOR THE AVERAGE DRINKER

The Hangover

Although it is not clear exactly how alcohol works to cause the so-called hangover, we do know that alcohol is a toxic chemical that affects both the stomach and the brain. If the person has ingested enough alcohol, he or she will experience a hangover the next day. Symptoms may include malaise, headache, tremor, and nausea (Kissin, 1985). While a severe hangover may make the victim wish for death (O'Donnell, 1986), in general the alcohol hangover is self-limiting and will respond to self-treatment that may include antacids and aspirin (Kissin, 1985).

For the majority, the hangover following a night's drinking is viewed as the price to be paid for a night's indulgence. Few people see it as a cause for major concern. The hangover may be considered a reflection of an early withdrawal syndrome from alcohol (Kissin, 1985; Ray and Ksir, 1987). Alcoholic hangovers are associated with the earlier stages of addiction, before the individual's body has started to adapt to the continued use of alcohol. The individual who is suffering from a hangover, be it after a single night of drinking or a more protracted period, is thus possibly going through a mild withdrawal process.

Sleep Disorders

Despite the fact that it is a CNS depressant, alcohol interferes with the normal sleep cycle. While it may bring about sleep, it does not allow for a normal dream cycle. This effect is not noted for the person who drinks only on a social basis. But for the chronic alcoholic, the cumulative effects might be quite disruptive. The impact of chronic alcohol use on the normal sleep cycle will be discussed fully in the next chapter.

Even the occasional drinker should be aware, however, that alcohol can impair an individual's ability to breathe during sleep. Within 2 hours of going to sleep, even moderate amounts of alcohol can contribute to *sleep apnea* (*Science Digest*, 1989). This is a potentially fatal disorder in which respiration temporarily stops during sleep. Complications caused by sleep apnea include high blood pressure and a disruption of the normal heart rate.

Individuals who consume even moderate amounts of alcohol prior to sleep have been found to experience twice as many apnea episodes as they experience when abstaining from alcohol use (*Science Digest*, 1989). Thus, individuals with breathing disorders, especially sleep apnea, should not drink, especially during the hours before bedtime.

Adverse Reactions from Drug Interactions

In addition to the potentiation effect that develops when one combines alcohol with the sedatives, alcohol interacts with other medications as well.[1] For individuals who are taking nitroglycerin, a medication often used in the treatment of heart conditions, the use of alcohol may result in significantly reduced blood pressure levels, possibly to the point of dizziness and loss of consciousness (Pappas, 1990). When combined with aspirin, alcohol may contribute to bleeding in the stomach. Oral medications for diabetes may negate the body's ability to metabolize alcohol, possibly resulting in acute alcohol poisoning from even moderate doses. Patients who are on the antidepressants known as *monoamine oxidase inhibitors* (or MAO inhibitors) should not consume alcohol. The fermentation process produces tyramine along with the alcohol. Tyramine is normally used by the body to produce an important amino acid, but it interacts with the MAO inhibitors, resulting in dangerously high, and possibly fatal, blood pressure levels.

SUMMARY

Following a brief overview of alcohol, we explored how it affects the body and described some of the more common complications of short-term alcohol use. The short-term effects of normal doses include a mild disinhibition effect, a mild sedative effect, and a vasodilation effect on the blood vessels on the

[1]Patients taking *any* medication should refrain from using alcohol along with it, except under a physician's supervision.

surface of the body. Above-normal doses may lead to heavy sedation, coma, and ultimately death. Research has demonstrated that, especially at the lower dosage levels, the individual's expectations for alcohol influence how its effects are interpreted.

In order to fully appreciate the effects of alcohol, one must consider the impact of long-term use on the individual, as well as the short-term effects. In the next chapter, we will turn our attention to the effects of chronic use.

Chapter 4

THE CHRONIC USE
OF ALCOHOL

T he focus of the last chapter was on the acute effects of alcohol on the "average" person. But because alcohol is a mild toxin, we must also consider the impact that chronic exposure has on an individual's body. Fortunately, only about 11% of the adults in the United States drink on a daily basis. However, for these individuals, chronic exposure to the toxic effects of alcohol often extracts a terrible price. In this chapter, the impact of chronic alcohol use on the individual will be explored.

THE SCOPE OF THE PROBLEM

Alcohol is a popular drug of choice for addicts. It is, by far, the most popular drug of abuse, accounting for an astounding 85% of the drug-addiction problem in the United States (J. Franklin, 1987). To put the problem of alcoholism in perspective, consider the fact that just 10% of the U.S. drinking population consumes fully 50% of all the alcohol produced in the United States (Kaplan & Sadock, 1988).

Viewing these statistics from another perspective, it has been estimated that there are approximately 10 million adult alcoholics in the United States (Bays, 1990). An additional 1 million (Ellis et al., 1988) to 3 million (Turbo, 1989) children and adolescents are also addicted to alcohol. Beasley (1987) holds out an even higher figure, reporting that between 10 and 15 million Americans are currently alcoholic, with an additional 10 million being "on the cusp of alcoholism" (p. 21).

To understand Beasley's (1987) statement, it is necessary to realize that the distinction between alcohol abuse and alcohol dependency is often an artificial one (Schuckit, Zisook, & Mortola, 1985). Indeed, Schuckit et al. found a group of men identified as abusers to be virtually identical to another group of men diagnosed as alcohol dependent. The major difference between the two groups was that the men in the latter drank more when they did drink and were more likely to have had alcohol-related medical problems.

From these findings, Schuckit et al. conclude that "it is not clear whether the distinction between alcohol abuse and alcohol dependence carries any important prognostic or treatment implications" (p. 1403). It is for this reason that, on the continuum of chemical use introduced in Chapter 2, category 2 is identified as "heavy social use/early problem use of drugs," while category 3 is identified as "heavy problem use/early addiction to drugs." When one's alcohol use has reached this level of intensity, the distinction between *abuse* and *dependence* becomes so vague as to have little relevance.

ALCOHOL TOLERANCE, DEPENDENCE, AND "CRAVING"

Tolerance to Alcohol

In the last chapter, it was noted that a person who was tolerant to the effects of alcohol might still be conscious and able to talk with a BAL of 0.78% (Schuckit, 1989). Alcohol, like the other CNS depressants, brings about a state of tolerance when used over an extended period of time. However, despite the development of tolerance the lethal dose of alcohol remains the same (P. R. Matuschka, 1985).

In the case of alcohol, both metabolic tolerance and pharmacodynamic tolerance develop as the individual's body adapts to the continual presence of the chemical. The chronic drinker's liver becomes more efficient at metabolizing alcohol, at least in the earlier stages of his or her drinking career. This is metabolic tolerance to alcohol, and one of the hallmarks of a serious alcohol problem is the individual's admission that it takes more for him or her to become intoxicated now than in the past.

Further, where an inexperienced drinker might be quite intoxicated after five or six mixed drinks, the chronic drinker might hardly have started to feel the effects of alcohol after "only" six drinks. This is an example of what is often called *behavioral tolerance*. The chronic drinker might appear quite sober, although he or she is actually legally intoxicated. If judged only on the basis of physical appearance, many chronic alcoholics manage to appear relatively sober, at least to the untrained observer, despite the fact that blood tests would reveal significant amounts of alcohol in their blood.

Behavioral tolerance is actually an expression of pharmacodynamic tolerance to the effects of alcohol. Remember that in pharmacodynamic tolerance the cells of the central nervous system attempt to carry out their normal function in spite of the continual presence of the toxin (in this case, alcohol). The cells of the brain become less and less sensitive to the intoxicating effects of the chemical; thus, the individual has to use more of the drug to achieve the same effect.

Dependence on Alcohol

Like the other CNS depressants, alcohol can bring about a state of both psychological and physical dependence (Segal & Sisson, 1985). *Psychological dependence* refers to a pattern of repeated self-administration of alcohol because the individual finds it rewarding. *Physical dependence* refers to a characteristic withdrawal syndrome, which comes about after the body adapts to the drug's effects. Over time, the alcoholic's body learns to function in spite of the use of alcohol. When the body adapts to the constant presence of the alcohol, it will take a period of time before its functions return to normal again if the person stops drinking.

The period of adjustment from intoxication to the normal state of being sober involves a great deal of discomfort for the chronic alcoholic. It is this withdrawal phase that many alcoholics attempt to avoid by drinking still more. The severity of the withdrawal from alcohol depends on (a) the intensity with which the individual used alcohol, (b) the duration of time over which the individual drank, and (c) the individual's state of health. The longer the period of alcohol use and the greater the amount ingested, the more severe the alcohol withdrawal syndrome. We will describe the symptoms of alcohol withdrawal for the chronic alcoholic in more detail later in this chapter.

Craving for Alcohol

Many alcoholics speak of a "craving" for alcohol long after they stop drinking. This craving may occur because chronic alcohol use can significantly reduce the brain's production of a group of opiatelike neurotransmitters—the *endorphins*, the *enkephalins*, and the *dynorphins* (Trachtenberg & Blum, 1987). These neurotransmitters function in the brain's pleasure center to help moderate an individual's emotions and behavior.

Blum (1988) suggests that a byproduct of alcohol metabolism combines with neurotransmitters normally found in the brain to form *tetrahydroisoquinoline* (TIQ). TIQ, in turn, is capable of binding to opiatelike receptor sites within the brain's pleasure center. In so doing, the individual experiences a sense of well-being (Blum & Payne 1991; Blum & Trachtenberg, 1988). This mechanism seems to be the reason why alcohol use is rewarding to the individual. However, TIQ's effects are short-lived, and the individual must drink more alcohol in order to regain or maintain the initial pleasurable feeling.

Chronic use of alcohol is thought to cause the brain to reduce its production of enkephalins, as the ever-present TIQ is substituted for naturally produced neurotransmitters (Blum & Payne, 1991; Blum & Trachtenberg, 1988). Furthermore, animal research suggests that the chronic use of alcohol reduces the amount of available dopamine and serotonin in the brain. The cessation of alcohol intake results in a neurochemical deficit, which the individual attempts to relieve through further chemical use. If the individual does not continue to use chemicals, this deficit is experienced as the "craving" for alcohol commonly reported by recovering alcoholics.

Recent research has also uncovered mechanisms by which alcohol seems to alter the brain's chemistry following both its short-term and its chronic use. The observed changes in brain chemistry underscore the potency of alcohol— a chemical that was long thought to be relatively harmless.

THE EFFECTS OF CHRONIC ALCOHOL USE

The chronic use of alcohol affects every organ of the body. Unfortunately, there is no simple formula by which to calculate the amount of damage done by drinking or to determine which organs will be affected. As stated by Segal and Sisson (1985):

> Some heavy drinkers of many years' duration appear to go relatively un-
> scathed, while others develop complications early (e.g., after five years) in
> their drinking careers. Some develop brain damage; others liver disease, still
> others, both. The reasons for this are simply not known. (p. 145)

It is known, however, that in different individuals the chronic use of alcohol will have an impact on different body systems.

The Digestive System

As we discussed in the last chapter, during distillation many of the vitamins and minerals that were in the original wine are lost. The body obtains carbohydrates from the alcohol it metabolizes, without the protein, vitamins, calcium, and other minerals. This may contribute to the state of vitamin depletion we referred to earlier, and which we will discuss in more detail later in this chapter.

It has been known for many years that chronic use of alcohol increases the risk of many forms of cancer. Schuckit (1989) notes that "alcoholics . . . have significantly elevated rates of cancers, especially [of] the esophagus and the stomach, as well as the head and neck" (p. 52). Nelson (1989) warns that the combination of cigarettes and alcohol is especially dangerous, as alcoholics who smoke tend to have "especially high rates of throat cancers" (p. 8 Ex).

In speaking of the impact of the chronic use of alcohol on the digestive system, Nace (1987) observes that "the organ most commonly thought to be affected by alcohol is the liver" (p. 23). Indeed, the human liver is the primary site at which alcohol is metabolized within the body (Frezza et al., 1990; Schenker & Speeg, 1990). Surprisingly, for reasons that are not fully understood, only 5% to 10% of alcoholics develop liver disease (D. W. Goodwin, 1989). The first manifestation of alcohol-related liver problems is the development of a *fatty liver*, a condition in which the liver becomes enlarged and does not function at full efficiency (Nace, 1987; Willoughby, 1984). This can usually be detected by physical examination, or through various blood tests (Schuckit, 1989).

If alcohol consumption continues, the individual is likely to develop *alcoholic hepatitis* which Nace (1987) characterizes as "a slow, smoldering process which may proceed or coexist with cirrhosis" (p. 25). Symptoms include a low-grade fever, malaise, jaundice, an enlarged and tender liver, and dark urine. A physical examination may reveal characteristic changes in the blood chemistry (Schuckit, 1989). Although it is thought that alcoholic hepatitis precedes the development of cirrhosis of the liver, this has not been proven.

Cirrhosis of the liver is the sixth leading cause of death in the United States (Nace, 1987). Over time, if the person continues to drink, fat deposits form in the liver. The repeated insults to the liver result in the formation of scar tissue, and large areas of the liver are permanently damaged. In many cases, a physical examination will reveal a hard, nodular liver, as well as an enlarged spleen, testicular atrophy, "spider" angiomas, tremor, jaundice, and a number of other symptoms (Nace, 1987).

Cirrhosis can lead to severe complications, including liver cancer and sodium and water retention (Nace, 1987; Schuckit, 1989). Furthermore, the scar tissue and fat deposits prevent the liver from filtering the blood as efficiently as before, causing toxins to build up in the blood. This then adds to the damage being done to the brain by the alcohol (Julien 1988; Willoughby, 1984). At the same time, the now-enlarged liver puts a greater workload on the heart, as the swelling of the liver puts pressure on the blood vessels that pass through it, causing the pressure to build up within the vessels. This condition is known as *portal hypertension*, and in turn may contribute to a swelling of the blood vessels in the esophagus. When the blood vessels in the esophagus swell, weak spots form on their walls, much like weak spots form on an inner tube of a tire. These weak spots in the walls of the blood vessels of the esophagus may rupture, leading to massive bleeding (Schuckit, 1989; Willoughby, 1984). This is a medical emergency that carries about a 33% mortality rate.

As if that were not enough, alcohol has been implicated as one cause of a painful inflammation of the pancreas, known as *pancreatitis*. Approximately one-third of pancreatitis cases are thought to be brought on by the chronic use of alcohol. According to Nace (1987), this condition usually occurs after 10 to 15 years of heavy drinking. The chronic use of alcohol also has been shown to cause *gastritis*, an inflammation of the lining of the stomach. This may result in bleeding from the stomach lining, or may contribute to the formation of ulcers (Willoughby, 1984). It has been estimated that about 30% of heavy drinkers will suffer from chronic gastritis (P. R. Matuschka, 1985).

If an ulcer forms over a major blood vessel, the individual may experience a "bleeding ulcer," as the stomach acid eats through the stomach lining and blood vessel walls. This is a severe medical emergency that frequently results in death. Willoughby (1984) notes that the medical treatment for this condition may include the surgical removal of part of the stomach, a condition that contributes to the body's difficulties in finding and absorbing suitable amounts of vitamins. This may lead to a chronic state of malnutrition, which in turn makes the individual a prime candidate for the development of tuberculosis (TB) (Willoughby, 1984). The treatment of TB is rather slow and difficult, often requiring that medication be taken on a regular basis for up to 18 months. Sometimes, surgery is necessary to remove the infected tissues, a process both painful and life-threatening in itself. Willoughby (1984) estimates that upwards of 95% of those alcoholics who have had a portion of their stomach removed secondary to bleeding ulcers and who continue to drink will ultimately develop TB.

Finally, the chronic use of alcohol lowers the effectiveness of the digestive system, resulting in malabsorption syndromes in which vitamins and needed nutrients are not absorbed in the quantities needed. When the body breaks down alcohol, one of the by-products is a sugar, which the body then burns in the place of normal food (Charness, Simon, & Greenberg, 1989). This results in a form of anorexia, as the body replaces the normal calorie intake with "empty" calories obtained from alcohol. In turn, this contributes to a decline in the effectiveness of the immune system in general. Beasley (1987) terms this condition a "leaky gut"—a common condition in chronic alcoholics.

The Heart and Circulatory System

Surprisingly, researchers have discovered that the moderate daily use of alcohol (that is, 1 to 2 drinks) has been found to have a beneficial effect on the cardiovascular system for men. The consumption of between ½ and 2½ drinks per day seems to be associated with a 25% reduction in the risk of heart attacks in men (Associated Press, 1991d).

For the chronic alcoholic, however, red-blood-cell formation is suppressed, and both blood-clotting problems and anemia are common. In fact, bacterial pneumonia is more than twice as common in alcoholics as in nonalcoholics (Nace, 1987). This is true for several reasons. First, the chronic use of alcohol lowers the resistance to disease by lowering the effectiveness of the immune system. Secondly, the individual might aspirate some of the material vomited during and after periods of drinking, a condition we referred to earlier as *aspirative pneumonia*. If the individual is unconscious when he or she vomits—a possibility if a great deal of alcohol has been consumed—there is a very real danger that the drinker will suffocate.

Alcohol is also implicated in damage to the cardiovascular system itself. In large amounts, alcohol is known to be *cardiotoxic*, which is to say that it is toxic to the muscle tissue of the heart. Prolonged exposure in high dosage levels may result in permanent damage to the heart-muscle tissue, resulting in *hypertension* (or high blood pressure), and inflammation of the heart muscle known as *myocardiopathy*. Approximately 25% of chronic alcoholics suffer from myocardiopathy (Schuckit, 1989).

The Central Nervous System

As we discussed in the last chapter, alcohol is toxic to the cells of the central nervous system. The chronic use of alcohol may result in a deterioration of the peripheral nerves in the hands and feet known as *peripheral neuropathies*. This condition is found in 5% to 15% of chronic alcoholics, and occasionally in nonalcoholic individuals, such as diabetics. Vitamin B deficiencies secondary to poor nutrition and vitamin malabsorption syndromes are thought to be the cause of this condition (Beasley, 1987; Charness et al., 1989; Nace, 1987). The chronic lack of proper vitamins causes nerve cells to die over time, with those in the hands and feet being the first to be affected (Schuckit, 1989).

Alcohol has also been implicated in damage to the brain tissue itself, and it has been estimated that 75% of chronic alcoholics will demonstrate some evidence of CNS dysfunction on standard neuropsychological tests (Tarter,

Ott, & Mezzich, 1991). The possibility that alcohol-induced brain damage might be detected even before the development of alcohol-related liver damage has been suggested (Berg, Franzen, & Wedding, 1987).

Ultimately, alcohol-induced brain damage may become so severe as to result in the need for nursing home placement. Indeed, Schuckit (1989) estimates that between 15% and 30% of all nursing home patients are admitted because of permanent alcohol-induced brain damage. Nace and Isbell (1991) state that alcohol-induced dementia is the second most common adult dementia, Alzheimer's disease being the first. Alcohol-induced dementia affects approximately 9% of alcoholics. It is also currently the single most preventable cause of dementia in the United States (Beasley, 1987).

One of the most frequent symptoms found in heavy drinking is that of memory disturbance, especially during the period when the person is drinking heavily. The person may find it impossible to remember events that took place while he or she was intoxicated, a condition commonly known as *blackout*. These periods of alcohol-induced amnesia may last for several days, although for the most part they are not that long (Segal & Sisson, 1985; Willoughby, 1984).[1]

During a memory blackout, the individual is able to carry out many complex tasks, often with great efficiency. However, he or she will not have any memory of having performed these tasks at a later time. The exact mechanism by which alcohol brings about a memory blackout is unknown; however, according to Zucker and Branchey (1984), blackouts are "among the most frequently reported symptoms in the progression of alcoholism" (p. 296).

Wernicke—Korsakoff's syndrome   Chronic alcohol use, as mentioned earlier, contributes to vitamin deficiencies, a condition known as *avitaminosis*. Avitaminosis is caused either by a lack of adequate vitamin intake or an inability of the body to use available vitamins effectively (Beasley, 1987). This process depletes the body's reserves of many vitamins, and over a period of time can result in a form of brain damage known as *Wernicke's encephalopathy* (Charness et al., 1989; Reuler, Girard, & Cooney, 1985).

Wernicke's encephalopathy develops when the body is deprived of adequate amounts of thiamine, one of the B family of vitamins, for extended periods of time. This chronic thiamine deficiency results in characteristic brain damage and has a 10% to 20% mortality rate (Reuler et al., 1985).

The individual suffering from Wernicke's disease may be confused to the point of being delirious and disoriented and exhibit a characteristic abnormal eye movement pattern known as *nystagmus*. Of those who survive this condi-

---

[1]Putnam (1989) cautions that an individual suffering from multiple personality disorder (MPD) might attribute the loss of memory often experienced by the main personality when another personality emerges to alcohol or drug use. This is because an alcohol- or drug-induced memory blackout is less threatening than one not caused by chemicals. Thus, the clinician must carefully determine whether the client has experienced episodes of memory loss when she or he has *not* been using alcohol or chemicals. Such non-drug-induced blackouts might indicate a neurological or psychiatric problem, such as MPD.

tion without treatment, up to 80% will go on to develop a condition known as *Korsakoff's psychosis,* or *Korsakoff's syndrome* (Charness et al., 1989; Reuler et al., 1985). Treatment consists of vitamin replacement therapy to limit the amount of damage to the brain. However, even when Wernicke's encephalophy is properly treated through aggressive thiamine replacement procedures, 25% of the patients who develop this disease will go on to develop Korsakoff's syndrome (Sagar, 1991).

Korsakoff's syndrome is a chronic organic brain syndrome, marked by inability to remember the past accurately, as well as difficulty in learning new information, ataxia, and neurological problems. In the earlier stages, the person who has Korsakoff's syndrome tends to "fill in" the gaps in his or her memory by making up answers to questions. This process is called *confabulation.* Confabulation tends to be most common in the earlier stages of Korsakoff's syndrome; as the individual adjusts to the loss of memory, he or she will not be as likely to confabulate (Brandt & Butters, 1986).

The exact mechanism of Korsakoff's syndrome is unknown at this time. The characteristic nystagmus seems to reflect a vitamin malabsorption syndrome, which may respond to massive doses of thiamine or vitamin B_1. However, the intellectual decline noted in Korsakoff's syndrome seems to come about differently. Brandt and Butters (1986) suggest that the person with Korsakoff's syndrome may be suffering from the toxic effects of long-term exposure to alcohol, which is a mild neurotoxin. They note that alcohol will cause a dose-related change in intellectual abilities which, when it reaches the stage evident in Korsakoff's syndrome, has become so severe that only 25% of the victims will return to their previous level of intellectual functioning.

In the author's clinical practice, one individual suspected of suffering from Korsakoff's syndrome reported that he was 53 years old, when according to the records he was almost 58. He was able to correctly identify his date of birth when asked to do so, but could not correctly recall his current age. He repeatedly confabulated an age for the one he could no longer recall. (Details have been changed to protect the identity of the client.)

Confabulation may involve different areas of memory, and sometimes is difficult to spot without collateral information or objective background data. Sacks (1970) notes that individuals will occasionally lose virtually all memories after a certain period of their lives and will almost be "frozen in time." He offers the example of a man who, in the mid 1970s, was convinced that it was just after World War II and was unable to recall anything after the late 1940s. This extreme example of confabulation, while extremely rare, can result from chronic alcoholism. More frequent are less pronounced cases, where significant portions of the memory are lost, but where the individual retains *some* memory.

At one point, Wernicke's encephalophy was thought to be a separate disorder from Korsakoff's syndrome. Now, both are understood to be different stages of the same disease. This disorder is now frequently referred to as *Wernicke–Korsakoff's syndrome.*

As previously stated, alcohol has been implicated as causing brain damage. Grant (1987), however, questions whether evidence of brain damage noted on neuropsychological testing is permanent, or whether some limited degree of recovery is possible for the chronic alcoholic. The work of Grant (1987) and Løberg (1986) suggests that a *limited* degree of improvement in cognitive function is possible in alcoholics who continue to abstain from alcohol for extended periods of time. This would seem to be true both for women (Fabian & Parsons, 1983) and for men (Grant, 1987).

One should keep in mind, however, that *limited* recovery of cognitive function does not mean *complete* recovery. Nace & Isbell (1991) suggest that perhaps only 20% of chronic alcoholics return to their previous level of intellectual functioning. Some limited degree of recovery is possible in perhaps 60% of the cases, and there is virtually no recovery of lost intellectual function in 20% of the cases. Charness et al. (1989) stated these statistics in a different way, concluding that 50% to 70% of chronic alcoholics will develop at least mild cognitive deficits, as measured by psychological tests.

Alcohol's effects on the sleep cycle   In Chapter 3, we noted that alcohol actually interferes with the normal sleep pattern, although it is a CNS depressant. Fredrickson, Richardson, Esther, & Lin (1990) report that 12% of the patients at a sleep disorder clinic for treatment of insomnia were found to have a history of alcohol abuse or alcohol dependence. Like the other CNS depressants, alcohol may bring about sleep, but it does not allow for a normal dream cycle. As a result of chronic alcohol use, the individual may experience a decrease in dream time, which takes place during the rapid-eye-movement (or REM) phase of sleep. When the individual stops drinking, he or she enters a period of abnormal sleep known as "REM rebound."

REM rebound is characterized by intense and vivid dreams, often to the point of frequent nightmares. These "rebound" dreams may be so frightening as to drive the individual to start drinking again in order to get a decent night's sleep. REM rebound can last for up to 6 months after a person has stopped drinking. In fact, Fredrickson et al. (1990) report that, in rare cases, the effects of alcohol can interfere with the normal sleep cycle over a year after detoxification.

The Emotional State

We have emphasized that alcohol is a CNS depressant. And as Willoughby (1984) notes, the depressant effects from just a single drink may last as long as 96 hours. The effects of an alcohol binge of 1 or 2 days might last for several weeks after abstinence (Segal & Sisson, 1985).

Chronic alcohol use often results in a range of neurotic and even psychotic symptoms that are thought to be secondary to the malnutrition and toxicity associated with alcoholism (Beasley, 1987). These symptoms can include depressive reactions (Schuckit, 1989) and generalized anxiety disorders and panic attacks (Beasley, 1987). Indeed, Beasley observes that of those patients diagnosed as having a generalized anxiety disorder, more than 20% were alcoholics whose "anxiety" was actually an early symptom of alcohol withdrawal. Stockwell and Town (1989) warn that many of those who seek help for anxiety attacks will be experiencing withdrawal-related "rebound anxiety" episodes, which will probably clear up after the use of alcohol is discontinued.

Unfortunately, anxiety attacks are often treated by physicians with antianxiety agents, known to be potentially addictive. It is common for chronic alcoholics to control their withdrawal symptoms during the day through the use of benzodiazepines. In this way, they can avoid the first stages of alcohol withdrawal during the work day, without the telltale smell of alcohol on their breath.

If the physician fails of obtain an adequate history and perform a physical exam (or if the patient lies about his or her alcohol use), there is a risk that the alcoholic might combine antianxiety medication with alcohol. The potential for an overdose exists when two different classes of CNS depressants are combined. Also, as Beasley (1987) notes, when the family of antianxiety agents known as benzodiazepines is combined with alcohol, a *paradoxical rage reaction* may result. In this situation, a drug that is normally a depressant brings about an unexpected period of rage in the individual to the point where he or she may attempt to physically harm others.

Occasionally, a person who is suffering from an actual anxiety disorder will try to self-medicate with alcohol. Since the effects of alcohol are very similar to those of the barbiturates, one should not be surprised to learn that alcohol has a fair antianxiety effect; that is, *in the short run*. Unfortunately, many of those who suffer from anxiety, whether alcohol induced or not, will turn toward further use of alcohol as a way to deal with the rebound anxiety that is experienced when the alcohol wears off.

The chronic use of alcohol will cause a paradoxical stimulation of the autonomic nervous system that the drinker will interpret as additional anxiety. A cycle is then started where the chronic use of alcohol actually sets the stage for further anxiety, resulting in the need for more alcohol. Stockwell and Town (1989) draw the following conclusion: "Many clients who drink heavily or abuse other anxiolytic drugs will experience substantial or complete recovery from extreme anxiety following sucessful detoxification" (p. 223). Thus, they recommend a drug-free period of at least 2 weeks in which to assess the need for pharmacological intervention for anxiety. While the topic of the pharmacological treatment of anxiety is outside of the scope of this text, the reader should keep in mind the need for a 2-week drug-free period in which to assess whether such treatment is indicated.

As noted, alcohol has been implicated in depressive reactions for chronic alcoholics. Surprisingly, many people who are clinically depressed will use alcohol in order to "numb" the depressive feelings they experience. This form of self-medication tends to add to the feelings of depression in the long run. Many people are unaware of this fact, thus setting up a vicious cycle. The depressed individual turns to alcohol to deal with the depression, then ends up feeling even more depressed because of the additional use of alcohol.

Schuckit (1983) estimates that between one-third and one-half of alcoholics display symptoms of depression at some point in their lives. According to Wolf-Reeve (1990), during the first 2 weeks of treatment, most alcoholics will meet the diagnostic criteria for major depression. However, in the vast majority of these cases, the individual is suffering from an *alcohol-induced* depression that will clear up shortly after detoxification from the alcohol (Schuckit, 1983; Willenbring 1986; Wolf-Reeve, 1990).

Primary depression in alcoholics is rare. It has been estimated that only 2% to 3% (Powell, Read, Penick, Miller, & Bingham, 1987) to perhaps as many as 5% (Schuckit, 1989) of the cases of depression seen in alcoholics is actually a primary depression. The vast majority of the cases of depression in chronic alcoholics is thought to be alcohol-induced; as such, it usually clears up within a short period after the person stops drinking.

However, it is well known that depression is significantly related to suicide (Hirschfeld & Davidson, 1988). One would expect, then, that alcoholics would be a high-risk group for suicide. Not surprisingly, research findings indicate a 15% lifetime risk for suicide among alcoholics, whether their depression is primary or secondary to their drinking (Hirschfeld & Davidson, 1988; Schuckit, 1986). Brent, Kupfer, Bromet, & Dew (1988) suggest that suicide is most likely to occur late in the course of alcoholism, when the individual first begins to experience such medical complications as cirrhosis of the liver.

Alcohol withdrawal for the chronic alcoholic   Unlike the social drinker, who may recover from a night's drinking with little more than a hangover, an alcoholic may experience an alcohol withdrawal syndrome when he or she attempts to stop drinking. This is an acute brain syndrome that develops within 24 to 96 hours after the last drink in 90% of the cases (Weiss & Mirin, 1988). However, alcohol withdrawal syndrome has been reported to occur up to 10 days following the last drink (Slaby, Lieb, & Tancredi, 1981).

As stated previously, the severity of alcohol withdrawal symptoms experienced by an individual depends on (a) the intensity with which that individual used alcohol, (b) the duration of time over which the individual drank, and (c) the individual's state of health. Approximately 6 to 8 hours after the last drink, the individual may experience any or all of the following symptoms: agitation, anxiety, diarrhea, hyperactivity, exaggerated reflexes, insomnia, nausea, restlessness, sweating, tachycardia, vomiting, and vertigo (Lieveld & Aruna, 1991).

In mild withdrawal cases, only few of these symptoms may be evident, and the individual may not progress to the next level of withdrawal. However, in more advanced cases, the symptoms may become more intense over a 6- to 24-hour period following the last use of alcohol. The individual may also begin to experience *alcoholic hallucinosis,* or hallucinations brought on by the withdrawal process.

In extreme cases of alcohol withdrawal, these symptoms will continue to become more intense over the next 2 days, and by the third day following the last drink the patient will start to experience fever, incontinence, and/or tremors in addition to the other symptoms. In approximately 16% of the cases, the withdrawal syndrome will also result in alcohol-related seizures (Nace & Isbell, 1991).

A further complication of chronic alcohol use seen in extreme cases is a condition known as the *delirium tremens* (DT's). It has been estimated that only about 5% (Lieveld & Aruna, 1991) to 10% (Weiss & Mirin, 1988) of alcoholics will develop the DT's, but they are certainly to be feared. The DT's involve a period of delirium, hallucinations, delusional beliefs that one is being followed, fever, and tachycardia (Lieveld & Aruna, 1991).

Throughout history, death from exhaustion has resulted in from 5% to 25% of the cases of individuals going through the full alcohol withdrawal syndrome (Schuckit, 1989). The causes of death for those going through the DT's include sepsis, cardiac and/or respiratory arrest, and cardia and/or circulatory collapse (Lieveld & Aruna, 1991). Individuals who are going through the DT's are also a high-risk group for suicide (Hirschfeld & Davidson, 1988; Weiss & Mirin, 1988).

In recent years, the benzodiazepines have been found to be quite useful in controlling the symptoms of alcohol withdrawal. According to Miller, Frances, and Holmes (1989), the judicious use of benzodiazepines controls the tremors, hyperactivity, convulsions, and anxiety associated with alcohol withdrawal. They note that after the withdrawal symptoms have been controlled, the daily dosage level of benzodiazepines should be reduced by 10% to 20% each day, until the drug is finally discontinued.

Bauman (1989) suggests that *controlled* intraveneous administration of alcohol, in combination with the benzodiazepines, may provide one method of controlling alcohol withdrawal symptoms in severe cases. He cites the case of a postsurgical patient whose alcohol withdrawal symptoms could not be controlled through the benzodiazepines alone. The controlled use of in-traveneous alcohol in combination with benzodiazepines allowed for a gradual withdrawal from alcohol with minimal discomfort or risk to the patient.

OTHER COMPLICATIONS OF CHRONIC ALCOHOL USE

Either directly or indirectly alcohol contributes to a large number of head injuries (Anderson, 1991; Sparadeo & Gill, 1989). It is not uncommon for an intoxicated person to fall and strike his or her head on furniture, or whatever happens to be in the way. And, of course there are those individuals who attempt to drive while intoxicated and subsequently suffer head injuries as a result of accidents. Researchers have found that approximately half of the estimated 1 million people who suffer a traumatic head injury each year have alcohol in their blood at the time of the injury (Anderson, 1991; Sparadeo & Gill, 1989).

Schuckit (1989) cautions that chronic alcohol use may reduce an in-dividual's life expectancy by 15 years, with the leading causes of death being (in decreasing order of frequency) heart disease, cancer, accidents, and suicide. Approximately 100,000 Americans die each year from alcohol-related diseases (L. Sigel, 1989), in addition to those who die in alcohol-related accidents or who commit suicide.

Chronic alcoholism also has been associated with a premature aging syndrome, in which an individual appears much older than he or she actually is (Brandt & Butters, 1986). In many cases, the overall physical condition of the individual corresponds to that of someone 15 to 20 years older. One alcoholic, a man in his 50s, was told by his physician that he was in good health—for a man about to turn 70!

It should be noted here that women who drink while pregnant run the risk of causing alcohol-induced birth defects, a condition known as *fetal alcohol syndrome*. We will discuss this condition in detail in Chapter 19 on "Hidden Victims."

Admittedly, every alcoholic will not suffer from every consequence we have reviewed. Some alcoholics will never suffer from stomach problems, for example, but may suffer from advanced heart disease. However Schuckit (1989) reports that, according to one research study, 93% of the alcoholics admitted to treatment had at least one important medical problem in addition to their alcoholism.

Research has demonstrated that an individual first demonstrates alcohol-related problems in his or her late 20s or early 30s. By the age of 31, approximately half of those who will at some time fit the criteria for alcoholism will already have done so (Schuckit, 1989). However, this means that a significant number of known alcoholics—again, approximately half—do not fit this "classic" picture.

The issue of whether or not there is an "addictive personality" will be discussed in a later chapter. About the only generalization that can be made about risk factors for alcoholism at this time is that children of alcoholics appear to be about three of four times as likely as children of nonalcoholics to themselves become alcoholic (Ackerman, 1983; Schuckit, 1987; Vaillant, 1983). Researchers interpret this tendency as reflecting a genetic predisposition toward alcoholism that is thought to be passed from one generation to another, especially in males.

Evidence would suggest that this genetic predisposition also requires certain environmental factors to trigger the development of alcoholism. However, if the individual has *ever* had an addiction disorder, then he or she should certainly be considered "at risk" for alcoholism.

SUMMARY

In this chapter we explored how alcohol affects the body and some of the more common complications of alcohol use and addiction. The course of alcoholism is a fluctuating one, according to Schuckit (1989), and in all too many cases the alcohol addiction is not recognized until too late. Alcohol at least contributes to numerous diseases, if it is not the sole causal agent of these different diseases.

Chapter 5

THE BARBITURATES AND
SIMILAR DRUGS

It is safe to assume that people have suffered from symptoms of anxiety and insomnia for thousands of years. Indeed, anxiety is a universal human experience in response to the stress of daily living. According to Sussman (1988), each year some 11% of American adults use an "antianxiety" agent at least once.[1] Furthermore, up to one-third of all adults suffer from at least transient insomnia (Gillin, 1991).

Anxiety can range from a mild uneasiness to a severe panic state in which an individual might sense impending doom or fear imminent death (Kaplan & Sadock, 1988). For hundreds of years, alcohol was thought to be the only chemical agent that could be used to control the symptoms of anxiety. It was only in the last century that a number of other drugs have been made available to treat this condition. These new antianxiety agents include the bromides, the barbiturate family of chemicals, and barbituratelike drugs, such as meprobamate. These drugs were the treatments of choice for insomnia and anxiety until the late 1960s and early 1970s, when the benzodiazepines were introduced (Feighner, 1987; Gillin, 1991).

Despite superficial differences in their chemical structure, these drugs are all central nervous system depressants. They all share common characteristics, and to a significant degree potentiate the effects of other CNS depressants. Although such drugs have a proven potential for abuse, they are also now preferred by physicians for the control of the symptoms of anxiety and insomnia.

Sedative abuse in this country has not received the same publicity as narcotic addiction. Although both the legitimate and illegal use of the barbiturates are declining (Kaplan & Sadock, 1988), the chemical dependency counselor or mental health professional will still occasionally be working with clients who may be using these drugs on a regular basis. In this chapter, we will review the barbiturates and barbituratelike drugs. In the next chapter, we will review the benzodiazepines.

---

[1]Occasionally, mental health professionals will use the term *anxiolytic* rather than *antianxiety*. For the purpose of this section, we will use antianxiety.

A HISTORY OF THE BARBITURATES

The history of alcohol is a long one, and has been discussed elsewhere (see Chapter 2). In brief, however, the major reason why alcohol was regarded as a medicine was because it could be used both to induce sleep and, if the person drank enough, to control pain. For much of history, alcohol was one of the few chemical agents that could be used with consistent, and usually predictable, results by physicians.

The barbiturates, as a class of drugs, are relative newcomers compared with alcohol. They were discovered in the last half of the nineteenth century by a German scientist. However, it was not until 1903 that the first barbiturate—Veronal—was introduced for human use (Peluso & Peluso, 1988). Since then, some 2,500 different barbiturates have been isolated in laboratories, although for the most part only about 50 of them are used today (Lingeman, 1974). They are now only rarely prescribed, having been largely replaced by the benzodiazepines (Gillin, 1991). In some surgical procedures and in the control of epilepsy, however, certain barbiturates remain the drugs of choice.

The barbiturates have a considerable abuse potential. In the past, up to half of the 300 tons of barbiturates manufactured in the United States each year was diverted to the black market (P. R. Matuschka, 1985). At this time, an unknown quantity is diverted to the black market, from which it is often obtained by the addict as a substitute for the more expensive narcotic, heroin (Kaplan & Sadock, 1988). When the heroin addict is unable to obtain narcotics, he or she may either ingest or inject a barbiturate to help control heroin withdrawal symptoms. Barbiturates thus continue to represent a significant part of the U.S. drug-abuse problem.

THE PHARMACOLOGY OF BARBITURATES

Snyder (1986) grouped the barbiturates into four different classes.[2] The criterion that determines which group a particular barbiturate falls into is the length of time that the drug will continue to have an effect on the person who has used it. Barbiturates are thus classified by their *duration of action*, as described in the following list:

1. The effects of the *ultrashort-acting* barbiturates begin to be felt in a matter of seconds and last for less than an hour. Examples of ultrashort barbiturates are Pentothal and Brevital. The ultrashort barbiturates are often used in surgical procedures, where a short duration of action is desirable (Snyder, 1986).
2. The effects of the *short-acting* barbiturates begin to be felt in a matter of minutes and last for 4 to 8 hours. Nembutal is one example of this class of barbiturates (Kaplan & Sadock, 1988).

[2]Sometimes only three classes are used—ultrashort, intermediate, and long-acting. However, both classification systems are based on the duration of action of the various barbiturates.

3. The effects of the *intermediate-acting* barbiturates begin to be felt within an hour and last for about 6 to 8 hours. Included in this group are such drugs as Amytal (Schuckit, 1989).
4. The effects of the *long-acting* barbiturates require over an hour to be felt and last for 10 to 12 hours (Snyder, 1986). Phenobarbital is perhaps the most common of the drugs in this class.

The barbiturates as a class are chemically similar, and thus tend to have similar effects on the person using them. The only major difference between the barbiturates is the length of time that it takes the individual's body to absorb, metabolize (break down), and excrete the different forms. Short-term barbiturates are rapidly inactivated ("metabolized") by the liver, whereas long-term barbiturates, such as phenobarbital, are eliminated from the body largely unchanged by the kidneys; thus, long-term barbiturates remain active for a longer period of time.

The barbiturate molecule is rapidly and completely absorbed from the stomach and small intestine, and is usually administered orally (Julien, 1988). Rarely, however, one of the ultrashort-acting barbiturates might be administered intraveneously, especially when used as an anesthetic in surgery. As previously mentioned, heroin addicts may also inject barbiturates as a substitute for their narcotics. The intravenous injection of barbiturates is quite dangerous and requires *immediate* access to life-support systems in case of adverse side effects. In the remainder of this chapter, we will focus on the effects of orally administered barbiturates.

As noted, the barbiturates, like alcohol, are well absorbed from the stomach and small intestine. According to the *Harvard Medical School Mental Health Newsletter* (1988), the barbiturates and alcohol act on the body in a similar manner, although some barbiturates have a longer effect than alcohol. Once they reach the bloodstream, the barbiturates are distributed throughout the body and affect all body tissues to some degree. P. R. Matuschka (1985) notes that at normal dosage levels the barbiturates depress not only the activity of the brain, but also to a lesser degree the activity of the muscle tissues, the heart, and the lungs.

The barbiturates are able to reach the brain itself rather quickly, and depending on the dose of the particular barbiturate used, it will act either as a sedative or a hypnotic. At normal dosage levels, the barbiturates have the greatest impact on the cortex itself, as well as on the reticular activating system (RAS) of the brain (which is responsible for awareness) and on the medulla oblongata (which controls respiration) (P. R. Matuschka, 1985).

TOLERANCE AND ADDICTION TO BARBITURATES

Tolerance to Barbiturates

Presently, barbiturates are used primarily to produce sedation or sleep, although they have also been found to be useful in controlling epilepsy (Julien, 1988; Ray & Ksir, 1987). Schuckit (1989) notes that the short-acting class of barbiturates, the class whose effects last longer than 3 hours, are the barbiturates most frequently abused.

Use of the barbiturate family of drugs, like use of alcohol, can lead to a state of tolerance. Jenike (1989) warned that while tolerance to the barbiturates might develop, there is no concomitant increase in the lethal dose. Thus, as the person abusing the barbiturates increases the dosage levels to achieve the same effect, he or she will come closer and closer to the lethal dose.

Also like alcohol, the effects of the barbiturates will vary depending on the amount of the drug ingested and the potency of the specific agent being used. At normal dosage levels, the effects of the barbiturates are very similar to those resulting from alcohol use (Peluso & Peluso, 1988). Cross-tolerance between alcohol and the barbiturates is common, as is some degree of cross-tolerance between the barbiturates and the opiates, which also have a depressant effect on the CNS (Kaplan & Sadock, 1988).

Dependence on Barbiturates

The phenomenon of addiction to this class of drugs was first reported in the late 1800s (Allgulander, Borg, & Vikander, 1984). Furthermore, it is particularly important to keep in mind that withdrawal from CNS depressants is potentially life-threatening and should be attempted only in a medical setting (Jenike, 1989; P. R. Matuschka, 1985). The barbiturates should *never* be abruptly withdrawn; to do so might bring about a state of confusion, seizures, possible brain damage, or even death.

Abrupt withdrawal from the barbiturates without medical supervision may result in death in approximately 5% of the cases (Ray & Ksir, 1987). According to Jenike (1989), the exact period in the withdrawal process in which seizures are likely to develop depends on the specific barbiturate being abused. For those that are short- to intermediate-acting, one may normally expect withdrawal seizures to begin on the second or third day, with such seizures being rare after 12 days. Approximately 80% of users may expect to experience withdrawal seizures in the absence of other medication (Jenike, 1989). Thus, barbiturate withdrawal, like alcohol withdrawal, carries with it a risk of death, which is not usually the case for opiate withdrawal.

THE EFFECTS OF BARBITURATES AT NORMAL DOSAGE LEVELS

At low doses for the occasional user, the barbiturates reduce feelings of anxiety and possibly bring on a sense of euphoria or feelings of drowsiness, depending on the individual's expectations (Kaplan & Sadock, 1988). The physical sensations resulting from low doses of barbiturates are very similar to those resulting from alcohol use and the subjective effects are "practically indistinguishable from alcohol's" (Peluso & Peluso, 1988, p. 54). This is to be expected because both alcohol and the barbiturates affect the cortex of the brain.

Clinically, the effects of the barbiturates may be indistinguishable from the effects of alcohol, especially when above-normal doses are utilized. As noted in the *Harvard Medical School Mental Health Letter* (1988), barbiturate intoxication closely resembles alcohol intoxication. At low dosage levels, the barbiturates bring about a decrease in motor activity, sedation, and possibly a feeling of elation or euphoria.

A person intoxicated by barbiturates will demonstrate such behaviors as slurred speech and unsteady gait, but he or she will not smell of alcohol (Jenike, 1989). Individuals intoxicated by barbiturates will *not* test positive for alcohol in blood or urine toxicology tests (unless they also happen to have alcohol in their systems). Specific blood or urine toxicology screens must be carried out to detect barbiturate intoxication (Kaplan & Sadock, 1988).

BARBITURATE COMPLICATIONS AT NORMAL DOSAGE LEVELS

The sleep that one achieves through the use of barbiturates is not the same as a normal state of sleep. The barbiturates suppress the rapid-eye-movement state of sleep (Peluso & Peluso, 1988). As reported by Foulkes (1989), research has shown that approximately 25% of a young adult's sleep time is spent in REM sleep. And because adequate and appropriate sleep patterns seem to play a role in emotional as well as physical health (Fiss, 1979), barbiturate-induced sleep may impact on the emotional and physical health of the individual.

Furthermore, tolerance begins to develop to the hypnotic effect of the barbiturates within a matter of days (Ray & Ksir, 1987). When used for long periods of time as a sleep aid and then discontinued, the barbiturates cause a person to enter a state of REM rebound. As previously mentioned, in this state a person will dream more intensely and more vividly for a period of time, as the body tries to catch up on lost REM sleep time. These dreams have been described as nightmares, strong enough to tempt an individual to start using drugs again, so as finally to get a good night's sleep. This rebound effect lasts for several nights, after which there is a gradual return to a normal sleep pattern. Further, the barbiturates have been found to add only about 20 to 40 minutes to the individual's actual sleep time (Ray & Ksir, 1987).

Another drawback of the barbiturates is the drug "hangover" (Govoni & Hayes, 1988). In a sense, the physical experience of the barbiturate hangover is similar to that of an alcohol hangover; that is, the individual is simply "unable to get going" the next day. This is because the barbiturates often require an extended period of time for the body to completely metabolize and excrete them.

The process of detoxification of a drug that has been ingested takes some time. The time necessary for the body to metabolize half of the original dose ingested is called the *half-life* of the drug. Small amounts of the barbiturates will remain in the person's bloodstream for hours, or even days, after a single dose of the drug. Julien (1988), for example, notes that the effects of barbiturates on judgment, motor skills, and behavior can last for as long as several days after only a single dose.

If a person continually adds to this reservoir of unmetabolized drug by repeated doses of the drug, there is a greater chance that he or she will experience a drug hangover. However, whether the result of a single dose or of repeated doses, the drug hangover is caused by traces of unmetabolized barbiturates remaining in the individual's bloodstream upon awakening the next day. The person might feel "not quite awake," or "drugged," as he or she attempts to meet the demands of the day. In some cases, individuals have been known to use CNS stimulants, such as the amphetamines, to counteract the effects of the depressants used the preceding night.

The elderly, or those with impaired liver function, are especially likely to have difficulty with the barbiturates. This is because it takes longer for their bodies to metabolize the drug. Sheridan, Patterson, and Gustafson (1982) advise that older individuals who receive barbiturates be started at half the usual adult dosage to compensate for possible difficulties in metabolizing larger doses efficiently.

As Barnhill, Ciraulo, and Ciraulo (1989) caution, it is especially dangerous to mix alcohol with barbiturates. Each drug potentiates the effects of the other by interfering with the metabolism of the other chemical in the liver. This allows the toxic effects of both drugs to build up with greater intensity than one would expect from either drug alone. In extreme cases, this process can result in death.

Research findings indicate that the barbiturates can interact with numerous other chemicals, increasing or decreasing the amount of these drugs in the blood through various mechanisms. For example, blood plasma levels of tricyclic antidepressants will drop by as much as 60% in patients who are taking both barbiturates and antidepressants (Barnhill et al., 1989). The barbiturates in such cases increase the speed with which the antidepressants are metabolized by activation of the liver's microsomal enzymes. In other cases, the barbiturates may slow the elimination process for a particular drug, making it more difficult for the body to metabolize that particular chemical. A physician should always be consulted before combining different medications.

THE EFFECTS OF BARBITURATES AT ABOVE-NORMAL DOSAGE LEVELS

If the dosage level is increased beyond that normally necessary to induce sleep, or if an individual has taken two or more CNS depressants at once, several things may happen. As the increasing blood levels of barbiturate interfere with the normal function of the medulla oblongata (the part of the brain that maintains respiration), there is a reduction in respiratory response.

There is also a progressive loss of reflex activity. If no action is taken in such situations, coma may result, and ultimately, death (Jenike, 1989).

When used for an extended period of time, barbiturates also may bring about a state of physical dependence, tolerance, and a characteristic withdrawal syndrome (similar to alcohol withdrawal). After tolerance to the effects of the barbiturates has developed, the individual's body becomes more efficient in breaking them down. Thus, he or she becomes better able to function, despite the continued presence of the drug. It is important to stress, however, that physical tolerance does not alter the lethal dose of the drug to any appreciable degree. Which is to say that while the individual may need increasing amounts of the drug to achieve the same effect once achieved at a lower dose because of the tolerance factor, the amount of the drug that would constitute an overdose remains pretty much the same.

The barbiturates are involved in some 3,000 drug-related deaths each year, many of which may be unintentional overdoses (Julien, 1988). Peluso and Peluso (1988) report that barbiturates accounted for upwards of 75% of all drug-related deaths as recently as a few years ago. Fortunately, the barbiturates do not directly cause any damage to the central nervous system. Therefore *if* the overdose victim can obtain medical support before he or she develops shock or hypoxia, complete recovery from the overdose may be possible (Sagar, 1991).

The barbiturates present a significant withdrawal danger. Schuckit (1989) notes that the severity of the withdrawal syndrome "in general parallels the strength of the drug, the number of doses taken, and the length of administration" (p. 21). As a general rule, abuse of 500 mg per day of barbiturates, *or the equivalent dose of other drugs*, will result in a significant risk of withdrawal seizures in the normal individual, usually within 72 hours of the last dose.

As we have noted, the barbiturates have a significant potential for physical dependence, as well as tolerance. As a rule of thumb, one should expect that individuals who abuse barbiturates, or who are addicted to them, will *underestimate* their daily dosage level; that is, the barbiturate addict/abuser will *minimize* his or her drug use (Jenike, 1989). The phenomenon of minimization will be discussed in more detail in Chapter 18.

Pregnant mothers may transmit barbiturates to the fetus through the placenta. Pregnant and nursing mothers should not use this class of drugs unless they are under a physician's care. An infant may be born with an addiction to barbiturates if the mother was herself addicted to this class of drugs at the time of delivery. According to Peluso & Peluso (1988), barbiturate withdrawal in the newborn is more complicated than narcotic withdrawal in the newborn.

BARBITURATELIKE DRUGS

Because of the many adverse side effects associated with barbiturate use, pharmaceutical companies have long searched for effective, yet safe, substitutes. During the 1950s, a number of new drugs were introduced to treat anxiety and insomnia in place of the barbiturates. These drugs include Miltown (meprobamate), Quaalude, and Sopor (two brands of names of methaqualone), Doriden (glutethimide), Placidyl (ethchlorvynol), and Noludar (methyprylon).[3]

The chemical structure of many of these drugs is quite similar to that of the barbiturates and, like the barbiturates, they are metabolized mainly in the liver. Although these drugs were all introduced as "nonaddicting," research has shown that they have an abuse potential that is very similar to that associated with the barbiturates.

Schuckit (1989) cautions that Placidyl (ethchlorvynol) and Doriden (glutethimide) are especially dangerous and recommends that neither be used. Harvey (1985) argues that there is "little to recommend [Doriden's] continued use as a sedative-hypnotic" (p. 363). Sagar (1991) notes that "glutethimide is notorious for its high mortality associated with overdose" (p. 304). And, as Sagar points out, the lethal dose of glutethimide is only 10 grams.

Meprobamate was a popular sedative in the 1950s, when it was sold under at least 32 different brand names, including Miltown and Equanil (Lingeman, 1974). Now, according to Rosenthal (1992), it is considered "obsolete" by current standards. Surprisingly, however, this medication is still quite popular with older patients and older physicians often continue to prescribe it. Meprobamate is quite addictive, although its addictive potential was not clearly recognized when it was first introduced. Some older patients have been using this medication for 30 years or more, and quite a few have been addicted to it for much of this period (Rosenthal, 1992).

Methaqualone is a drug that achieved significant popularity in the drug world, especially in the late 1960s and early 1970s. It was purported to have aphrodisiac properties, although this remains conjecture (Mirin, Weiss, & Greenfield, 1991). It also was said to provide a mild sense of euphoria for the user. Although methaqualone was withdrawn from the market in the United States, it is still smuggled in or manufactured illegally in U.S. laboratories (Kaplan & Sadock, 1988). Thus, while there are no legitimate sources of methaqualone in the United States, one still encounters the American drug user who abuses this chemical.

Methaqualone users report feelings of euphoria, well-being, and behavioral disinhibition. The usual hypnotic dose is between 150 and 300 mg, but some individuals have been known to use upwards of 2,000 mg in a single day (Mirin, Weiss, & Greenfield, 1991). As with the barbiturates, while tolerance to the drug's effects quickly develop, the lethal dosage of methaqualone remains the same. Death from methaqualone overdose has occurred, especially when the drug is taken in combination with alcohol, or when the individual accidentally overdoses while trying to overcome his or her tolerance to the drug's effects.

---

[3]The brand name of each drug precedes the generic name in parentheses.

SUMMARY

For thousands of years, people relied on alcohol as the only effective antianxiety or hypnotic drug. In the early 1900s, the barbiturates were introduced. The barbiturates act on the body in much the same way as alcohol does. And, like alcohol, they also have a significant potential for addiction. In the post–World War II era, synthetic drugs with chemical structures very similar to those of the barbiturates were introduced, often with the claim that these drugs were "nonaddicting." However, the new drugs were ultimately found to have an addiction potential similar to that of the barbiturates. Since the introduction of the benzodiazepines (to be discussed in the next chapter), the barbiturates and similar drugs have fallen into disfavor.

Chapter 6

THE BENZODIAZEPINES

T he first of a new class of drugs, the *benzodiazepines*, was introduced in the 1960s. Since then, the benzodiazepines have become the treatment of choice for anxiety (Rickels, Giesecke, & Geller, 1987) and insomnia (Gillin, 1991). Examples of drugs in this family include Valium, (diazepam), Librium (chlordiazepoxide), Dalmane (flurazepam), Xanax (alprazolam), and Ativan (lorazepam). Each of these drugs was initially introduced as a nonaddicting substitute for the barbiturates or barbituratelike drugs. In this chapter, we will look at the benzodiazepines and the role they play in the drug-abuse problem.

THE ADDICTION POTENTIAL OF BENZODIAZEPINES

The benzodiazepines were first introduced as safe, nonaddicting drugs. Over the years, however, many researchers have found that they present a significant danger of addiction (Schuckit, 1989). For example, according to Jenike (1989), a person who took 80 to 120 mg of diazepam a day for 40 to 50 days would become addicted to this chemical. Also, between 300 and 600 mg of chlordiazepoxide a day for 60 to 180 days would result in addiction. Jenike added that the time required for dependence to develop to the other benzodiazepines was not yet known.

According to Juergens and Morse (1988), however, withdrawal symptoms for alprazolam (or other benzodiazepines) would be observed in patients who had taken prescribed dosage levels for longer than 4 months. They note that the pharmacological characteristics of Xanax (a brand of alprazolam), which reaches peak blood levels in 1 to 2 hours and is fully metabolized in from 6 to 16 hours, make it especially attractive as a drug of abuse.

Juergens and Morse describe the case histories of patients, 6 of them women, who became addicted to alprazolam after receiving prescriptions for the treatment of anxiety or depression. They state that all 7 patients had withdrawal symptoms when the medication was discontinued, concluding that 6 of them demonstrated some degree of tolerance to the drug's effects. In light of these findings, it is quite disturbing to note that the journal *American Druggist* (1989, 1990) reported that Xanax (alprazolam) was the third most commonly prescribed drug in the United States in 1988 and the fourth most commonly prescribed drug in 1989.

The phenomenon of benzodiazepine abuse does not seem to be limited to the United States. Shepherd (1990) reports that the per capita consumption of tranquilizers in France was five times that found in the United States. Indeed, Shepherd claims that "more anti-anxiety pills [are] sold in France than aspirin" (p. 2EX). Considering the amount of aspirin sold in the United States each day, this has to be a staggering amount.

Peluso and Peluso (1988) estimate that some 10 million Americans have used benzodiazepines for nonmedical purposes at some point in their lives. They also estimate that some 4 million Americans did so in 1987. Woods, Katz, & Winger (1988) are somewhat more conservative. They estimate that about 1% of the U.S. population uses benzodiazepines for nonmedical purposes each year, and in general they downplay the danger of addiction to this class of drugs.

MEDICAL USES OF BENZODIAZEPINES

The benzodiazepine family of drugs is one of the most frequently prescribed (Rickels, Schweizer & Lucki, 1987). Valium (diazepam) is often used as muscle relaxant after a person has suffered a strain and also is of value in the emergency treatment of seizures. Clonopin (clonazepam) has been found to be effective in the long-term control of seizures (Morton & Santos, 1989). Some other members of the benzodiazepine family of drugs have been reported to be useful as short-term sleep aids. These include Restoril (temazepam), Halcion (triazolam), Dalmane (flurazepam), and the recently introduced Doral (quazepam) (Gillin, 1991; Hussar, 1990).

The benzodiazepines also have been found to be most useful in the short-term control of the anxiety symptoms and are "by far the most widely used of the anxiolytics and hypnotics" (Rickels et al. 1987, p. 781). Specific benzodiazepines used in treating anxiety include Valium (diazepam), Librium (chlordiazepoxide) Tranxene (clorazepate), Xanax (alprazolam), and Ativan (lorazepam).

Two different benzodiazepines, Xanax (alprazolam) and Deracyn (adinazolam), are reportedly of value in the treatment of depression. Alprazolam is said to be useful in treating the anxiety that often accompanies depression. Cardoni (1990) reports that Deracyn (adinazolam) binds to the same receptor sites within the brain thought to be utilized by other benzodiazepines. Further, research reviewed by Cardoni suggests that the antidepressant effects of this medication are a result of Deracyn's (adinazolam's) ability to increase the sensitivity of certain neurons within the brain to serotonin, giving this benzodiazepine a true antidepressant potential lacking in other drugs of this class.

Schuckit (1989) contends that the benzodiazepines reduce anxiety only for about 1 to 2 months, and that they are not useful in treating anxiety continuously over a long period of time. The *Harvard Medical School Mental Health Letter* (1988) does not support this conclusion. It states that while patients might develop some tolerance to the sedative effects of benzodiaz-epines, they do not become tolerant to the antianxiety effects.

According to Woods et al. (1988), there is some question as to whether the benzodiazepines are effective in the long-term control of anxiety. They es-timate that upwards of 15% of those who use benzodiazepines take the medication on a daily basis for a year or longer. They also note that those who take them for extended periods tend to be older, to have a history of treatment by mental health professionals, and to suffer from multiple health problems.

The possibility of suicide through a drug overdose is a very real concern for the physician. The benzodiazepines are considered to be very "safe" because there is a large range between normal therapeutic doses and the lethal dose. Where some of the barbiturates have a ratio of therapeutic dosage to lethal dosage of 1:3, the benzodiazepines have a ratio of therapeutic dosage to lethal dosage of 1:200 (Kaplan & Sadock, 1988). It should be emphasized that any drug overdose should *always* be treated by a physician.

THE PHARMACOLOGY OF BENZODIAZEPINES

Whereas the barbiturates depress the normal function of the *entire* neuron, the benzodiazepines are more selective in their action. Clinical research suggests that the benzodiazepines will affect only the action of a single neurotransmit-ter. This neurotransmitter, known as *gamma aminobutyric acid* (or GABA), serves as a biochemical "brake" (Andreasen, 1984). GABA serves to shape and slow neurotransmitter activity in the brain. Neurons that utilize GABA are widely distributed throughout the cortex of the brain.

The benzodiazepines facilitate the action of GABA by binding to the GABA receptor site and a chloride channel on the neuron surface. This facilitates the action of GABA, reducing the level of nerve excitement, especially in the portion of the brain called the locus ceruleus (Cardoni, 1990; Upjohn Company, 1989). Nerve fibers from this portion of the brain connect with other parts of the brain thought to be involved in fear and panic reactions. By blocking the stimulation of the neurons of the locus ceruleus, the benzodi-azepines are thought to reduce the individual's anxiety level.

By contrast, the barbiturates depress the *entire* range of activity of neurons in many different parts of the brain, including the cortex. The barbiturates achieve a more global reduction in nerve-cell activity and tend to cause sedation, along with a reduction in anxiety levels.

Because their action is more selective than that of barbiturates the benzo-diazepines have become the drug of choice for the treatment of anxiety and insomnia. The *Harvard Medical School Mental Health Letter* (1988) notes that the benzodiazepines are very similar in their actions, differing mainly in the duration of action. Unlike the barbiturates, excessive sedation at normal dosage levels of the benzodiazepines is rare.

Rickels et al. (1987) note that when CNS depression *is* observed with benzodiazepines, it is usually a result of too large a dose being used for the particular person. Sussman (1988) suggests that advancing age may make an individual more susceptible to the sedation, impaired motor coordination, memory loss, and respiratory depression occasionally experienced as a side effect of benzodiazepine use. One exception to this rule might be Deracyn (adinazolam). Cardoni (1990) estimates that up to 66% of those who receive Deracyn might experience some degree of drowsiness, at least until their bodies adapt to the drug's effects.

L. S. Cohen (1989) attributes this to the fact that the liver becomes less efficient at metabolizing benzodiazepines with advanced age. Bleidt and Moss (1989) suggest that an age-related decline in regional blood flow to the liver and kidneys make it difficult for the elderly to metabolize and excrete many drugs, including many benzodiazepines. Cohen (1989) states that the elderly may take three times as long to fully metabolize diazepam and chlordiazepoxide as young adults. Bleidt and Moss suggest that lorazepam or oxazepam might be better benzodiazepines than diazepam for use with the elderly. Lorazepam and oxazepam have a shorter half life, and are thus more easily metabolized.

BENZODIAZEPINE ABUSE AND ADDICTION

It has been reported that the benzodiazepines are frequently overprescribed (Snyder, 1986). Peluso and Peluso (1988) state that approximately 75% of the prescriptions written for benzodiazepines are for conditions inconsistent with the recommended uses of these drugs. However, both Woods et al. (1988) and Appelbaum (1992) disagree, suggesting that in the vast majority of cases the benzodiazepines *are* appropriately prescribed and used according to instructions.

It has been claimed that 1.5 million Americans are addicted to benzodiazepines, with the vast majority being women (Peluso & Peluso, 1988). Indeed, approximately 65% of Valium users are women.

Withdrawal from Benzodiazepines

Schuckit (1989) notes that with the exception of differences in the potency of the various antianxiety agents, virtually all of the CNS depressants have demonstrated tolerance and withdrawal patterns quite similar to those associated with the barbiturates. The *Harvard Medical School Mental Health Letter* (1988) does concede that at normal dosage levels, physical dependence to the benzodiazepines is possible in 4 to 6 weeks. In most cases, however, it would require about 4 to 6 months for dependence to develop to this class of medication. After 8 months of benzodiazepine use at normal dosage levels, "most" patients would experience withdrawal symptoms, and after a year, "almost all" would experience these symptoms, according to the *Harvard Medical School Mental Health Letter*.

Benzodiazepine withdrawal can be quite difficult. Schweizer, Rickels,

Case, and Greenblatt (1990) attempted to reduce dosage levels by 25% each week in 63 patients judged to be dependent upon benzodiazepines. They found that in spite of the gradual reduction in daily benzodiazepine dosage levels, approximately 33% of those addicted to benzodiazepines with long half-lives and 42% of those addicted to short half-life forms of benzodiazepines were unable to complete the withdrawal program. This was attributed to personality factors, suggesting that some patients may have greater psychological difficulty during withdrawal than others.

According to Rickels, Schweizer, Case, and Greenblatt (1990), the severity of benzodiazepine withdrawal is dependent on five "drug-treatment factors," as well as several "patient factors." The drug-treatment factors include (1) the total daily dose of benzodiazepines being used, (2) the total time over which benzodiazepines have been used, (3) the half-life of the benzodiazepine being used, (4) the potency of the benzodiazepine being used, and (5) the rate of withdrawal (gradual, tapered withdrawal or abrupt withdrawal).

The patient factors influencing the withdrawal from benzodiazepines include (1) the patient's premorbid personality structure, (2) expectations for the withdrawal process, and (3) individual differences in the neurobiological structures within the brain thought to be involved in the withdrawal process. Rickels et al. suggest that interactions between treatment and patient factors determine the severity of the withdrawal process.

Woods et al. (1988) support the contention that the benzodiazepines have some abuse potential. They warn physicians that

> a mild degree of physiological dependence is likely to develop in some patients taking benzodiazepines on a regular basis for several months. (p. 3478)

In general, it would seem that the abuse potential of benzodiazepines is quite low, except for those with a history of drug abuse (Appelbaum, 1992; Woods et al., 1988). Woods et al. suggest that the benzodiazepines possess no significant reinforcement potential, and claim that most patients do not increase the dosage levels above what is prescribed, even if they are addicted to these drugs. However, this theory has not been tested in practice.

BENZODIAZEPINE COMPLICATIONS AT NORMAL DOSAGE LEVELS

The benzodiazepines are not perfect drugs. Tolerance to their anticonvulsant effects is possible; hence, they are of limited value only in the control of epilepsy (Harvey, 1985; Morton & Santos, 1989). Also, while the benzodiazepines at normal dosage levels are not general neuronal depressants as are the barbiturates, excessive sedation occasionally occurs, even at normal dosage levels.

For reasons that are not clearly understood, the elderly are especially vulnerable to being oversedated by benzodiazepines (Gillin, 1991; Rickels et al., 1987). As already noted, it has been suggested that a progressive reduction in blood flow to the liver that begins at about middle age may make it more difficult for the elderly to metabolize benzodiazepines. Younger individuals with liver damage also are potentially vulnerable to the sedation often accompanying benzodiazepine use.

Even when used at low doses, elderly patients often become confused and disoriented on Halcion (triazolam) (Gillin, 1991; Salzman, 1990). Other possible side effects of triazolam include behavioral disinhibition, hyperexcitability, daytime anxiety, amnesia, and confusion (Gillin, 1991). Dalmane also tends to cause confusion and oversedation, especially in the elderly. When introduced into the body, Dalmane (flurazepam) is transformed into the metabolite desalkylflurazepam. Unfortunately, this metabolite tends to accumulate in the body, especially when used over the course of several nights by older patients. The half-life of desalkylflurazepam is between 40 and 280 hours (Gillin, 1991). Thus, the effects of a single dose can last for up to 12 days in some patients.

If a person uses Dalmane for even a few days, he or she might experience significant levels of CNS depression. Further, if the person ingests alcohol or an over-the-counter cold remedy after using Dalmane for even a few days, the unmetabolized drug could combine with the depressant effects of the alcohol or cold remedy to produce serious levels of CNS depression.

Cross-tolerance between the benzodiazepines, alcohol, the barbiturates, and meprobamate is possible (Barnhill et al., 1989, Snyder, 1986). The benzodiazepines may also potentiate the effects of such other CNS depressants as antihistamines, alcohol, or narcotics, presenting a danger of oversedation or even death.[1] Thus, if there is some doubt about whether two or more medications should be used together, it is wise to consult a physician or the local poison control center. When oversedation occurs, an individual is likely to experience feelings of drowsiness, fatigue, lightheadedness, dizziness, and mental or physical slowing. By adjusting the dosage level or schedule, it is usually possible to avoid such problems.

Occasionally the benzodiazepines bring about a degree of irritability, hostility, or aggression even at normal dosage levels. According to Beasley (1987), it is common for the combination of alcohol and benzodiazepines to bring about this paradoxical rage reaction. He states that "hundreds of reports on [this reaction] in individuals combining alcohol and diazepam are now on file" (p. 123). However, the paradoxical rage reaction is also seen on occasion in individuals using benzodiazepines alone at therapeutic doses.

This paradox—a rage reaction in someone who has used a tranquilizer—is thought to be the result of the disinhibition effects of benzodiazepines. Which is to say that as the benzodiazepines lower social inhibitions, the person is more likely to engage in behavior that he or she had successfully controlled previously. A similar effect is often seen in those who drink alcohol, which also has a disinhibition effect.

[1]For example, the singer/movie star Judy Garland died as a result of the effects of alcohol in combination with the benzodiazepine diazepam (Snyder, 1986).

The possibility that benzodiazepine may contribute to memory problems has also been suggested (Rickels et al., 1987; Schuckit, 1989). Indeed, there is evidence that even at therapeutic dosage levels, the benzodiazepines may interfere with the formation of memory patterns (Harvey, 1985; Plasky, Marcus, & Salzman, 1988). Hand (1989) reports that one benzodiazepine commonly used as a sleep aid, Halcion (triazolam), can cause memory disturbance when used at therapeutic dosage levels. Salzman (1990) agrees, but notes that the effect "is more likely to develop when [Halcion] is used at high doses or together with alcohol" (p. 8).

This type of memory disturbance is termed *anterograde amnesia*; that is, a form of amnesia involving the formation of memories after a specific event (Plasky et al., 1988). A person might be unable to remember information presented to him or her after the ingestion of the drug. At normal dosage levels, the benzodiazepines can also disrupt the normal psychomotor skills necessary to drive an automobile or work with power tools.

This effect is not as apparent when individuals are allowed to compensate for the difficulty of a task by performing it more slowly (Rickels et al., 1987). However, tasks that require vigilance or speed of motor performance can be markedly affected by benzodiazepine use. Obviously, caution should be exercised by patients who use benzodiazepines and who also drive. Woods et al. (1988) report that impaired psychomotor coordination may persist for several days following the initial use of benzodiazepines.

The benzodiazepine family of drugs occasionally will produce mild respiratory depression, even at normal therapeutic dosage levels. This is especially true for people with pulmonary disease. Thus, use of the benzodiazepines should be avoided in patients who suffer from sleep apnea, chronic lung disease, or other sleep-related breathing disorders (Rickels et al., 1987). Doghramji (1989) cautions against using CNS depressants for patients who suffer from Alzheimer's disease, as such medications might potentiate pre-existing sleep apnea problems. Urinary incontinence, hyperactivity, and rage reactions have been noted in some patients who have used Clonopin (Morton & Santos, 1989).

Creelman, Ciraulo, and Shader (1989) note that there are a "few anecdotal case reports" of patients who have suffered adverse effects from the use of benzodiazepines while on lithium carbinate. The authors reviewed one case report involving the combined use of Valium (diazepam) and lithium in which the patient suffered profound hypothermia (subnormal temperature of the body). Creelman et al. also note that the sedative effects of diazepam appear to be potentiated by lithium in rats, although the implications of this research on human subjects is not yet clear.

Although clinical depression is not commonly encountered as a side effect of benzodiazepine use, Smith and Salzman (1991) state that rare cases of drug-induced depression have been reported as a possible side effect of this group of medications. The exact mechanism by which the benzodiazepines might cause these depressive episodes is not clear at this time, but Smith and Salzman warn that suicide is a possible outcome of a benzodiazepine-induced depressive episode. They add, however, that this drug-induced depression is quite responsive to either a reduction in benzodiazepine dosage levels or to antidepressant medications.

The benzodiazepines also have been found to interfere with normal sexual functioning, even when used at therapeutic dosage levels. We will discuss this effect in more detail in Appendix IV, "Drugs and Sex."

The trials of Halcion   According to Hand (1989), since the benzodiazepine Halcion (triazolam) was introduced, some 2,300 adverse reactions have been reported to the manufacturer, Upjohn Pharmaceuticals. Hand concludes that

> compared with other benzodiazepines, triazolam causes more agitation, confusion, amnesia, hallucinations, and bizarre or abnormal behavior. Suicides, attempted suicides, deaths, and violent crimes have been associated with triazolam administration. In most of the adverse reaction reports, the drug was taken as recommended. (p. 3)

Because of the dangers associated with the use of triazolam, Salzman (1990) warns that this drug "should be used at the lowest possible dose and for the briefest possible time—ideally, only one or two nights" (p. 8). So serious were the concerns over the side effects of triazolam in Britain, the British government saw fit to ban Halcion (sales) in England as of October 1991 (*Washington Post*, 1991). This action, in combination with recent reviews of triazolam by the American Food and Drug Administration, places the future of this benzodiazepine in doubt at this time.

THE EFFECTS OF ANTIANXIETY-AGENT USE

As antianxiety agents, the benzodiazepines have very similar effects on the user. At normal dosage levels, the person will experience a state of gentle relaxation. When used in the treatment of insomnia, the benzodiazepines initially reduce the sleep latency period; that is, the duration of time between when the individual first goes to bed and when he or she finally falls asleep. They also reduce the number of times a person awakens during the night (Harvey, 1985). At first, those who use one of the benzodiazepines to help them sleep often report a sense of deep and refreshing sleep.

However, the benzodiazepine family of drugs also interferes with the normal sleep cycle, reducing the amount of rapid-eye-movement sleep. It is during the REM phase of sleep that we dream, and research findings suggest that dreaming is necessary for mental health (Hobsen, 1989). Alcohol, the barbiturates, and the benzodiazepines have all been noted to interfere with the amount of REM sleep the user achieves.

When a person discontinues the use of such CNS depressants as alcohol, the barbiturates, or the benzodiazepines, he or she will experience REM rebound (Woods et al., 1988). This is an *increase* in the amount of sleep time spent in REM sleep. After a bad night's sleep, if the CNS depressants have not been used habitually, REM rebound will result in an insignificant increase in total REM sleep the next night.

However, chronic use of CNS depressants, or even limited use of CNS depressants in some individuals, can cause a significant rebound effect. According to the *Harvard Medical School Mental Health Letter* (1988), there have been cases of rebound anxiety and insomnia lasting from 3 days to 3 weeks involving individuals who had used a benzodiazepine as a sleep aid for only 1 to 2 weeks. These cases are unusual, however. Most people will experience REM rebound only after a more protracted period of drug use.

Rosenbaum (1990) has proposed one way of dealing with the problem of "rebound anxiety" experienced when a patient on alprazolam experiences an abrupt drop in medication blood levels. Because alprazolam has a short half-life, blood levels drop rather rapidly, and the individual may experience an increase in anxiety symptoms just before it is time for the next dose. This process results in a phenomenon known as clock watching, in which the patient counts down the time for the next dose.

In withdrawing patients from benzodiazepines with short half-lives, such as alprazolam, Rosenbaum recommends that they be gradually switched to clonazepam, a long-acting medication. Clonazepam is about twice as potent as alprazolam, but has a longer half-life. The transition from alprazolam to clonazepam takes about a week, after which time the patient should be taking only clonazepam. This medication may then be gradually withdrawn, resulting in a slower decline in blood levels. However, Rosenbaum notes that the patient still should be warned that there will be some "rebound anxiety" symptoms. These symptoms are not a reflection of the original anxiety; they are simply a sign that the body is adjusting to the gradual reduction in clonazepam blood levels.

CONSEQUENCES OF CHRONIC BENZODIAZEPINE ABUSE

Although introduced as safe and nonaddicting substitutes for the barbiturates, it has been shown that the benzodiazepines do indeed have a significant abuse potential. As noted above, according to Peluso and Peluso (1988), some 4 million Americans have used Valium for nonmedical purposes in the past year, and 10 million have done so at some point in their lives.

Dietch (1983) proposes several criteria by which to identify benzodiazepine abuse. These criteria include (1) use of the drug after the medical/ psychiatric need for it has passed, (2) symptoms of physical or psychological dependence on one of the benzodiazepines, (3) use of the drug in amounts greater than the prescribed amount, (4) use of the drug to obtain an euphoriant effect, and (5) use of the drug to decrease self-awareness, or the possibility of change.

The development of physical dependence on the benzodiazepines is a function of the specific drug being used, the daily dosage level, and the length of time the person has used the drug. For example, Valium (diazepam) has a long half-life. A Valium addict might experience minimal withdrawal symptoms in the first 5 days after stopping the drugs with the withdrawal symptoms reaching their peak from 5 to 9 days after the last dose.

Dietch (1983) reports that withdrawal symptoms of benzodiazepine addiction can include anxiety, insomnia, dizziness, nausea and vomiting, muscle weakness, tremor, confusion, convulsions (seizures), and a drug-induced withdrawal psychosis. Rapport and Covington (1989) point to a long list of symptoms that may be experienced, including anxiety, irritability, depression, emotional lability, paranoia, delusions, memory problems, feelings of being in motion, hallucinations, disorientation, weight loss, muscle spasms and cramps, seizures, ataxia, headaches, nausea, vomiting, thirst, diarrhea, constipation, insomnia, hypertensive episodes, blurred vision, and possible death.

In addition to the problems of physical dependence, Dietch (1983) contends that it is possible to become psychologically dependent on benzodiazepines. Indeed, he states that "psychological dependence on benzodiazepines appears to be more common than physical dependence" (p. 1140). Psychologically dependent users may take the drug continuously or intermittently because they *believe* they need benzodiazepines. This belief may be inconsistent with their actual medical requirements. No statistics are available on how many people are psychologically dependent on benzodiazepines.

There is a tendency, at least among some users of the benzodiazepines, to increase their dosage levels above those prescribed by their physician. This phenomenon is not well understood. In a study by Dietch (1983), patients tended to augment their dose according to the level of environmental stress they were experiencing. The subjects in this study were patients who were prescribed one of the benzodiazepines for medical/psychiatric reasons. There is virtually no information on how drug abusers might utilize this class of drugs, or what dosage level might be preferred by addicts. Woods et al. postulates that those most likely to abuse benzodiazepines would be individuals with a history of polydrug abuse.

All of the CNS depressants, including the benzodiazepines, are capable of producing a *toxic psychosis*, especially in overdose situations. This condition is also referred to as *organic brain syndrome* by some professionals. Schuckit (1989) states that toxic psychosis includes auditory hallucinations and/or paranoid delusions, and notes that this drug-induced psychosis should clear in from 2 to 14 days.

As with the barbiturates, withdrawal from benzodiazepines should only be attempted under the supervision of a physician. Severe withdrawal symptoms may include hyperthermia, delirium, convulsions, a drug-induced psychosis, and possible death (Jenike, 1989). Detoxification may be necessary on an inpatient basis in some cases, although Woods et al. (1988) contend that most patients can be slowly withdrawn from benzodiazepines with few or no side effects.

Surprisingly, despite all that is known about the barbiturates and the CNS depressants in general, people still abuse them in significant numbers. It has been reported that many individuals who abuse the amphetamines and cocaine (see the following chapter on CNS stimulants) will use depressants either to control some of the side effects of their stimulant use or to "come down" from the stimulants in order to sleep. (Peluso & Peluso, 1988). Alcoholics will often use CNS depressants during working hours, so as not to exude the telltale smell of alcohol.

ENTER BUSPIRONE: A NEW ERA IN THE CONTROL OF ANXIETY?

A new medication, BuSpar (buspirone), was recently introduced as an anti-anxiety agent. BuSpar is not a member of the benzodiazepine family; it is chemically unrelated to currently available antianxiety compounds. Moreover, clinically it has fewer side effects and has been compared to both diazepam and clorazepate in terms of its ultimate effectiveness (Feighner, 1987; Manfredi et al., 1991).

Clinical testing suggests that buspirone does not cause significant sedation or fatigue (Rosenbaum & Gelenberg, 1991). Further, no evidence of potentiation between Buspirone and select benzodiazepines, or between alcohol and buspirone, has been reported (Feighner, 1987; Manfredi et al., 1991).[3]

Clinical trials of buspirone have resulted in complaints of gastrointestinal problems, drowsiness, decreased concentration, dizziness, headache, feelings of lightheadedness, nervousness, diarrhea, excitement, sweating/clamminess, nausea, depression, and fatigue (Feighner, 1987; Manfredi et al., 1991; Newton, Marunycz, Alderdice, & Napoliello, 1986).

Unlike the benzodiazepine family of drugs, buspirone has no anti-convulsant action, nor is it useful as a muscle relaxant (Eison & Temple, 1987). Indeed, buspirone has been found to be of little value in those cases of anxiety that involve insomnia, which is a significant proportion of anxiety cases (Manfredi et al., 1991).

The mechanism of action for buspirone is thought to differ from that of the benzodiazepines (Eison & Temple, 1987). Buspirone binds to dopamine and serotin type 1 receptors in the hippocampus, a different portion of the brain that benzodiazepines impact on (Manfredi et al., 1991). Further, buspirone is not immediately effective; it must be used for up to 2 or 3 weeks before maximum effects are evident (Thornton, 1990).

Research into the addictive potential of buspirone is mixed at this time. According to Lader (1987), buspirone has not been shown to demonstrate any abuse liability in animal or human studies. This conclusion is supported by Thornton (1990) and Rosenbaum and Gelenberg (1991). But while Lader suggests that there is no evidence of a withdrawal syndrome such as that seen

[3]This is *not*, however, a recommendation that these substances be mixed. As before, alcohol should not be mixed with medication under any circumstances.

in chronic benzodiazepine abuse, Murphy, Owen, & Tyrer (1989) state that
they have found evidence of both an addictive effect and a withdrawal
syndrome. At this time, then, we cannot say with certainty that buspirone is
nonaddictive.

As you will recall, one of the side effects of benzodiazepine use is
occasional memory problems. Rickels et al. (1987) found that buspirone
failed to demonstrate any impact on memory in a sample of 39 subjects
suffering from generalized anxiety disorder as measured by psychological
tests, suggesting that buspirone does not cause amnesia, as do many benzodiazepines.

Rickels, Schweizer, Csanalosi, Case, and Chung (1988) note that buspirone has not been shown to lessen the intensity of withdrawal symptoms
experienced by patients who are addicted to benzodiazepines. They attempted
to identify the long-term effects of buspirone and found no evidence of
tolerance to buspirone's effects over a 6-month period. They also failed to
uncover any evidence of a physical dependence or withdrawal syndrome from
buspirone in that time frame.

Unfortunately, the manufacturer's claim that buspirone offers many advantages over the benzodiazepines in the treatment of anxiety states has not yet
been totally fulfilled. Indeed, Rosenbaum and Gelenberg (1991) caution that
"many clinicians and patients have found buspirone to be a generally disappointing alternative to benzodiazepines" (p. 200). This assessment
notwithstanding, they recommend a trial of buspirone for those patients who
exhibit persistent anxiety symptoms. Further, buspirone would seem to be the
drug of choice in the treatment of anxiety states in the addiction-prone
individual.

SUMMARY

Since their introduction in the 1960s, the benzodiazepines have become one
of the most frequently prescribed medications. As a class, the benzodiazepines are the treatment of choice for the control of anxiety, insomnia, and
many other conditions. They have also become a significant part of the
drug-abuse problem. Although many of the benzodiazepines were first introduced as nonaddicting and safe substitutes for the barbiturates, there is
evidence to suggest that they have an abuse potential similar to that of the
barbiturate family of drugs.

The new drug buspirone, sold under the brand name BuSpar, is a recent
addition to the numerous antianxiety drugs currently available. The first of a
new class of antianxiety agents, buspirone works through a different mechanism than the benzodiazepines. While it was introduced as nonaddicting,
this claim has been challenged by at least one team of researchers. The actual
addictive potential of buspirone is not clear at this time.

Chapter 7

THE AMPHETAMINES AND SIMILAR DRUGS

T he CNS stimulants include cocaine; the amphetamine family of drugs; and amphetaminelike drugs, such as Ritalin. The behavioral effects of these drugs are remarkably similar, despite their individual chemical differences (Gawin & Ellinwood, 1988). In this chapter, we will review the amphetamines and amphetaminelike drugs. In Chapter 8, we will review cocaine.

The *amphetamine* family of chemicals was first discovered in 1887 (Kaplan and Sadock, 1988; Lingeman, 1974). However, it was not until 1927 that these drugs were found to be useful to medicine. It was in that year that Benzedrine was introduced, in an inhaler similar to "smelling salts," for use in the treatment of asthma (Grinspoon & Bakalar, 1985). The ampoule (also called *ampule*), which could be purchased over the counter, would be broken, releasing the concentrated amphetamine liquid into the surrounding cloth. The Benzedrine ampoule would then be held under the nose and inhaled, much like "smelling salts" are.[1]

Another use for amphetamines was in treating depression and heightening one's capacity to work (Grinspoon & Bakalar, 1985). It was not long, however, before it was discovered that ampoules of Benzedrine could be unwrapped, carefully broken open, and the concentrated Benzedrine injected. Drug users quickly discovered that the effects of the amphetamines were quite similar to those of cocaine. Indeed, amphetamines came to be viewed by many as a "safe" substitute for cocaine, which by the early 1920s was known to be a very dangerous drug.

During World War II, the amphetamines were used by American, British, German and Japanese armed forces to counteract fatigue and heighten endurance (Brecher, 1982). For reasons that are not well understood, there was a wave of amphetamine abuse in Sweden (Snyder, 1986) and in Japan immediately following World War II.

By the late 1960s and early 1970s, American physicians were routinely prescribing amphetamines for depression and for weight loss. By 1970, some 8% of all prescriptions were for some form of amphetamines (Peluso & Peluso, 1988). Indeed, so popular were the amphetamines that by the early 1970s some 10 billion 5-mg tablets of amphetamine were legally produced in the

[1]Needless to say, amphetamines are no longer sold over the counter to treat asthma.

United States alone (Kaplan & Sadock, 1988). An unknown quantity was also produced in various illegal laboratories. During the late 1960s and early 1970s, amphetamine use in the United States reached "epidemic proportions" (Kaplan & Sadock, 1988, p. 238).

It is ironic that just a generation later we would be seeing drug users drift away from the amphetamines and all the dangers associated with their use to the "safety" of cocaine (Estroff, 1987). Chronic users of the amphetamines found that the drug ultimately came to dominate their lives. The amphetamines would bring about agitation when used at high doses; they also caused a drug-induced depression when one's supply ran out.

Eventually, people began to understand that "speed kills"—either directly (by impacting on the heart and vascular system) or indirectly (by causing a person's self-care activities to deteriorate). Amphetamine use died out during the late 1970s and early 1980s, as cocaine became a popular drug of abuse. Now, with the trend away from cocaine, a new generation of drug abusers is exploring the amphetamines. Although we have not returned to the levels of amphetamine use that characterized the late 1960s and early 1970s, some believe that the amphetamines are again becoming popular as drugs of abuse.

MEDICAL USES OF AMPHETAMINES AND SIMILAR DRUGS

The amphetamine family of drugs is one of the more powerful groups of CNS stimulants (Jaffe, 1990). The amphetamines and similar drugs (Ritalin, for example) bring about their main action through improvement of the action of the smooth muscles of the body (Weiner, 1985). They have been known to improve athletic performance to some degree, and are often abused for this purpose. These effects are not uniform, however. Weiner cautions that stimulants can actually bring about a *decrease* in athletic abilities.

The amphetamines were once thought to be useful in the control of weight. This was due to their anorexic side effect. *Anorexia* refers to a loss of appetite, especially when prolonged. Subsequent research, however, has demonstrated that the amphetamines are only minimally effective as a weight-control agent, with tolerance to their appetite-suppressing side effect appearing in only 4 weeks (Snyder, 1986). Presently, the amphetamines are not recognized as effective adjuncts in weight-control programs (Weiner, 1985).

Although the amphetamines were once thought to be antidepressants, they are no longer used for this purpose (Potter, Rudorfer, & Goodwin, 1987). The amphetamines and related compounds do have a limited medical value, however. First, in a limited number of cases, they have been found to be useful in the control of hyperactivity in children (Kaplan & Sadock, 1988). Surprisingly, although the amphetamines are CNS *stimulants*, they have a calming effect on children who are hyperactive as a result of a condition known as *minimal brain damage*, which is also referred to as "hyperactivity" or "attention deficit syndrome."

The amphetamines are able to exert a calming effect by enhancing the function of the reticular activating system (RAS) of the brain. This is the portion of the brain thought to be involved in focusing one's attention (Gold & Verebey, 1984). The RAS is thought to "screen out" extraneous stimuli to allow for concentration on a specific task. In children who suffer from hyperactivity, the RAS is thought to be underactive, causing them to be easily distracted. The amphetamines are believed to stimulate the RAS to the point where the child is able to function more effectively.

Further, the amphetamines have come to be the treatment of choice for a rare neurological condition known as *narcolepsy*—a lifelong condition in which a person is subject to sudden spells of falling asleep during waking hours (*Harvard Medical School Mental Health Letter*, 1990; Mirin et al., 1991). Doghramji (1989) described narcolepsy as an incurable disorder thought to reflect a chemical imbalance within the brain. One of the chemicals involved, dopamine, is the neurotransmitter that the amphetamines cause to be released from neurons in the brain. Current thinking is that the amphetamines may at least partially correct the dopamine imbalance that causes narcolepsy.

Not infrequently, the amphetamines are abused by college students, especially around the final-examination period. Conrad, Hughes, Baldwin, Achenbach, and Sheehan (1989) estimate that approximately half of the medical students in the 1960s used amphetamines at some point in their medical school training or internship in order to remain awake. However, with increasing restrictions on the manufacture of amphetamines, Conrad et al. suggest that medical students may have turned to the use of cocaine to help them meet the demands of their training in the 1980s.

THE PHARMACOLOGY OF AMPHETAMINES AND SIMILAR DRUGS

The amphetamines are easily absorbed through the gastrointestinal tract and when used orally begin to have an effect within 20 minutes (R. K. Siegel, 1991) to 30 minutes (Mirin et al., 1991). Amphetamines may also be used intraveneously, and when injected they reach the brain very quickly. The chemical structure of the amphetamines closely resembles that of two different neurotransmitters: norepinephrine and dopamine, and because of this similarity they are thought to impact on many different parts of the central nervous system and also on the muscles of the body.

The exact mechanism by which amphetamines stimulate the brain and central nervous system is still not clear. We do know, however, that these drugs facilitate the release of norepinephrine within the brain (Mirin et al., 1991). Once in the brain, the amphetamines stimulate the medulla (which is involved in the control of respiration), causing the individual to breathe more deeply and more rapidly. At normal dosage levels, the cortex is also stimulated, resulting in reduced fatigue and possibly increased concentration abilities (Kaplan & Sadock, 1988). Many users of amphetamines also report a feeling of euphoria when they ingest this drug.

The amphetamines are mainly metabolized by the liver. After an oral dose of an amphetamine, however, at least 50% of the drug will be excreted unchanged by the kidneys (Mirin et al., 1991). The half-life of the amphetamines is between 10 and 30 hours, depending—at least in part—on the acidity of the urine (Govoni & Hayes, 1988).

METHODS OF AMPHETAMINE ABUSE

Because of the ease with which they may be manufactured, amphetamines (especially the form known as *methamphetamine*) are often sold in homemade tablet form for oral use. These tablets are often white with crossed score marks on one side; hence, the street name "white cross" (Doweiko, 1979). Some amphetamines may also be diverted from legitimate sources. These "pharmaceutical" amphetamines will come in a variety of capsules or tablets. Recently, methamphetamine crystals known as "ice" have also become available in many parts of the United States. (Ice will be discussed in a separate section later in the chapter.)

The tablets (or powder, if purchased in power form) may be crushed, and prepared for intravenous use, as is done with heroin. Methamphetamine is especially potent, and thus favored by amphetamine users. The injected methamphetamine reaches the brain in seconds, causing an effect described as "instant eurphoria" by the late Truman Capote (cited in R. K. Siegel, 1991, p. 72).

Amphetamine powder may be "snorted," in a manner similar to the way in which cocaine is used. When abused in this manner, it takes only about 3 minutes for the drug to be absorbed and reach the brain (R. K. Siegel, 1991). The amphetamines are also smoked, according to Siegel, especially the ice form of methamphetamine. The effects of ice are felt by the user in only 6 seconds.

THE EFFECTS OF AMPHETAMINE USE

The amphetamine experience is, to a large extent, very similar to the cocaine experience. However, while (1) the effects of cocaine may last from a few minutes to an hour at most, the effects of the amphetamines may last many hours (Schuckit, 1989). Furthermore, unlike cocaine, the amphetamines are effective when used orally and, also unlike cocaine, the amphetamines have only a small anesthetic effect (Weiner, 1985).

The effects of the amphetamines on any given individual will depend upon that individual's mental state, the dosage level, the relative potency of the specific form of amphetamine, and the manner in which the drug is used. The usual oral dosage level is between 15 and 30 mg/day (Lingeman, 1974); it varies, however, according to the potency of the amphetamine or amphetaminelike drug being used (Julien, 1988).

At low-to-moderate oral dosage levels, the individual will experience increased alertness, mood elevation, a mild euphoria, reduction of mental fatigue, and improved ability to concentrate (Kaplan & Sadock, 1988; Weiner, 1985). Gawin and Ellinwood (1988) note that the amphetamines and cocaine will initially produce "a neurochemical magnification of the pleasure experienced in most activities" (p. 1174). As they describe it, the initial use of amphetamines or cocaine will

> produce alertness and a sense of well-being . . . they lower anxiety and social inhibitions, and heighten energy, self-esteem, and the emotions aroused by interpersonal experiences. Although they magnify pleasure, they do not distort it; hallucinations are usually absent. (p. 1174)

Some people will experience insomnia and anxiety, as well as irritability and hostility during periods of initial use (Grinspoon & Bakalar, 1985). It is not uncommon for drug users to try to counteract these side effects through the use of alcohol or benzodiazepines. Indeed, Peluso and Peluso (1988) estimate that *half* of all regular users of amphetamines also may be classified as heavy drinkers. It is also not uncommon for alcoholics to use amphetamines to counteract the sedating effects of the alcohol.

As tolerance to the euphoria brought about by oral doses of amphetamines develops, there is a tendency for the user to increase his or her dosage levels (Peluso & Peluso, 1988). Eventually, the obsessive user substitutes intraveneously administered amphetamines for the orally administered forms of stimulants. Individuals who "graduate" to the intravenous use of amphetamines usually do so when they are no longer able to achieve the desired effects through oral use or by "snorting" the drug. If the intravenous user of amphetamines fails to use proper sterile techniques, he or she runs the risk of endocarditis (Burden & Rogers, 1988) and a wide range of other blood infections, including the AIDS virus (Wetli, 1987).

When injected or smoked, users have reported an almost orgasmic experience. However, as the individual begins to develop tolerance to the effects of the drug, this euphoria becomes less and less pronounced. As the individual experiments with the drug, she or he will discover that, initially, higher doses also intensify the euphoria experienced (Gawin & Ellinwood, 1988). There is thus a tendency for intraveneous amphetamine users to increase their daily dosage level over time.

However, higher dosage levels of amphetamines can also result in confused behavior, irritability, fear, suspicion, hallucinations, and delusions (Julien, 1988; Weiner, 1985). Davis and Bresnahan (1987) report that in nonpsychotic abusers, amphetamines can bring about paranoid psychosis within hours, and that this condition will continue at least as long as the amphetamine remains in the body. As we will discuss shortly, this amphetamine-induced psychosis occasionally becomes permanent.

Chronic users of amphetamines will often embark on "speed runs," repeatedly using amphetamines in order to recapture and maintain the elusive euphoria that was initially experienced. During such speed runs, the user will inject larger and larger doses of the drug to overcome tolerance for its effects. Indeed, long-term users of amphetamines have been known to inject upwards of 1,700 mg/day in divided doses. They build up gradually to this total daily dosage level as their tolerance for the drug increases (Weiner, 1985).

The development of tolerance to the effects of the amphetamines is not inevitable. For example, when the amphetamines are used in the treatment of narcolepsy, a person can be maintained on a specific dosage level for years, without tolerance developing (Brecher, 1972; Weiner, 1985). Tolerance to the euphoria effect of the amphetamines does develop, however, making it neces-sary for the abuser to continue to increase the dosage.

High dosage levels of the amphetamines can result in a drug-induced psychosis, indistinguishable from schizophrenia (Kaplan & Sadock, 1988). At one point, it was thought that the amphetamines essentially brought on a latent schizophrenia in a person who was vulnerable to this condition. It has now been suggested, however, that they can cause drug-induced psychosis even in essentially normal people (Grinspoon & Bakalar, 1985).

This drug-induced psychotic state is often characterized by confusion, suspiciousness, hallucinations and delusional thinking, as well as by episodes of violence. Kaplan and Sadock (1988) note that, in contrast to actual schizophrenia, the hallucinations experienced by an individual suffering from an amphetamine psychosis tend to be mainly visual. Further, the amphet-amine-induced hyperactivity and absence of a thought disorder helps to distinguish an amphetamine psychosis from actual schizophrenia. Under normal conditions, this drug-induced psychosis clears up within days after the drug is discontinued (Kaplan & Sadock, 1988; Schuckit, 1989). In some cases, however, it may last for weeks or even months. On occasion, the amphetamine-induced psychosis seems to become permanent.

Nobody is able to predict who will become addicted to amphetamines. While there *is* evidence that most amphetamine users will not become addicted (Gawin & Ellinwood, 1988), every person who uses amphetamines runs the risk of potential addiction.

CONSEQUENCES OF PROLONGED USE OF CNS STIMULANTS

The consequences of prolonged amphetamine use include the drug-induced psychosis we have discussed, as well as various complications associated with neglect of dietary requirements or lack of sleep for extended periods of time. Gold and Verebey (1984) note that vitamin deficiencies are commonly found in chronic amphetamine abusers, a side effect of malnutrition.

Julien (1988) notes that "fatalities directly attributable to the use of amphetamines are rare" (p. 92). Indeed, he states that naive drug users have survived doses of 400–500 mg. However, according to Weiner (1985), chronic use can result in confusion, assaultiveness, irritability, weakness, insomnia, anxiety, delirium, paranoid hallucinations, panic states, and suicidal and homicidal tendencies. The individual also may experience a condition known as *formication*, the sensation that unseen bugs are crawling either on the skin or just underneath (*Harvard Medical School Mental Health Letter*, 1990; R. K. Siegel, 1991). Amphetamine addicts, like cocaine addicts, have been known to scratch or burn their skin in an attempt to rid themselves of these unseen bugs. In addition to these consequences, prolonged use of the amphetamines may result in vomiting, anorexia, cardiac arrhythmias, angina, and diarrhea. Convulsions, coma, and death are all possible from amphetamine use (Kaplan & Sadock, 1988).

Fatigue and depression follow prolonged periods of amphetamine use, with the depression often reaching suicidal proportions (Slaby et al., 1981). Amphetamine-induced feelings of depression can last for extended periods of time, possibly for *months* following cessation of amphetamine or cocaine use. Gawin and Ellinwood (1988) note that prolonged use of the amphetamines also seems to bring about a "sustained neurophysiologic change" in the brain of the user (p. 1178).

Thus, evidence seems to suggest that prolonged use of the amphetamines brings about actual physical damage to the cells of the brain, which in turn affects how the brain functions. Research in this area is quite limited, however. The long-term impact of amphetamine use on brain function is not yet clear.

As noted by Gawin and Ellinwood (1988), periods of drug-induced euphoria experienced during the amphetamine or cocaine "binge" may create "vivid, long-term memories" (p. 1175). These memories, in turn, help trigger the craving that many cocaine or amphetamine users report when they stop using the drug.

"ICE"—THE NEXT WAVE OF AMPHETAMINE ABUSE?

Earlier in the chapter, we discussed the abuse potential of one amphetamine—methamphetamine. Recently, a colorless, odorless form of crystal methamphetamine that resembles a chip of ice or clear rock candy has become popular in the United States (*Minneapolis Star-Tribune*, 1989b; *Playboy*, 1990b). Referred to as "ice" on the streets, it is often sold as a "safe" alternative to the form of cocaine known as "crack." (*Mayo Clinic Health Letter*, 1989). "Glass" and "crystal" are other street names for this form of crystal methamphetamine (*The Economist*, 1989).

It has been suggested that ice was brought to Hawaii from Japan by army troops following World War II and that its use was endemic to Hawaii for many years (*Health News*, 1990). Police and drug-abuse professionals now believe that it may have reached the U.S. mainland in the late 1970s or early 1980s (*The Economist*, 1989). However, the drug did not gain much notoriety until the news media began to give it a certain mystique by reporting its effects and dangers.

Although it is between two and three times as expensive as crack, this new form of methamphetamine has become a popular drug of abuse in Hawaii. On the mainland, its use was thought to be limited to the West Coast (R. K. Siegel, 1991), but according to *The Economist* (1989), it has become readily available on the streets of Texas and Florida and is spreading across the country.

How Ice Is Used

Ice is smoked; that is, its fumes are inhaled. The drug crosses into the blood through the lungs, and reaches the brain in a matter of seconds. Crack cocaine is also smoked, but the "high" from crack lasts perhaps 20 minutes, while that from ice is thought to last from 8 hours (*Playboy*, 1990b) to 12 hours (*Health News*, 1990; *Minneapolis Star-Tribune*, 1989b) to 14 hours (*The Economist*, 1989), or even for as long as 18 hours (McEnroe, 1990). This is consistent with the pharmacological properties of the amphetamines as compared with those of cocaine. The stimulant effects of the amphetamines in general last for hours, whereas cocaine's stimulant effects usually last for a shorter period of time.

How Ice Is Produced

Like crack, this form of methamphetamine is manufactured in clandestine laboratories. However, unlike crack, which must be processed from cocaine that is smuggled into the country, ice may be manufactured from chemicals legally purchased from any chemical supply store (R. K. Siegel, 1991). Further, because it is odorless, ice may be smoked in public without alerting passersby that it is being used.

Dose for dose, ice is cheaper than crack, and, because of its duration of effect, it *seems* to be more potent. Furthermore, ice will cool and reform as a crystal if the user decides to stop smoking it for a moment or two. This makes it highly transportable, and offers an advantage over crack in that only a piece of the drug may be used, instead of having to use it all at once.

Complications of Ice Use

Although it is often sold as a safe alternative to crack, there have been reports of fatal ice overdoses (*Health News*, 1990; *Mayo Clinic Health Letter*, 1989). Researchers have discovered that the addiction potential of ice is at least as great as that of crack, if not greater (*Health News*, 1990). Indeed, Hong, Matsuyama, and Nur (1991) suggest that ice users may ultimately use dosage levels up to 1,000 times the maximum recommended therapeutic dosage for methamphetamine—dosage levels that pose serious risks to the user.

Long-term use of ice at these dosage levels can result in kidney and/or lung damage, as well as permanent damage to the structure of the brain itself (*Health News*, 1990). According to Hong et al. (1991), ice shares the well-documented complications of other forms of amphetamine abuse, including pulmonary edema, vascular spasm, cardiomyopathy, drug-induced psychotic reactions, and acute myocardial infarction (that is, "heart attack").

Hong et al. also suggest that ice may cause "systemic and coronary vasospasm that results in an increased cardiac workload but impaired myocardial blood supply" (p. 1154). This hypothesis is similar to that advanced by Lange et al. (1989) with respect to cocaine. Lange et al. propose that cocaine (discussed in the next chapter) causes a spasm in the coronary arteries at a time when the heart's workload is increased by the drug's effects on the rest of the body. Often, the result is a heart attack that may prove fatal. If ice does indeed act on the body in the same way cocaine does, this may account for the often lethal effects of ice in particular and the amphetamines in general.

THE TREATMENT OF STIMULANT ADDICTION

Because the effects of the amphetamines are similar to those of cocaine in many ways, it should not be surprising that the treatment of amphetamine abuse is very similar to that of cocaine abuse. Thus, in order to avoid duplication of material common to the treatment of both the abuse of the amphetamines and cocaine, we will reserve discussion of the treatment of stimulant addiction for the following chapter on cocaine.

SUMMARY

Although they were discovered in the 1880s, it was not until the 1930s—some 50 years later—that the amphetamines were first introduced as a treatment for asthma. The early forms of amphetamines were sold over the counter in cloth-covered ampoules that were used in much the same way as smelling salts are used today. Within a short time, however, it was discovered that the ampoules were a source of concentrated amphetamine that could be injected. The resulting "high" was similar to that of cocaine—a drug that had gained a reputation as being dangerous—but the amphetamine high was found to last much longer.

The amphetamines were used extensively both during and after World War II. Following the war, American physicians prescribed amphetamines for the treatment of depression and as an aid for weight loss. By 1970, amphetamines accounted for 8% of all prescriptions written. However, in the time since then, physicians have come to understand that the amphetamines present a serious potential for abuse. They have come under increasingly strict controls limiting their manufacture and distribution.

Unfortunately, the amphetamines are manufactured easily, and there has always been an underground manufacture and distribution system for these drugs. In the late 1970s and early 1980s, street drug users drifted away from the amphetamines to the supposedly safe stimulant of the early 1900s—

cocaine. But recent evidence suggests that the pendulum has now started to swing back in the opposite direction. Cocaine is now known to be dangerous, and a new generation has discovered the amphetamines. This new generation of amphetamine addicts is not yet fully aware of the lesson so painfully learned by the amphetamine users of two or three decades ago; namely, "speed kills."

Chapter 8

Cocaine

A s noted in the previous chapter, cocaine is a CNS stimulant, as are the amphetamine family of drugs and amphetaminelike drugs, such as Ritalin. These drugs are all very similar with respect to the behavioral effects they produce, although they differ chemically (Gawain & Ellinwood, 1988). Having reviewed the other CNS stimulants in the last chapter, we will now turn our attention to cocaine.

INTRODUCTION TO COCAINE

Cocaine is obtained from the coca bush *Erythroxylon coca*, which grows in the higher elevations of Peru, Bolivia, and Java (DiGregorio, 1990). For thousands of years natives chewed the leaves of the coca plant (Byck, 1987). The drug was, and still is, used as a stimulant to help the natives reduce feelings of fatigue and hunger and be able to function in the high mountains of South America (White, 1989). Prior to the invasion of Peru by the Spanish conquistadors in the sixteenth century, cocaine was used in religious ceremonies and as a medium of exchange (Ray & Ksir, 1987). As described by Byck (1987), cocaine is "a mysterious gift of the gods, used in ancient burials" (p. 5).

According to White (1989), the modern natives of the mountain regions of Peru mix the leaves with lime obtained from sea shells. When the mixture is chewed, the lime works with the saliva to release the cocaine from the leaves. The lime also helps to mask the bitter taste of the coca leaf. Although in recent years the majority of bushes have been grown for the international cocaine trade, *some* coca bushes are still grown for native use. White estimates that 60% of the world's supply of the coca plant is grown in Peru, 22% in Bolivia, and 15% in Colombia.

Jaffe (1990) has observed that the natives of Peru who continue to chew cocaine on a regular basis "appear to have little difficulty in discontinuing use of the drug when they move to lower altitudes" (p. 541). He attributes this to the fact that chewing the leaves is a rather inefficient method of using cocaine. Byck (1987) challenges this conclusion, noting that appreciable blood levels of cocaine can be achieved through oral use, and that "coca chewers are *de facto* users" (p. 4). White (1989) states that recent research indicates that chewing coca leaves is not as harmful as was once thought; in fact, the practice may actually help the chewer absorb some of the phosphorus, vitamins, and calcium contained in the mixture.

COCAINE IN MODERN HISTORY

Although cocaine has been in use for thousands of years, the active agent of cocaine was not isolated until 1859 by Albert Neimen (Scaros, Westra, & Barone, 1990).[1] Following the isolation of the drug, researchers began to concentrate large amounts of relatively pure cocaine for human use. The newly developed hypodermic needle also made it possible to introduce cocaine directly into the bloodstream for the first time. The combination of the hypodermic needle and relatively pure cocaine was to prove a dangerous one.

During the late 1800s even Sigmund Freud experimented with the drug, at first thinking it a cure for depression (Rome, 1984). (Surprisingly, subsequent research has cast doubt as to its antidepressant properties [Post, Weiss, Pert, & Uhde, 1987]). At that time, cocaine was easily available without a prescription. Freud also advocated cocaine as a "cure" for the withdrawal symptoms associated with opiate addiction (Byck, 1987; Lingeman, 1974). However, when Freud discovered the drug's previously unsuspected addictive potential, he discontinued his research on cocaine.

In the late 1800s and early 1900s, cocaine found its way into a wide variety of produce and medicines, often without it being listed on the label as an active ingredient. The new drink "Coca-Cola," introduced by John Stith-Pemberton, was one of many beverages and elixirs that contained cocaine (White, 1989). Following the passage of the Pure Food and Drug Act of 1906, however, it became necessary to list the ingredients of a patent medicine or elixir on the label. As a result of this law, cocaine was removed from many patent medicines.

With the passage of the Harrison Narcotics Act of 1914, nonmedical cocaine use was prohibited (Maranto, 1985). This served to drive recreational cocaine use underground, where it remained until the late 1960s. By then, cocaine had the reputation of being the "champagne of drugs" for those who could afford it (White, 1989, p. 34). In the period from the 1960s until the mid-1980s, cocaine use became increasingly popular, eventually reaching epidemic proportions. Its popularity as a drug of abuse appears to have peaked sometime around 1986, and now seems to be on the decline (Kleber, 1991). However, cocaine remains a significant part of the drug-abuse problem.

There are many reasons why cocaine became so popular in the late 1960s. First, there was a growing disillusionment with the amphetamines, which had proven to be killers. Cocaine had the reputation of being able to bring about

[1]According to Shuckit (1989), cocaine was isolated in 1857, not in 1859.

many of the same sensations associated with amphetamine use, but it was not thought to be addicting (Gawin & Ellinwood, 1988; Maranto, 1985). Also, cocaine had been all but forgotten following the Harrison Narcotics Act of 1914, including the bitter truth about its dangers, which were dismissed as "moralistic exaggerations" (Gawin & Ellinwood, 1988, p. 1173). In the late 1960s and early 1970s, a few respected pharmacologists even attested—incorrectly—to the "fact" that cocaine was nonaddicting (Maranto, 1985).

In addition to its reputation as a "nonaddicting" substitute for the amphetamines, cocaine was also known as a special drug, a "society high" (Doweiko, 1979). These features added to the glamour of cocaine use (White, 1989). Furthermore, during the late 1960s and early 1970s, increasing restrictions on amphetamine manufacture served to tighten the supply of these stimulants (Lingeman 1974). Thus, the amount of amphetamines that could be diverted to illegal markets was reduced, which added to a growing demand for a substitute.

It should be noted that amphetamines were *the* stimulant of choice until the latter half of the 1960s, and there was little cocaine use being reported. Thus, few living professionals had first-hand experience with cocaine addiction. The dangers of cocaine addiction, so well known three-quarters of a century earlier, had disappeared from the public consciousness.

By the late 1960s, the trend away from the amphetamines back to cocaine had started. This is the reverse of what had happened a half-century earlier, when cocaine was replaced by the recently introduced amphetamines as the stimulants of abuse. The trend away from cocaine to the amphetamines was brought about by several factors.

First, there was the fact that it was so difficult to obtain cocaine. Secondly, there was the high cost of cocaine as compared with the amphetamines. Third, there were the known dangers of cocaine use, which in the late 1920s and early 1930s were well documented in the medical literature. Fourth, and finally, the effects of cocaine would last only a short time, whereas the effects of amphetamines tended to last for hours (Weiner, 1985).

But, as we have noted, by the late 1960s the rise of cocaine had begun, although it did not reach the United States until the mid-1970s and early 1980s. By the mid-1970s the practice of smoking coca paste was popular in parts of South America and had started to gain a foothold in the United States. "Crack" cocaine did not become popular until the early 1980s, as cocaine dealers and users attempted to find a form of cocaine that was easily prepared and easily smoked, without the elaborate equipment necessary to make cocaine "freebase" (*U.S. News & World Report*, 1991).

In retrospect, by the mid-1970s and most certainly by the early 1980s, cocaine had once again become a significant part of the U.S. drug scene. It remains a popular drug of abuse and a significant number of people are currently addicted to it, although its popularity seems to be on the wane once again.

MEDICAL USES OF COCAINE

Cocaine is not just a drug of abuse. It is a topical analgesic used by physicians in the ear, nose, throat, rectum, and vagina. Cocaine is also one ingredient in a mixture called Brompton's cocktail, which is used to control the pain of cancer; however, this mixture has fallen out of favor (Scaros et al., 1990). The onset of cocaine's action when used as a local analgesic is approximately 1 minute, with a duration of effect that can last as long as 2 hours (Govoni & Hayes, 1988). However, according to House (1990), with the introduction of a range of new drugs that offer the advantages of cocaine without its side effects, cocaine now "has virtually no clinical use" (p. 41).

THE SCOPE OF THE PROBLEM

Cocaine remains a rather popular drug of abuse. Perhaps some 30 million Americans have at least tried the drug at some point in their lives (DiGregorio, 1990; House, 1990). The Department of Health and Human Services (1990) estimated that over 6 million Americans over the age of 12 had used cocaine in the preceding year and that 662,000 of this number had used it at least once a week. Kleber (1991) suggests that 1.75 million Americans are heavy cocaine users; however, he does not specify what he means by "heavy."

According to Gold and Palumbo (1991), cocaine abuse peaked in the mid-1980s. They point out that whereas an estimated 5.8 million Americans were using cocaine in 1985, only 1.6 million were doing so in 1990. Louie (1990) estimates that 2.2 million Americans are addicted to cocaine. This estimate is higher than either the total number of people estimated to be using cocaine by Gold and Palumbo (1991) or the total number of people who used it at least once a week suggested by the Department of Health and Human Services (1990). However, it is close to the figure of 2 million cocaine addicts in the United States, suggested by Peluso and Peluso (1988).

That form of cocaine known as crack has a reputation of being especially addictive. It is thought that perhaps as many as 600,000 adolescents between the ages of 12 and 17 are addicted to crack cocaine (Gelman et al., 1990), although *U.S. News & World Report* (1991) reports a lower estimate of 500,000 Americans of all ages being addicted to crack. Mayes, Granger, Borenstein and Zuckerman (1992) state that some 6.6 million Americans used crack at least once in 1989 (the last year for which statistics are available). As these often conflicting estimates suggest, we do not know with certainty how many Americans are currently using cocaine.

According to Byrne (1989b), 300–400 tons of cocaine are smuggled into the United States each year; Silvers (1990) would put this figure at 700 tons. This is a staggering amount considering that on the street cocaine is sold in 1-gram packages, on average only 49% pure cocaine with the rest being "fillers" or adulterants (Scaros et al., 1990).

As noted, estimates of the full extent of the problem of cocaine abuse and addiction vary widely. At one point, it was estimated that as many as 5,000 people a day were being introduced to cocaine (Decker, Fins, & Frances, 1987). According to Kirsch (1986), annual expenditures for cocaine are $60 billion to $70 billion. This is significantly higher than the estimate of $18 billion being spent on cocaine each year suggested by the journal *Alcoholism & Drug Abuse Week* (1991b).

Obviously, in spite of the so-called war on drugs and the many dangers associated with cocaine use, there is still a thriving demand for this drug, no matter which of the estimates you believe. As depressing as these estimates are, however, there is evidence suggesting that the number of Americans using cocaine has either leveled off, or possibly even declined, in recent years (White, 1989; *U.S. News & World Report*, 1991).

HOW COCAINE IS PRODUCED

The steps involved in producing cocaine for sale on the streets have been outlined by Byrne (1989b) and White (1989). In the first step, the coca leaves are harvested. In some parts of Bolivia harvesting may take place as often as once every 3 months, as the climate is especially well suited for the plant's growth. In the second step, the leaves are dried, usually by letting them sit in the open sunlight for a few hours or days. Although the practice technically is illegal, coca leaves are openly set out to dry in some parts of Bolivia, according to Byrne.

The third step in the production of cocaine begins when the dried coca leaves are put in a plastic-lined pit and mixed with water and sulfuric acid (White, 1989). After the mixture is crushed by workers, who wade into the pit barefooted, diesel fuel and bicarbonate are added. After a period of time, during which workers reenter the pit several times to continue to stomp through the mixture, the liquids are drained off. Lime is then mixed with the residue, forming the paste that constitutes cocaine base. White states that 500 kg of leaves are needed to produce 1 kg of cocaine base.

The fourth step begins when water, gasoline, acid, potassium permanganate, and ammonia are added to the cocaine paste obtained in the previous step. This forms a reddish-brown liquid, which is then filtered. A few drops of ammonia, when added to the mixture, produces a milky solid, which is filtered and dried. The fifth step begins when the dried cocaine base is dissolved in a solution of hydrochloric acid and acetone. A white solid forms and settles to the bottom of the tank (Byrne, 1989b); White, 1989). This is cocaine hydrochloride.

In the sixth step, the cocaine is filtered and dried under heating lights, causing it to form a white crystalline powder. This is gathered up, packed, and shipped, usually in kilogram packages (1 kg is equal to 2.4 lb). Before each kilogram is repackaged for sale on the street, it is diluted either with mannitol or with local anesthetics, such as lidocane (Byrne, 1989b). The cocaine is then packaged in 1-gram units and sold to individual users. (For more information about how street drugs are adulterated, see Chapter 31, "Drugs and Crime.")

HOW COCAINE IS USED

Cocaine may be used in a number of ways. First, cocaine hydrochloride powder can be inhaled through the nose ("snorted"). It may also be injected directly into a vein. Cocaine hydrochloride is a water-soluble form of cocaine; thus, it is well adapted to either intranasal or intraveneous use (Sbriglio & Millman, 1987).

Schuckit (1989) notes that when cocaine is snorted, the powder is usually arranged on a glass in thin lines 3–5 cm long, each of which contains approximately 25 mg of cocaine. The powder is diced up, usually with a razor blade, and then inhaled through a drinking straw, or rolled paper. When it reaches the nasal passages, which are richly supplied with blood vessels, the cocaine is quickly absorbed. It gains rapid access to the bloodstream, usually in 30–90 seconds, and is carried to the brain (House, 1990).

Cocaine is also injected intravenously. Cocaine hydrochloride powder is mixed with water and then injected into a vein. Jones (1987) states that cocaine administered intravenenously will reach the brain in approximately 15–20 seconds. The user will experience a rapid, intense feeling of euphoria.

Another form of cocaine use, sublingual, is becoming increasingly popular, especially with the hydrochloride salt of cocaine (Jones, 1987). On this method of administration, the drug is placed under the tongue where there is a rich supply of blood vessels. Large amounts of the drug will enter the bloodstream quickly, with results similar to those associated with intranasal administration.

The fourth major method of cocaine use involves inhaling the fumes. This is the process known as "freebasing." Actually, the practice of burning or smoking different parts of the coca plant dates back to at least 300 B.C. R. K. Siegel (1982) relates how the Incas would burn coca leaves at religious festivals. In the late 1800s, coca cigarettes were used to treat hay fever and opiate addiction, and by the year 1890 cocaine was being used for the treatment of whooping cough, bronchitis, asthma, and a range of other conditions.

Despite this long history, the practice of smoking cocaine for recreational purposes is apparently a relatively new phenomenon. According to Kirsch (1986), it was discovered in the mid-1960s that it was easier to smoke freebase cocaine than cocaine hydrochloride. This is because the freebase form is more volatile than cocaine hydrochloride, and will decompose less when heated. House (1990) notes that cocaine hydrochloride tends to turn into a liquid when heated, making it impossible to smoke.

As described by R. K. Seigel (1982), the process of transforming cocaine hydrochloride into freebase involves treating cocaine hydrochloride with various solutions, then filtering out the precipitated cocaine freebase. This will increase the cocaine concentration of the obtained powder, but will not burn off the impurities in the cocaine (R. K. Siegel, 1982). The process of preparing cocaine freebase is quite complex; hence, smoking cocaine freebase tends to be limited to a small proportion of those who abuse cocaine (Gawin, Allen, & Humblestone, 1989).

When heated, the cocaine powder vaporizes and the user inhales the fumes. According to Gonzales (1985), the effects are felt in a mere 7 seconds. Dr. Ronald Siegel (cited in Gonzales, 1985) notes that "there is no such thing as a social-recreational free-baser" (p. 200). In effect, by the time a person has moved to the point of freebasing cocaine, he or she has passed through the phase of casual use and is addicted to the drug. So potent is the process of freebasing cocaine that Gold and Verebey (1984) describe it as "tantamount to intraveneous administration without the need for a syringe" (p. 714).

Crack cocaine (also called "rock") is also smoked, resulting in "an intense, wrenching rush in a matter of seconds" (Lamar, Riley, & Samghabadi, 1986, p. 16). Like freebase, crack is cocaine base, freed from its hydrochloride salt. It is sold in ready-to-use form, in containers that allow the user one or two inhalations for a relatively low price (Gawin et al., 1989). The convenience of crack makes it a preferred form of cocaine (Kirsch, 1986). It is also less expensive than freebase, making it more attractive to the under-eighteen crowd (Bales, 1988; Taylor & Gold (1990).

The operation of one crack "factory" was vividly described as follows:

> Curtis and his girlfriend dropped the cocaine and baking soda into the water, then hit the bottle with the blowtorch. The cocaine powder boiled down to its oily base. The baking soda soaked up the impurities in the cocaine. When cold water was added to the bottle, the cocaine base hardened into white balls. Curtis and Iris spooned them out, placed them on a table covered with paper, and began to measure the hard white cocaine. (Breslin, 1988, p. 212).

The effects of crack are short-lived, lasting only a few minutes (Breslin, 1988; Lemar et al., 1986; *U.S. News & World Report*, 1991). More and more crack must be used in order to reachieve the initial "rush." Eventually, the user will experience a period of severe postcocaine depression. This encourages further use of cocaine, simply to feel normal again.

THE SUBJECTIVE EFFECTS OF COCAINE

As with many drugs of abuse, it has been found that an individual's *expectancies* for cocaine influence how its effects are perceived. Schafer and Brown (1991) report that experienced cocaine users anticipate both positive effects (for example, euphoria) and negative effects (for example, depression). Further, experienced cocaine users expect a generalized feeling of arousal as a result of their cocaine use, some feelings of anxiety, feelings of relaxation, a decrease in hunger, and indifference to pain and fatigue. According to Weiner (1985), the intravenous administration of cocaine will result in a rush that is "somewhat akin to sexual orgasm" (p. 552). Freebasing cocaine, or using crack, will result in the same subjective experience. This rush, however, does not result from oral or intranasal administration of cocaine.

Gold and Verebey (1984) state that the cocaine rush is so intense that "it alone can replace the sex partner of either sex" (p. 719). They note that some male users have experienced spontaneous ejaculation without direct genital stimulation after either injecting or freebasing cocaine. Indeed, cocaine users have been known to speak of their drug of choice as they would a lover. However, as tolerance develops to the effects of cocaine, the male will begin to experience impotence and the female, frigidity.

Within seconds, the initial rush is replaced by a period of excitation that lasts for several minutes (R. K. Siegel, 1982). During this period, the individual will feel more competent and energetic (Gold & Verebey, 1984) or extremely self-confident (Taylor & Gold, 1990). Schuckit (1989) notes that there is no objective evidence suggesting that a person under the effects of cocaine actually is stronger, but because of the effects of cocaine on the nervous system, the person is likely to *feel* more powerful. This sense of increased power is one of the positive effects that experienced cocaine users anticipate.

According to Byck (1987), the euphoric initial rush lasts only a few minutes. However, Gonzales (1985) reports that it can last for minutes to an hour, depending on the method by which the cocaine is used. Kirsch (1986) states that although crack contains the same adulterants and impurities found in cocaine,

> it feels purer because smoking the concentrated alkaloid gives a more immediate, intensified rush. This happens because the smoke is absorbed into the blood-stream through the lung tissue—the most direct route to the brain. (p. 46)

The rush obtained from crack begins almost instantly and subsides quickly. This makes the drug *seem* more pure than when cocaine is used intranasally. When "snorted," cocaine must be absorbed through the the mucous membranes of the nose, which is a slower process, and the high is less intense (Kirsch, 1986).

Cocaine's effects are very short-lived. Julien (1988) noted that the body is able to fully break down (metabolize) cocaine quite rapidly, with the effects of intravenously administered cocaine lasting for only 5 to 15 minutes. To maintain the initial effect, the user must repeatedly use the drug (Lingeman, 1974). Eventually, the person is using cocaine not to gain the initial euphoria, but simply to avoid the postcocaine depression that is ultimately experienced by every cocaine user.

To complicate matters, Schuckit (1989) notes that tolerance to cocaine may develop within hours or days. Thus, the individual will begin to require more and more cocaine in order to achieve the same effect that was initially experienced. This urge to increase the dosage and continue using the drug can reach the point where "users become totally preoccupied with drug-seeking and drug-taking behaviors" (R. K. Seigel, 1982, p. 731).

At this point, the person is addicted to cocaine. Gold and Verebey (1984) termed cocaine "deceptively addictive" (p. 720), while Kirsch (1986) called crack "extraordinarily addictive" (p. 47). Some individuals have been known to routinely administer huge amounts of cocaine in a day's time as a result of their tolerance to the drug's effects (Gonazles, 1985; Schuckit, 1984). R. K. Seigel (1982) notes that some cocaine users have been known to use upwards of 30 grams a day, administering a dose as frequently as once every 5 minutes.

It should be pointed out that these dosage levels are quite toxic and could be fatal to the "naive" drug user. In this sense, "naive" describes a person who has not had time to develop a tolerance to the drug's effects.

Surprisingly, although it is a potent CNS stimulant, cocaine can also function as an effective local anesthetic—a capability that was discovered approximately 100 years ago (Byck, 1987). Cocaine is thought to be capable of blocking the nerve signals, or impulses, of the peripheral nerves. It changes the electrical potential of these peripheral nerves, preventing them from passing on their nerve impulses to the brain. Thus, the body is unable to sense pain from the part of the body under the influence of cocaine, at least for a period of time. However, as we have mentioned, cocaine is rarely used in medicine today (House, 1990).

THE PSYCHOLOGICAL EFFECTS OF COCAINE

In humans, the cortex is the first part of the brain to be affected by cocaine, followed by the brainstem at higher doses (Julien, 1988). This is true no matter how the drug first enters the body. The drug is thought to cause the nerve cells in the brain to release vast amounts of the neurotransmitters normally utilized in small amounts to carry messages between neurons (Lamar et al., 1986), and then to block the reabsorption of these chemicals (Potter et al., 1987). This overstimulation serves to lower the amount of stimulation needed to activate the brain's reward system (Kornetsky & Bain, 1987).

Cocaine thus causes the brain's reward system to function more easily, with less than normal stimulation. Needless to say, this experience is quite pleasurable for the user. Cocaine is thought to accomplish this by blocking "the reuptake of released monoamines including norepinephrine, dopamine and serotonin" (Woods, Winger, & France, 1987, p. 23). These are neurotransmitters thought to be involved in the normal function of the human brain.

After the neurons in the brain release neurotransmitters, they are normally reabsorbed for future use. However, since cocaine blocks the reabsorption process, the supplies of neurotransmitters gradually become depleted. The user, then, falls deeper and deeper into a cocaine-induced depression.

Cocaine is self-reinforcing. The person who uses it is likely to experience pleasurable effects and to want to repeat the experience again. As noted earlier, smoking (or injecting) cocaine can bring about an intense rush that has been described in terms of a sexual orgasm (Gold & Verebey, 1984). According to one cocaine addict quoted by Lamar et al. (1986), "It feels like the top of your head is going to blow off" (p. 16).

Also as noted earlier, smoking crack cocaine or freebasing will result in euphoria in just 7 seconds—an immediacy of reinforcement that is quite powerful. To reexperience this effect, a person might go into a cycle of continuous cocaine use known as "coke runs"—using cocaine for hours or days at a time. Individuals have been known to use cocaine until they simply cannot stay awake any longer, or until the available supply is exhausted (R. K. Seigel, 1982; Weiner, 1985).

Animal research has demonstrated that rats who are given intraveneous cocaine for pushing a bar set in the wall of their cage will do so repeatedly, ignoring food or even sex (Hammer & Hazelton, 1984; Maranto, 1985). According to Hammer and Hazelton, these rats will continue to use the drug to the point of death from convulsions or infection. This reflects both how potent a reinforcer cocaine is and how addictive it can be for the person who uses it.

COMPLICATIONS OF COCAINE ABUSE

Cocaine is hardly a safe drug. It may kill an individual the very first time she or he uses it, or an any subsequent time it is used. There is no way to predict when cocaine use will result in serious complications, or even death.

Since 1976, which is approximately when cocaine again became a popular drug of abuse, there has been more than a fifteenfold increase in cocaine-related emergency-room visits (DiGregorio, 1990). Indeed, in 1990 alone cocaine abuse resulted in 79,400 emergency-room visits (*Alcoholism & Drug Abuse Week*. 1991a). Furthermore, significant number of these cases resulted in death. Moreover, according to House (1990), 5 of every 1,000 deaths in hospital emergency rooms are caused either directly or indirectly by cocaine abuse.

Cocaine can kill through a variety of mechanisms. A small percentage of the population simply cannot detoxify cocaine, no matter how small the dosage level. In these people, the liver is unable to produce an essential enzyme necessary to break down the cocaine—a condition known as a *pseudocholinesterase deficiency* (Gold, 1989). The use of even a small amount of cocaine can result in serious, if not fatal, complications for people with this condition.

As stated by Estroff (1987), "cocaine is much more deadly than heroin when abused in unlimited quantities" (p. 25). Death may be brought about by uncontrolled seizures following cocaine use or from paralysis of the breathing muscles. Cocaine use also may result in strokes in both the brain and the spinal cord (Jaffe, 1990). Such cocaine-induced strokes may kill or simply cause paralysis. Indeed, cocaine-induced death can come about so quickly that "the victim never receives medical attention other than from the coroner" (Estroff, 1987, p. 25).

Cocaine has been reported to bring about damage to the heart muscle and death through heart failure (Maranto, 1985). Whether used intranasally or injected, cocaine can cause cardiac arrhythmias (irregularities in the heartbeat) that may be fatal (Jaffe, 1980; Schuckitt, 1989). It can also cause full-blown heart attacks and sudden death from cardiac arrest (Maranto, 1985).

As we mentioned in the last chapter, it has been suggested that cocaine may cause heart attacks or sudden cardiac arrest in the same manner reported for the form of methamphetamine known as ice; that is, by increasing the heart rate while simultaneously decreasing the blood flow through the coronary arteries (Lange et al., 1989). This process is thought to bring about a decrease in the supply of oxygen to the heart muscle at the very time when the cocaine is causing an increase in the demand on this same muscle tissue. The outcome, even in individuals with no known coronary artery disease, may be a cardiac infarction (damage to the heart muscle), or even a fatal arrhythmia.

The question of whether cocaine's cardiac complications are caused by the cumulative effects of cocaine use or by impurities in the cocaine is still unclear (Decker et al., 1987; Isner & Chokshi, 1989). However, Decker et al. report that cocaine use is often associated with

> profound cardiovascular effects such as sudden death from cardiac arrest, pericardial chest pain, myocardial infarction, hypertension, ventricular tachyarrhythmias, and angina pectoris. (p. 464)

In layperson's terms, cocaine can bring about pain in the region over the heart and the lower thorax ("pericardial chest pain"). The term *ventricular tachyarrhythmias* refers to a pattern of abnormally fast contractions of the ventricles of the heart, usually in excess of 150 contractions per minute, which may rapidly prove to be fatal. *Myocardial infarction* is a technical term for what we know as a heart attack.

Decker et al. (1987) also state that reexposure to cocaine after a period of abstinence, or even first exposure to cocaine, might predispose an individual user to myocardial infarction, angina pectoris, or both. They warn that chest pain in young people may be misinterpreted as a symptom of anxiety or some other psychological problem "when it actually may signal cardiac damage resulting from remote or recent drug use" (p. 465).

In addition to cardiovascular problems, chronic intranasal use of cocaine can result in inflamed sinuses, hoarseness, breakdown of the cartilage of the nose, pulmonary hemorrhage, chronic bronchitis (also known as "crack lung"), chronic inflammation of the throat, and irreversible lung damage (House, 1990; Taylor & Gold, 1990).

If the person who injects cocaine uses a "dirty" needle, or fails to use sterile techniques, he or she runs the risk of endocarditis (Burden & Rogers, 1988); hepatitis B; AIDS; various other blood infections; and skin abscesses (S. Cohen, 1984; Taylor & Gold, 1990). Wetli (1987) reports that in addition to these infections there are occasional isolated reports of unusual infections, such as fungus infections of the brain, associated with intravenous cocaine use.

Opiate addicts frequently are forced to inject medications intended for oral use. Oral medications often include "fillers," substances that are added to the active agent of an oral medication to give it form and make it easier to handle. These "fillers" are not intended to enter the bloodstream, and are harmless when the medication is taken orally. Repeated injections of these foreign materials cause extensive scarring at the site of injection, forming the characteristic "tracks" of chronic opiate addicts. By contrast, cocaine addicts usually inject soluble materials, and are thus less likely to develop extensive scars at the site of injection (Wetli, 1987).

There is a danger of adverse interactions between cocaine and medications being used to treat conditions or other drugs being abused by the individual (S. Cohen, 1984). Barnhill et al. (1989) report that cocaine is often used in conjunction with marijuana, and that both drugs are capable of significantly increasing heart-rate levels associated with the use of either drug alone. Indeed, they report heart-rate increases of almost 50 beats per minute. This is a matter of some consequence for those whose heart muscle has been damaged.

Cocaine has also been implicated as causing panic reactions (DiGregorio, 1990). According to Louie (1990), 25% of the patients seen at one panic-disorder clinic eventually admitted to the use of cocaine. Further, up to 64% of cocaine users experience some degree of anxiety as a side effect.

Chronic use of cocaine has been implicated in the development of a drug-induced psychosis very similar in appearance to paranoid schizophrenia. The exact mechanism by which cocaine might bring about a drug-induced psychosis is not clear at this time, although Satel and Edell (1991) suggest that those individuals who do develop a cocaine-induced psychosis may possess a biological vulnerability toward schizophrenia that is activated by cocaine use. This condition is known on the streets as "coke paranoia"; it usually clears within a few hours (Davis & Bresnahan, 1987) to a few days (Schuckit, 1989) after cocaine use is discontinued. On occasion, however, the cocaine-induced paranoid state seems to become permanent (Maranto, 1985).

Drug-induced periods of rage, or outbursts of anger and violent assaultive behavior have been reported following chronic use of cocaine (Gonzales, 1985). Cocaine often bring about seizures in the user, which may be fatal without proper medical intervention. Finally, Maranto (1985) notes that either a few hours after snorting the drug, or within 15 minutes of injecting it, a person may slide into a state of depression. After prolonged use this depression may reach suicidal proportions (S. Cohen, 1984).

The depression associated with cocaine use is the result of cocaine's depleting the nerve cells in the brain of the neurotransmitter *norepinephrine*, one of the chemical messengers passed between nerve cells. In many cases, this period of depression will resolve itself in a few hours to a few weeks. Not surprisingly, some people fall into a cycle of using more cocaine in order to relieve the feelings of depression brought on by previous cocaine use. They will go on extended "coke runs," during which they continue to use cocaine until exhausted or until their supply runs out. These are similar to the "speed runs" associated with amphetamine use, discussed in the last chapter.

Findings from medical research suggest the possibility of liver damage from cocaine use in *any* form (Moranto, 1985). Also after periods of extended use, some people have experienced the so-called cocaine bugs. As discussed in the last chapter, this hallucinatory experience in which the person senses bugs crawling on or just under the skin is also associated with prolonged amphetamine use. The technical term for this condition is *formication* and, as noted previously, some individuals go so far as to burn their arms or legs with matches or cigarettes in an attempt to rid themselves of these unseen bugs (Gonzales, 1985; Lingeman, 1974).

Animal research suggests that, after repeated exposures to cocaine, an animal may develop seizures at a dose that previously had not brought on such convulsions. This process has been termed a "pharmacological kindling," and it was found that while cocaine itself might have a short half-life, the sensitization effects are long lasting (Post et al., 1987). Moreover, Post et al., report that

> repeated administration of a given dose of cocaine without resulting seizures
> . . . *in no way assure[s] the continued safety of this drug* **even for that given
> individual.** (p. 159) (italics and boldface added)

Thus, while the *immediate effects* of cocaine may last only a short time, the body can become hypersensitive to cocaine for long periods of time. If this should happen, the person could suffer possibly fatal side effects from a dosage level once easily tolerated.

Enough is now known about cocaine that few would challenge its addictive potential. According to Lamar et al. (1986), individuals who "snort" cocaine will develop an addiction in 3 to 4 years; those who smoke crack may be fully addicted in just 6 to 10 weeks. But, after a protracted period of use, many users reach the point where they will continue to use the drug not to experience a rush, but just to maintain a feeling of being normal.

WITHDRAWAL FROM CNS STIMULANTS AND RECOVERY

Although the treatment process will be discussed in more detail later on in the text, brief mention of the treatment of addiction to CNS stimulants should be made here. Unfortunately, although a great deal is known about the manifestations of cocaine addiction, very little is known about the natural history of cocaine dependence (Jaffe, 1990; Weiner, 1985).

Gawin and Ellinwood (1988) report that "of 30 million Americans who have tried cocaine intranasally, 80 percent have *not* become regular users, and 95 percent are *not* addicted to the drug" (p. 1174, italics added). Thus, not everybody who uses cocaine by "snorting" it is addicted to the drug. However, people do frequently become addicted to cocaine.

Hospital-based detoxification from CNS stimulants such as the amphetamines is rarely necessary as a direct result of the abuse of this class of drugs (*Harvard Medical School Mental Health Letter*, 1990). However, hospital-based observation and treatment may be necessary to protect an individual during postamphetamine or postcocaine depression. A decision as to whether to hospitalize an individual should be made on a case-by-case basis according to such factors as the individual's state of mind, his or her medical status, and informed judgment as to whether the individual has adequate resources to deal with withdrawal on an outpatient basis.

There is very little research addressing the factors that bring about addiction to the CNS stimulants; thus, it is not possible to determine which person who abuses cocaine is likely to become addicted. Furthermore, in contrast to the research into the genetics of alcoholism, "research on genetic factors in stimulant abuse has not been pursued" (Gawin & Ellinwood, 1988, p. 1177).

Evidence does exist that cocaine may cause a withdrawal syndrome (Hammer & Hazelton, 1984; Satel et al., 1991). Gawin and Ellinwood (1988) compare this withdrawal syndrome to the acute withdrawal of the alcohol hangover. Although the cocaine withdrawal syndrome does not include the severe symptoms associated with opiate withdrawal, cocaine withdrawal is marked by such complaints as paranoia, depression, fatigue, "craving" for cocaine, agitation, chills, insomnia, nausea, and vomiting. DiGregorio (1990) points to muscle tremors, headache, ravenous hunger, and altered sleep patterns as symptoms of cocaine withdrawal. These begin between 24 and 48 hours after the last dose of cocaine and persist for 7 to 10 days.

The Stages of Recovery

Gawin and Kleber (1986) suggest a triphasic model for the postcocaine-binge recovery process, including the following stages:

1. *Stage 1.* In the early part of the first stage, which lasts from 1 to 4 days, the person experiences agitation, depression, and anorexia, as well as a strong craving for cocaine. As the person progresses through the second half of the first stage, he or she loses the craving for cocaine, but experiences insomnia and exhaustion combined with a strong desire for sleep. The second half of the first phase begins on day 4 and lasts until day 7.

2. *Stage 2.* After the seventh day of abstinence, the person returns to a normal sleep pattern and gradually experiences stronger cravings for cocaine and higher levels of anxiety. Conditioned cues exacerbate the individual's craving for stimulants, possibly drawing him or her back to chemical use. If the person is able to withstand the environmental and intrapersonal cues for further drug use, he or she moves into the "extinction" phase, in which there is a gradual return to a more normal level of function.

3. *Stage 3.* The extinction phase begins after 10 weeks of abstinence. If the person cannot maintain sobriety and again goes on a stimulant "binge," the cycle will repeat itself. If however, the person can withstand the drug craving, chances are likely that he or she will achieve sobriety. For example, Hall, Havassy, and Wasserman (1991) state that approximately 80% of those cocaine addicts who are able to abstain from cocaine use for 12 weeks after treatment are still drug-free after 6 months.

It is not known how long an individual may need to fully recover from his or her cocaine addiction. Cocaine and amphetamine addicts might suddenly experience craving for these drugs "months or years after its last appearance" (Gawin & Ellinwood, 1988, p. 1176), and long after the last period of chemical use.

Satel et al. (1991) report findings that fail to support the Gawin and Kleber (1986) model. In the study by Satel et al., the cocaine withdrawal process was marked by withdrawal symptoms that declined over the first 3 weeks of inpatient treatment. These withdrawal symptoms were much milder than anticipated and failed to follow the triphasic model suggested by Gawin and Kleber.

At this point, there is consensus among researchers that there is a withdrawal syndrome following prolonged cocaine use; however, there is still controversy surrounding the exact nature of the postcocaine withdrawal syndrome. Various theoretical models are now being explored to better understand what happens when a cocaine addict attempts to lead a drug-free life.

As part of the process of exploring different ways of working with cocaine addicts, a number of pharmacological agents are being investigated in the hope of finding a drug, or combination of drugs, that will control postcocaine craving. These agents will be discussed in Chapter 19.

The treatment of stimulant addiction involves more than just helping the addict stop using the drug. One common complication of stimulant addiction is that the addict has often forgotten what a drug-free life is like (Siegel, 1984). Further, Gold and Verebey (1984) point out that cocaine addiction may lead to vitamin deficiencies, especially of the B complex and C vitamins. Since the stimulant effects of the amphetamines are so similar to those of cocaine, one would expect that the amphetamines would also lead to vitamin deficiencies in a pattern similar to that associated with cocaine.

Gold and Verebey (1984) found that 73% of a sample of cocaine abusers tested had at least one vitamin deficiency. They concluded that the vitamin deficiencies were a reflection of the cocaine abuse, since cocaine may cause anorexia. They recommended vitamin replacement therapy as part of the treatment of cocaine addiction. One would expect, then, that vitamin replacement therapy could be valuable in the rehabilitation of amphetamines abusers as well.

It should be emphasized that total abstinence from drugs of abuse is essential in the treatment of cocaine or amphetamine addiction. In addition, follow-up treatment should include behavior modification and psychotherapy (Gold & Verebey, 1984). Indeed, according to Hall, Havassy, and Wasserman (1991), those cocaine addicts who make a commitment to full abstinence following treatment are more likely to avoid further cocaine use than addicts who do not declare abstinence as a treatment goal. Group support in the form of Alcoholics Anonymous, Narcotics Anonymous, and Cocaine Anonymous is often of great help. As with the other forms of drug addiction, recovering individuals are at risk for cross-addiction to other chemicals and must avoid other drug use for the rest of their lives.

SUMMARY

Although humans have used cocaine for hundreds if not thousands of years, the active agent of the coca bush was not isolated until 1859. This accomplished, it was possible to concentrate large amounts of cocaine. The introduction of the hypodermic needle in the 1850s allowed for the intravenous administration of large amounts of cocaine, which immediately became a rather popular drug of abuse.

At the turn of the century, government regulations limited the availability of cocaine, which had been mistakenly classified as a narcotic. The emergence of the amphetamine family of drugs in the 1930s, along with increasingly strict enforcement of the laws against cocaine use, allowed addicts to substitute legally purchased amphetamines for the increasingly rare cocaine. In time, the dangers of cocaine use were forgotten by all but a few medical historians.

However, in the late 1960s and early 1970s, government regulations began to limit the availability of amphetamines and cocaine regained its popularity. Moreover, it is now also smoked in the forms of freebase and crack, both dangerously addictive. Evidence suggests, however, that the current wave of cocaine addiction peaked around 1986 and that fewer and fewer people are now becoming addicted to it.

Chapter 9

Marijuana

A lthough nobody is sure exactly when people began to smoke marijuana, historical evidence points to its use at least since the reign of the Chinese Emperor Shen Nung (2737 B.C.) (Scaros et al., 1990). Since then, marijuana has been used for both medicinal and recreational purposes. Grinspoon and Bakalar (1985) state, for example, that as late as the nineteenth century marijuana was being used by European and American physicians as an analgesic, hypnotic, and anticonvulsant.

During the early part of this century, marijuana was found to be ineffective, or at least less effective, than many other pharmaceuticals being introduced to fight disease. For a long time, there did not appear to be any legitimate medical use for marijuana, and it was removed from the doctor's pharmacopoeia. In recent years, however, there has been interest in the possible medical use of marijuana to control the nausea sometimes associated with cancer chemotherapy (Grinspoon & Bakalar, 1985; Jaffe, 1990). It has also received attention as an agent that may be useful in the control of certain forms of glaucoma.

The practice of smoking marijuana cigarettes was apparently introduced to the United States by Mexican immigrants who had come north to find work in the 1920s. According to Musto (1991), the practice was quickly adopted by Americans, particularly jazz musicians. With the start of Prohibition, the working class turned to growing and importing marijuana as a substitute for the now-banned alcohol (Gazzaniga, 1988). Its use declined with the end of Prohibition, when alcohol could once again be easily obtained. In the 1960s, however, marijuana reemerged as a popular drug of abuse, and it has remained a popular recreational drug ever since. Currently, marijuana is the most frequently used drug in the United States and the fourth most commonly abused chemical in Canada, afer caffeine, alcohol, and tobacco (*Health News*, 1990).

Marijuana is obtained from the plant *Cannabis sativa*, which grows naturally in a wide variety of climates and is also frequently cultivated both for personal use and for sale. Over the past 20 years, as a result of selective breeding programs, the potency of "street" marijuana has significantly increased. Indeed, some of the marijuana now sold on the streets is two and a half times as potent as the marijuana sold in the 1970s (American Academy of Family Physicians, 1990a).

A little-known fact is that the United States is the world's foremost producer of marijuana (Nadelmann, Kleiman, & Earls, 1990). Indeed, several years ago, *Playboy* (1988) reported that when the Asthma and Allergy Foundation of America examined air samples from the Los Angeles area to determine which pollen particles were drifting in the air—a matter of some interest to those with allergies to pollen—it was found that fully 40% of the pollen was from marijuana plants.

THE SCOPE OF THE PROBLEM

Marijuana is used on a regular basis by an estimated 200 million people around the world (Kaplan & Sadock, 1988). It is difficult to clearly assess the extent of marijuana use in the United States, at least in part because the pattern keeps changing. However, marijuana is undoubtedly a popular drug of abuse. According to the Department of Health and Human Services (1990), 20 million Americans had used marijuana at least once in the preceding year.

Mirin et al. (1991) report that 15 million young people use marijuana approximately once a month, 9 million use it weekly, and 6 million use it daily. The journal *Health News* (1990) estimates that perhaps 9% to 12% of all people surveyed over the age of 15 use marijuana at least once a year. Weiss and Mirin (1988) contend that 60% of the population between the ages of 18 and 25 have used marijuana at least once.

It is difficult to estimate the total percentage of the U.S. population that has at least tried marijuana. Kaplan and Sadock (1988), for example, estimate that over 40 million Americans have used the drug at least once. According to the Department of Health and Human Services (1990), more than 66 million Americans over the age of 12 have used marijuana at least once.

Obviously, estimates vary on the number of Americans who have used marijuna or are currently using it. This is because, as Peluso and Peluso (1988) note, "a few puffs on a joint is this generation's social martini" (p. 110). Social sanctions against marijuana use have been relaxed, and in many states possession of a small amount of marijuana has been decriminalized. Over time, then, a greater and greater percentage of the population is likely to have tried marijuana at some point in their lives.

The majority of marijuana users experiment with the drug briefly and then give it up for good. However, for many, marijuana becomes a popular drug of choice. The Department of Health and Human Services (1990) concludes that 5.5 million Americans use marijuana at least once a week and that 3.3 million use it daily. Kaplan and Sadock (1988) estimate that 10 million Americans use marijuana on a regular basis. Both Jenike (1989) and L. Siegel (1989) estimate that 20 million Americans use marijuana on a regular basis.

THE PHARMACOLOGY OF THC

The hemp plant that yields marijuana contains over 400 different identified compounds, of which an estimated 61 have psychoactive properties (University of California, Berkeley, 1990b). But the active ingredient of marijuana appears to be the chemical delta-9-tetrahydrocannabinol, abbreviated THC (Bloodworth, 1987; Mirin et al., 1991; Schwartz, 1987).

The highest concentrations of THC are found in the small upper leaves and flowering tops of the plant (Mirin et al., 1991). As noted by Berger and Dunn (1982), *marijuana* is the term used to identify the relatively weak preparations of the cannabis plant that are used for smoking or eating, whereas *hashish* refers to a preparation with a higher concentration of THC.

After it is ingested or inhaled, THC is detoxified by the liver. About 65% of the metabolites are excreted in the feces and the rest are excreted in the urine (Schwartz, 1987). Tolerance to the effects of THC develop rapidly, and in order to continue to achieve the initial effects, the chronic marijuana user must use "more potent cannabis, deeper, more sustained inhalations, or larger amounts of the crude drug" to achieve the same effect (Schwartz, 1987, p. 307).

Because the liver is unable to immediately metabolize all the THC in the system, and because the THC binds to fat cells, significant amounts of THC may be stored in the body's fat reserves. The THC may then may be slowly released back into the bloodstream after the person has stopped using marijuana. According to Schwartz (1987), this could explain why heavy marijuana users may test positive for THC in urine toxicology screens weeks after their last use of the drug. The casual user of marijuana will usually test positive for only 3 days after the last use of the drug.

An ongoing search by various scientists has finally resulted in the discovery of what appears to be a receptor site within the brain that is used by the THC molecule. In an attempt to isolate certain neuropeptides that transmit pain signals between cells, Matsuda, Lolait, Brownstein, Young, and Bonner (1990) discovered a process through which THC inhibits the function of the enzyme *adenylate cyclase*, which is involved in the transmission of pain messages. This research opens the way for scientists to identify the naturally occuring substances that utilize that receptor site, to learn how marijuana works on the body, and to explore the nature of memory and pain perception.

HOW MARIJUANA IS USED

In the United States, marijuana is most often smoked, although occasionally it is ingested. Marijuana cigarettes, called "joints" or "reefers," contain between 5 mg and 20 mg of THC. These cigarettes usually contain between 500 mg and 750 mg of marijuana, the exact potency of which varies from batch to batch.

The technique of smoking a marijuana cigarette is somewhat different from that used with regular cigarettes. The user must inhale the smoke deeply into the lungs, then hold his or her breath for about 25 seconds to get as much THC into the blood as possible (Schwartz, 1987). About 18% of the available THC is absorbed through the lungs into the blood by this method of smoking (Scaros et al., 1990).

When smoked, the effects begin almost immediately, usually within seconds (Weiss & Mirin, 1988) to perhaps within 10 minutes (Bloodworth, 1987). The effects reach peak intensity within 30 minutes and begin to decline in an hour (Weiss & Mirin, 1988). Estimates of the duration of the subjective effects of marijuana range from less than 3 hours (Brophy, 1990) up to 4 hours (Bloodworth, 1987; Grinspoon & Bakalar, 1985). The half-life of THC in the body has been estimated as being approximately 3 days (Schwartz, 1987) to a week (Bloodworth, 1987).

When ingested by mouth, the user will absorb only a small percentage of the available THC. Schwartz (1987) states that the oral user would have to ingest three times as much THC in order to achieve the effects produced by smoking one joint. Also, the oral user will not experience the immediate effects that result from smoking marijuana. Usually, from 30 to 60 minutes (Mirin et al., 1991) to perhaps 2 hours (Schwartz, 1987) must elapse before the effects of the ingested drug are felt. Estimates of the duration of marijuana's effects when ingested orally range from 3 to 5 hours (Mirin et al., 1991; Weiss & Mirin, 1988) to 5 to 12 hours (Grinspoon & Bakalar, 1985; Kaplan & Sadock, 1988).

THE SUBJECTIVE EFFECTS OF MARIJUANA

At moderate dosage levels, marijuana will bring about a two-phase reaction (Brophy, 1990). The first phase begins shortly after the drug enters the bloodstream, when the individual will experience a period of mild anxiety, followed by a sense of well-being or euphoria, as well as a sense of relaxation and friendliness (Kaplan & Sadock, 1988). According to Friedman (1987), there is evidence suggesting that marijuana causes "a transient increase in the release of the neurotransmitter dopamine" (p. 47). Dopamine is thought to be involved in the experience of euphoria.

As with many drugs of abuse, the individual's expectancies will influence how he or she will perceive the effects of marijuana. Schafer and Brown (1991) report that experienced marijuana users expect the drug to (a) impair cognitive function and behavior, (b) facilitate relaxation, (c) facilitate social interaction and enhance sexual function, (d) enhance creativity, (e) alter perception, and (f) bring about a sense of "craving."

Individuals who are intoxicated on marijuana will experience an altered sense of time, as well as mood swings (Kaplan & Sadock, 1988). Marijuana also seems to bring about a splitting of consciousness, in which users will possibly experience the sensation of observing themselves while under the influence of the drug (Grinspoon & Bakalar, 1985; Kaplan & Sadock, 1988).

Marijuana users have often referred to a sense of being on the threshold of a significant personal insight but without being able to put this insight into words. These reported drug-related insights seem to come about during the first phase of the marijuana reaction. The second phase of the marijuana experience begins when the individual becomes sleepy, which takes place following the acute intoxication caused by marijuana (Brophy, 1990).

There are few immediate adverse reactions to marijuana (Mirin et al., 1991). Panic reactions, while rare, are thought to be one consequence of marijuana use (Kaplan & Sadock, 1988). Factors that influence the development of marijuana-related panic reactions are the individual's prior experience with marijuana, his or her expectations for the drug, the dosage level being used, and the setting in which the drug is used. Such panic reactions are most often seen in the inexperienced marijuana user (Bloodworth, 1987; Mirin et al., 1991) and respond to simple reassurance (Kaplan & Sadock, 1988).

According to Nahas (1986), marijuana use may trigger an underlying psychosis in an individual who has suffered a previous psychotic episode, or who may be predisposed to psychosis. He adds that the role of marijuana in the emergence of these psychotic episodes has not been determined. Grinspoon and Bakalar (1985) and Kaplan and Sadock (1988) report that although marijuana may cause an individual to experience some distortion of body image, paranoid reactions, and increased anxiety, there is no evidence to suggest that it is likely to bring about a psychotic reaction in the well-adjusted individual.

CONSEQUENCES OF CHRONIC MARIJUANA USE

As previously mentioned, the hemp plant from which marijuana is obtained contains some 400 different chemicals. Tests have shown that more than 2,000 separate metabolites of these chemicals may be found in the body after marijuana has been smoked (Jenike, 1989). Many of these metabolites may remain in the body for weeks after a single dose of marijuana, and their long-term effects have not been studied in detail. In addition, if the marijuana is adulterated (as it frequently is), the various adulterants will add their own contribution to the flood of chemicals being admitted to the body when a person uses marijuana.

The active agent of marijuana, THC, has been demonstrated to cause lung damage and reduce the effectiveness of the body's immune system. Smoking marijuana can also result in increased levels of carbon monoxide in the blood (Oliwenstein, 1988). Indeed, it has been reported that the marijuana smoker absorbs *five times* as much carbon monoxide per joint as a cigarette smoker from a single regular cigarette (Oliwenstein, 1988; University of California, Berkeley, 1990b).

Furthermore, marijuana users who smoke only a few joints a day seem to develop the same type of damage to the cells lining the airways as do cigarette smokers who go on to develop lung cancer (Oliwenstein, 1988; University of California, Berkeley, 1990b). The chronic use of marijuana often brings about obstructive pulmonary diseases similar to those seen in cigarette smokers (University of California, Berkeley, 1990b).

According to Bloodworth (1987), marijuana smoke contains 5 to 15 times the amount of a known carcinogen, benzpyrene, as does tobacco smoke. Indeed, the heavy use of marijuana has been suggested as a cause of cancer of the tongue in at least one case (Almadori, Paludetti, Cerullo, Ottavini, & D'Altari, 1990). Almadori et al. suggest that marijuana smokers who also smoke tobacco products are at higher risk for cancer of the mouth, an effect of marijuana use that had not previously been identified.

It has been reported that marijuana smokers have an increased frequency of bronchitis and other upper respiratory infections (Mirin et al., 1991). Furthermore, marijuana is now known to damage the lungs (Siegel, cited in Engelman, 1989). Peluso and Peluso (1988) state that marijuana also suppresses part of the immune system, a conclusion supported by Siegel (cited in Engelman, 1989). Bloodworth (1987) states that there is conflicting evidence as to whether marijuana affects the immune system; however, even if it does, it would be a matter of little importance to the healthy individual. He cautions, though, that even a weak immunosuppressant effect could have "a devastating effect on AIDS patients" (p. 180).

Marijuana has been implicated in reduced sperm counts (Brophy, 1990). Also, decreased blood testosterone levels have been reported for male chronic marijuana users (Bloodworth, 1987). According to the *Mayo Clinic Health Letter* (1989), chronic marijuana use in women could result in abnormal menstruation. With pregnant women, fetal damage may result (Bloodworth, 1987). Wray and Murphy (1987) conclude that chronic marijuana use can result in fertility problems in women.

According to Jenike (1989), those who have previously used hallucinogenics may also experience marijuana-related "flashback" experiences. Such flashbacks are usually limited to the 6-month period following the last marijuana use. They will eventually stop if the person does not use any further mood-altering chemicals (Weiss & Mirin, 1988). (Flashbacks will be discussed in more detail in Chapter 13 on hallucinogenic drugs.)

It has been suggested that there is no known evidence of marijuana-related brain damage, even in chronic users of marijuana (Jenike, 1989). However, Peluso and Peluso (1988) challenge this conclusion, noting evidence that suggests that chronic marijuana use may result in physical changes in the brain similar to those associated with aging. Bloodworth (1987) states that marijuana has been found to cause microscopic changes in the synaptic cleft in the brain of animals; however, the significance of this finding for humans is not clear.

Research on the effects of THC on the brain suggests that it changes the way in which the brain handles sensory information (Friedman, 1987). Furthermore, chronic exposure to THC "damages and destroys nerve cells and causes other pathological changes in the hippocampus" (p. 47). This portion of the brain is thought to be involved with processing sensory information.

Most certainly, there is evidence that chronic marijuana use may cause memory problems (American Academy of Family Physicians, 1990a; Wray & Murthy, 1987). This seems to be because marijuana interferes with the retrieval mechanisms of memory (Wray & Murthy, 1987), although this effect may be only temporary and clear up in a few weeks after the last marijuana use (American Academy of Family Physicians, 1990a). Thus, there does appear to be evidence that chronic use of marijuana can cause at least temporary brain dysfunction.

Jenike (1989) states that marijuana may cause impaired reflexes, decreased short-term memory, and decreased attention spans. Mirin et al. (1991) note that automobile drivers under the influence of marijuana will frequently misjudge speed and length of time required for braking. According to Schwartz (1987), marijuana use may impair coordination and reaction time for 12 to 24 hours after the eurphoria from the last marijuana use ends. Furthermore, teenagers who smoke marijuana as often as six times a month are more than twice as likely to be involved in traffic accidents.

In a study by Meer (1986), 10 private airplane pilots were tested on a flight simulator 24 hours after they had smoked one marijuana cigarette. Although their performance had improved over their simulator performance 1 to 4 hours after smoking the marijuana cigarette, these pilots still demonstrated significant impairment. One pilot's simulation performance would have landed the plane off the runway, for example. The exact significance of these findings is not clear at this time, but the study does suggest that marijuana's effects on coordination might be longer-lasting than was once thought.

Marijuana use can cause a significant increase in heart rate, a matter of some consequence to persons who suffer from heart disease (Barnhill et al., 1989; Bloodworth, 1987). Moreover, cocaine users will often augment their use of cocaine with marijuana so that the sedative effects of the marijuana will counteract the excessive stimulation caused by the cocaine. The combination of marijuana and cocaine can increase a person's heart rate above the increase from either drug alone, raising the heart rate an additional 50 beats per minute (Barnhill et al., 1989). Again, this is a matter of some importance to those with heart disease, although it should be pointed out that marijuana by itself apparently does not cause heart disease (Brophy, 1990; Jenike, 1989).

There is conflicting evidence as to whether chronic marijuana use can bring about an "amotivational syndrome." Mirin et al. (1991) report that this condition has been described as consisting of decreased drive and ambition, short attention span, easy distractibility, and a tendency not to make plans beyond the present day. Although the existence of this syndrome has been challenged (Mirin et al., 1991), Schwartz (1987) contends that further research is needed to determine once and for all whether chronic marijuana use can cause the amotivational syndrome.

In terms of *immediate* lethality, marijuana is a "safe" drug. There have been no clearly documented cases of a lethal overdose involving marijuana alone (Kaplan & Sadock, 1988; Nahas, 1986). Weil (1986) describes marijuana as "among the least toxic drugs known to modern medicine" (p. 47). In contrast to the estimated 346,000 deaths in the United States each year from tobacco and the total of 125,000 yearly fatalities from alcohol use, marijuana estimates indicate 75 deaths each year—and these are mainly from accidents (Crowley, 1988).

Grinspoon and Bakalar (1985) estimate that the effective dose of marijuana is between 1/20,000th and 1/40,000th of the lethal dose, which is to say that marijuana is a very safe drug in terms of immediate lethality. However, according to the University of California, Berkeley, (1990b), there is virtually no information available on the effect of chronic exposure to the chemicals found in the typical marijuana cigarette.

THE ADDICTION POTENTIAL OF MARIJUANA

As the reader will recall from earlier chapters, two essential indicators of addiction to any chemical are the development of tolerance to that chemical and the onset of a withdrawal syndrome when the drug is discontinued. Bloodworth (1987) states that smoking as few as three marijuana cigarettes a week may result in tolerance to the effects of marijuana.

Because of its long half-life in the human body, the symptoms associated with marijuana withdrawal are not so severe as those resulting from narcotic or barbiturate withdrawal (Bloodworth, 1987). Symptoms of marijuana withdrawal include irritability, anxiety, insomnia, nausea, and loss of appetite (Bloodworth, 1987; Group for the Advancement of Psychiatry, 1991). According to Nahas (1986), the withdrawal syndrome from heavy use of marijuana includes sweating, vomiting, nausea, and sleep disturbance. Thus, it now appears that marijuana is addictive, despite earlier claims to the contrary.

THE TREATMENT OF MARIJUANA ABUSE

Short-term, acute reactions to marijuana do not require any special intervention (Brophy, 1990). According to Mirin et al. (1991), panic reactions usually respond to "firm reassurance in a nonthreatening environment" (p. 304). However, they note that patients should be watched to ensure that they do no harm to themselves or to others. Grinspoon and Bakalar (1985) note that marijuana may cause transient feelings of anxiety during the initial period following the drug's use.

Marijuana users usually do not present themselves for treatment, unless there is some form of coercion (Bloodworth, 1987). Even when chronic marijuana users enter treatment, there are no well-developed methods for working with them (Mirin, Weiss, & Greenfield, 1991). Roffman and George

(1988) attribute this to the mistaken belief that marijuana abuse was not a cause of major concern to health care providers because it was less toxic than other drugs of abuse. Thus, health care providers failed to address the issue of how to deal with the chronic marijuana user.

As stated previously, total abstinence from *all* psychoactive drugs is required if treatment is to work (Bloodworth, 1987). A treatment program that identifies why the individual is using drugs and explores alternatives to further drug use is thought to be most effective. Supplemental groups that focus on vocational rehabilitation and socialization skills are also of value in the treatment of the chronic marijuana user (Mirin et al., 1991). Jenike (1989) recommends that treatment efforts focus on understanding the abuser's disturbed psychosocial relationships.

Bloodworth (1987) states that "family therapy is almost a necessity" (p. 183). He also emphasizes group therapy as a means of dealing with peer pressure to use chemicals, as well as self-help support groups, such as Alcoholics Anonymous and Narcotics Anonymous.

SUMMARY

Marijuana has been a controversial drug for several generations. In spite of its popularity as a drug of abuse, surprisingly little is known about it. Indeed, after a 25-year search, researchers just recently have identified what appears to be the specific receptor site used by the THC molecule to cause at least some of its effects on perception and memory.

Despite our relative ignorance about marijuana, some groups continue to advocate its complete decriminalization. Other groups maintain that marijuana is a serious drug of abuse with a high potential for harm and should not be legalized in any circumstances. Even the experts differ as to the potential for marijuana to cause harm. Whereas Weil (1986) classifies marijuana as one of the safest drugs known, Oliwenstein (1988) terms it a dangerous drug.

The evidence to date suggests that marijuana is not as benign as was once thought. Either alone or in combination with cocaine, marijuana will increase the heart rate—a matter of some significance to those with cardiac disease. There also is evidence that chronic use of marijuana will cause physical changes in the brain, and the smoke from marijuana cigarettes has been found to be even more harmful than tobacco smoke. In the years to come, marijuana will likely remain a most controversial drug.

Chapter 10

NARCOTIC ANALGESICS

K nowledge of narcotic analgesics dates back thousands of years. Indeed, opium, which is to say the dried juice from the opium poppy plant, *Papaver somniferum*, has been used for medicinal purposes for at least 3,500 years (Jaffe, 1989). Records dating back to approximately 7000 B.C. refer to the use of opium in treating children suffering from colic (Thomason & Dilts, 1991). Thus, it is safe to assume that opium has been known to folk healers for quite some time.

Narcotics also have been used as drugs of abuse for some time. In this chapter, we will explore the role that narcotic analgesics have in modern medicine. Then, we will discuss their role as drugs of abuse.

THE CLASSIFICATION OF ANALGESICS

Abel (1982) defined an analgesic as a drug capable of relieving pain without producing general anesthesia. There are two such groups of drugs. In one group are those drugs that bring about a *local anesthesia;* in the second are those that change the perception of pain—the *global analgesics.* Cocaine, for example, is a local anesthetic, and as such will block the transmission of nerve impulses from the site of the injury to the brain. In so doing, cocaine (or any of the other local anesthetics developed after cocaine) prevent the brain from receiving the nerve impulses that transmit the pain message from the site of the injury.

As mentioned, the global analgesics change a person's perception of pain. This group of analgesics was further divided into two subgroups by E. L. Abel (1982). The first of these is the *narcotic* family of drugs, which have both a CNS-depressant capability and an analgesic effect. The second subgroup of global analgesics consists of *nonnarcotic* analgesics, such as aspirin, acetaminophen, and similar agents.

The nonnarcotic analgesics are thought to interfere with the action of chemicals released by injured tissues of the body, resulting in a reduction of pain and inflammation. They are also useful in the control of fever and do not have a major impact on the CNS. We will discuss the nonnarcotic analgesics in detail in Chapter 12. In this chapter, we will focus on the narcotic family of drugs.

Many of the narcotic analgesics may be traced either directly or indirectly to opium. Indeed, the term *opiate* was once used to designate those drugs derived from opium (Jaffe & Martin, 1985). Recently, a number of synthetic and semisynthetic opiatelike painkillers have emerged. In current terminology, *opioid* in a generic sense refers to any drug that is similar to morphine in its actions, although sometimes the terms *opiate* and *opioid* are used interchangably. For the purpose of this text we will use the traditional terms, *opiate* or *narcotic*.

Opium is made by extracting a milky juice from the plant *Papaver somniferum* and then letting the juice dry. The powder that is formed is opium. Opium was used by European physicians in the sixteenth and seventeenth centuries for virtually every ailment they encountered (Melzack, 1990). According to Ray and Ksir (1987), until recently opium was perhaps the only medicine that physicians could use with predictable results. It was useful in controlling mild to severe levels of pain and (in the absence of modern sanitation) could be used to treat dysentery.

It was not until 1803 that a German scientist, Friedrich W. A. Serturner, isolated a pure alkaloid base from opium. This chemical was later named morphine, after Morphius, the Greek god of sleep. Morphine was soon identified as the major active ingredient in opium. Codeine, which also has mild analgesic properties, was isolated from opium in 1832 (Melzack, 1990).

NARCOTIC ADDICTION IN HISTORY

The invention of the hypodermic needle by Alexander Wood in 1857 made it possible to inject drugs into the body quickly and relatively painlessly. This, combined with the availability of relatively large quantities of pure morphine, resulted in a rather severe outbreak of morphine addiction (Jaffe, 1989). Furthermore, injected morphine was not thought to be addicting, at least during the early 1850s, and could be obtained without a prescription (Callahan & Pecsok, 1988; Melzack, 1990).

This is not to say that the opiate family of drugs had not been abused before this time. Indeed, Ray and Ksir (1987) point to evidence from 1500 B.C. that opium was used to prevent excessive crying in children. They also note evidence from A.D. 129 to A.D. 199 that opium cakes were sold in the streets of Rome. By 1729, China had found it necessary to outlaw opium smoking, and within a little more than a century fought a major war with England over the English importation of opium to China (Franklin, 1987; Ray & Ksir, 1987).

Morphine was freely used in battlefield hospitals during the American Civil War. It was also used in the Franco-Prussian and Prussian-Austrian wars in Europe (Callahan & Pecsok, 1988). Intravenous administration of morphine was found to be effective in providing pain relief from battlefield wounds. A second major use of morphine was in the control of dysentery.[1] The crowded, unsanitary army camps of the last century were prime breeding grounds for infection. In their text *The Civil War*, Ward, Burns, and Burns (1990) state that in a single year "995 of every thousand men in the Union army contracted diarrhea and dysentery" (p. 184).

Because of morphine's side effect of slowing down the wavelike muscle contractions of the muscles surrounding the intestines, it was found to be a valuable treatment for dysentery. Given the high infection rates for dysentery, it is no wonder that so many soldiers on both sides of the Atlantic became addicted to morphine. By the mid-1800s, morphine addiction was known as the "soldier's disease" (Ray & Ksir, 1987, p. 34).

During the last half of the nineteenth century, the United States suffered from a wave of opiate addiction. Both opium and morphine were freely available without the need for a prescription. Like cocaine, morphine was included in patent medicines. Many became addicted to the opiates in various patent medicines without being aware of the contents of the bottle they had purchased.

Further, the practice of smoking opium was brought to this country by Chinese immigrants, many of whom came to the United States to work on the railroad in the late 1800s. While this practice did not become very popular, it was reported that by 1900 25% of the opium imported into the United States was for smoking (Ray & Ksir, 1987).

According to Brecher (1972), by 1900 approximately 1% of the total U.S. population was addicted to narcotics. This included patients who had become addicted to opiates as a result of medical treatment of various diseases or injuries, individuals who had become addicted through various patent medicines, and those who had become addicted through the practice of smoking opium. Keep in mind that opiates were freely available through both mail-order houses and over-the-counter sales.

Concern over the growing numbers of people addicted to cocaine, the opiates, or both, prompted passage of the Pure Food and Drug Act of 1906. This law required that the contents of medicines be printed on the labels, so that the purchaser could see what was contained in the medicine. Eight years later, the Harrison Narcotics Act of 1914 was passed, prohibiting the use of certain drugs without a prescription. These laws were intended to help contain the growing drug-addiction problem in the United States. In the ensuing years, various other legal restrictions have come into play as the drug-abuse problem has waxed and waned. However, the problem of narcotic abuse/addiction has never entirely disappeared.

---

[1]Dysentery is an infection of the lower intestinal tract that causes a great deal of pain and severe diarrhea mixed with blood and mucus. It is caused by contaminated water (often found in crowded army camps) and could prove rapidly fatal. Dehydration was the usual cause of death if the diarrhea could not be controlled.

MEDICAL USES OF THE ANALGESICS

Following the introduction of aspirin, narcotics were no longer used to control mild to moderate levels of pain. However, the opiates are used to control acute pain, and codeine has been found to be quite useful as a cough suppressant (Reiss & Melick, 1984). The opiates also continue to be used in the control of *severe* diarrhea, by suppressing the motility of the gastrointestinal tract. We will discuss this use later on in the chapter.

Several different forms of opiates have been developed over the years. Some of these are natural opiates, whereas others are semisynthetic or totally synthetic opiatelike chemicals. Morphine is still considered the prototype of the opiates, however, and continues to be the standard against which other opiates are measured (Jaffe & Martin, 1985). Surprisingly, because the synthesis of morphine in the laboratory is difficult, most morphine is still obtained from the opium poppy.

The Mystique of Heroin

Except for differences in potency, the effects of the various forms of narcotic analgesics are very similar. Researchers are thus at a loss to explain why heroin (actually, diacetylmorphine) is one of the preferred narcotics among addicts. When diacetylmorphine was first tried by chemists at the Bayer pharmaceutical company in 1898, they reported that it made them feel "heroic" (Mann & Plummer, 1991, p. 26). The drug was thus given the brand name "Heroin." At the time, it was thought to be both nonaddictive and a cure for morphine addiction. It was not until 12 years later that the true addiction potential of heroin was recognized.

Heroin is used in England to control severe pain, especially the pain caused by cancer, but the drug has been outlawed in the United States. It is more potent than morphine. According to the standard conversion formula, 4 mg of heroin is as powerful as 10 mg of morphine (Lingeman, 1974). Further, because of differences in its chemical structure, heroin is able to cross the blood–brain barrier 100 times faster than morphine (Angier, 1990). This is because heroin is a lipid-soluble chemical, and the blood–brain barrier allows lipids to easily cross over from the bloodstream into the brain. By contrast, morphine is not fully lipid soluble. Thus, it takes morphine from 20 to 30 minutes to cross the blood–brain barrier.

As Lingeman (1974) points out, one of the factors that seems to influence addicts in choosing between heroin and morphine is their *expectation* that heroin will produce a greater degree of euphoria. Surprisingly, when used in equipotent doses, narcotics addicts are unable to tell the difference between morphine and heroin when these drugs are injected intramuscularly. However, in the case of intravenous injections, most addicts can immediately distinguish between heroin and morphine, according to Lingeman.

Historically, morphine was the drug of choice for American narcotics users at the turn of the century. The actions of heroin are quite similar to those of morphine, which is to be expected since morphine is a metabolite of heroin (Scaros et al., 1990). In other words, once heroin is injected into the body, it is transformed back into morphine by the liver.

The main advantage of heroin over morphine is that heroin has only half the bulk. Thus, it is transported more easily by addicts and their suppliers (Lingeman, 1974). The preferred method of use is intraveneous injection, however, there is also evidence to suggest that addicts increasingly may be smoking heroin because of the very real fear of contracting AIDS from contaminated needles (Pinkney, 1990). To avoid using hypodermic needles that may have been used by other addicts, many individuals will heat heroin powder in a piece of aluminum foil, using a cigarette lighter or match as the heat source. The fumes are then inhaled and the user experiences the high without the risk of exposure to contaminated needles (*Alcoholism & Drug Abuse Week*, 1991c; Scaros et al., 1990).

Unfortunately, preliminary evidence would suggest that heroin may become the "latest" drug of abuse. As addicts turn away from cocaine, many are turning to heroin as their drug of choice. Substance-abuse professionals have started to suspect that the United States may experience a new wave of heroin addiction in the middle to late 1990s, just as it experienced a wave of cocaine addiction in the 1980s.

MECHANISMS OF ACTION

The analgesic effect of the opiates is attributed to a number of different factors (Reiss & Melick, 1984). First, the opiates seem to mimic the actions of the body's natural painkillers, a group of three opiatelike neurotransmitters that include the *endorphins*, the *enkephalins*, and the *dynorphins*. As mentioned previously, these chemicals are thought to be used by the brain to control pain and moderate the emotions. The opiates seem to utilize the same receptor sites in the brain used by these natural painkillers to reduce the patient's awareness of pain. Jaffe and Martin (1985) note that the morphinelike drugs are able to achieve analgesia without a significant loss of consciousness—a decided advantage in many cases.

The opiates also appear to be able to reduce anxiety, promote drowsiness, and allow an individual to sleep in spite of severe pain (Brown, 1987; Govoni & Hayes, 1988). When therapeutic doses of morphine are given to a patient in pain, he or she will usually report that the pain is less intense, less discomforting, or entirely gone (Jaffe & Martin 1985). According to Brown (1987), some of the factors that influence the analgesia achieved through the use of morphine include the route by which the medication is administered, the interval between doses, and the dosage level being used.

The cough-suppressant action of codeine, a close chemical relative of morphine, is thought to result from the ability of codeine to suppress the cough reflex (Thomason & Dilts, 1991). The cough reflex is controlled by the medulla, a portion of the brain responsible for the maintenance of the body's internal state (Jaffe & Martin 1985).

THE EFFECTS OF NARCOTICS AT NORMAL DOSAGE LEVELS

At normal dosage levels, in the person who is using narcotics for medical reasons, these drugs will change that person's perception of pain (Thomason & Dilts, 1991). In order to understand how this is achieved, one must understand that pain is a multifaceted phenomenon. According to Melzack (1990), there are two forms of pain. The first form of pain, what Melzack terms *phasic,* is a sharp expression of discomfort experienced at the instant of injury. This is followed by a steady, less intense, but more enduring *tonic* form of pain.

Not surprisingly, these two forms of pain seem to have different neurological pathways. The neuropathways for phasic pain are dampened quickly; thus, this type of pain serves to warn the organism that injury has occurred without overwhelming it with needless pain messages. Tonic pain, on the other hand, seems to serve the function of warning the organism to rest until recovery can take place. Although morphine is of little value in the control of phasic pain, it seems well suited in controlling the enduring tonic form of pain (Melzack, 1990).

An individual's experience of pain is at least partially influenced by his or her anxiety level, expectations, and general state of tension. The more tense, frightened, and anxious a person is, the more likely that he or she will experience pain in response to a given pain stimulus. The opiates are able to raise the individuals' pain threshold by moderating some of the fear, anxiety, and tension that normally accompany pain states (Jaffe & Martin, 1985). Thus, the individual will not attach as much importance to the pain, and will experience less distress than before the opiates were administered.

Narcotic analgesics produce some drowsiness and sedation (Schuckit, 1989), but without a general loss of consciousness (Jaffe & Martin, 1985). They also will cause the pupils of the eyes to constrict. According to Govoni and Hayes (1988), this constriction of the pupils may occur even in total darkness. Some patients also report a sense of euphoria after using one of the narcotic analgesics.

The effects we have described so far are seen in normal individuals who are experiencing some degree of pain. However, when pain-free individuals receive the same dose of morphine, they are likely to experience nausea and vomiting, as well as some degree of drowsiness and an inability to concentrate (Jaffe & Martin, 1985). Many will experience a sense of euphoria. Unlike alcohol, however, even large doses of morphine will not cause slurred speech or significant incoordination.

The mechanism by which opiates are able to produce a sense of euphoria are not well understood. However, since the discovery of a class of neurotransmitters known as the *endorphins* in 1975, one theory has been that the opiates mimic the actions of this family of neurotransmitters (Kirsch, 1986). The endorphins are thought to be responsible for stress management, and are also thought to be "natural painkillers." When the brain is flooded with opiates, it reacts as if massive amounts of endorphins were released. Where there is no stress or pain, the individual will often experience a sense of euphoria.

Snyder (1977) postulates that this mechanism may also account for the addictive potential of the opiates. According to this theory, the future opiate addict would be a person who had suffered a great deal of emotional distress throughout life, possibly because of a biological deficit. Such a person would lack normal levels of endorphins. Since the person had always known psychological suffering, he or she would have no way of knowing the suffering was not normal and thus would not seek help in dealing with this pain.

However, when that person injected opiates, the brain would be flooded with a chemical that mimicked the lacking endorphins and he or she would suddenly gain release from the long-standing emotional pain. When the dose began to wear off, the individual would seek out more opiates in an attempt to regain the euphoria and comfort only just discovered. Over time, as the body reduced production of natural endorphins, the individual would have to continue the use of narcotics to avoid the painful withdrawal symptoms that are the hallmark of narcotic addiction.

NARCOTIC ANALGESIC COMPLICATIONS AT NORMAL DOSAGE LEVELS

Even at therapeutic dosage levels, the opiates will cause some degree of constriction of the pupils and will depress respiration. Indeed, following even therapeutic doses of morphine (or a similar agent), respiration might be affected for 4 to 5 hours. Therefore, narcotic analgesics should be used with caution in individuals who suffer from such respiratory problems as asthma, emphysema, chronic bronchitis, and pulmonary heart disease.

According to Supernaw (1991) however, "fear of respiratory depression [caused by morphine] appears to be misplaced" (p. H-11). Thomason and Dilts (1991) would argue this claim, cautioning that health care workers should anticipate that the narcotics will cause the respiratory center of the brain to become less sensitive to rising blood levels of carbon dioxide, resulting in respiratory depression.

When used at therapeutic dosage levels, morphine and similar drugs cause some degree of nausea and vomiting as a side effect (Brown, 1987). Research has demonstrated that, at normal dosage levels, approximately 40% of ambulatory patients will experience some degree of nausea and approximately 15% will vomit (Jaffe & Martin, 1985). Brown (1987) notes that ambulation increases the chances that a patient will experience nausea or vomiting, and suggests that patients not walk around immediately after receiving medication.

These side effects are dose-related, which is to say that as the dosage level increases, these side effects are seen with greater frequency. Some individuals will be quite sensitive to the opiates and experience adverse reactions to narcotics at even low dosage levels. Melzack (1990) advanced the theory that an individual's response to the narcotics may be genetically mediated, going on to hypothesize that a genetic mechanism might account for the phenomenon of addiction to narcotics.

At therapeutic dosage levels, there is evidence that morphine and similar drugs are able to decrease the secretion of hydrochloric acid in the stomach. Peristalsis, the waves of muscle contractions that force the contents of the intestines forward, is restricted (Govoni & Hayes, 1988), possibly to the point of spasm in the muscles involved (Jaffe & Martin, 1985). (As noted previously, this is the side effect that made morphine so useful in the treatment of dysentery.) Further, the smooth-muscle tissue surrounding the bladder is stimulated by narcotic analgesics, resulting in a sensation of constantly having a full bladder.

Oral versus Injected Doses for Medical Purposes

The opiates are well absorbed from the gastrointestinal tract, but, when used orally, there is great variation in obtained blood levels of narcotics (Govoni & Hayes, 1988). Thus, the oral method of administration is not the most effective, and is used only in cases of moderate levels of pain. The narcotics are well absorbed through the lungs (as in when heroin or opium are smoked) and the nasal mucosa (when heroin powder is inhaled).

In addition to the uneven absorption rates associated with oral doses of narcotics, Brown (1987) points out that the liver will metabolize at least 50% of the morphine that is absorbed through the gastrointestinal tract *before* it reaches the brain. It is thus difficult to determine how much of an oral dose of morphine will reach the blood, or how much will actually reach the brain before being metabolized by the liver. For this reason, larger doses are prescribed when oral doses are used than when morphine is injected.

Because a greater degree of control over the amount of narcotics that reach the blood is achieved when narcotics are injected, the opiates are most often injected when used for medical purposes (Jaffe & Martin, 1985). For this same reason, the most common method of narcotic abuse also involves the injection of narcotics.

METHODS OF OPIATE ABUSE

Although the narcotic analgesics are quite useful in the treatment of a range of medical conditions, there are those who will abuse this family of drugs by self-administering them for personal pleasure. These individuals will usually inject the narcotic, either under the skin ("skin popping"), or into a vein ("mainlining"). The practice of smoking opium is not common in the United States, where supplies of opium are limited. It is more common in parts of the world where supplies are plentiful.

Those who are addicted to narcotics obtain their daily supply of the drug from many sources. In the case of health care professionals with access to pharmaceutical supplies, they might divert medications to themselves. The usual practice for the "street" addict is to buy "street" narcotics, unless he or she has access to "pharmaceuticals." The "street" narcotic is a drug that has usually been smuggled into the United States, then distributed for sale at the local level. The narcotics are usually sold in powder form, in small packets. The powder is mixed with water and the mixture heated in a small container (usually a spoon) over a flame from a cigarette lighter, candle, or the like. The mixture is then injected.

"Pharmaceuticals" are medications intended for legal use that have been diverted to the streets. When using a pharmaceutical, an addict will crush the tablet, or take the capsule apart, and mix the powder with water. Again, the mixture is then heated in a small container (a spoon, a bottlecap or the like) over a small flame (from a match, candle, or cigarette lighter), which helps mix the powder with the water. The resulting mixture is then injected.

The addict does not inject the narcotic in the same way as a physician or nurse injects medication into a vein. The technique the addict uses is called "booting," and has been described for heroin as follows:

[The heroin is injected] a little at a time, letting it back up into the eye dropper, injecting a little more, letting the blood–heroin mixture back up, and so on. The addict believes that this technique prolongs the initial pleasurable sensation of the heroin as it first takes effect—a feeling of warmth in the abdomen, euphoria, and sometimes a sensation similar to an orgasm. (Lingeman, 1974, p. 32)

In the process, however, the hypodermic needle and the syringe (or the eye dropper attached to a hypodermic needle) become contaminated with the individual's blood. When other addicts use the same needle, as is common practice with cocaine and opiate addicts, contaminated blood from one individual is passed to the next, and the next, and the next. . . . It is for this reason that many heroin addicts now choose to inhale the fumes, rather than run the risk of exposing themselves to AIDS.

Intraveneous narcotic addicts who inject medication intended for oral use will inject starch or other "fillers" directly into the bloodstream (Wetli, 1987). These fillers, which are not meant to reach the blood, are mixed with the medication to give it body and form. They are usually destroyed by stomach acid when the medication is taken orally, but cannot be destroyed by the body's defenses when injected. Street narcotics are usually adulterated with a wide variety of substances (see Chapter 31, "Drugs and Crime"). Repeated exposure to pharmaceutical fillers or adulterants from street drugs can cause extensive scarring at the point of injection. These scars form the so-called tracks caused by repeated injections of narcotics.

According to Jaffe (1986, 1989), it is not clear at this time how the opiates function as a reinforcer, as they impact on a number of different parts of the brain. But both animal research and clinical evidence with human subjects suggest that the opiates are indeed powerful reinforcers. Kirsch (1986) notes that opiates are thought to activate the same reward system of the brain that cocaine does, however this is not known for certain.

It is known, however, that a single dose of opiates will reduce anxiety and enhance self-esteem. When abused through injection, many opiates will bring about a rush or "flash." This sudden, brief, pleasurable sensation, which has been described as similar to a sexual orgasm (Jaffe, 1986, 1989; Lingeman, 1974), lasts about 30 to 60 seconds (Mirin et al., 1991). The individual will then experience drowsiness and euphoria that will last for several hours (Scaros et al., 1990).

As tolerance to the opiates develops, however, the individual will no longer experience the rush with as much intensity, and the opiates will lose the initial antianxiety effect. According to Kline and Miller (1986), the opiates cause the brain's natural endorphin system, which is involved in regulation of the emotions, to at least partially shut down. In other words, over time, the brain substitutes the chemical opiates for natural endorphins.

When the supply of opiates is eliminated from the body, the brain no longer has the necessary amounts of either natural endorphins or opiates to utilize in the regulation of emotions and pain. In time, the brain will again start to produce endorphins on its own; however, until it does, the individual will experience withdrawal symptoms. We will discuss these symptoms later in the chapter.

Over time, the individual will develop differential tolerance to the various effects of the opiates (Jaffe, 1989). The individual can develop remarkable tolerance to both the analgesic and respiratory depressant effects of opiates, but less to the constipation that can result from opiate use. Chronic use of narcotics often results in significant problems with constipation.

OPIATE ADDICTION

As we have noted, the narcotic family of drugs possesses a significant potential for addiction. Indeed, the potential for addiction is so serious that it is one of the major factors limiting the medical use of narcotics (Jaffe & Martin, 1985). According to Melzack (1990), many health care workers fail to use these drugs in the most effective manner because they fear the patient may become addicted. However, as Melzack points out, patients who receive narcotics for the control of pain are unlikely to become addicted, unless they have a prior history of addiction. By contrast, those who use narcotics for psychological effects are most likely to become addicted.

In spite of the reputed addiction potential of the narcotics, only a fraction of those who briefly experiment with opiates will become addicted (Jaffe, 1989). Jenike (1989) states that "opioid dependence develops in about half of the individuals who engage in opioid abuse" (p. 3). He goes on to point out that addiction to narcotics can develop in under 2 weeks if the drugs are used on a daily basis in regularly increasing doses.

Casual narcotics abusers take great pains to avoid being identified. Such individuals will not volunteer information about their addiction, possibly out of fear of losing their jobs. This factor makes it difficult to identify how many people actually use narcotics only occasionally. Although it is possible for an individual to abuse narcotics without becoming addicted, there is no way at this time to predict who will ultimately become addicted and who will not. Thus, the practice of narcotics abuse is a dangerous one, since the possibility of addition cannot be ruled out.

According to Khantzian (1985) there may be a dynamic interaction between a person's psychological distress and the vulnerability of that person to narcotics addiction. Opiate addicts may be drawn to the drug because of its ability to help them control powerful feelings of rage and anger, as opposed to the depression and hypomania experienced by cocaine addicts. Franklin (1987) agrees, stating that some individuals are at risk for opiate addiction because of their "constant psychic pain" (p. 87). It is of interest to note that there is a significant interrelationship between the experience of pain and the experience of depression, and for some individuals this inner pain might be a reflection of depression (Franklin, 1987).

Research has not identified the primary cause of this inner pain. Possibilities include a lack of maternal love during a critical phase of childhood or a biological deficit. However, since some individuals grow up with this inner pain, they tend accept it as a "normal" state of being. That is, until they began to experiment with opiates. At this point the opiate-addict-to-be suddenly and forcefully learns that life without constant psychic pain is possible. Such individuals become "instantly and forever addicted" (Franklin, 1987, p. 87).

Melzack (1990) estimates that perhaps as many as 50% of those who abuse narcotics have suffered from periods of depression. Research *does* suggest that those who are actively abusing narcotics on a daily basis tend to be significantly more depressed than those who occasionally abuse them, and both groups tend to be more depressed than those who do not use narcotics (Maddux, Desmond, & Costello, 1987). However, it is not clear at this time whether this depression is a cause or a result of the narcotics abuse. In either case, evidence points to a significant relationship between depression and opiate addiction. It should be kept in mind that *all* opiates have the potential for abuse and are capable of causing tolerance, psychological dependence, and physical addiction to various degrees.

In addressing the question of diagnosing opiate addiction, Jaffe (1986) notes that current diagnostic criteria usually include only the existence of opiate tolerance or opiate withdrawal symptoms. The presence of either, or both, is sufficient to establish a diagnosis of opiate addiction.

Following an extended period of use, the exact duration of which is unknown, the opiates will bring about a classic pattern of withdrawal symptoms when discontinued. As previously mentioned, Jenike (1989) suggests that a person can become addicted to narcotics in less than 2 weeks of daily use at ever-increasing dosage levels. Jaffe (1989) points out that after addiction has developed withdrawal from narcotics will vary in intensity as a result of the dosage level of the opiate that was abused, the length of time over which the person used the drug, and the speed with which withdrawal is attempted.

In theory, then, an opiate addict who had used the equivalent of 50 mg of morphine a day for 3 months would have an easier detoxification than an individual who had used the equivalent of 50 mg of morphine a day for 3 years. Also, an opiate addict who was gradually withdrawn from opiates at the rate of the equivalent of 10 mg of morphine a day would have an easier detoxification than an addict who suddenly stopped using the drug ("cold turkey").

Peele (1985) challenges the concept of withdrawal from narcotics as we currently understand it. He states:

> In all cases, what is identified as pathological withdrawal is actually a complex self-labeling process that requires users to detect adjustments taking place in their bodies, to note this process as problematic, and to express their discomfort and translate it into a desire for more drugs. (p. 19)

This statement is consistent with the work of Jay, Elliott, and Varni (1986), who found that an individual's perception of pain and discomfort is actually the result of a complex interaction between such factors as knowledge, attention, motivation, and suggestibility. In other words, an individual's perception of and response to the withdrawal process will be influenced to a large degree by his or her "cognitive set."

This phenomenon has been observed in real-life settings, in which narcotics addicts are forced to go through the withdrawal process "cold turkey." For example, in a therapeutic community that actively discourages reports of withdrawal discomfort, narcotics addicts will not go through the dramatic withdrawal displays so often noted in methadone detoxification programs (Peele, 1985). Further, when narcotics addicts are incarcerated and denied further access to drugs, they are often able to go through withdrawal without the dramatic symptoms noted in detoxification programs. Thus, the withdrawal process following addiction to narcotics is not simply a physical phenomenon. Cognitive factors are involved as well.

Use of Narcotics During Pregnancy

Narcotics, like a large number of other drugs, cross the placenta in the woman who is pregnant. Thus, when a woman who is pregnant uses narcotics, both mother and fetus are exposed to opiates. Infants of addicts are, in a very real sense, hidden victims of addiction, as will be discussed in Chapter 19. At this point, it is sufficient to be aware that the narcotics easily cross the placenta of the woman who is pregnant, putting the fetus at risk.

THE SCOPE OF THE PROBLEM

It has been reported that there are between 400,000 and 600,000 known heroin addicts in the United States (American Academy of Family Physicians, 1989; Kaplan & Sadock, 1988). Between 200,000 (Ross, 1991) and 300,000 (Kaplan & Sadock, 1988), which is to say fully half of all heroin addicts in the United States, live in New York City. Another 275,000 are thought to be concentrated in California (Pinkney, 1990). Surprisingly, in spite of the "war on drugs" of the 1970s and 1980s, the number of active narcotics addicts has remained relatively constant over the past decade (*Alcoholism & Drug Abuse Week*, 1991c; Horgan, 1989).

Male addicts are thought to outnumber female narcotics addicts by a ratio of 3:1 according to Kaplan and Sadock (1988). The American Academy of Family Physicians (1989) estimates that, in addition to those who are addicted to narcotics, 2 million Americans abuse heroin occasionally.

Heroin has a reputation as an addictive drug. However, the number of individuals who occasionally use heroin but who never "graduate" to the intensive, compulsive use that is the hallmark of addiction is simply not known. Lingeman (1974) contends that "the majority go on to mainlining" (p. 106). Jaffe, (1989, 1990) disagrees, stating that only a fraction of those who briefly experiment with opiates will actually become addicted.

According to DuPont (1987), heroin use in the United States peaked in 1971. While the number of heroin addicts may not be increasing, it should be taken into account that many former addicts, who have subsequently become addicted to other substances, admit that they would return to narcotic use if it were possible for them to regain the euphoria they previously experienced.

There are also individuals who are apparently able to use narcotics off and on for years, without becoming addicted (Shiffman, Fischer, Zettler-Segal, & Benowitz, 1990). Admittedly, these individuals ("chippers") are a distinct minority of narcotics users. They seem to use narcotics more in response to social stimuli than to physiological stimuli. While they are not technically heroin addicts, they are certainly part of the spectrum of narcotics abuse in the United States.

Finally, there are those individuals who use narcotics other than heroin. These drugs are usually obtained from prescriptions that are diverted to the streets. Because it is difficult to determine the percentage of prescriptions used by legitimate patients and the percentage misused, it is impossible to obtain an estimate of nonheroin narcotics addiction. Thus, a figure of 600,000 known heroin addicts must be viewed only as a baseline figure. By nature, the addict avoids the spotlight of scientific inquiry; hence, accurate data about the extent of this problem are not available.

WITHDRAWAL SYMPTOMS IN THE NARCOTICS ADDICT

According to Jaffe (1989), opiate withdrawal symptoms generally begin 8 to 12 hours after the last dose of the drug, depending on the speed with which the individual's body is able to metabolize the specific chemical being used. In order to avoid these withdrawal symptoms, the addict must either inject the drug again, or begin using another drug.

Withdrawal symptoms for the narcotics addict include tearing of the eyes, a running nose, repeated yawning, sweating, restless sleep, dilated pupils, anorexia, irritability, insomnia, weakness, abdominal pain, ejaculation in male addicts, and gastrointestinal upset (Scaros et al., 1990). Constipation is a significant problem, which can result in fecal impaction or, in rare cases, intestinal obstruction (Jaffe, 1989, 1990).

It has been suggested that these withdrawal symptoms might make an addict so uncomfortable as to reinforce the tendency toward continued drug use (Bauman, 1988). This is true even if drug tolerance precludes the initial rush (Jaffe, 1986, 1989). Indeed, perhaps "as many as one-third of [narcotics] addicts have a pathologic fear of detoxification" (Jenike, 1989; p. 4). In other words, there is evidence to suggest that even after the initial rush no longer can be achieved, the addict may continue to use narcotics mainly to avoid withdrawal symptoms.

Opiate addicts in a medical setting will often emphasize the distress they experience during withdrawal, possibly as a ploy to obtain additional medications. The manipulativeness demonstrated by addicts in maintaining their drug habits has been documented by Jenike (1989), among others. However, while withdrawal from narcotics may be uncomfortable, it is not fatal, except in the case of infants who are born addicted to narcotics (Group for the Advancement of Psychiatry, 1991). Kaplan and Sadock (1990) argue that the narcotic withdrawal syndrome is "seldom a medical emergency" (p. 40). Symptoms of the opiate withdrawal syndrome will eventually abate in the healthy individual even in the absence of treatment.[2]

OPIATE OVERDOSE

The abuse of narcotics may result in death. Indeed, in 1990 at least 33,700 heroin-related emergency-room admissions were reported to the Drug Abuse Warning Network (*Alcoholism & Drug Abuse Week*, 1991a). Consider, too, that this number does not include individuals who overdosed, but who never lived long enough to reach a hospital emergency room.

The exact mechanism of death in a narcotics overdose appears to be respiratory arrest (Thomason & Dilts, 1991). However, this is only for cases of overdose with pharmaceutical opiates. Scaros et al. (1990) report that a typical sample of street heroin will contain between 68 and 314 mg of quinine—a common adulterant added to heroin. If one assumes that by "booting" the drug the typical heroin addict will prolong the process of injection for 10 seconds, and given the amount of quinine in the usual street sample of heroin, the addict will be injecting quinine at up to *182* times the

[2]This assumes that the individual is addicted *only* to opiates. If the individual is addicted to other chemicals as well, this will complicate the withdrawal process. Thus, *withdrawal from chemicals should be attempted only under medical supervision.*

maximum recommended rate for medical applications. This rate of quinine injection is in itself capable of causing a fatal reaction in many individuals. The question remains open, then, as to whether deaths by "narcotics overdoses" are indeed caused by the narcotics themselves, or by other substances that are mixed in with narcotics sold on the streets (Khuri, 1989).

Street Myths and Narcotics Overdose

In the drug subculture, there are several myths concerning the treatment of opiate overdose. First, there is the myth that cocaine (or some other CNS stimulant) will help to control an opiate overdose. Another myth is that symptoms of an overdose can be controlled by putting ice packs under the arms and in the groin area of the overdose victim.

Unfortunately, the treatment of an opiate overdose does not lend itself to such easy solutions. Even in the best-equipped hospitals, a narcotics overdose may result in death. According to Khuri (1989), the current treatment of choice is Narcan (naloxone hydrochloride). This chemical is thought to bind at the narcotic receptor sites within the brain, preventing the narcotic molecules from reaching the receptors and causing respiratory depression.

Even if Narcan is administered, oxygen and possibly mechanical ventilation may also be necessary (Sheridan et al., 1982). The effects of Narcan are short-lived, as the drug has a half-life of only 60 to 90 minutes (Khuri, 1989). There is also need for continual monitoring for 24 hours or more after an overdose to make sure the individual has fully recovered. It cannot be overemphasized that known or suspected opiate overdose is a life-threatening emergency that always requires immediate medical support and treatment.

A WORD ON FENTANYL AND RELATED "DESIGNER" DRUGS

In recent years, a new synthetic narcotic known as Sublimaze (fentanyl is the generic name of this drug) has been introduced. Like other opiates, fentanyl is intended for the control of pain. Because of its short duration of action, it is especially useful as an analgesic during and immediately after surgery (Govoni & Hayes, 1988).

Although fentanyl is extremely potent, there is some controversy over exactly how potent. According to Kirsch (1986), fentanyl is "approximately 3,000 times stronger than morphine [and] 1,000 times stronger than heroin" (p. 18). Kirsch (1986) notes that the active dose in humans is 1 microgram. By contrast, he points out, the average postage stamp weighs 60,000 micrograms.

Khuri (1989) estimates that one-tenth of a milligram (0.10 mg) of fentanyl is as potent as 10 mg of morphine administered subcutaneously. Gallagher (1986) agrees with this estimate of fentanyl's potency and believes it to be 20 to 40 times as potent as heroin. Govoni and Hayes (1988) state that fentanyl is 80 times as potent as morphine.

When used in a medical setting, fentanyl is administered only by injection. There are no oral forms of this drug on the market. According to Kirsch (1986), there is evidence suggesting that some people who abuse the drug might be smoking or snorting it. Khuri (1989) reports that fentanyl is sold on the streets under the name of "Sub" or "China White."

Fentanyl is so potent a drug that extremely small doses are effective in humans. Its detection is extremely difficult and routine drug toxicology screens might overlook the presence of such small amounts of fentanyl in the blood or urine of a suspected drug user (Gallagher, 1986; Kirsch, 1986). Thus, even a "clean" urine or blood drug screen might not rule out fentanyl use.

Adverse Effects of Fentanyl

Among the side effects of fentanyl abuse are respiratory depression, constipation, and, because of its potency, a significant risk of fatal overdose. Kirsch (1986) states that fentanyl can produce a 25% decrease in heart rate and a 20% drop in blood pressure. He also notes that some addicts die so rapidly after using fentanyl that they are found with the needle still in their arms. Some researchers attribute the rapid death to the narcotic itself; others postulate that death is brought on by the various chemicals added to the drug to "cut" or dilute it on the street.

When used in a medical setting, some of the side effects of fentanyl include blurred vision, a sense of euphoria, nausea, vomiting, dizziness, delirium, lowered blood pressure, and possible respiratory depression or respiratory arrest (Govani & Hayes, 1988). Govani and Hayes also note that cardiac arrest is possible as an adverse effect of fentanyl.

The Subjective Effects of Fentanyl

Although it is entirely synthetic, fentanyl is still a member of the opiate family of drugs. As such, it will produce analgesia, for which it is used in medical settings. When abused, it will also produce a sense of drowsiness and euphoria. Addicts also report a short-lived rush, apparently of a shorter duration than the rush from heroin abuse (Kirsch, 1986).

Fentanyl has a rather short half-life in the body; that is, it tends to be a very short-acting drug. According to Govani and Hayes (1988), the duration of the analgesic effects of this drug last only for 1 to 2 hours. However, its effects on respiration might last longer. One advantage of fentanyl over morphine in a medical setting is that fentanyl produces a more rapid analgesic response.

It is difficult to understand the addictive potential of fentanyl. Dr. William Spiegelman (cited in Gallagher, 1986) states that "it can take years to become addicted to alcohol, months for cocaine, and one shot for fentanyl" (p. 26). To further complicate matters, "street chemists" are manipulating the chemical structure of fentanyl—adding a few atoms to the basic chain here, snipping a few atoms there—to produce what are known as "drug analogs."

Fentanyl and its analogs are rapidly becoming a significant part of the drug-abuse problem in the United States. According to Gallagher (1986), in California fentanyl analogs are currently being used by 20% of the opiate addicts. It is clear that to serve the public well, the health professional must have a basic understanding of these new "designer" drugs.

THE TREATMENT OF OPIATE ADDICTION

A commonly held belief is that once an opiate addict, always an addict. Indeed, research findings indicate that approximately 90% of those addicts who achieve sobriety will return to chemical use within 6 months (Schuckit, 1989). However, on the positive side, more than a third of all opiate addicts will *ultimately* be able to achieve sobriety and remain drug-free. For those addicts who survive their addiction, abstinence from opiate use is finally achieved about 9 years after the addiction first developed (Jaffe, 1989; Jenike, 1989). This is a far brighter picture than the one that health care professionals usually paint when the subject of treatment is brought up. We will discuss the treatment of opiate addiction in more detail in Chapter 27.

SUMMARY

Physicians have been using narcotics to treat pain and disease for several thousand years. Indeed, after alcohol, the narcotics can be considered our oldest drugs. Various members of the narcotic family have been found to be effective in the control of several pain, severe cough, and severe diarrhea. The only factor that limits their application in the control of less severe conditions is their addiction potential.

Although the addiction potential of narcotics has long been known, narcotics have been a significant part of the drug-abuse problem for generations. With the advent of the chemical revolution, recently developed synthetic narcotics are likely to become a part of the drug-abuse problem for generations to come.

Chapter 11

INHALANTS AND AEROSOLS

T
he inhalants are a group of toxic substances, some of which are meant to be used for nonmedical purposes; for example, as cleaning agents, herbicides, pesticides, and various types of glue. These compounds contain chemicals that, when inhaled, alter the manner in which the brain functions. They cause the user to feel euphoric, and because of this effect they are occasionally abused by adults, and also by children and adolescents, who have easy access to many of them. Because these chemicals are inhaled, they are called inhalants.

A HISTORY OF INHALANT ABUSE

There have been numerous historical references to the practice of anesthetic abuse in the past century. Indeed, the earliest documented use of the anesthetic gases appears to have been for recreation, and historical records from the 1800s document the use of such agents as nitrous oxide for "parties." The use of gasoline fumes in order to get high is thought to have begun prior to World War II (Morton, 1987). Documentation of this practice dates from the early 1950s (Blum, 1984).

By the mid-1950s and early 1960s, the popular press had begun to headline "glue sniffing" (Anderson, 1989a; Morton, 1987; Westermeyer, 1987). This is the practice whereby an individual uses model airplane glue, the active agent of which is toluene in many cases, as an inhalent to get high. Nobody knows how the practice of glue sniffing first started, but Berger and Dunn (1982) suggest that it began in California, when teenagers accidently discovered the intoxicant powers of toluene-containing model-airplane glue.

The first known reference to this practice was in 1959, in the magazine section of a Denver newspaper (Brecher, 1972). Local newspapers soon began to carry stories on the dangers of inhalant abuse, in the process giving explicit details on how to use airplane glue and what effects to expect. According to Brecher, within a short period, a "nationwide drug menace" had emerged (p. 321).

Brecher contends that the "problem" was essentially manufactured through distorted media reports. He points out that in response to media reports of numerous deaths due to glue sniffing, one newspaper tracked down several stories and found only nine deaths that could be attributed to this practice. Of this number, six deaths were due to asphyxiation—each victim had used an airtight plastic bag and had suffocated. Furthermore, Brecher notes, "among tens of thousands of glue-sniffers prior to 1964, no death due unequivocally to glue vapor had as yet been reported" (p. 331). Thus, according to Brecher, children needed to be warned only to avoid sniffing glue with plastic bags over their heads.

In light of Brecher's (1972) argument, one is left with the question of how serious the glue-sniffing problem was before the news media began to publish reports about it. Indeed, one is left with the impression that the so-called problem was a media fabrication, at least to some degree. However, we do know now that the use of inhalants may introduce toxic chemicals into the body, possibly causing damage to any of a number of different organs (Brunswick, 1989; Jaffe, 1989).

THE PHARMACOLOGY OF INHALANTS

Many chemical agents reach the brain more rapidly and efficiently when they are inhaled than when they are ingested by mouth or injected. Unlike drugs taken by mouth or injected into the body, the inhalants enter the bloodstream directly from the lungs, without their chemical structure being altered in any way by the liver. The inhalants may reach the brain in an extremely short period of time, usually within seconds (Blum, 1984; Watson, 1984).

There are four classes of inhalants: (1) volatile organic solvents, such as those found in paint and fuel; (2) aerosols, such as hair sprays, spray paints, and deodorants; (3) volatile nitrites such as *amyl nitrite* (or its close chemical cousin, *butyl nitrite*); and (4) general anesthetic agents, such as nitrous oxide (Anderson, 1989a). Of the different classes of inhalants commonly abused, children and adolescents will most often abuse the first two classes of chemicals. Children and adolescents have limited access to the third category, and extremely limited access to general anesthetics, the final class of inhalants.

The chemistry of inhalants is quite complex, especially in light of the fact that these chemicals are designed for industrial or household use—not for human consumption. Multiple chemical agents are often combined to meet the needs of industry. The exact combination of chemicals included in any mixture depends on the specific purpose for which the solvent is to be used and the conditions under which it is to be used.

All of the chemicals in the mixture are introduced into the body when an individual inhales fumes from an industrial solvent. There are so many different chemicals in the mixture that it is difficult to identify the specific agent(s) that cause the euphoria, or the physical damage, to any individual (Anderson, 1989a; Jaffe, 1989; Morton, 1987). Since the inhalants are all toxic to the human body to some degree (Blum, 1984; Fornazzari, 1988; Morton, 1987), one would wonder why an individual would willingly inhale concentrations of toxic chemicals that often are *a hundred times higher* than the permitted level of exposure for industrial workers.

THE SCOPE OF THE PROBLEM

Sporadic use of inhalants usually lasts for a year or two among teenagers, and in general is a fad (Schuckit, 1989). According to Newcomb and Bentler (1989), inhalants are usually the first consciousness-altering agents used by children. They tend to be most popular among boys in their early teens, especially in poor or rural areas where more expensive drugs of abuse are not easily available (Jaffe, 1989). However, inhalant abuse also has been reported in children as young as 5 years of age (Beauvais & Oetting, 1988).

McHugh (1987) suggests that the inhalants are most often abused by grade-school children and agrees with Newcomb and Bentler that they are often the first consciousness-altering chemicals children use. McHugh notes that after a year or two, and certainly by adolescence, one tends to find that the user has abandoned the use of inhalants. However, as noted by Brunswick (1989), approximately one-third of the children who abuse inhalants are found to be using traditional drugs of abuse 4 years later. Thus, for some, inhalants may be "gateway" chemicals that lead the way to further drug use later in life (Anderson, 1989a).

According to Morton (1987), of those adolescents who *do* abuse inhalants, between 30% and 40% do so only sporadically. Another 40% to 50% abuse inhalants over a period of a few weeks to a few months before stopping, and only about 10% seem to become habitual abusers. Thus, while some individuals continue to use inhalants for 15 years or more (Schuckit, 1989; Westermeyer, 1987), these people are apparently a minority of those who use inhalants. The majority of those who use inhalants during childhood and adolescence either go on to other forms of drug use in later years or discontinue further experimentation with chemicals.

The actual percentage of individuals currently using solvents is not known (Miller & Gold, 1991). As stated previously, the practice of abusing inhalants appears to involve boys more often than girls—usually boys between the ages of 10 and 15. In a study by Schuckit (1989), 20% of the adolescent girls and 33% of the adolescent boys questioned admitted to using solvents at least once. According to Anderson (1989a), almost 2 million adolescents have admitted to using inhalants at least once. Thus, it is safe to say that a sizable number of school-aged children and teenagers experiment with inhalants.

S. Cohen (1977) points out several reasons why the inhalants are popular chemicals of abuse. First, they have a rapid onset of action, usually on the order of a few seconds. Secondly, inhalant users report pleasurable effects, including a sense of euphoria, when they use these chemicals. Third, and perhaps most importantly, the inhalants are relatively inexpensive and are easily obtained.

Most of the commonly used inhalants may be freely purchased by people of all ages.[1] They are inexpensive and usually available in small, easily hidden packages. Brunswick (1989) describes them further, as follows:

> They are found at the corner drug store, in the garage, or under the kitchen sink. They take the form of magic markers, glue and fingernail polish. They produce a short but intense high that some have likened to the rush from rock cocaine, or "crack." (p. 6A)

HOW INHALANTS ARE USED

McHugh (1987) describes inhalent abuse as "a group activity" (p. 334). In the case of glue, as noted by Lingeman (1974), the most common method of abuse is for the user to squeeze some of it into a paper bag. The bag is then held tightly over the nose and the fumes inhaled, so that the chemical is introduced into the lungs.

Volatile gases are usually inhaled from a handkerchief or rag that has been soaked with the chemical being used (Brunswick, 1989). The effects may last up to 45 minutes, depending upon the individual's exposure to the chemical being abused (Mirin et al., 1991).

THE SUBJECTIVE EFFECTS OF INHALANTS

The initial effects of the fumes include a feeling of hazy euphoria, somewhat like the feeling of intoxication from alcohol (Blum, 1984). Other symptoms emerge after a period of time, including slurred speech, excitement, double vision, ringing in the ears, and hallucinations (Blum, 1984; Lingeman, 1974; Morton, 1987). Occasionally, the individual will feel omnipotent, which may lead to episodes of violence (Lingeman, 1974; Morton, 1987).

As noted, one of the initial experiences of inhalant abuse is a feeling of euphoria, although nausea and vomiting also may occur (McHugh, 1987). After this initial euphoria CNS depression develops. The individual may become confused, disoriented, and experience a loss of inhibitions. If he or she continues to inhale the fumes beyond this stage, stupor, seizures, or cardiorespiratory arrest may develop. After 30 minutes to an hour, McHugh notes that the person will usually return to a normal state of consciousness, if he or she has an adequate air supply.

According to Schuckit (1989), the mental changes that follow inhalation of glues or solvents or aerosol gases from spray cans generally disappear relatively quickly. Except for headache, hangovers tend to be mild. Westermeyer (1987) states that the impairment of the CNS that results from the occasional use of inhalants usually clears up in a few minutes to a few hours.

---

[1]Adolescents usually have only limited access to the volatile nitrites, although butyl nitrite is sold without prescription in some states and thus would be available to anyone. Obviously, except in rare cases, the general anesthetic agents, such as nitrous oxide, are most often used only by medical personnel.

However, according to Miller and Gold (1991), it is not uncommon for the user to experience a residual sense of drowsiness and stupor for several hours after the last use of inhalants.

COMPLICATIONS OF INHALANT ABUSE

Although Lingeman (1974) states that there are no withdrawal symptoms associated with these substances, Blum (1984) documents a withdrawal syndrome similar to the DT's. Miller and Gold (1991) state that the nature of the withdrawal syndrome would depend on the specific chemicals being abused, the duration of inhalant abuse, and the dosage levels being utilized. They suggest that some of the symptoms of inhalant withdrawal might include tremors, irritability, anxiety, insomnia, seizures, and muscle cramps.

According to Schuckit (1989), damage to various organs as a result of inhalant abuse is rare but not unknown. Physical complications from inhalant abuse include possible cardiac arrythmias, damage to the liver, kidney failure, transient changes in lung function, reduction in blood-cell production possibly to the point of aplastic anemia, and possible permanent organic brain damage.

There is also evidence that these agents might cause toxic reactions involving respiratory depression, as well as kidney and liver damage (Anderson, 1989a; Brunswick, 1989; Morton, 1987). Inhalants have been shown to cause damage to the central nervous system, including cerebellar ataxia (loss of coordination) and deafness (Fornazzari, 1988). The possibility that various inhalants may cause coma, convulsions, brain damage, or even death is noted by McHugh (1987) and Mirin et al. (1991).

As reported by Parras, Pathier, and Ezpeleta (1988), gasoline sniffing by children has resulted in occasional cases of lead poisoning, a serious condition that may have long-term consequences for a child's physical and emotional growth. Westermeyer (1987) notes that liver damage, bone marrow suppression, sinusitis (irritation of the sinus membranes), erosion of the nasal mucosal tissues, and laryngitis may result from inhalant abuse. He states further that these complications "usually resolve after some weeks of abstinence" (p. 903). But, as noted previously, permanent organ damage, while rare, is possible from inhalant abuse (Schuckit, 1989).

Neurological Complications

In a study of 37 chronic inhalant users conducted by Sharp and Brehm (1977), 40% of the subjects scored in the brain-damaged range on a test designed to detect neurological dysfunction. However, Sharp and Brehm do not attribute this finding to the subjects' chronic use of inhalants. Rather, they suggest that the results may reflect preexisting brain damage. In any case, Westermeyer (1987) recommends that patients known to abuse inhalants should be routinely assessed for damage to the central nervous system and peripheral nervous system, as well as for damage to the kidneys, liver, lungs, heart, and bone marrow.

Mirin et al. (1991) report that a condition similar to the delirium tremens (DT's) of alcoholism has been noted in some chronic users of inhalants. Chronic exposure to toluene (the solvent found in various forms of glue) may result in intellectual impairment, ataxia secondary to damage to the cerebellum, deafness, and loss of the sense of smell (Maas et al., 1991; Rosenberg, 1989). In fact, chronic exposure to toluene may result in such extensive injury to the brain as to be visible on magnetic resonance imaging (MRI) tests used by physicians to study the brain's physical structure.

THE MISUSE OF ANESTHETICS

As noted by Berger and Dunn (1982), *nitrous oxide* and *ether* were used as recreational drugs prior to their emergence as surgical anesthetics. Indeed, these gases were routinely used as intoxicants for quite some time before they found medical application. Horace Wells, who introduced nitrous oxide to the field of medicine, noted the pain-killing properties of this gas when he observed a person under its influence trip and gash his leg, without any apparent pain (Brecher, 1972).

As medical historians know, the first planned demonstration of nitrous oxide as an anesthetic was something less than a success. The patient returned to consciousness in the middle of the operation and began to scream in pain. However, the use of nitrous oxide gradually found acceptance as an anesthetic gas, especially in the field of dentistry (Brecher, 1972).

Julien (1988) states that the pharmacological effects of the general anesthetics are the same as those of the barbiturates. There is a dose-related range beginning with an initial period of sedation and anxiety reduction on through sleep and analgesia. Furthermore, nitrous oxide is often abused because it cannot induce unconsciousness if the person's supply of oxygen is adequate (Julien, 1988). It is for this reason that it is rarely used as an anesthetic, unless it is combined with other agents. In the absence of sufficient oxygen, the patient runs the risk of *hypoxia* (a decreased oxygen level in the blood), which can result in permanent brain damage if not corrected immediately. In surgery, the anesthesiologist takes special precautions to ensure that the patient has an adequate oxygen supply.

Obviously, when someone uses nitrous oxide for recreational purposes, he or she will lack the support resources available to a surgical team, thus, serious injury, or even death, may result. It is possible to achieve a state of hypoxia from virtually any of the inhalants (Julien, 1988).

Despite the risks associated with its use, nitrous oxide is a popular drug of abuse in some circles (Schwartz, 1989). Dental students, dentists, medical school students, and anesthesiologists, all of whom have access to this gas through their professions, will occasionally abuse it, as they will ether, chloroform, trichloroethylene, and halothane. Also, because nitrous oxide is used as a propellent in certain whipping-cream cans, such as "Reddi Whip," children and adolescents will occasionally abuse this chemical by finding ways to release the gas from the container. Recreational users report that nitrous oxide brings about a feeling of euphoria, giddiness, hallucinations, and loss of inhibitions (Lingeman, 1974). It is sometimes referred to as "laughing gas."

The volatile anesthetics are not metabolized by the body to any significant degree; rather, they enter and leave the body essentially unchanged (Glowa, 1986). Once the source of the gas is removed, the concentration of the gas in the brain begins to drop and normal circulation returns the brain to a normal state of consciousness within moments. While the person is under the influence of the anesthetic gas, however, the ability of the brain cells to react to painful stimuli seems to be reduced.

THE ABUSE OF NITRITES

Two forms of nitrites are commonly abused: *amyl nitrite* and its close chemical cousin, *butyl nitrite*. Amyl nitrite functions as a coronary vasodilator; that is, it causes the coronary arteries to dilate, allowing more blood to flow to the heart. Because of this property, amyl nitrite was once commonly used in the control of angina pectoris. The drug was administered in small glass containers embedded in cloth layers. The user would "snap" or "pop" the container with the fingers and inhale the fumes in order to control the chest pain of angina pectoris.[2]

With the introduction of nitroglycerine preparations, which are equally as effective as amyl nitrite and which lack many of its disadvantages, few physicians now use amyl nitrite in treating heart disease (Schwartz, 1989). It does continue to have a limited role in diagnostic medicine and in the emergency treatment of cyanide poisoning. For the most part, however, its role in medicine has been superceded by nitroglycerine.

Butyl nitrite became popular as an aid to sexual pleasure in the 1970s. It is often sold legally by mail-order houses or specialty stores, depending on specific state regulations. It is sold as a "room deodorizer," in small bottles that may be purchased for under $10. Both amyl nitrite and butyl nitrite, when abused, will cause a brief (90-second) rush, characterized by dizziness, giddiness, and rapid dilation of blood vessels in the head (Schwartz, 1989). This in turn causes an increase in intracranial pressure (*AIDS Alert*, 1989). On occasion, the increased intracranial pressure may contribute to the rupture of unsuspected aneurysms, which may prove fatal.

Nitrites are thought to cause the user to experience a prolonged, more intense orgasm. After-effects include an intense, sudden headache; increased pressure of the fluid in the eyes (a danger for those with glaucoma); possible weakness; nausea; and possible cerebral hemorrhage (Schwartz, 1989). The

[2]It was from the distinctive sound of the glass breaking that both amyl and butyl nitrite have been called "snappers" or "poppers."

use of nitrites is common among male homosexuals, and may contribute to the spread of the virus that causes AIDS (*AIDS Alert*, 1989; Schwartz, 1989). By causing the dilation of blood vessels in the anus, either amyl or butyl nitrite may actually aid the transmission of the HIV from the active to the passive partner during anal intercourse (*AIDS Alert*, 1989).

SUMMARY

The use of inhalants seems to be a fad that mainly involves teenagers. Moreover, individuals who use these agents do not usually do so for more than a year or two. A minority of users, however, will persist in inhaling the fumes of gasoline, solvents, and certain forms of glue for many years.

The effects of inhalants seem to be rather short-lived, although prolonged use of certain agents has been shown to result in permanent damage to the kidneys, brain, and liver. Death, either through hypoxia or through prolonged exposure to inhalants, is possible. Very little is known about the effects of prolonged use of this class of chemicals.

Chapter 12

OVER-THE-COUNTER ANALGESICS

Medications that are used to control pain can be classified into three groups. First, there are the *local anesthetics*, which interfere with the transmission of pain messages from the site of the injury to the brain. When used properly, cocaine is one such agent. Although cocaine is now viewed with disfavor, it is still the local anesthetic of choice for certain procedures.

The next group of analgesics are the *global analgesics*. These drugs work within the brain to nonselectively alter the perception of pain. The narcotic family of drugs are most frequently utilized as global analgesics. Finally, there are the *nonnarcotic analgesics*, which are thought to interfere with the chemical sequence that results in pain at the site of an injury. This last class of medications includes aspirin, ibuprofen, and acetaminophen—chemicals that are normally considered over-the-counter (or OTC) medications.[1,2] Cocaine and the narcotic family of analgesics have been reviewed in earlier chapters. In this chapter, we will discuss the OTC analgesics.

A SHORT HISTORY OF PAIN MANAGEMENT

Until the introduction of aspirin in the late 1800s, physicians were forced to use narcotic-based analgesics to control even mild to moderate levels of pain. However, the opiates are addictive and have a depressant effect on the central nervous system—factors that limit their usefulness in pain control. Physicians hesitate to use narcotic-based analgesics except in the case of severe pain (Giacona, Dahl, & Hare, 1987).

Aspirin, or *acetylsalicylic acid*, was first isolated from the bark of certain willow trees in 1827 and commercially marketed in 1898 (G. R. Gay, 1990; Mann & Plummer, 1991). Actually, the very name "aspirin" is a historical

---

[1]Aspirin is one of a family of related compounds, many of which are analgesic, anti-inflammatory, antipyretic (antifever) actions. However, none of these aspirinlike drugs appear to be as powerful as aspirin. For purposes of this text, we will limit our discussion to aspirin in connection with this family of compounds.

[2]An *over-the-counter* medication is one that can be purchased legally over the counter without a prescription.

accident. "Aspirin" (with a capital *A*) was introduced by the Bayer pharmaceuticals company as the brand name for acetylsalicylic acid around the turn of the century. Over time, however, "aspirin" (with a small *a*) has come to mean *any* preparation of acetylsalicylic acid. The manner in which this happened is reviewed in excellent detail by Mann and Plummer (1991).

Shortly after it was isolated, researchers quickly discovered that aspirin is effective in controlling mild to moderate levels of pain without risk of addiction, as is common with the narcotic family of analgesics. Further, aspirin was found to have other applications that the narcotic family of analgesics did not, such as the control of inflammation. For these reasons, aspirin has continued to be a very popular drug. As noted by Mann and Plummer (1991), it is the most frequently used drug in the world.

Since the 1950s, a number of aspirinlike nonnarcotic analgesics have been put on the market (Reiss & Melick, 1984). The most popular of these nonaspirin OTC analgesics are *acetaminophen* and *ibuprofen.* Since the time of their introduction, they have collectively come to take away from aspirin the lion's share of the billions of dollars spent on OTC analgesics in the United States (Mann & Plummer, 1991).

The generic name *acetaminophen* is actually a form of chemical shorthand. The true name of this chemical is *N-acetyl-para-aminophenol*, from which acetaminophen is obtained. The drug was actually first isolated in 1878, and its ability to reduce fever was identified even then. But at the time it was thought that acetaminophen would share the dangerous side effects found in a close chemical cousin, para-aminophenol, so it was set aside until the early 1950s (Mann & Plummer, 1991).

In the early 1950s, sufficient evidence had accumulated to show that acetaminophen was quite a bit safer than para-aminophenol, and that it did not have the same potential for harm that aspirin does. A massive advertising campaign followed the introduction of acetaminophen, playing on the fact that aspirin tends to irritate the stomach, whereas acetaminophen does not. By the early 1970s, acetaminophen had carved a small but respectable nitch for itself in the OTC analgesic market, under the brand name Tylenol.

Ibuprofen was introduced as a prescription-only drug in the United States in 1974, although it was available in Europe as a prescription drug before then. In 1984 the Food and Drug Administration approved the sale of ibuprofen as an over-the-counter medication in modified dosage forms. Since its introduction as an OTC medication, ibuprofen has captured more than 20% of the nonprescription painkiller market (Squires, 1990). Motrin and Nuprin are two popular brands of ibuprofen.

While these medications are indeed quite useful, each has the potential for adverse, and possibly fatal, side effects, even at normal dosage levels (Aronoff, Wagner, & Spangler, 1986). Aspirin itself was introduced before the development of modern regulations that govern medication distribution in the United States. In fact, aspirin is such a potent drug that had it been discovered today rather than a century ago, it would be available by prescription (Cousins, 1989).

Both acetaminophen and ibuprofen have been known to be abused. Under certain conditions, both have potentially harmful side effects. Clearly, then, chemical-dependency professionals should have a sound working knowledge of the OTC analgesics—aspirin, ibuprofen, and acetaminophen.

MEDICAL USES OF THE OTC ANALGESICS

As we have mentioned, aspirin is used in the control of mild to moderate levels of pain (Giacona et al., 1987; Supernaw, 1991). Aspirin also has been found effective in treating common headaches, neuralgia, the pain associated with oral surgery, and other musculoskeletal pain (Giacona et al., 1987). Aspirin in low doses is sometimes recommended for preventing migraines. Aspirin is often used to relieve the symptoms of dysmenorrhea and to reduce inflammation and fever. Fever reduction is brought about partly by aspirin's ability to cause peripheral vasodilation and sweating (Govoni & Hayes, 1988).

Both ibuprofen and acetaminophen have also been found to be useful in controlling fever (Govoni & Hayes, 1988). However, the control of a fever provides only symptomatic relief for the individual. It must be emphasized that the cause of the fever must still be identified and treated to ensure adequate medical care for the patient (McGuire, 1990).

While acetaminophen only has a minor anti-inflammatory action (Mitchell, 1988; Morgenroth, 1989; Supernaw, 1991), aspirin has been found most useful in the control of inflammation caused by rheumatoid arthritis, osteoarthritis, and other forms of arthritis (Giacona et al., 1987; McGuire, 1990). Ibuprofen also has an antiinflammatory potential. Both aspirin and ibuprofen have a different chemical structure from the steroids, another class of anti-inflammatory drugs, and they are often called *nonsteroidal antiinflammatory drugs* (or NSAIDs). (Because acetaminophen has no significant anti-inflammatory effects, it is not classified as a NSAID.)

The OTC analgesics are quite potent. Indeed, recent research would suggest that aspirin, acetaminophen, and ibuprofen are even effective in controlling the pain associated with some forms of cancer (McGuire, 1990). Currently, researchers are exploring the possibility that aspirin, acetaminophen, and/or ibuprofen, when used in combination with narcotic analgesics, might actually reduce the patient's need for narcotic painkillers in some cases.

THE PHARMACOLOGY OF THE OTC ANALGESICS

Surprisingly, aspirin does not seem to work within the brain itself (Gazzaniga, 1988). Rather, it appears to work at the site of the injury. Each cell in the human body produces chemicals called the *prostaglandins*. When the cell is injured, these chemicals are released, causing inflammation and pain. Aspirin's analgesic effect may be attributed to its power to inhibit the production of prostaglandins (Aronoff et al., 1986; Giacona et al., 1987; McGuire, 1990).

Thus, by blocking the action of the prostaglandins, aspirin helps to control both mild to moderate levels of pain and also inflammation caused by injury to the body. Aspirin also inhibits the clotting of blood platelets, reducing the ability of the blood to form clots. Although the exact mechanism by which aspirin is able to achieve this effect is unknown, it is a useful side effect in the control of transient ischemic attacks (TIAs) (Govoni & Hayes, 1988), and either the initial or subsequent heart attacks (*Internal Medicine Alert*, 1989; *Medical Letter*, 1989; Govoni & Hayes, 1988; Graedon, 1980).

Aspirin's ability to reduce cardiovascular disease was discovered in a research project involving 22,000 male physicians (*Psychiatry Drug Alerts*, 1989). After a 5-year period of time, it was found that those physicians who took just one 325-mg aspirin tablet every other day suffered 44% fewer heart attacks compared to the physicians who took a placebo. This beneficial effect was noted only for individuals over 50 years of age and was strongest for those individuals with lower cholesterol levels. Unfortunately, findings also revealed that the use of aspirin slightly *increased* the chances of death from hemorrhagic stroke for the user; therefore, the benefits of aspirin use must be weighed against the increased risk of a stroke.

According to Thun, Namboodiri, and Heath (1991), nonsteroidal anti-inflammatory drugs such as aspirin have also been identified as inhibiting the growth of tumors in the colon. They suggest that aspirin's ability to inhibit prostaglandin synthesis might interefere with tumor cell growth, or it might stimulate the body's immune response in some unknown manner, allowing the body to fight the invading cancer more effectively.

Another theory is that because aspirin increases the possibility of gastrointestinal bleeding it might increase the tendency for a tumor within the colon to bleed. If a tumor in the colon bleeds, it is more likely to be discovered. Tumors that are discovered early in the growth process are easier to treat. At this point, the exact mechanism by which aspirin might inhibit the growth of tumors in the colon is still unknown (Thun et al., 1991). Acetaminophen does not seem to have any impact on tumor growth, and the impact of ibuprofen on tumors in the colon is yet to be explored.

As an analgesic, acetaminophen is thought to have a mechanism of action very similar to that of aspirin (Giacona et al., 1987), and in terms of its ability to reduce fever and pain it is thought to be equipotent with aspirin (Supernaw, 1991). But the exact manner by which acetaminophen reduces pain is unknown (Morgenroth, 1989). It is thought that this drug, like aspirin, interferes with the synthesis of prostaglandins through some unknown mechanism. Unlike aspirin, acetaminophen does not possess a significant anti-inflammatory potential; it also does not interfere with the normal clotting of the blood (Govoni & Hayes, 1988). These features often make acetaminophen an ideal substitute for individuals who are unable to take aspirin.

Ibuprofen, like aspirin, has been found to be effective in the control of mild to moderate levels of pain and in the control of fever (Govoni & Hayes,

1988). Ibuprofen's analgesic action is thought to result from the drug's ability to interfere with the production of the prostaglandins (Squires, 1990). While ibuprofen has some anti-inflammatory effect, it is thought to be somewhat less effective in treating inflammation than the older drug, aspirin (Morgenroth, 1989). Graedon (1980) disagrees with this assessment, however. He argues that ibuprofen is equally as effective as aspirin at dosage levels of between 1,600 and 2,400 mg/day.

Fischer (1989) expresses a middle-of-the-road position on the potential of ibuprofen, observing that the drug's anti-inflammatory effects are seen only after 2 to 4 weeks of continuous drug use, and then only at close to the maximum recommended dosage levels for this analgesic. This would suggest that one might do better to take aspirin for the control of inflammation; however, one must remember that aspirin is quite irritating to the stomach.

Because ibuprofen is about one-fifth to one-half as irritating to the stomach as aspirin (Giacona et al., 1987), ibuprofen is often used in cases where the individual is unable to tolerate gastrointestinal irritation. Still, it has been estimated that between 4% and 14% of those who use ibuprofen will also experience some degree of gastrointestinal irritation (Graedon, 1980). Further, just as aspirin can cause gastrointestinal bleeding when used for prolonged periods of time, a small percentage of those who use ibuprofen for prolonged periods of time will also experience this side effect. Researchers estimate that approximately 3 out of every 1,000 people will experience some degree of ibuprofen-induced gastrointestinal bleeding (Carlson et al., 1987).

NORMAL DOSAGE LEVELS OF OVER-THE-COUNTER ANALGESICS

There is conflicting evidence as to whether aspirin's analgesic effects are dose-related (Giacona et al., 1987), and there is mixed evidence suggesting little or no additional analgesic benefits from increasing the dosage levels to above 600 mg every 4 hours. However, even at normal dosage levels, aspirin and acetaminophen have a significant analgesic potential. McGuire (1990) states that 650 mg of aspirin or acetaminophen—a standard dose of 2 regular-strength tablets of either medication—provide an analgesic effect equal to that of 50 mg of the narcotic painkiller meperidine (Demerol). Kaplan and Sadock (1990) state that 650 mg of aspirin has the same analgesic potential as 32 mg of codeine, 65 mg of propoxyphrene (Darvon), or a 50-mg oral dose of pentazocine (Talwin).

In a study by Seymore and Rawlins (1982), a single dose of 1,200 mg of aspirin seemed to provide a greater degree of relief from dental pain than did 600 mg in a single dose. However, Aronoff et al. (1986) contend that there is a "ceiling effect" for aspirin, beyond which higher dosage levels do not provide greater pain relief. They put this ceiling level at approximately 1,000 mg every 4 hours. According to McGuire (1990), dosage levels of aspirin or acetaminophen higher than this only increase the risk of a toxic reaction.

It has been recommended that aspirin be taken at a normal adult oral dosage level of 325 to 650 mg every 4 hours as needed for the control of pain (U.S. Pharmacopeial Convention, 1990a). This recommendation includes the warning that aspirin should not be continuously used for longer than 10 days by an adult and longer than 5 days for a child under the age of 12, except under a doctor's orders. (Note: When used in the treatment of arthritis, aspirin may be used at higher-than-normal dosage levels. In this case, the aspirin is usually administered under a doctor's direct care and supervision; as such it represents a specialized application of aspirin. This application of aspirin, because it is carried out under the supervision of a physician, will not be discussed here.)

Aspirin is rapidly and completely absorbed from the gastrointestinal tract, although the speed with which it is absorbed depends on the acidity of the stomach contents (Sheridan et al., 1982). When taken on an empty stomach the rate at which aspirin is absorbed depends on how quickly the tablet crumbles after reaching the stomach (Rose, 1988). The aspirin will then pass through the stomach lining and, when taken on an empty stomach, begin to reach the bloodstream in as little as 1 minute, according to Rose. However, when the individual takes aspirin either with food, or right after eating, it may take up to ten times longer to reach the bloodstream; thus, the therapeutic effect on the individual will be delayed (Pappas, 1990).

As noted by McGuire (1990), while food may slow the rate at which aspirin is absorbed, it does not reduce the amount that is absorbed. Ultimately, *all* of the aspirin is absorbed, with peak blood levels being achieved in 1 to 2 hours when a single dose is ingested (McGuire, 1990), or between 5 and 18 hours when repeated dosage levels are utilized (Govoni & Hayes, 1988).

Aspirin is sold both alone and in combination with agents designed to reduce the irritation that aspirin might cause to the stomach. According to Govoni and Hayes (1988), timed-released and enteric-coated tablets have been known to bring about erratic absorption rates. Graedon (1980) warns that when antacids are taken along with aspirin to reduce stomach irritation, blood levels of aspirin are found to be between 30% and 70% lower than when aspirin is used without antacids—a matter of some concern for individuals who are taking the drug for the control of inflammation or pain.

The recommended adult dose of acetaminophen is also 325 to 650 mg every 4 hours as needed for the control of pain (U.S. Pharmacopeial Convention, 1990a). According to Aronoff et al. (1986), acetaminophen's antipyretic and analgesic effects are equal to those of aspirin, and the ceiling level of acetaminophen is the same. Peak blood concentrations are achieved in 30 minutes to 2 hours after an oral dose of acetaminophen (Govoni & Hayes, 1988), and the half-life of an oral dose is from 1 to 4 hours. Individuals with significant liver damage may experience a longer acetaminophen half-life, as this drug is metabolized by the liver.

Govoni and Hayes (1988) recommend that 300 to 600 mg of ibuprofen be used 3 to 4 times a day for the control of rheumatoid arthritis; for the control of mild to moderate pain, they recommend 200 to 400 mg every 4 to 6 hours. The

Upjohn Company, the manufacturer of Motrin (a brand of ibuprofen available by prescription only), advises that total daily dosage levels not exceed 3,200 mg/day in divided doses (Medical Economics Company, 1991).

Ibuprofen is rapidly absorbed when used orally, with peak blood plasma levels being achieved 1 to 2 hours following ingestion of the drug. Within 4 hours of the time that a normal dose is ingested, blood plasma levels will fall to about half that of the peak plasma level (Govoni & Hayes, 1988). The drug is metabolized by the liver, and only 10% is excreted unchanged, according to Govoni and Hayes.

COMPLICATIONS CAUSED BY USE OF OVER-THE-COUNTER ANALGESICS

Aspirin

Aspirin is quite popular as a home remedy, and has been in use for close to 85 years (Graedon, 1980). It has been estimated that Americans use approximately 20 tons of aspirin per day (Olson, 1988); or, in other terms, approximately 30 billion tablets of aspirin a year (Mann & Plummer, 1991). On a worldwide basis, 100 million pounds of aspirin are consumed each year, according to Mann and Plummer.

Indeed, so popular is aspirin that many people underestimate its usefulness (Graedon, 1980; Jaffe & Martin, 1985). They also tend to underestimate its potential for causing serious side effects (Reiss & Melick, 1984). In speaking of the dangers presented by the OTC analgesics, Morgenorth (1989) states that these medications "can be harmful, even deadly, if used too often, in combination with one another, or by the wrong people at the wrong time" (p. 36).

Approximately 0.2% of the general population is allergic to aspirin. However, of those individuals with a history of allergic disorders, approximately 20% will be allergic to aspirin. Symptoms of an allergic reaction to aspirin may include a rash and asthmalike reactions that may be fatal (Graedon, 1980). Govoni and Hayes (1988) warn that patients with the "aspirin triad" (a history of nasal polyps, rhinitis, and asthma) not use aspirin (p. 89).

In reviewing the symptoms of an allergic reaction to aspirin, Graedon (1980) notes that they include wheezing, abdominal pain, and breathing problems. Death is possible as a result of an allergic reaction to aspirin. Both Govoni and Hayes (1988) and Fischer (1989) warn that patients who are sensitive to aspirin are likely also to be sensitive to ibuprofen, as cross-sensitivity between these two drugs is common.

According to *Comsumer Reports* (1989), between 2% and 10% of those who use aspirin, even if they do so only occasionally, will experience some degree of gastric irritation. It was suggested by Mortensen and Rennebohm (1989) that this gastric irritation might be caused by aspirin's nonselective ability to interfere with production of prostaglandin. Aspirin use can result in the disruption of the prostaglandin production necessary for the proper function of the gastric lining, causing irritation and bleeding in the stomach while blocking the production of prostaglandins at the site of an injury elsewhere in the body.

Sheridan et al. (1982) warn that some of aspirin's side effects include anorexia, nausea, and vomiting. As we have noted, those who use aspirin, even if only occasionally, may experience some degree of gastrointestinal bleeding (Pappas, 1990). Normally, this internal bleeding is minimal and causes no significant problems. However, individuals who use aspirin on a regular basis may become anemic as a result of the constant use of the drug.

Aspirin should not be used by those with a history of ulcers, bleeding disorders, or other gastrointestinal disorders (U.S. Pharmacopeial Convention, 1990a). Further, it is suggested that people avoid taking aspirin together with acidic foods that irritate the gastrointestinal system, such as coffee, fruit juices, or alcohol (Pappas, 1990).

Due to their effects on blood clotting, neither aspirin or ibuprofen should be used by individuals with a bleeding disorder, such as hemophilia (Govoni & Hayes, 1988; U.S. Pharmacopeial Convention, 1990a). According to Govoni and Hayes, a single dose of aspirin can prolong bleeding time for between 3 and 7 days after the last use of the drug. Persons who are undergoing anticoagulant therapy, which reduces the ability of the blood to form clots, obviously should not use aspirin, except when directed by a physician.

Govoni and Hayes (1988) also point out that aspirin should not be used by people with a history of chronic rhinitis. Those being treated for hyperuricemia (a buildup of uric acid in the blood) also should not use aspirin. This drug inhibits the action of probenecid, one of the drugs used to treat hyperuricemia. Even if the patient is not taking probenecid, aspirin at normal dosage levels reduces the body's ability to excrete uric acid, thus contributing to the problem of uric-acid buildup within the body. Acetaminophen has been advanced as a suitable substitute for patients suffering from gout and who need a mild analgesic, according to Govoni and Hayes.

Aspirin also should not be used by patients who are receiving medications for the control of their blood pressure. It has been found that aspirin may interfere with the effectiveness of some antihypertensive medications (Fischer, 1989). Also, prolonged use of aspirin can result in iron deficiency anemia in some patients (Govoni & Hayes, 1988). Additionally, both aspirin and ibuprofen can bring about some loss of hearing and a persistent ringing in the ears known as "tinnitus." The patient's hearing will usually return to normal when the aspirin or ibuprofen is discontinued.

A very rare side effect of aspirin use is *hepatotoxicity*, which is to say that aspirin may prevent the liver from filtering the blood effectively (G. R. Gay, 1990). This will allow for the buildup of certain toxins in the blood—a buildup that may appear suddenly. The literature to date suggests that hepatotoxicity caused by the use of aspirin or ibuprofen is extremely rare; nevertheless, it has been documented. Another rare complication from aspirin use is a drug-induced depression (Mortensen & Rennebohm, 1989).

The elderly are especially susceptible to toxicity from aspirin and similar agents because their bodies are unable to metabolize and excrete this family of drugs as effectively as younger adults. Bleidt and Moss (1989) attribute this to the reduced blood flow to the liver and kidneys in the elderly. Sussman (1988) warns that one complication of aspirin use in the elderly is the development of anxiety states.

Aspirin or related compounds should never be used with children who are suffering from a viral infection. Research strongly suggests that aspirin might increase the possibility of the child developing *Reye's syndrome* (Morgenroth, 1989, Sagar, 1991). This is a serious, potentially fatal, condition that affects children between the ages of 2 and 12 for the most part (Sagar, 1991). Reye's syndrome usually follows a viral infection, such as influenza or chickenpox. Symptoms include swelling of the brain, seizures, disturbance of consciousness, and a fatty degeneration of the liver (*Dorland's Illustrated Medical Dictionary*, 1988).

It has also been found that individuals should not use aspirin immediately prior to drinking or while they are actively drinking. According to Roine et al. (1990), the use of aspirin prior to the ingestion of alcohol will decrease the activity of gastric alcohol dehydrogenase, an enzyme produced by the stomach that starts to metabolize alcohol even before it reaches the bloodstream. This will result in a higher than normal blood alcohol level, even in the rare social drinker who takes aspirin shortly before drinking.

Surprisingly, aspirin has been implicated in the failure of intrauterine devices (IUD's) to prevent pregnancy. Its anti-inflammatory action is apparently what causes it to interfere with the effectiveness of these devices.

Ibuprofen

Ibuprofen has been implicated as the cause of blurred vision in some individuals who use it (Nicastro, 1989). Graedon (1980) recommends that people using ibuprofen who experience some change in their vision discontinue the medication and consult with a physician immediately. In addition to the 3% to 9% of the patients on ibuprofen who experience skin rashes or hives as a side effect of this medication, ibuprofen has been implicated in the formation of cataracts (Graedon, 1980). It has also been said to cause migraine headaches in both men and women (Nicastro, 1989).

According to the Upjohn Company (manufacturer of Motrin), ibuprofen has a number of side effects, including heartburn, nausea, diarrhea, vomiting, nervousness, hearing loss, changes in vision, and elevation of blood pressure (Medical Economics Company, 1991). Furthermore, in individuals with heart problems, it has been known to cause congestive heart failure.

Recent research has also suggested that ibuprofen can cause or contribute to kidney failure in those suffering from hypertension, kidney disease, or other health problems (Squires, 1990). This may be associated with ibuprofen's ability to block the production of prostaglandin. Research has shown that by blocking the body's production of prostaglandin, ibuprofen also reduces the blood flow throughout the body, especially to the kidneys. If an individual is suffering from a reduction in blood flow to the kidneys for any reason, including "normal aging, liver or cardiovascular disease, or simply dehydration from vomiting, diarrhea and fever accompanying the flu," ibuprofen could cause or contribute to acute kidney failure (Squires, 1990, p. 4E).

When used by individuals who are also taking lithium, ibuprofen can increase the blood levels of lithium by 25% to 60% (Jenike, 1989). This effect is most pronounced in older individuals, and may contribute to lithium toxicity in some cases, according to Jenike. Therefore, patients who are using both lithium and ibuprofen concurrently should be closely monitored. Moreover, patients who are on lithium should report *any* use of ibuprofen, even over-the-counter preparations, to the physician who is prescribing the lithium, so that appropriate steps may be taken.

Acetaminophen

Acetaminophen is metabolized by the liver. And, as outlined in Chapter 4, the liver may be damaged by the chronic use of alcohol. It has been observed (Mitchell, 1988; Morgenroth, 1989) that chronic use of alcohol may lower the dosage level at which a person may develop acetaminophen toxicity. According to Mitchell (1988), there are a few documented cases of chronic alcoholics developing acetaminophen toxicity at dosage levels only slightly higher than the normal recommended dose. Thus, has been recommended that active or recovering alcoholics not use acetaminophen for *any* reason (*Consumer Reports*, 1989; Govoni & Hayes, 1988; Graedon, 1980).

According to Morgenroth (1989), taking just 7.5 grams (7,500 mg) of acetaminophen (just 15 "extra-strength" tablets) in a single dose will bring about a toxic reaction in the healthy individual. Supernaw (1991) states that individuals who use acetaminophen at high dosage levels for extended periods of time (that is, 5,000 mg/day for 2 to 3 weeks) are likely to develop liver damage.

OTC ANALGESIC OVERDOSE

While an antidote to acetaminophen overdose is available, it must be administered *within 12 hours* of ingestion of the overdose. However, in many cases, the toxic effects of an acetaminophen overdose require 3 or 4 days to develop, so that by the time that an individual begins to show symptoms of acetaminophen toxicity, it may be too late to prevent permanent liver damage, or even death.

Aspirin, ibuprofen, and acetaminophen have all been implicated as the cause of death in cases of overdose. Aspirin overdose is a serious medical emergency that may result in death, even with the best medical care and support. To gain an appreciation for the dangers inherent in the abuse of aspirin, consider that almost the same number of Americans died from aspirin overdose as from heroin overdose in 1990 (*Playboy*, 1991).

Symptoms of aspirin toxicity are most often seen in patients who take large doses. However, even small doses of aspirin may result in toxicity for the individual who is aspirin-sensitive. Symptoms of aspirin toxicity include headache, dizziness, tinnitus, mental confusion, increased sweating, thirst, dimming of sight, and hearing impairment (Govoni & Hayes, 1988). Other symptoms of aspirin toxicity include restlessness, excitement, apprehension, tremor, delirium, hallucinations, convulsions, stupor, coma, and possible death.

According to Lipscomb (1989), OTC overdose is most frequent with acetaminophen. Adolescents will often initiate an overdose of acetaminophen as a suicide gesture, without the actual intent to commit suicide (Morgenroth, 1989). However, because of the relatively low dose necessary to produce a toxic reaction to acetaminophen, and because its effects are not immediately apparent, the individual might not seek medical assistance until several days after the initial overdose.

It was reported by Mitchell (1988) that in Great Britain, aspirin overdoses result in an estimated 200 to 250 deaths per year, while acetaminophen poisoning causes an estimated 150 deaths per year. Acetaminophen poisoning may cause death through liver failure. This is because large doses of acetaminophen destroy *glutathione,* a chemical produced by the liver to protect itself from toxins. When *N-acetylcysteine* is administered within several hours of the initial overdose, it is quite effective in the treatment of acetaminophen poisoning (Mitchell, 1988).

As we have noted, however, the symptoms of an overdose of acetaminophen may not be observed for between 48 hours (Graedon, 1980) and 96 hours (Morgenroth, 1989) after the overdose—well *after* the liver has been damaged. *In the case of an overdose of acetaminophen, treatment must begin* **immediately** and not when signs of liver toxicity or kidney damage are finally noted.

Ibuprofen's popularity as an OTC analgesic has resulted in an increasing number of overdose attempts involving this drug (Lipscomb, 1989). As noted by Lipscomb, symptoms of overdose include seizures, acute renal failure, abdominal pain, nausea, vomiting, drowsiness, and metabolic acidosis. There is no specific antidote for ibuprofen toxicity, and medical care often involves supportive treatment only.

SUMMARY

Over-the-counter analgesics are often discounted as not being "real" medicine. Indeed, aspirin is perhaps America's most popular "drug," with more than 20,000 tons being manufactured and consumed in the United States alone. Aspirin, acetaminophen, and ibuprofen are quite effective in the control of mild to moderate levels of pain, without the side effects found with narcotic analgesics. However, even if they are available over the counter, these drugs carry significant potential for harm.

Acetaminophen has been implicated in toxic reactions in chronic alcoholics at near-normal dosage levels. It also has been implicated as the cause of death in people who have taken acetaminophen overdoses. Aspirin and ibuprofen have been implicated in fatal allergic reactions, especially in those who suffer from asthma. The use of aspirin in children with viral infections may result in Reye's syndrome, a potentially fatal condition. The use of some OTC analgesics is not advised for pregnant women. Women who plan to nurse their babies are advised to check with a physician to determine whether they should avoid the use of any of the OTC analgesics during lactation.

Chapter 13

THE HALLUCINOGENS

It has been estimated that about 6,000 different species of plants can be used for their psychoactive properties (Brophy, 1990). From these plants, we have obtained approximately 100 different hallucinogenic drugs (Kaplan & Sadock, 1988), many of which have been used for centuries in religious ceremonies, healing rituals, and esoteric rites (Berger & Dunn, 1982).

By the middle of this century, hallucinogenic substances were the subject of much scientific inquiry. The effects of lysergic acid diethylamide-25 (LSD-25, or simply LSD)—a substance obtained from the rye ergot fungus *Claviceps purpurea* (Lingeman, 1974)—were first recorded in 1943. At that time, a scientist accidently ingested a small amount of LSD-25 and experienced its hallucinogenic effects.

Following World War II, there was a great deal of scientific interest in the hallucinogens, especially with respect to similarities between the effects these chemicals produced in humans and various indicators of mental illness. However, in the 1960s use of the hallucinogens moved from the laboratory into the streets, and these substances became drugs of abuse (Brown & Braden, 1987).

The widespread abuse of LSD in the 1960s prompted the classification of this drug as a controlled substance in 1970 (Jaffe, 1990). While the prevalence of hallucinogen abuse declined in the late 1970s, the use of LSD appears to again be on the upswing (*Mayo Clinic Health Letter*, 1989; Miner, 1989). Other hallucinogens have consistently remained popular drugs of abuse. One hallucinogen, *phencyclidine* (PCP), has waxed and waned in popularity. In the 1970s, because of its toxicity, PCP fell into disfavor (Jaffe, 1989). But in the 1980s a form of PCP that could be smoked was introduced, and it again became a popular drug of abuse. Currently, PCP seems to be in disfavor, although it is still being sold, either alone or in combination with other drugs.

A relative newcomer, *N, alpha-dimethyl-1,3-benzodioxole-t-ethanamine* (MDMA), became quite popular as a chemical of abuse in the late 1970s and early 1980s. This drug is frequently sold on the streets under the name of "Ecstasy." Both PCP and MDMA will be discussed in later sections of this chapter.

THE SCOPE OF THE PROBLEM

The majority of those who use hallucinogens such as LSD experiment with the drug a few times, possibly out of curiosity or the desire to intensify a certain experience, and then either avoid further hallucinogen use or use hallucinogens only on an episodic basis (Jaffe, 1989). According to Johnston, Bachman, and O'Malley (1989), 8.3% of the high school seniors in the class of 1989 had used LSD at least once, however significant numbers of students who admitted to the frequent use of this chemical were not reported.

It is difficult to estimate the number of casual drug users in the United States, partly because of the illegality of drug use. Individuals who use chemicals are unlikely to admit readily to the practice. The difficulty is compounded by lack of consensus among experts on exactly what constitutes experimental, casual, and abusive use of chemicals. Statistics on drug use/abuse should be regarded with these difficulties in mind. The problem of drug abuse, by its very nature, will tend to remain hidden.

THE PHARMACOLOGY OF HALLUCINOGENS

The commonly abused hallucinogenics can be divided into two major groups on the basis of their pharmacology (Jaffe, 1989). First, there are the hallucinogens that bear a structural resemblance to a neurotransmitter known as *serotonin*. Hallucinogenics in this group include LSD, psilocybin, and dimethyltryptamine (DMT). A second group of hallucinogenics is chemically related to the neurotransmitters dopamine and norepinephrine. The chemical structure of these agents also resembles that of the amphetamine family of drugs (Jaffe, 1989). These hallucinogenics include, among others, mescaline, MDMA, and DOM (also known as STP).

In spite of the chemical differences between the hallucinogens, their effects are remarkably similar. Although a person under the influence of a hallucinogen might believe that he or she has a new insight into reality, these drugs do not generate new thoughts so much as alter one's perception of existing sensory stimuli (Snyder, 1986). Also, despite their chemical differences, these drugs all produce hallucinations that are usually recognized by the user as being drug-induced (Lingeman, 1974).

In order to avoid duplication of material, our focus in this chapter will be on the hallucinogens LSD, MDMA, and PCP. Other hallucinogens will be discussed only briefly.

The Pharmacology of LSD

Neither LSD nor any of the other hallucinogenic drugs have any legitimate medical use at present. LSD is quite potent, its effects being felt at doses as low as 50 micrograms (Mirin et al., 1991).[1] According to Lingeman (1974), the usual dose in illicit drug use is from 100 to 700 micrograms.

[1]There are 1,000 micrograms in 1 milligram.

When taken by mouth, LSD is rapidly absorbed and quickly distributed to all body tissues (Mirin et al., 1991). Lingeman (1974) notes that only about 0.01% of the ingested drug actually reaches the brain. Thus, for a 50-microgram dose, only one-half of a microgram actually reaches the brain. This makes it quite difficult to trace LSD once it reaches the brain.

The exact mechanism of action for LSD is still unknown (Jaffe, 1989), although Mirin et al. (1991) postulate that it inhibits the activity of serotonin in the dorsal midbrain raphe. This view was challenged by Jaffe (1989), who reports that LSD is now thought to act at various sites in the central nervous system, ranging from the cortex of the brain itself down to the spinal cord, including the midbrain sites identified by Mirin et al. However, as we have noted, the exact mechanism by which LSD and similar drugs work is still unknown.

The usual method of administration is by mouth, and the effects are first experienced from 20 minutes (Jaffe, 1989) to an hour (Lingeman, 1974) after the drug is ingested. These effects include tachycardia, increased blood pressure, increased body temperature, pupillary dilation, nausea, muscle weakness, an exaggeration of normal reflexes (hyperreflexia), dizziness, and some degree of tremor (Jaffe, 1989). Lingeman (1974) characterizes these changes as "relatively minor" (p. 133).

Factors that influence the speed with which LSD begins to act include the amount of the drug ingested and the development of tolerance to the drug (Mirin et al. 1991). Tolerance to the effects of LSD develops quickly, often within 2 to 4 days (Brown & Braden, 1987). It abates just as rapidly when the drug is discontinued (Jaffe, 1989; Lingeman, 1974). Cross-tolerance between the different hallucinogens is common, according to both Jaffe and Lingeman.

In terms of direct physical mortality, LSD is a relatively safe drug (Brown & Braden, 1987). In fact, Weil (1986) classifies LSD as one of the safest drugs known to modern medicine. Although the lethal dose of LSD in humans is not known, Lingeman (1974) notes that an elephant given a massive dose of LSD (297,000 micrograms, or 5,940 doses at 50 micrograms each) died.[2] In terms of direct mortality, many other hallucinogens are not as benign, and have been implicated in physical harm to the user. Further, LSD has been known to contribute *indirectly* to a number of fatalities, and thus its use is not entirely without risk.

The plasma half-life of LSD is rather short, with approximately half of the drug being metabolized into nonhallucinogenic substances by the liver in 2 to 3 hours (Jaffe, 1989; 1990). Surprisingly, the effects of LSD in humans seem to last about 8 to 12 hours (Kaplen & Sadock, 1988), a phenomenon that is not understood at this time.

Research has shown LSD to be a complex, somewhat puzzling, chemical. It is active in extremely small doses, yet appears to effect many different body systems. Only a small portion of the LSD that is ingested actually enters the brain. But, as we will discuss in the next section, the drug has a profound impact on consciousness.

---

[2]Lingeman (1974) did not report how the elephant came to ingest the LSD.

THE SUBJECTIVE EFFECTS OF HALLUCINOGENS

The effects of LSD vary according to the individual's mental state at the time that the drug is ingested and the setting in which the drug is used (Lingeman, 1974). According to Kaplan and Sadock (1988), an individual's personality makeup, expectations, and the environment in which the drugs are used all impact the way in which the effects of the hallucinogens are perceived.

Brophy (1990) describes the LSD "trip" as passing through several distinct phases. First, within a few minutes of taking LSD, there is a release of inner tension. This stage, which will last for 1 to 2 hours, is characterized by laughter or crying, as well as a feeling of euphoria (Jaffe, 1989). The second stage usually begins from 30 to 90 minutes (Brown & Braden, 1987) to 2 to 3 hours (Brophy, 1990) following the ingestion of the drug. During this portion of the LSD trips, the individual will experience such perceptual distortions as visual illusions and hallucinations.

Mirin et al. (1991) describe the second phase as being marked by "wave-like perceptual changes" and the phenomenon of synthesthesia. *Synthesthesia* refers to the "slipping over" of information from one sense into another sensory system. Thus, a person experiencing synthesia may report that he or she can "taste" colors or "see" music.

The third phase of the hallucinogenic experience begins 3 to 4 hours after the drug is ingested (Brophy, 1990). During this phase of the LSD trip, the person will experience temporal distortion. The person may also experience marked mood swings and a feeling of ego disintegration. Feelings of panic are often experienced during this phase, as are occasional feelings of depression (Lingeman, 1974). It is during this stage that the LSD user often expresses a belief that he or she possesses quasimagical powers or a magical control (Jaffe, 1989). This break with reality has resulted in fatalities; for example individuals have jumped from windows, believing they could fly. It is for this reason that LSD has been indirectly implicated as the cause of death in a number of cases.

If a person *does* develop a panic reaction to the LSD experience, he or she will often respond to calm, gentle reminders from others that these feelings are drug-induced and that they will pass. Brophy (1990) notes that antipsychotic medications, such as Haldol, might be used in low doses by medical personnel until the individual is back in control. Jenike (1989) recommends the use of benzodiazepines to help the individual deal with the anxiety, while phenothiazines have been found useful in aborting the LSD experience. However, even with such intervention, some patients remain psychotic and require weeks to months of psychiatric care.

Many hallucinogens are adulterated with belladonna or other anti-cholinergics (Kaplan & Sadock, 1988). These substances, when mixed with phenothiazines, may bring about coma and death through cardiorespiratory failure. Thus, it is imperative that the physician treating a "bad trip" know precisely what drugs have been used (and if possible be provided with a sample) to determine what medication is best in a given case. Kaplan and

Sadock (1988) recommend that if a sedative is indicated, diazepam (or, in extreme cases, haloperidol) be utilized by the physician.

Hallucinogens and "Bad Trips"

The likelihood of a bad trip is determined by three factors: (a) the individual's expectations for the drug (which is known as the "set"), (b) the setting in which the drug is used, and (c) the psychological health of the user (Mirin et al., 1991). Inexperienced users are more likely to experience bad trips than experienced LSD users, according to Mirin et al. LSD is thought to be capable of activating a latent psychosis (Lingeman, 1974), which may require long-term psychiatric care.

The effects of LSD start to wane 4 to 6 hours after ingestion. As the individual begins to recover, he or she will experience "waves of normalcy" (Mirin et al., 1991), which gradually blend into the normal. Within 12 hours, the acute effects of LSD have cleared although "a sense of psychic numbness . . . may last for days" (p. 290).

The "flashback" is a consequence of hallucinogenic use that is not well understood. Approximately 25% of those who use hallucinogenic drugs will experience some form of flashback (Kaplan & Sadock, 1988). In brief, the flashback may be described as a spontaneous reoccurrence of the drug experience that may take place days, weeks—or in some cases, even months—after the last hallucinogenic use (Mirin et al., 1991). Flashback experiences may be brought on by illness; stress; fatigue; marijuana use; or sudden bright light (as experienced, for example, on emerging from a dark room). Sometimes individuals try to induce flashbacks. They usually last from a few seconds to a few minutes, although occasionally they may last for as long as 2 days or even longer (Kaplan & Sadock, 1988).

Flashback experiences are often frightening, although some individuals seem to enjoy the visual hallucinations: "flashes" of color, halos around objects, things growing smaller or larger, and feelings of depersonalization (Mirin et al., 1991). Some individuals respond to flashbacks by becoming depressed, panicky, or occasionally suicidal (Kaplan & Sadock, 1988).

In about 50% of the cases, the flashbacks gradually cease within months, although some individuals may continue to experience them for as long as 5 years after the last use of a hallucinogen. The only treatment is reassurance that the flashback will end or perhaps the use of benzodiazepines to help control the anxiety.

PHENCYCLIDINE (PCP)

The drug *phencyclidine*, also known as PCP, was first developed in the 1950s and was initially used as a "highly potent, but relatively nontoxic" anesthetic for animals (Berger & Dunn, 1982, p. 98). Research into its possible use in humans was discontinued in 1965, when it was discovered that patients who had received PCP experienced a drug-induced delirium (Brown & Braden, 1987). In 1978, all legal production of PCP was discontinued and the drug was declared a controlled substance as defined by the Comprehensive Drug Abuse Prevention and Control Act of 1970 (Slaby et al., 1981).

By the mid-1970s, however, PCP had become one of the most frequently abused drugs in this country (Grinspoon & Bakalar, 1990). Its popularity seems to have peaked in the late 1970s and has been declining since that time. Whereas 13% of high school students in a 1979 survey admitted to having used PCP (Grinspoon & Bakalar, 1990), only about 4% of high school seniors in the class of 1989 admitted to having used it at some point in their lives (Johnston, O'Malley, & Bachman, 1989). In the latter survey, 2.4% of the 17,000 subjects admitted having used PCP in the past year, while 1.4% claimed to be currently using the drug.

It should be kept in mind, however, that PCP is often used unknowingly. The drug is easily manufactured (Slaby et al., 1981), and thus may be produced by amateur chemists and either mixed into other street drugs or passed off as other chemicals (Brophy, 1990). Thus, someone who thought that they had purchased LSD, for example, might actually have purchased PCP instead. PCP is often mixed with marijuana to increase the effects of marijuana sold on the street.

The Effects of PCP

Phencyclidine is an unusual drug. Depending upon the dosage level and route of administration, it will demonstrate anesthetic, stimulant, depressant, or hallucinogenic effects (Brown & Braden, 1987; Weiss & Mirin, 1988). The drug may be smoked, used intranasally, taken by mouth, or injected intraveneously (Brown & Braden, 1987; Slaby et al., 1981). The most common method of administration is to smoke a cigarette that contains PCP (Grinspoon & Bakalar, 1990). Tolerance is not known to develop to PCP (Jeinke, 1989), and there is no evidence of PCP addiction (Newell & Cosgrove, 1988).

The absorption of PCP after smoking is rapid and the effects will be felt within minutes (Brophy, 1990; Kaplan & Sadock, 1988) to within an hour's time (Mikkelsen, 1985) after the drug is used. Jaffe (1990) observes that "few drugs seem to induce so wide a range of subjective effects" (p. 557). Not all of these effects are desired by the user; indeed, unwanted effects are common (Mirin et al., 1991). Some of the more common negative effects include anxiety, restlessness, and disorientation. The possibility that PCP may contribute to suicidal thinking has also been suggested (Weiss & Mirin, 1988).

Berger and Dunn (1982), from observations based on the wave of PCP abuse that took place in the 1970s, report that the PCP brings the user either to "the heights, or the depths" of emotional experience (p. 100). Besides depression, other negative effects of PCP include mental confusion, assaultiveness, anxiety, irritability, and paranoia, according to Berger and Dunn. Indeed, so many people have experienced so many different undesired effects from PCP that researchers are at a loss to explain why the drug is so popular (Newell & Cosgrove, 1988).

Symptoms of mild levels of PCP intoxication   Small doses of PCP, usually under 5 mg, will produce a state resembling that of alcohol intoxication (Mirin et al., 1991), or intoxication resulting from the use of other CNS depressants (Weiss & Mirin, 1988). The individual will experience in-coordination, staggering gait, slurred speech, and numbness of the extremities (Jaffe, 1989). Other effects include agitation, some feelings of anxiety, flushing of the skin, visual hallucinations, irritability, and feelings of euphoria.

The acute effects last between 4 and 6 hours, after which the user will "come down," or gradually return to normal, over an additional period of 6 to 24 hours (Berger & Dunn, 1982).

Symptoms of moderate levels of PCP intoxication   As the dosage level increases to between 5 and 10 mg, many users will experience a disturbance of body image; that is, different parts of their bodies will no longer seem real (Brophy, 1990). The user may exhibit slurred speech, twitching of the eyes, and increased muscle tone (Weiss & Mirin, 1988).

Other symptoms of moderate levels of PCP intoxication include paranoia, severe anxiety, belligerence, and assaultiveness (Grinspoon & Bakalar, 1990). The individual may demonstrate unusual feats of strength (Brophy, 1990; Jaffe, 1989). Some people also experience drug-induced fever, excessive salivation, drug-induced psychosis, and violence.

Symptoms of severe levels of PCP intoxication   As the dosage level reaches the level of 10 to 20 mg, coma and seizures are possible, as well as hypertension and severe schizoid behavior (Grinspoon & Bakalar, 1990; Kaplan & Sadock, 1988; Weiss & Mirin, 1988). The coma that is brought on by an overdose of PCP may last up to 10 days (Mirin et al., 1991). The individual may develop heart arrhythmias, encopresis, visual and tactile hallucinations, and drug-induced paranoia. Death from respiratory arrest, convulsions, and hypertension have all been reported in cases of PCP over-dose (Brophy, 1990).

According to Kaplan and Sadock (1988), PCP may remain in the blood and urine for more than a week. The half-life of PCP following an overdose may range from 72 hours (Jaffe, 1985) to a period of weeks (Grinspoon & Bakalar, 1990). It is possible to reduce the half-life of PCP in the body by acidifying the urine. This is done by having the patient take vitamin C tablets or drink cranberry juice (Grinspoon & Bakalar, 1990; Kaplan & Sadock, 1988).

Complications of PCP Use

PCP has been implicated as causing a drug-induced psychosis that may last for days or weeks following the last use of the drug (Jaffe, 1989; Jeinke, 1989; Weiss & Mirin, 1988). This PCP psychosis seems to be most likely for those who either have suffered a previous schizophrenic episode (Mirin et al., 1991) or who are vulnerable to such an episode (Jaffe, 1989). There is no way to predict in advance who might develop a PCP psychosis, although Grinspoon and Bakalar (1990) report that 6 out of 10 patients who develop this psychosis

go on to develop chronic schizophrenia. This might suggest a predisposition
for schizophrenia in at least some of those who experience a PCP psychosis.

The PCP psychosis usually will progress through three different stages,
each of which lasts approximately 5 days (Mirin et al., 1991; Weiss & Mirin,
1988). The first stage is usually the most severe, and is characterized by
paranoid delusions, anorexia, insomnia, and unpredictable assaultiveness.
During this phase, the individual is extremely sensitive to external stimuli
(Jaffe, 1989; Mirin et al., 1991), and the "talking down" techniques that may
work with an LSD bad trip are not likely to be effective with someone
experiencing a PCP psychosis (Jaffe, 1990).

The middle phase is marked by continued paranoia and restlessness, but
the individual is usually calmer and in intermittent control of his or her
behavior (Mirin et al., 1991; Weiss & Mirin, 1988). This phase will again
usually last 5 days, and will gradually blend into the final phase of the PCP
psychosis recovery process. This final phase is marked by a gradual recovery
over a week or two, although in some patients the PCP psychosis may last for
months (Mirin et al., 1991; Slaby et al., 1981; Weiss & Mirin, 1988). Social
withdrawal and severe depression are also common following chronic use of
PCP (Jaffe, 1990).

There would appear to be some minor withdrawal symptoms following
prolonged periods of hallucinogen use. Chronic PCP users have reported
memory problems, although these seem to clear when the drug is discontinued
(Jaffe, 1990; Newell & Cosgrove, 1988). Recent evidence suggests that
chronic PCP users demonstrate the same pattern of neuropsychological deficits found in other forms of chronic drug use, suggesting that PCP might cause
subtle brain damage (Grinspoon & Bakalar, 1990; Newell & Cosgrove, 1988).

ECSTASY: THE LATEST IN A LONG LINE OF "BETTER" HALLUCINOGENS

Over the past decade, a "new" hallucinogen became increasingly popular
among college students. This drug, *N,alpha-dimethyl-1,3 benzodioxole-t-
ethanamine* (MDMA), is called "Ecstasy," "XTC," or "Adam" on the streets
(Barnes, 1988). Although classified by some as a new "designer" drug, it was
actually first synthesized in 1914 (Climko, Roehrich, Sweeney, & Al-Razi,
1987; Mirin et al., 1991).

It was not until the early 1970s that MDMA began to be abused widely
(Hayner & McKinney, 1986); thus, it was not classified as a controlled
substance in the 1960s. It was manufactured legally (sometimes in very large
quantities) until the Drug Enforcement Administration finally classified it as a
controlled substance, on July 1, 1985 (Climko et al., 1987).

Chemically, MDMA is related to another hallucinogen, MDA (Kirsch,
1986), and is one of the hallucinogenic chemicals whose structure resembles
that of the amphetamines. It briefly surfaced as a drug of abuse during the

1960s, then disappeared, as drug-users turned to other hallucinogens, such as LSD. Because LSD was more potent and did not cause the nausea or vomiting associated with MDMA, LSD became *the* popular drug of abuse and MDMA was all but forgotten for some 20 years.

Then, during the mid-1970s illicit drug manufacturers "decided to resurrect, christen, package, market, distribute, and advertise [MDMA]" (Kirsch, 1986, p. 76). For a time, "Empathy" was considered as a name for the drug, but "Ecstasy" was finally selected (Kirsch, 1986). In effect, with this drug, the marketing techniques of business found their way into the drug world. Unknown drug manufacturers first created a demand for a "product." Then, these same people conveniently met the demand they had created.

According to Kirsch (1986), samples of the "new" Ecstasy contained a "package insert," including "unverified scientific research and an abundance of 1960s mumbo-jumbo" (p. 81). However, the package insert did warn the user not to mix Ecstasy with other chemicals (including alcohol). It also recommended that the drug be used only occasionally and that the user take care to ensure a proper "set." Thus, with Ecstasy, drug abuse had become Big Business.

The Scope of the Problem of MDMA Abuse

According to Hayner and McKinney (1986), hundreds of thousands of doses of MDMA have been taken, although the exact number is not known. Kirsch (1986) notes that in 1976 one drug "lab" was reported to have manufactured and distributed an estimated 10,000 doses of MDMA per month. By the year 1984, this same lab was manufacturing and distributing approximately 30,000 doses of the drug per month. And in 1985, the year that the manufacture of MDMA was declared illegal, the lab was thought to be turning out some 500,000 doses per month. Moreover, more than one drug lab was known to be in operation.

After the Drug Enforcement Administration classified MDMA as a controlled substance, "trafficing in MDMA [was made] punishable by fifteen years in prison and a $125,000 fine . . ." (Kirsch, 1986, p. 84). Several labs were shut down by the DEA, so that the supply was diminished somewhat. The demand was still there, however, fueled by news stories in the popular press about Ecstasy's supposed value in psychotherapy and its cheap ($10) price (*Health News*, 1990). This demand was largely met by street drug dealers, who either knowingly or unknowingly passed off other substances as "Ecstasy" (Kirsch, 1986).

Despite the misrepresentation problem, it was reported that a significant number of students on one college campus admitted to having used MDMA at least once (Peroutka, 1989). For those students, the average number of doses was 5.4 per student. The dosage levels were reported as being between 60 and 250 mg—a dosage level found to cause neurotoxicity in animals. Furthermore, in at least 5 cases, Peroutka identified MDMA or related compounds as being the cause of death.

The Effects of MDMA

There is little objective research into the behavioral effects of MDMA in humans. According to Barnes (1988), since controlled clinical trials with the drug have never been performed, "its precise toxicity or efficacy in people [is] impossible to determine" (p. 239).

Some psychiatrists advocate the use of MDMA as an aid to psychotherapy (Price, Ricaurte, Krystal, & Heninger, 1989, 1990). Climko et al. (1987) note that in one "uncontrolled" study MDMA brought about a positive change in mood. However, they go on to state that MDMA also has been reported to cause undesirable symptoms; for example,

> tachycardia, an occasional "wired" feeling, jaw clenching, nystagmus, a nervous desire to be in motion, transient anorexia, panic attacks, nausea and vomiting, ataxia, urinary urgency . . . insomnia, tremors, inhibition of ejaculation, and rarely, transient hallucinations. (p. 365)

According to Hayner and McKinney (1986), at normal doses MDMA causes an increased heart rate, tremor, tightness in jaw muscles, bruxism (grinding of the teeth), nausea, insomnia, headache, and sweating. Furthermore, people who are particularly sensitive to the drug may experience numbness and tingling in the extremities of the body, vomiting, increased sensitivity to cold, visual hallucinations, ataxia, crying, blurred vision, and nystagmus.

Peroutka (1989) observed that recreational users of MDMA tend to use the drug only once every 2 to 3 weeks, if not less frequently. This rather unusual drug-use pattern could reflect a gradual weakening of the drug's desired effects and an increased likelihood of experiencing its negative side effects. Taking a double dose of the drug does not increase the desired effects of MDMA according to Peroutka; rather, it makes it more likely that the individual will experience unpleasant side effects.

One very interesting drug effect at normal dosage levels is that users will occasionally "relive" past events. The memories associated with these events often have been suppressed because they are painful memories (Hayner & McKinney, 1986). Thus, individuals may find themselves reliving experiences they wanted to forget. This phenomenon, which many psychotherapists thought might prove beneficial to patients in the confines of a therapeutic relationship, seem to be so frightening that Hayner and McKinney characterized them as "detrimental to the individual's mental health" (p. 343).

Furthermore, Hayner and McKinney report that symptoms of an MDMA overdose include tachycardia, hypertension, hypotension, heart palpitations, hyperthermia, renal failure, and visual hallucinations. MDMA, they note, "can potentially kill at doses that were previously tolerated in susceptible individuals" (p. 342). The exact mechanism of death is still not certain. Residual effects of MDMA include anxiety attacks, persistent insomnia, rage reactions and a drug-induced psychosis, according to Hayner and McKinney.

Although the exact mechanism of action for MDMA is not clear, animal research suggests that the drug influences the action of serotonin, a neurotransmitter in the brain (Chimko et al., 1987). Also, MDMA appears to be a rather toxic drug compared with the traditional hallucinogens, such as LSD. Animal research also has demonstrated that MDMA is *neurotoxic*, specifically to those neurons that use serotonin as a neurotransmitter (Barnes, 1988). Whereas a rat might receive 10,000 times the normal human dose of LSD and not demonstrate any neurotoxicity, rats, guinea pigs, and monkeys that received only two or three times the normal dose of MDMA were found to have developed symptoms of neurotoxicity (Barnes, 1988; Roberts, 1986).

Clinical evidence now suggests that this drug is neurotoxic in humans as well as animals, although there is no information on whether this brain damage is permanent or not (Barnes, 1988; Grob, Bravo, & Walsh, 1990; *Health News*, 1990). While there is no evidence to suggest that MDMA is addictive, Peroutka (1989) argues that there *is* evidence to suggest "a long-term, and potentially irreversible, effect of MDMA on the human brain" (p. 191).

In a study by Price et al. (1989), it was found that MDMA users responded differently than normal control subjects in a test designed to measure serotonin levels in the body. Although the measured differences between MDMA users and the control group were not statistically significant, Price et al. concluded that the results were suggestive of neurotoxicity caused by use of MDMA.

In recent years, MDMA has become popular to the point of being dubbed a "yuppie hallucinogen" (*Health News*, 1990). This is despite the fact that there is evidence suggesting that it is toxic to certain brain cells in animal brains. It is reasonable to assume that MDMA is also toxic to portions of the human brain, especially those that utilize serotonin as a neurotransmitter. This latest drug to emerge from America's illicit laboratories may very well cause organic brain damage in the user.

SUMMARY

Weil (1986) suggests that people initially used hallucinogens to alter their normal state of consciousness. Hallucinogen use in the United States has waxed and waned in a series of waves, as first one drug and then another become the current drug of choice for achieving this altered state of consciousness. In the 1960s, LSD was the major hallucinogen, and in the 1970s and early 1980s, it was PCP. Currently, MDMA seems to be gaining ground as the hallucinogen of choice, although research suggests that this drug may cause permanent brain damage, especially to those portions of the brain that utilize serotonin as a primary neurotransmitter.

It is logical to assume that other hallucinogens will emerge over the years, as people continue to look for a more effective way to alter their state of consciousness. In time, these drugs also will fade, as they are replaced by still newer hallucinogens. Just as cocaine faded from the drug scene in the 1930s and was replaced for a time by the amphetamines, so one might expect wave after wave of hallucinogen abuse, as new drugs become available. It is likely that chemical-dependency counselors will have to maintain a working knowledge of an ever-growing range of hallucinogens in the years to come.

Chapter 14

CIGARETTES AND NICOTINE

The use of tobacco was well established in the New World hundreds of years before Europeans first arrived. Tobacco was used in religious ceremonies by the natives of North America for hundreds, if not thousands, of years before the arrival of European explorers. Following the arrival of Columbus, the art of smoking was carried across the Atlantic to Europe by sailors who adopted the habit of smoking tobacco. The practice of smoking became quite popular in Europe, and within a few years of its introduction there, the use of tobacco had spread across Europe and into Asia (Schuckit, 1989).

The spread of tobacco use across Europe took place despite harsh opposition from the Church and various governments. Berger and Dunn (1982) report, for example, that public smoking in Germany was once punishable by death. In Russia, castration was the sentence for the same crime, according to Berger and Dunn, while in China, the use or distribution of tobacco was punishable by death. Smokers were executed as infidels in Turkey.

Tate (1989) relates the history of a certain Rodrigo de Jerez, a member of one of Columbus's early expeditions to the New World. When de Jerez (who had adopted the habit of smoking from the Indians of America) lit up his first cigar, the townspeople thought that he had become possessed by an evil spirit. For the "good of his soul," he was imprisoned by the Inquisition for an extended period of time, although ultimately he was released.

Despite this initial strong stance against smoking, the practice soon became at least moderately acceptable in society. Over the centuries, society has interpreted tobacco use differently. In the years following its introduction to Europe, tobacco was thought to be a medicine. More recently, in the past two centuries, smoking was viewed as a mark of sophistication. Only in the last generation or two has tobacco use met with wide public criticism.

Centuries ago, tobacco in the New World was possibly "more potent and may have contained high concentrations of psychoactive substances" compared with the tobacco of today (Schuckit, 1989, p. 215). Starting in the mid-nineteenth century, new varieties of tobacco were planted, allowing for a greater yield than in previous years. Also, new methods of curing the leaf of the tobacco plant were discovered, speeding up the process by which the leaf could be prepared for use.

153

The advent of the industrial age brought with it machinery capable of manufacturing the cigarette, a smaller, less expensive, neater way to smoke than cigars offered. One machine, invented by James A. Bonsack, could produce 120,000 cigarettes a day. Finally, changes in the tax laws made it possible to lower the price of the cigarettes, which soon became a favorite of the poor (Tate, 1989). By 1909, no fewer than 10 different states had laws on the books prohibiting the use of cigarettes.

Prior to the introduction of the cigarette, the major method of tobacco use was chewing. The practice of chewing tobacco, then spitting into the ever-present cuspidor, contributed to the spread of tuberculosis and other diseases (Brecher, 1972). In response, public health officials began to campaign against the practice of chewing tobacco after the year 1910. The new cigarette, manufactured in large numbers by the latest machines, provided a more sanitary, and relatively inexpensive, alternative to chewing tobacco. By 1890, for example, the price of domestic cigarettes had fallen to the price of a nickel for a pack of 20 (Tate, 1989). Thus, cigarettes were affordable for all but the poorest smoker.

Smokers soon discovered that, unlike cigars, the smoke of cigarettes was mild enough so that it could be inhaled (Jaffe, 1989). This allowed the nicotine to enter the lungs and bloodstream. For many, cigarette smoking became the method through which their nicotine addiction was serviced. The world has never been the same since.

THE SCOPE OF THE PROBLEM

Following World War I, the use of cigarettes grew in popularity and peaked in the mid-1960s (Schuckit, 1989). According to Jaffe (1989) the social climate was one of total social acceptance. In fact, "until quite recently, tobacco use was so common and socially acceptable . . . [that] almost everyone tried smoking" (p. 680). By the mid-1960s approximately 52% of adult American males and 32% of adult American females were cigarette smokers (Schuckit, 1989).

In 1964 the Surgeon General of the United States released a report stating that cigarette smoking was a health hazard and outlining the various problems that might be caused by smoking. In issuing this report, the Surgeon General joined a battle against smoking that had been going on since the late 1800s (Tate, 1989). Since the 1964 report was issued, the number of adult smokers has gradually declined. However, despite the growing body of information on the dangers of tobacco use, a total of 5.2 *trillion* cigarettes were smoked around the world in 1988 (*Playboy*, 1990b). In that year, Americans smoked an average of 2,285 cigarettes per individual.

It is difficult to determine the exact number of Americans who are still smoking cigarettes. The Department of Health and Human Services (1990) estimates that approximately 54 million Americans over the age of 12 are smokers. This estimate is close to that of Henningfield and Nemeth-Coslett

(1988), who suggest that some 50 million Americans still smoke, while another 10 million use "smokeless" tobacco products. L. Siegel (1989) offers the highest estimate of all, stating that some 60 million Americans continue to smoke.

Within the past generation, researchers have discovered that the roots of nicotine addiction may lie in childhood or adolescence. The problem of cigarette smoking by children and adolescents will be discussed in a later chapter. However, for now the reader should keep in mind that cigarette smoking is often a lifelong problem.

THE PHARMACOLOGY OF SMOKING

The primary method by which tobacco is used is by smoking (Schuckit, 1989), although in recent years chewing tobacco has made a comeback. The exact pharmacology of tobacco smoking is quite complicated. According to Jaffe (1990), variables that influence the composition of the smoke obtained from tobacco include: the (a) the exact composition of tobacco being used, (b) the density with which the tobacco is packed in the cigarette, (c) the length of the column of tobacco (for cigarette or cigar smokers), (d) the characteristics of the filter being used (if any), (e) the paper being used (for cigarette smokers), and (f) the temperature at which the tobacco is burned.

Tobacco smoke contains some 4,000 different compounds (Jaffe, 1990; Schuckit, 1989). When an individual smokes, these chemicals are inhaled into the lungs. Jaffe (1990) provides a partial list, including

> carbon monoxide, carbon dioxide, nitrogen oxides, ammonia, volatile nitrosa-mines, hydrogen cyanide, volatile sulfur-containing compounds, nitrites and other nitrogen-containing compounds, volatile hydrocarbons, alcohols, and aldehydes and keytones (e.g., acetaldehyde, formaldehyde and acrolein). (p. 545)

Some of these chemicals are documented carcinogens. A *carcinogen* is a chemical that is known to cause cancer in humans, or strongly suspected of having this capacity. Thus, cigarette use introduces carcinogenic chemicals directly into the body. Cigarette smoke also contains radioactive compounds, such as polonium 210 (Jaffe, 1990), and a small amount of arsenic (Banerjee, 1990).

The major psychoactive agent in tobacco is thought to be nicotine. However, tobacco smoke also includes *acetaldehyde*, a chemical that is the first metabolite produced by the liver when alcohol is metabolized. Acetaldehyde is more potent than alcohol and, like alcohol, has a sedative effect on the user (Rustin, 1988). Thus, while nicotine is thought to be the chemical that has the strongest effect on the user, other compounds in tobacco smoke also have some impact on the smoker's state of mind.

Nicotine is known to have "properties similar to those of cocaine and amphetamines" (Rustin, 1988, p. 18). Researchers disagree as to the relative potency of nicotine, however. Jaffe (1989) contends that nicotine is less powerful than cocaine or the amphetamines. By contrast, Weil (1986) claims that nicotine is a more powerful reinforcer than the amphetamines. Henningfield and Nemeth Coslett (1988) state that *intraveneous* nicotine is five to ten times more potent than intraveneous cocaine in terms of its reward potential. Bertone, Gomez, Jacques, and Mattiko (1988) reach a similar conclusion, noting that "milligram for milligram, nicotine is more potent than cocaine in modifying behavior" (p. 14).

Thus, researchers are in agreement that nicotine is a powerful reinforcer. Smoking cigarettes delivers the nicotine to the brain more effectively than an intraveneous injection (Weil, 1986). Each cigarette contains approximately 0.5 mg of nicotine (Kaplan & Sadock, 1988), which, when smoked, will reach the brain in just 7 seconds (Lichtenstein & Brown, 1980) to 8 seconds (Jaffe, 1990). Once in the body, nicotine will be rapidly distributed to virtually every blood-rich tissue in the body, including the brain (Henningfield & Nemeth-Coslett, 1988).

Nicotine impacts on the *medulla oblongata,* the small section of the brain that controls, among other things, respiration, swallowing, vomiting, and blood-pressure levels (Restak, 1984). It is here that nicotine has its main effect, causing many first-time smokers to experience nausea and vomiting (Jaffe, 1990). Heart rate is also modified by nerve impulses from the medulla, which accounts at least in part for nicotine's effects on the cardiovascular system. These effects include an increase in heart rate, blood pressure, and strength of heart contractions and a reduction of peripheral blood flow (Schuckit, 1989).

Nicotine decreases the strength of stomach contractions (Schuckit, 1989), and cigarette smoke itself can cause irritation of the tissues of the lungs and pulmonary system. It can also deposit potentially harmful chemicals in the lungs and slow down the motion of the cilia (the small hairlike projections that help to clean the lungs).

The mechanism by which nicotine affects the central nervous system is unknown. Smokers are known to experience brain stimulation (Schuckit, 1989) and decreased muscle tone (Jaffe, 1990). Animal research suggests that nicotine stimulates the release of the neurotransmitters norepinephrine and dopamine (Jaffe, 1990), as well as acetylcholine (Restak, 1991). Research has revealed that nicotine binds selectively to the neurons in the brain that utilize acetylcholine, some of which mediate pleasurable sensations. Thus, over time, smoking will be associated with pleasurable sensations involving these neurotransmitter groups.

Drug Interactions Between Nicotine and Other Chemicals

Drug interactions between nicotine and various other therapeutic agents are well documented. According to Bond (1989) and Jaffe (1990), cigarette smokers may require more morphine for the control of pain. Furthermore, they may experience less sedation from benzodiazepines than nonsmokers.

However, Creelman, Sands, Ciraulo, Greenblatt, and Shader (1989) argue that there is no evidence to support the latter theory. Creelman et al. state that "smokers should not require different dosing of benzodiazepines than nonsmokers" (p. 167).

Nicotine also seems to counteract some of the sedation associated with alcohol use and, as Schuckit (1989) suggests, this may be one reason why alcoholics seem to smoke so much. Tobacco also interacts with many anti-coagulants, with the beta-blocker propranolol, and with caffeine (Bond, 1989). Women who use oral contraceptives and who smoke are more likely to experience strokes, myocardial infarction, and thromboembolism (Bond, 1989). Individuals who use "smokeless" tobacco are more likely to develop oropharyngeal cancer than those who do not use tobacco products (Kaplan & Sadock, 1988).

NICOTINE ADDICTION

It has been known for some time that nicotine is addictive. But not everybody who smokes is actually *addicted* to nicotine (Hughes, Gust, & Pechacek, 1987). As noted by Henningfield and Nemeth-Coslett (1988):

> Simple exposure to tobacco does not ensure that dependence will develop, nor is everyone who uses tobacco dependent on nicotine. (p. 38s)

Indeed, the first-time smoker generally experiences not pleasure, but nausea and possibly even vomiting (Rystak, 1991). However, if the individual persists in his or her attempts to smoke, the stimulation of the neurotransmitter systems will eventually result in an association between smoking and pleasurable sensations, according to Rystak.

Not surprisingly, as people attempt to repeat and maintain nicotine-induced pleasurable sensations, many will become addicted. As such, they will demonstrate all the characteristics necessary for a diagnosis of drug addiction: (a) tolerance, (b) withdrawal symptoms, and (c) drug-seeking behaviors (Rustin, 1988). Furthermore, according to Rustin, tobacco users will develop drug-using rituals that may provide them with a measure of security in an insecure world. This may account for a person's tendency to smoke when he or she is anxious.

According to Jaffe (1989), those individuals who have smoked at least 100 cigarettes will go on to become daily smokers. However, he does not specify how many of them will eventually become addicted to nicotine. It is bound to be a sizable number if, as Shiffman et al. (1990) contend, 90% of cigarette smokers are addicted to the nicotine in tobacco.

Smokers who are not addicted to nicotine seem to exhibit a pattern of cigarette use that differs from the pattern of those who are addicted. Shiffman et al. (1990) examined the smoking habits of "chippers" (individuals who use chemicals—in this case tobacco—without evidence of addiction). They found that chippers do not appear to smoke in response to social cues or to avoid the symptoms of withdrawal. Indeed, one characteristic of the tobacco chipper is a tendency *not* to experience withdrawal symptoms from nicotine. The phenomenon of tobacco "chipping" is not well understood and warrants further inquiry.

Unfortunately, for 90% of those who smoke, addiction to nicotine is a very real problem. To place the tenacity of nicotine addiction in perspective, Kozlowski et al. (1989) asked some 1,000 individuals in treatment for drug addiction to rate the relative difficulty of quitting smoking and giving up their drug of choice. Surprisingly, 74% rated quitting smoking at least as difficult as giving up their drug of choice—a finding that underscores the addiction potential of tobacco.

Some researchers believe the chronic smokers tend to smoke in such a way as to regulate the nicotine level in their blood. Smokers will increase or decrease their cigarette use to achieve, and then maintain, a person-specific blood level of nicotine (Lichtenstein & Brown, 1980; Shiffman et al., 1990). According to Jaffe (1990), when given cigarettes of a high nicotine content, smokers will cut back; when given low-nicotine cigarettes, they will tend to smoke more often.

Henningfield and Nemeth-Coslett (1988) challenge Jaffe's (1990) conclusion. They point out that cigarette smokers have been shown to be "remarkably insensitive" to changes in nicotine levels in the blood (p. 45a). In reviewing the rapid changes in blood plasma nicotine levels across the span of a single day, they contend that the data do not support the constant-level hypothesis. However, this issue has not yet been completely resolved.

Nicotine Withdrawal

Withdrawal symptoms usually begin within 2 hours of the last use of tobacco and peak within 24 hours (Kaplan & Sadock, 1988). Then, they gradually decline over the next 10 days to several weeks (Jaffe, 1989). In a study of nicotine withdrawal symptoms, Hughes, Gust, Skoog, Keenan, and Fenwick (1991) found that up to 25% of their sample population continued to experience withdrawal symptoms a full month after they had stopped smoking. Additionally, up to 75% experienced at least occasional craving for nicotine even after 6 months had passed.

Withdrawal symptoms vary from one individual to the next. It has been suggested that a higher daily intake of nicotine may be associated with stronger withdrawal of symptoms (Jaffe, 1990). Specific symptoms of nicotine withdrawal include irritability, impatience, decreased attentiveness, and increased aggressiveness. Insomnia, drowsiness, hunger, tremulousness, anger or irritability, and strong tobacco "cravings" have also been reported (Hughes et al., 1991). Over time, the former smoker will experience a decrease in heart rate and blood pressure, and improved peripheral blood-flow patterns. The possibility that the withdrawal process might exacerbate depressive disorders has been suggested (Jaffe, 1990).

Smokers who quit their habit often report weight gain over time, although the exact mechanism by which this comes about is unknown. Jaffe (1990) pointed out that cigarette smoking seems to help suppress an individual's appetite; it is logical to assume that this process is reversed when the person stops smoking.

While many ex-smokers attempt to avoid this weight gain, researchers have come to view it in a more positive light within the past few years. According to Hughes et al. (1991), those individuals who gain weight are more likely to remain abstinent following the decision to stop smoking. In their sample population, weight levels "returned to precessation levels at 6 months" (p. 57), suggesting that weight gain may be a time-limited phenomenon for those individuals who experience this side effect of abstinence.

In a study by Williamson et al. (1991) to explore the problem of weight gain in ex-smokers, a group of 748 male and 1,137 female smokers was contrasted with a group of 409 men and 359 women who had abstained from the use of tobacco for a year. It was found that the average male ex-smoker gained 2.8 kg (6.7 lb) and the average female ex-smoker gained 3.8 kg (9.1 lb).[1] For a minority of the ex-smokers (some 10% of the men and 13% of the women), an average weight gain of 13 kg (31.2 lb) was reported.

The Williamson et al. (1991) study yielded an additional interesting finding; namely, that the average smoker in the sample population actually weighed less than the average nonsmoker in a control group. Further, according to Williamson et al., by the end of the study "the mean body weight of those who had quit had increased only to that of those who had never smoked" (p. 743). The conclusion was that tobacco use interferes with weight gain through some unknown mechanism. The weight gain following the decision to quit smoking was interpreted as possibly reflecting the body's readjustment to the same level as those individuals who never smoked to begin with.

COMPLICATIONS OF THE CHRONIC USE OF TOBACCO

The exact amount of nicotine, "tar," and carbon monoxide obtained from a specific brand of cigarette is evident when the cigarette is "smoked" by a test machine (Jaffe, 1989). However, individual differences in people's smoking methods results in significant variation in specific chemical combinations generated by each cigarette. Thus, it is difficult to determine exactly what chemicals, and in what concentrations, may be introduced into the body of an individual smoker.

Around the turn of the century carcinoma of the lung was a relatively rare disease; indeed, it was not until 1923 that lung cancer was included in the International Classification of Diseases (*Smithsonian*, 1989). Furthermore, as noted by Foa (1989), as late as 1921 the association between tobacco use and cancer had not been recognized. But by the year 1980, tobacco use and various forms of cancer were known to be linked. According to the Council on

[1]There are 2.4 pounds per kilogram.

Scientific Affairs of the American Medical Association (1990a) "globally . . . tobacco use is responsible for almost 2.5 million excessive or premature deaths per year" (p. 3312). If present trends continue, it is estimated that by the year 2030 cigarette smoking will cause 10 million deaths a year around the world (*The Lancet,* 1991).

According to the Centers for Disease Control (Associated Press, 1991a), over 434,000 Americans died from smoking in 1988. Of this number, an estimated 106,000 died from lung cancer and almost 31,000 died from other forms of cancer associated with smoking. Furthermore, some 200,800 individuals died from smoking-related cardiovascular disease, 82,800 died from respiratory diseases associated with smoking other than lung cancer, and 1,300 died from burns received in fires started by cigarette smoking, as estimated by the Centers for Disease Control.

It also has been estimated that at least 126,000 women die each year as a result of smoking-induced illness (University of California, Berkeley, 1990c). Women who smoke are at risk for "invasive cervical cancer, miscarriages, early menopause, and osteoporosis, among other disorders" (p. 7); and, in fact, lung cancer has now surpassed cancer of the breast as the leading cause of cancer-related deaths in women.

According to the American Cancer Society (1990), fully 83% of all lung cancer and one-third of all cancer in general is connected with cigarette smoking. Klag and Whelton (1987) point out that cigarette smoking significantly increases the chance of stroke in males and emphasize the need for a program to "promote smoking cessation on a national, as well as on an individual, level" (p. 628).

The risk of premature death from cigarette smoking is dose-related. Individuals who smoke only 1 to 9 cigarettes a day are five times as likely to develop lung cancer as nonsmokers (University of California, Berkeley, 1991). Those who smoke between 10 and 19 cigarettes a day, are nine times as likely to develop lung cancer. And, according to the University of California, Berkeley, "no amount of smoking is free of risk" (p. 8).

Schuckit (1989) claims that, after alcohol, tobacco use results in the highest annual death rate of any abused substance. Scott (1987) goes even further, stating that nicotine-related deaths exceed even those caused by alcohol. According to Nelson (1989), cigarette smoking accounts for more than three times as many deaths as alcohol and ten times as many deaths as all other drugs combined.

Chronic cigarette smokers are known to suffer increased rates of cancer of the lung, mouth, pharynx, larynx, and esophagus; increased rates of cardiovascular disease; and increased mortality from pulmonary disease (Jaffe, 1990; Schuckit, 1989). Alcoholics who also smoke cigarettes are especially vulnerable to cancer of the throat (Nelson, 1989). Why this is so is not clear, although it stands to reason that if the use of either agent increases the risk of cancer, the use of *both* would involve an even higher risk.

The risks associated with smoking are not limited to the smoker alone. Researchers estimate that "passive smoking" (that is, inhaling the smoke from the cigarettes of others) results in the deaths of an additional 28,027 Americans (Steenland, 1992) to 53,000 Americans (Associated Press, 1990a) each year.

To put the problem of smoking-related mortality in perspective, it has been suggested that fully *one-fifth* of all deaths in the United States (Roper, 1991) and *one-sixth* of all deaths in the United Kingdom (*The Lancet*, 1991) are caused by smoking. According to Nunn-Thompson and Simon (1989), when estimated annual smoking-related health care costs are combined with cigarette-related lost-productivity figures, the annual cost of cigarette smoking in the United States comes to $65 *billion* dollars a year, or approximately $2.17 per package of cigarettes sold. This is the cost for cigarette smoking only; it does not include costs incurred by chewing tobacco or cigar and pipe smoking. Obviously, tobacco use in the United States extracts a significant price.

THE TREATMENT OF NICOTINE ADDICTION

Nicotine is thought to be the substance in tobacco that causes addiction to cigarettes (Nunn-Thompson & Simon, 1989). So powerful is this addiction to nicotine that thousands of people are unsuccessful at breaking their cigarette habit. Weil (1986) contends that it is easier to withdraw from heroin than from nicotine. As he puts it, "I have never seen anyone have as much physical trouble giving up heroin as . . . giving up cigarettes" (p. 42).

There is a definite advantage to breaking the nicotine habit. The former smoker's risk of developing heart disease drops 50% in the first year. Moreover, within 15 years of the last cigarette the risk is approximately the same as that of a nonsmoker. In spite of this obvious medical incentive, however, research findings indicate that only one person in four is able to permanently stop smoking before the age of 60 (Lichtenstein & Brown (1980).

Many attempts have been made to apply behavior modification techniques to help individuals stop smoking. However, as Stevens and Hollis (1989) note, while behavioral training programs usually help between 70% and 80% of the participants to stop smoking on a short-term basis, between 50% and 75% of those who do stop smoking relapse within a year. In other words, of those who attempt to stop smoking, most will stop for a short time, but less than half will be tobacco-free a year later (Jaffe, 1989). Hughes et al. (1991) found that 65% of their experimental sample relapsed within the first month of quitting, suggesting that the first month is especially difficult for those who are trying to quit.

Early relapse could be attributed to the vulnerability of the individual in the first 3 to 4 weeks after quitting to smoking "cues," such as being around other smokers (Bliss, Garvey, Heinold, & Hitchcock, 1989). At such times, the individual is less likely to cope effectively with the urge to smoke and is in danger of a relapse into active cigarette smoking again (Hughes et al., 1991).

Cohen et al. (1989), in their review of the data from 10 different research projects involving a total of 5,000 subjects who were attempting to stop smoking, found that light smokers (those who smoked fewer than 20 cigarettes each day) were significantly more likely to be able to stop smoking on their own than were heavy smokers. They also found that the number of unsuccessful previous attempts was *unrelated* to whether or not the smoker would be successful on the current try. They conclude that "most people who fail a single attempt [to quit smoking] will try again and again and eventually quit" (p. 1361). However, they also characterize quitting as a "dynamic process" in which periods of abstinence are intermixed with periods of relapse.

Nicotine-containing gum has been shown to be helpful (although not totally effective) in both controlling the craving for cigarettes and the irritability associated with withdrawal from cigarettes (Hughes et al., 1991; Nunn-Thompson & Simon, 1989). After 30 minutes of chewing the nicotine-containing gum, approximately 90% of the nicotine in the gum has been released. Moreover, the gum does not raise the blood level of nicotine to that found in cigarette smokers, and the gum itself may cause such side effects as sore gums, excessive salivation, nausea, ulcers on the gums, anorexia, and headache (Nunn-Thompson & Simon, 1989).

In a study by Gottlieb, Killen, Marlatt, and Taylor (1987), subjects who believed they were chewing nicotine-containing gum reported fewer withdrawal symptoms than those who were not given gum to chew, whether or not the gum actually contained nicotine. Thus, the individuals' *expectations* for the gum seemed to moderate their withdrawal symptoms from cigarettes. This study raises questions as to the role of the individual's expectations in the tobacco-withdrawal process.

A nasal spray that contains nicotine has also been used in the control of tobacco craving (Jaffe, 1989; Nunn-Thompson & Simon, 1989). Preliminary findings suggest that blood plasma levels of nicotine obtained from this nasal-spray approach those obtained from smoking, but neither its effectiveness as an aid to stop smoking, nor its safety, have been demonstrated.

Glassman et al. (1988) explored the application of an antihypertensive drug, Catapres (clonidine), to the craving for nicotine often reported by cigarette smokers who stop. This medication has been found to be of value in the control of drug craving in narcotics withdrawal. Findings revealed that more than twice as many subjects who received clonidine were able to stop smoking and remain abstinent over a 4-week time span than subjects who received a placebo.

However, in another study involving clonidine, Franks, Harp, and Bell (1989) found that this drug failed to produce statistically significant effects. Franks et al. suggest that earlier research studies exploring the application of clonidine to nicotine withdrawal utilized small numbers of highly motivated subjects, who were not representative of the general-practice population encountered by most physicians.

Other agents that have been utilized in the treatment of nicotine withdrawal include buspirone, tricyclic antidepressants, and lobeline (a drug derived from a variety of tobacco) (Nunn-Thompson & Simon, 1989). Despite extensive research, however, there is no single substance that has proven effective in treating the symptoms of nicotine withdrawal beyond a reasonable doubt.

In 1992, the Food and Drug Administration approved the manufacture and sale of transdermal nicotine patches as an aid to smoking cessation. The theory behind the use of these patches is that the user will achieve a moderate, but steady, nicotine level in his or her blood without actually smoking. Then, after a period of time, the amount of nicotine in the patches could be reduced, gradually weaning the user off cigarettes.

From the perspective of sales, these patches were an immediate success. Pharmacists had a hard time filling the numerous prescriptions for the patches, and there were shortages reported in various parts of the country. However, there has been little published research on the effectiveness of this technique, and the initial response seemed to indicate that there were many problems associated with the use of transdermal nicotine patches. Some users have reported skin irritation, and questions have been raised concerning safety. A number of users have reported that they relapsed while they were using the patches or shortly thereafter.

Thus the question of how effective transdermal nicotine patches might be has not been answered. Even if research does ultimately demonstrate that these patches are an effective adjunct to smoking cessation, little is known about how best to use them in a smoking cessation program.

Bertone et al. (1988) describe a treatment program they developed for nicotine withdrawal. Based on the fact that nicotine addiction is similar to other forms of chemical addiction, this program first of all includes a detoxification component. Nicotine detoxification involves the use of clonidine (the antihypertensive drug previously discussed) and nicotine chewing gum for controlled withdrawal over a 10-day period.

The program also includes dietary monitoring on the theory that "eating and drinking behaviors play an important role in the activation of the smoking response" (Bertone et al., 1988, p. 15). Furthermore, emphasis on proper diet helps to control the weight gain often reported by smokers who quit.

Another component of the treatment program consists of therapeutic activities designed to enhance cardiovascular fitness. Stress-management techniques and individual and group therapy are also employed. Finally, a twelve-step program known as "Smokers Anonymous" is incorporated into the overall program.

Although the treatment program appears to be reasonable from a clinical standpoint, long-term statistics demonstrating the usefulness of this particular approach to nicotine addiction are not yet available. So far, it has not demonstrated a higher "cure" rate than other, less complex, treatment programs. Indeed, according to Cohen et al. (1989), formal treatment programs for cigarette smokers have a "disappointing performance" (p. 1355).

Kozlowski et al. (1989) state that "most cigarette smokers give up smoking without formal treatment" (p. 901). This conclusion is confirmed by Peele (1989), who points out that 95% of those who quit smoking do so without formal treatment. Jaffe (1989) contends that the individual's motivation to quit smoking is a critical predictor of success. These observations raise serious questions as to whether extensive treatment programs are necessary. Fiore et al. (1990) argue that formal treatment programs are useful for heavy smokers and those at risk for tobacco-related illness, despite the fact that the vast majority of those who quit manage to do so on their own.

SUMMARY

Tobacco use, once limited to the New World, was first introduced to Europe by members of Columbus's expeditions. Once the practice of smoking or chewing tobacco reached Europe, tobacco use rapidly spread. Following the introduction of the cigarette around the turn of the century, smoking became more common, rapidly replacing tobacco chewing as the accepted method of tobacco use.

Nicotine, the active agent of tobacco, has been found to have an addiction potential similar to that of cocaine or narcotic drugs. A significant percentage of those who are currently addicted to nicotine will attempt to stop smoking but will be unsuccessful initially. Current treatment methods have been unable to achieve a significant cure rate, and more comprehensive treatment programs have been suggested for nicotine addiction. Although they are patterned after treatment programs for alcohol addiction, these comprehensive programs also have not demonstrated a significantly improved cure rate for cigarette smoking. It has been suggested, however, that such programs might be of value for individuals whose tobacco use has put them at risk for tobacco-related illness.

Chapter 15

THE UNRECOGNIZED PROBLEM OF STEROID ABUSE

The *anabolic steroids* (or simply, *steroids*) are not well understood in terms of their addiction potential (Bower, 1991). However, on the street there is a certain aura surrounding them. Indeed, so common has the use of steroids become in athletic training programs that some athletes look upon these drugs not as potent chemical agents, but rather as a "nutritional supplement" (Breo, 1990, p. 1697).

An unknown percentage of teenagers and young adults are using steroids, in spite of their considerable potential to cause harm to the user. It is for this reason that health-care and chemical-dependency professionals should have a working knowledge of the effects of this class of medications.

AN INTRODUCTION TO ANABOLIC STEROIDS

The term *anabolic* refers to the action of these drugs to increase the speed of growth of body tissues; the term *steroids* refers to their chemical structure (Redman, 1990). These drugs are chemically similar to testosterone, the male sex hormone, and thus have a masculinizing (androgenic) effect on the user (Hough & Kovan, 1990; Landry & Primos, 1990). At times, this class of drugs is referred to as the *anabolic-androgenic steroid* family of drugs.

It has been suggested that these drugs may, when abused, bring about a feeling of euphoria (M. D. Johnson, 1990; Lipkin, 1989). However, it is not for this reason that they are primarily abused. Rather, the main reason why steroids are abused is because they stimulate protein synthesis, a process that indirectly promotes muscle-tissue development and increases muscle strength (Hough & Kovan, 1990; Kimmage, 1990; Pettine, 1991; Pope & Katz, 1990).

Steroids are also abused in the belief that they will enhance attractiveness (Bahrke, 1990; Brower, Blow, Young, & Hill, 1991; M. D. Johnson 1990; Pettine, 1991; Pope, Katz, & Champoux, 1986). Indeed, Fultz (1991) reports that 25% of adolescent steroid abusers take steroids because they think it will help them look better. It has even been suggested that some law enforcement personnel abuse steroids to increase their strength and aggressiveness (Bahrke, 1990).

165

MEDICAL USES OF ANABOLIC STEROIDS

The anabolic steroids are used by physicians to promote tissue growth and help damaged tissue recover from injury (Govoni & Hayes, 1988). According to the U.S. Pharmacopeial Convention, (1990b), physicians may also use one of the steroid family of drugs to treat certain kinds of anemia and help patients regain weight after periods of severe illness. This steroid is also used as an adjunct to the treatment of certain forms of breast cancer in women. In certain cases, the steroids may also promote the growth of bone tissue following injuries to the bone (Govoni & Hayes, 1988). The Council on Scientific Affairs of the American Medical Association (1990b) suggests that the steroid family of drugs could also be useful in the treatment of osteoporosis.

In 1990 the use of anabolic steroids was outlawed by Congress, *except for medical purposes*. This made the sale of 28 different forms of anabolic steroids a crime that could be punished by a prison term of up to 5 years (10 years if the steroids were sold to minors) (Fultz, 1991). Thus, the steroids are now considered controlled substances.

THE SCOPE OF THE PROBLEM

There has been very little research into how widespread steroid abuse actually is (Bower, 1991; Pope et al., 1986). In a survey by Johnson, O'Malley, and Bachman (1989), an estimated 11.1% of the male high school students and 5% of the female students who responded admitted to the use of anabolic steroids at some point in their lives.

According to Daigle (1990), 6% to 10% of male high school students are current users of anabolic steroids. This estimate is in the same range as that provided by Dreyfuss (1990), who reported that almost 7% of male high school seniors in a sample of 3,403 admitted that they were currently using steroids or that they had used them in the past. Gannon (1989) contends that 7% of all male high school students have used steroids at least once. Finally, according to the *Los Angeles Times* (1990), 250,000 high school students are either currently using steroids or have used them in the past. Bahrke (1990) would put this figure at 500,000 high school students.

As for steroid abuse on college campuses, it has been estimated that approximately 20% of college athletes have used steroids on at least one occasion (Hough & Kovan, 1990). In fact, although steroid abuse became common among althetes first, there is now evidence of a growing trend for nonathletes to abuse them as well (Landry & Primos, 1990). This trend is reflected in Porterfield's (1991) estimate that as many as 1 million people are abusing these drugs.

HOW STEROIDS ARE USED

Physicians will often prescribe steroids on the assumption that they will be able to monitor and control the use of these drugs (Breo, 1990). However, athletes frequently do not limit themselves to the prescribed medications; they obtain steroids from other sources to increase their daily dosage on their own. Anabolic steroids are smuggled into this country from overseas, or diverted to the "black market" from legitimate sources, and are often available through an informal distribution network that exists in health clubs or gyms (M. D. Johnson, 1990).

Another common source of steroids are veterinary products, which are sold on the street for use by humans. These medications may be injected into muscle tissue or taken orally. Sometimes both intramuscular and oral doses of the medication are taken together—a practice is known as "stacking" steroids (Medical Economics Company, 1989). Steroids that are injected are known as "injectables"; those that are taken by mouth are called "orals" (Bahrke, 1990) or "juice" (Fultz, 1991). In a study by Brower, Blow, Young, and Hill (1991), 61% of their sample of steroid-abusing weight lifters were engaged in the practice of "stacking."

Another way in which the steroids are abused is through the practice of *pyramiding* (Daigle, 1990). Initially, the user takes the smallest dose. The daily dosage level is then gradually increased, so that by midcycle the user is taking the maximum dosage of steroids. Then, the daily dosage level is gradually tapered, until by the last week in the cycle the abuser is again taking a relatively small daily dose. Episodes of pyramiding are interspaced with periods of abstinence from anabolic steroid use that may last several weeks, or even months (Landry & Primos, 1990).

Many of the steroids smuggled into the United States originate in Mexico and Europe (M. D. Johnson, 1990). According to Bahrke (1990), between 50% and 80% of the steroids used by athletes comes from the "black market"—a term applied to any steroid used for other than medical purposes. Black market sales are big business, bringing in from $100 million (Miller, 1990; Pettine, 1991) to between $300 and $500 million (Council on Scientific Affairs, 1990b; Fultz, 1991) annually in the United States.

Much of what is known about the anabolic steroids is based on data obtained from patients who were taking steroids under a physician's care, using specific recommended dosage levels to achieve a specific goal (Medical Economics Company, 1989). Adverse side effects have been documented at relatively low doses in cases where these medications were used to treat medical conditions (Hough & Kovan, 1990).

The U.S. Pharmacopeial Convention (1990b) warns that even at recommended dosage levels, steroids are capable of causing sore throat or fever, vomiting (with or without blood), dark-colored urine, bone pain, nausea, unusual weight gain, and headache. The adverse effects of anabolic steroids depend on (a) the route of administration, (b) the specific drugs taken, (c) the dose utilized, (d) the frequency of use, (e) the health of the individual, and (f) the age of the individual (M. D. Johnson, 1990).

Unfortunately, many adolescents and young adults who abuse steroids do so at dosage levels that are often much higher than the maximum recommended dosage level. They may be 100 times as high (Brower, Catlin, Blow, Eliopulos, & Bereford, 1991) or even 1,000 times as high (Council on Scientific

Affairs, 1990b; Medical Economics Company, 1989). Brower, Blow, Young, and Hill (1991), for example, found that the dosage range of steroids being used by a sample of weight lifters was between 2 and 26 times the recommended dosage level for steroids. Landry and Primos (1990) note that in one study the *lowest* dose of anabolic steroids being used by a group of weight lifters was 3½ times the usual therapeutic dose.

There is very little information available on the effects of this family of drugs at these dosage levels (M. D. Johnson, 1990). We do know, however, that the effects on the anabolic steroids on muscle tissue last for several weeks after the drugs are discontinued (Pope & Katz, 1991). Thus, muscle-builders who abuse steroids may discontinue the drugs shortly before a competition to avoid having their steroid use detected by urine toxicological screens. A "clean" urine sample, then, does not rule out steroid use in modern sporting events. It only provides evidence that steroids were not used in the period *immediately prior* to the competition.

COMPLICATIONS OF STEROID ABUSE

The Reproductive System

Adult males who use steroids at the recommended dosage levels might experience enlargement of breasts, increased frequency of erections or continual erections (a condition known as *priapism*, which is itself a medical emergency), unnatural hair growth, and a frequent urge to urinate. Steroid *abuse* in males may bring about such side effects as breast enlargement, degeneration of the testicles, enlargement of the prostate gland, impotence, and sterility (Council on Scientific Affairs, 1990b; Hough & Kovan, 1990; Mendelsohn & Arthur, 1989). On rare occasions, steroid abuse has resulted in carcinoma (cancer) of the prostate (M. D. Johnson, 1990; Landry & Primos, 1990) and urinary obstruction (Council on Scientific Affairs, 1990b).

Women who use steroids at recommended dosage levels may experience enlargement of the clitoris, irregular menstrual periods, unnatural hair growth or unusual hair loss, a deepening of the voice, and reduction in the size of the breasts (Hough & Kovan, 1990; Mendelsohn & Arthur, 1989; Pope & Katz, 1988; Redman, 1990). The Council for Scientific Affairs (1990b) suggests that women who use steroids may experience beard growth. Crawshaw (1985) warns that the baldness experienced by many women who use steroids in large doses is irreversible. However, menstrual irregularities caused by steroid use will often disappear after the steroids are discontinued (M. D. Johnson, 1990).

The Liver, Kidneys, and the Digestive System

The anabolic steroids may cause hepatoxicity (liver failure), and there is evidence to suggest that, when used for long periods of time at excessive doses, steroids might contribute to the formation of both cancerous and benign liver tumors (Council for Scientific Affairs, 1990b; Medical Economics Company, 1989). Steroid abusers may experience altered liver function, which may be detected through appropriate blood tests (M. D. Johnson, 1990).

The Cardiovascular System

There is evidence to suggest that steroid use may contribute to the development of heart disease for those who abuse this family of drugs—complications that may last for months after the drug is discontinued (Hough & Kovan, 1990; M. D. Johnson, 1990; Kimmage, 1990; Wolkowitz, 1990). Apparently, there is a tendency for this class of drugs to increase the levels of low-density lipoprotein cholesterol and blood pressure levels while decreasing the levels of high-density lipoproteins (Council for Scientific Affairs, 1990b; Crawshaw, 1985; Fultz, 1991; M. D. Johnson, 1990). These are well-documented risk factors for heart disease that may have lifelong consequences for the person abusing steroids.

In effect, the anabolic steroids may contribute to accelerated atherosclerosis of the heart and its surrounding blood vessels. There is a documented case of a 34-year-old weight lifter who suffered a stroke while using steroids (Council on Scientific Affairs, 1990b). Fultz (1991) notes that high doses of the anabolic steroids may cause blood platelets to clump together, contributing to both heart attacks and strokes.

The Central Nervous System

The anabolic steroid family of drugs is thought by some to be capable of causing behavioral changes in the user. To explore this hypothesis, Wolkowitz et al. (1990) administered an 80-mg daily dose of a pharmaceutical steroid known as *prednisone* to a sample of healthy volunteers for 5 days. Findings revealed "prednisone administration [to be] associated with decreases in . . . levels of several biologically and behaviorally active neuropeptides or neurotransmitters" (p. 966).

In other words, Wolkowitz et al. found measurable changes in the levels of neuropeptides or neurotransmitters in their sample population after a period of only 5 days. However, in spite of these measured changes in biochemical levels, they found "no significant prednisone-associated changes . . . in group mean behavioral ratings" (p. 967). That is, no apparent behavioral changes were evident in their sample population.

It should be noted, however, that the preceding study involved *only* a five-day period in which to explore whether prednisone might cause behavioral changes. Individuals who abuse steroids often do so for extended periods of time, and may do so at dosage levels far above the daily 80 mg used by Wolkowitz et al. Indeed, individuals who abuse steroids, as we have noted, often do so at dosage levels up to 1,000 times the maximum recommended dosage level (Medical Economics Company, 1989). It requires several weeks of constantly increasing dosage levels to achieve this level of steroid abuse.

Further, at these grossly inflated dosage levels, anabolic steroids are suspected of causing psychotic symptoms in the chronic user (Crawshaw, 1985; M. D. Johnson, 1990; Mendelsohn & Arthur, 1989; Pope et al., 1986). Pope and Katz (1987) examined 31 weight lifters who admitted to the use of steroids and found that 22% had experienced some symptoms of psychosis, apparently as a side effect to their steroid use. In a later study, Pope and Katz (1988) examined 41 athletes who had used steroids and found that 9 of them (22%) had experienced either a manic or a depressive reaction while using steroids. Another 5 subjects (12%) had experienced other psychotic reactions, apparently drug-induced.

In 1990 Pope and Katz reported that, in their opinion, steroid abuse had contributed to the violent behavior of 3 individuals, to the point where homicide or attempted homicide was the end result in all three cases. This drug-induced reaction is often known as a "roid rage" by illicit steroid users (Fultz, 1991; Redman 1990). According to M. D. Johnson (1990), up to 90% of those who abuse steroids may experience an increase in aggressive or violent behaviors.

Steroids may cause depression in both men and women who use this family of drugs at recommended dosage levels or at higher levels. These drugs may also produce a toxic reaction if the individual is using too high a dose for his or her individual body chemistry. Symptoms of a toxic reaction to steroids include a drug-induced psychotic reaction, manic episodes, delirium, dementia, or a drug-induced depressive reaction that may reach suicidal proportions (Lederberg & Holland, 1989).

Complications in General

Patients who have medical conditions, such as certain forms of breast cancer; diabetes mellitus; diseases of the blood vessels, kidney, liver, or heart; and prostate problems (males), should not use steroids unless prescribed by a physician who is aware of these conditions (U.S. Pharmacopeial Convention, 1990b). The anabolic steroids are thought to be possibly carcinogenic (M. D. Johnson, 1990); thus, their use is not recommended for patients with either active tumors or a history of tumors, except under a physician's supervision.

Other side effects caused by steroid use include acne (especially across the back), and possibly a foul odor on the breath (Redman, 1990). Pettine (1991) reviewed one case of unnatural bone degeneration that was *possibly* caused by long-term steroid use in a weight lifter, and suggests that users of anabolic steroids be warned of this additional potential danger.

Growth patterns in the adolescent   Adolescents who use steroids run the risk of stunted growth, as these drugs may permanently stop bone growth (Council on Scientific Affairs, 1990b; Crawshaw, 1985; M. D. Johnson, 1990; Mendelsohn & Arthur, 1989). A further complication of steroid abuse by adolescents is that the tendons do not grow at the same accelerated rate as the bone tissues, resulting in increased strain on the tendons and a higher risk of injury to these tissues (Hough & Kovan, 1990; M. D. Johnson, 1990).

Anabolic steroids and blood infections   In addition to the complications of the steroids themselves, individuals who abuse steroids through intramuscular or intraveneous injection run the risks associated with contaminated needles. Indeed, there have been cases of athletes contracting AIDS from using a "dirty" needle (Crawshaw, 1985; Scott & Scott, 1989).

ANABOLIC STEROIDS AND DRUG INTERACTIONS

The anabolic steroids interact with a wide range of medications, including several drugs of abuse. Potentially serious drug interactions have been noted in cases where the individual took high doses of acetaminophen while on steroids. The combination of these two drugs—steroids and acetaminophen—should be avoided, except when the individual is being supervised by a physician. Patients who are taking antabuse (disulfiram) should not take steroids, nor should individuals who are taking Trexan (naltrexone); anticonvulsant medications, such as Dilantin (phenytoin); Depakene (valproic acid); or the phenothiazines (U.S. Pharmacopeial Convention, 1990b).

ARE ANABOLIC STEROIDS ADDICTIVE?

In recent years, evidence has been uncovered suggesting that long-term steroid use at high dosage levels may result in steroid addiction. The steroids have been known to bring about a sense of euphoria (Fultz, 1991; Lipkin, 1989). For some, this may be why steroid use is so attractive. According to Bower (1991), up to 57% of weight lifters who use steroids ultimately become addicted to these drugs.

There have been reports that steroids might be capable of bringing about a withdrawal syndrome similar to that associated with cocaine addiction. Symptoms of withdrawal from steroids include depressive reactions, possibly to the point of suicide attempts (Hough & Kovan, 1990; Kashkin & Kleber, 1989). Other symptoms often reported during or after withdrawal from steroids include sleep and appetite disturbances, which seem to be part of the poststeroid depressive syndrome (Bower, 1991), fatigue, restlessness, anorexia, insomnia, and decreased libido (Brower, Blow, Young, & Hill, 1991).

Like other drug abusers, many steroid abusers require gradual detoxification from the drugs and intensive psychiatric support to limit the impact of withdrawal and prevent a return to steroid use (Bower, 1991; Hough & Kovan, 1990; Kashkin & Kleber, 1989). According to Robert Dimeff, Donald Malone, and John Lombardo (cited in Bower, 1991), some of the symptoms of steroid addiction include the following:

- the use of higher doses than originally intended;
- a loss of control over the amount of steroids used;

- a preoccupation with further steroid use;
- the continued use of steroids in spite of an awareness of the problems caused by their use;
- the development of tolerance to steroids and the need for larger doses to achieve the same effects as once brought on by lower doses;
- the disruption of normal daily activities; and
- the use of steroids to control or avoid withdrawal symptoms.

These researchers suggest that three or more of these symptoms would identify those individuals who were dependent on steroids.

Dreyfuss (1990) concludes that fully 25% of the current users of steroids are either physically of psychologically dependent on these drugs. According to Bower (1991), up to 57% of weight lifters who use steroids ultimately become addicted. Further, in addition to their physical addiction potential, it is possible for the user to become psychologically dependent on anabolic steroids (M. D. Johnson, 1990). The percentage of users who are psychologically dependent has not been estimated.

THE TREATMENT OF ANABOLIC STEROID ABUSE

Obviously those individuals who are indeed abusing anabolic steroids must first be identified before treatment can be initiated. On the basis of clinical history and blood and/or urine tests a physician may be the first one to suspect that a patient may be abusing steroids, and the physician may be in the best position to comfront the user. At this point, a chemical-dependency counselor is not thought to have a significant role in the treatment of the anabolic steroid user.

Once a steroid abuser has been identified, close medical supervision is required to identify potential complications of his or her steroid abuse. Further, medical supervision of the withdrawal from anabolic steroids is necessary, and a gradual detoxification program may need to be established. Although most medical complications caused by steroid abuse will usually clear up after the individual discontinues use (Hough & Kovan, 1990), some of the complications (such as heart-tissue damage) may be permanent. Furthermore, surgical intervention may be necessary to correct some of the side effects of steroid abuse, according to Hugh and Kovan.

Following detoxification from anabolic steroids, counseling personnel should attempt to determine why the patient started using steroids in the first place. Self-concept issues may be salient; some patients may need to learn to accept themselves without resorting to "crutches," such as anabolic steroids. Proper nutritional counseling may be necessary to help the athlete learn how to enhance body strength without using potentially harmful drugs. Support groups may help the patient substitute social support for chemical support.

SUMMARY

Within the past decade, a surprising new group of drugs, the anabolic steroids, have emerged as drugs of abuse in many circles. However, steroids are not the "typical" drug of abuse. Adolescents and young adults abuse steroids because they believe these substances will increase aggressiveness, improve athletic ability, and enhance personal appearance. Little is known about the effects of these drugs at the dosage levels typical of the steroid abuser. The identification and treatment of steroid abusers is primarily a medical issue, but substance-abuse counselors should have a working knowledge of the effects of steroid abuse and the complications associated with such abuse.

Chapter 16

THE MEDICAL MODEL
OF CHEMICAL ADDICTION

In the first section of this book, which is made up of Chapters 1–15, we examined the various drugs of abuse, including the effects they have on the user and the damage they may cause. This is important information for professionals in the areas of chemical dependency and health care. However, knowledge of what each drug of abuse might do to the user does not answer two deceptively simple questions. First *why do people use these drugs* and, second, *why do people become addicted?* In this chapter, we will explore these questions from the perspective of what has come to be known as the "medical" or "disease" model of addiction.

WHY DO PEOPLE USE CHEMICALS?

At first, this question might seem simplistic. People use drugs because they choose to do so.[1] Furthermore, drugs of abuse are part of the environment. Every day, perhaps several times a day, each of us has to make a decision whether or not to use chemicals. Admittedly, for most of us, this choice is relatively simple, and perhaps it is made without conscious thought. But the fact remains that we are constantly faced with opportunities to use recreational chemicals, and we must decide whether or not to do so.

Stop for a moment and think: Where is the nearest liquor store? *If you wanted to do so*, where could you buy some marijuana? How about cocaine or narcotics? If you are over the age of 15, you probably know the answers, or at least you probably could find someone who does. But why didn't you go out and buy any of these chemicals on your way to work or school this morning? Why didn't you buy some recreational drug on your way home last night?

The answer is that you chose not to. Although your decision not to use chemicals might have been made without conscious thought, on some level, you made the choice. In one sense, then the answer to the question of why people use drugs of abuse is because they choose to do so. We will now consider some of the factors that influence this decision.

---

[1]We are referring here to recreational users of chemicals, not to those who are addicted.

Reward Potential

Actually, the question of why a person might use alcohol or another drug of abuse is rather complex. The novice chemical user may make the decision to try one or more drugs in response to peer pressure or in anticipation of pleasurable effects. Researchers call this the "pharmacological potential,"or the "reward potential," of the chemical or chemicals being used (Meyer, 1989a), and many of the drugs of abuse have a high reward potential (Crowley, 1988).

Stated very simply, many drugs of abuse make the user feel good. As an example, consider that cocaine's effects have been likened to sexual orgasm. The rush from intraveneously administered narcotics has also been described as orgastic. Indeed, so powerful is cocaine for some users that they prefer the drug to a sex partner!

Human beings tend to follow the same rules of behavior that animals do. If a certain behavior increases an individual's sense of pleasure or decreases his or her discomfort, the person is likely to repeat that behavior. On the other hand, if a certain behavior increases the individual's sense of discomfort or reduces his or her sense of pleasure, the person is unlikely to repeat that behavior. Furthermore, an *immediate* consequence (either reward or punishment) has a stronger impact on behavior than a *delayed* consequence.

When these rules of behavior are applied to substance abuse, one discovers that the immediate consequence of chemical use (the immediate pleasure) has a stronger impact on behavior than the delayed consequence (possible addiction or disease at an unspecified later date). Thus, it should not be surprising that people are tempted to use chemicals again and again, given the immediate pleasure they derive. If every time you used a certain drug you ended up feeling like a horse had just kicked you in the head, how tempted would you be to use that drug again and again?

Social Learning

Surprisingly, there are many people who do not find drugs of abuse immediately pleasurable. Indeed, sometimes an individual must be taught first to recognize the drug's effects and then to interpret them as pleasurable. For example, first-time marijuana users must often be taught by their drug-using peers how to smoke it and how to recognize its effects. Then, they need to be told why marijuana intoxication is so pleasurable (Kandel & Raveis, 1989; Peele, 1985). A similar learning process takes place with heroin users. First-time heroin users are often taught by those who are more experienced what to look for in terms of effects and why the drug-induced feelings are so desirable (Lingeman, 1974).

First-time drinkers also need coaching. It is not uncommon for the first-time drinker to become so ill after a night's drinking that he or she will swear never to drink again. However, more experienced drinkers will help the novice learn *how* to drink, *what* effects to look for, and *why* these alcohol-induced physical sensations are so pleasurable. This feedback is often informal—it may come from a "drinking buddy," newspaper articles, advertisements, television programs, conversations with friends and coworkers, or casual observations of others who are drinking. The outcome of this social-learning process is that the novice drinker is taught how to drink and how to enjoy the alcohol he or she consumes.

Individual Expectations

Another factor that influences an individual's decision as to whether or not to use a specific chemical is the person's expectations for the drug. We have already mentioned that expectations for a drug exert a strong influence on how the drugs' effects are perceived. For example, recall the study by Gottleib et al. (1987) in which subjects who believed they were chewing nicotine-containing gum reported fewer withdrawal symptoms than those who were not given gum. It did not matter whether or not the gum actually contained nicotine. The critical factor was the expectations for the gum.

Brown, Goldman, Inn, and Anderson (1980) attempted to identify the common expectations that people in this culture have for alcohol. They found that their subjects expected alcohol to enhance life experiences, magnify physical and social pleasure, and improve sexual performance. Further, they found that their subjects fully expected that moderate alcohol use would increase social aggressiveness, make them more assertive, and reduce tension.

Mirin, Weiss, and Greenfield (1991) have found that an individual's expectations for LSD is one of the factors that might contribute to the so-called bad trip. Novice LSD users are more likely to anticipate adverse consequences as a result of using the drug than are more experienced users. This anxiety seems to help set the stage for a negative drug experience, or bad trip.

Thus, an individual's expectations for alcohol or any other chemical is one factor that influences his or her decision as to whether or not to use it. Individual expectations express themselves in two ways. First, if a person's expectations concerning the use of a specific drug are extremely negative, he or she will not even experiment with that chemical. For example, if you suggest to someone that he or she experiment with a well-known poison, such as cyanide, the usual response will be something like "Are you, nuts, or something?"

Secondly, for the individual who does choose to use a certain drug, his or her expectations for that drug will influence how its effects are perceived. The individual's expectations for a drug's effects are often learned from other, more experienced, chemical users. As stated previously, through formal and informal feedback mechanisms, a given individual might learn (a) how to use a drug of abuse, (b) what to look for from that drug, and (c) why the effects are so desirable. Based on all of this information, the individual will then evaluate his or her experience with the drug to decide if it was rewarding or not.

Social Reinforcement

In exploring why people choose to use drugs, cultural factors also must be considered. A given individual's decision to use or not use chemicals is made within the context of the culture of which that person is a member. Each culture is marked by certain attitudes and beliefs that govern the use of mood-altering chemicals (Leigh, 1985). These cultural attitudes and beliefs, which have evolved over generations, form the framework within which the individual's decision about chemical use is made. They also provide a standard by which the individual's chemical use is measured.

As we noted in Chapter 1, there was class-specific patterns of drug use, at least prior to the Vietnam conflict (Franklin, 1987). This implies that an individual's social class helped to shape his or her drug-use pattern. Different social groups had different "acceptable" drugs of abuse. This fact is also attested to by Nathan (1980).

Peele (1985) agrees that cultural influences are significant determinants of drug-use patterns. Indeed, he states:

> In cultures where use of a substance is comfortable, familiar, and socially regulated both as to style of use and appropriate time and place for such use, addiction is less likely and may be practically unknown. (p. 106)

Thus, according to Peele, it is only if a given society fails to regulate how, when, and where a chemical may be used that chemical abuse becomes a problem. It is Peele's position that substance abuse is a problem because society fails to regulate *appropriate* substance use—not because it fails to eliminate drug use by the members of the society.

The Jewish and Italian-American cultures provide excellent examples of the power of social rules to govern chemical use. In both of these cultures, drinking traditionally has been limited mainly to religious or family celebrations. Excessive drinking is strongly discouraged, and "proper" (socially acceptable) drinking behavior is modeled by adults during religious or family activities. It is no coincidence that these two cultural groups have relatively low rates of alcoholism.

Peele (1984) notes that Chinese-American adults also model proper drinking behavior for their children. Traditionally, alcohol has not been viewed as a rite of passage into adulthood nor has its use been associated with social power. By contrast, Irish-Americans viewed alcohol use far more liberally, as a rite of passage, and peer groups encouraged the use of alcohol. It is for this reason that Peele (1984, 1985) concludes that the Irish-American subculture subsequently demonstrated higher rates of alcoholism than the Chinese-Americans.

Kunitz and Levy (1974) explored the different drinking patterns of the Navaho and Hopi Indians. These tribes co-exist in the same part of the country and share similar genetic histories. However, Navaho tribal customs hold that public group drinking is acceptable, while solitary drinking is a mark of deviance. For the Hopi, however, drinking is more likely to be a solitary experience because alcohol use is not tolerated within the tribe. Those who are seen drinking are shunned. These two groups, living in close geographic proximity, clearly demonstrate how different social groups develop different guidelines regulating alcohol use.

In some subcultures, an individual's use of chemicals is seen as a sign of maturity, with the specific drugs being abused serving as a signpost of the individual's "growth." For example, in the United States, adolescents often look upon drinking as a sign of their entry into adulthood, almost as a "rite of passage" (Leigh, 1985). Within this context, it should not be surprising to learn that the adolescent subculture frequently encourages repeated episodes of chemical abuse (Swaim, Oetting, Edwards, & Beauvais, 1989).

In this section, our discussion so far has been limited to the use of alcohol. This is because alcohol is the most common recreational drug in the United States. However, the American Indians of the Southwest frequently ingest mushrooms with hallucinogenic potential as part of their religious ceremonies. In the Mideast, alcohol is prohibited, but hashish is an accepted recreational drug. In both cultures, strict social rules dictate when these substances can be used, the conditions under which they can be used, and the penalties for unacceptable substance use.

The point to remember is that each culture provides its members with guidance about what is acceptable or unacceptable substance use. But within each culture there are various subgroups that may adopt the parent culture's standards only to a limited extent. For example, in one subgroup the use of alcohol might be strictly prohibited. Another subgroup might permit the use of alcohol only on religious holidays, while still a third might allow the rare social use of alcohol. Finally, other subgroups might permit free use of alcohol, but with limits as to an acceptable level of intoxication or frequency of use.

Thus, even within a single culture, there will be subgroups (or social groups) that have different standards from those of the parent culture. The relationship between the various social groups and the parent culture is illustrated in Figure 16-1.

However, it should be pointed out that there is also a feedback mechanism between individuals and the social groups they belong to. While an individual's behavior is shaped, at least in part, by the social group that he or she might belong to, the individual will also help to shape the behavioral expectations of the social group by choosing whom to associate with. For example, alcoholics (and, other drug users) tend to drift towards social groups where the use of their drug is at least tolerated, if not actively encouraged. At the same time, addicts avoid social groups where their drug use is discouraged.

Kandel and Raveis (1989) found that one important predictor of whether or not an individual will use cocaine is whether he or she has friends who use cocaine. Furthermore, a given individual's cocaine-use pattern is extremely similar to that of his or her friends. Those individuals who use cocaine tend to

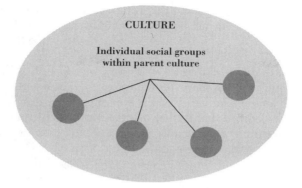

FIGURE 16-1   The relationship between individual social groups and the parent culture.

associate with others who also use cocaine; those who avoid cocaine use tend to associate with other nonusers.

In a study by Simpson, Crandall, Davage, and Pava-Krueger (1981), 60% of their sample population of narcotics addicts spent a lot of time engaged in "street" leisure activities prior to their participation in a substance-abuse treatment program. Their recreational activities centered on behaviors involving other addicted individuals. After the completion of treatment, only 13% of the sample continued to associate with active narcotics addicts.

Once an individual is aware of societal guidelines and has been provided with information about the effects of different chemicals, he or she is then faced with a decision. One option is to adopt the cultural standards and find a social group to join that also endorses these standards. Or, the individual might find that the cultural standards are inconsistent with personal values and choices and seek a different social group to belong to that is more consistent with his or her beliefs.

In terms of drug use, the individual who has tried chemicals and has found them physically and psychologically rewarding must then evaluate whether there are social rewards for the drug use or social sanctions against it. If there are social rewards, and if the user has found the drug experience to be rewarding, then he or she is likely to use the chemical again.

If, on the other hand, there are social sanctions against the use of the chemical, the individual must (a) try to find a way to reconcile further use of the drug while remaining in the same social group, (b) try to discontinue use of the drug, or (c) try to find a different group that will tolerate continued drug use.

Although most people do not think in these exact terms, their thinking parallels these themes. For example, there are many people who, if questioned, will admit to being "closet" drug users. They go to great trouble to hide their use of alcohol or other recreational chemicals from neighbors and friends. The man or woman who sneaks around the neighborhood hiding empty alcohol bottles in the trash cans of neighbors is attempting to reconcile personal use of alcohol with social expectations. If too many empty alcohol bottles were noticed in his or her own trash, it might lead to unpleasant questions or suspicions. So, it is better to hide the evidence than run the risk of discovery.

There are also those who will, if closely questioned, admit to having experimented with one or more of the drugs of abuse. But, these same individuals will also explain that while they found the drug's effects to be pleasurable, they decided that further use was not possible given their social status, and so gave it up. For example, if one were to question people who had used marijuana and hallucinogens during the "hippie" era of the late 1960s and early 1970s, many of them would refer to the "phase" that they were going through, adding that as they grew older they found chemical use to be inconsistent with their growing maturity.

Unfortunately, there are also those who find that the chemical's effects are so desirable as to encourage further use, even in the face of social sanctions. Further, in the service of their drug use, they will drift toward social groups that accept and support it.

Life Goals

Still another factor that influences an individual's decision regarding drug use is whether or not the use of a specific drug or drugs is consistent with his or her long-term goals. This is rarely a problem with socially approved drugs, such as alcohol, and, to a lesser degree, tobacco. However, the junior executive who has just won a much hoped-for promotion, only to find that the new position is with a company with a "no smoking" policy, might find that giving up the smoking habit is a serious problem if he or she smokes.

In such a case, the individual in question has evaluated the degree to which further use of tobacco is consistent with the life goal of a successful career. However, there are also many cases in which the individual would elect to search for a new position rather than accept the restriction on chemical use. The point to remember is that the individual must evaluate whether or not the use of alcohol or other recreational drugs is consistent with his or her long-term goals.

A Summary of Factors

All of the factors we have discussed have been found to play a role in a given individual's decision to begin to use alcohol or other drugs. A flow chart of the decision-making process is shown in Figure 16-2.

It should be noted, however, that we are discussing the individual's decision to use alcohol or drugs on a recreational basis. The factors that play a role in *initiating* chemical use are different from those that play a role in *maintaining* chemical use (Zucker & Gomberg, 1986). There is increasing evidence that many people will use alcohol or other drugs of abuse strictly on a recreational basis. As such, these people will limit their chemical use to

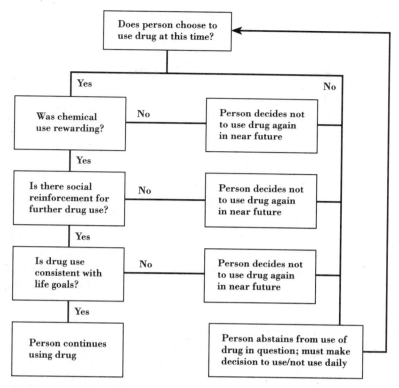

FIGURE 16-2 The decision-making process.

specific periods or use one or more drugs for a period of time on an experimental basis and then discontinue the practice.

Unfortunately, some people will not be able to limit their chemical use
only to occasional episodes of recreational use. Although at first they use
drugs on a recreational basis, they progress to more serious levels of abuse, or
perhaps even addiction. It is not possible to determine which people are at
risk of progressing to these more serious levels. We do know, however, that
drug addiction is a very real problem for many people. We will now consider
this problem more closely.

WHY DO PEOPLE BECOME ADDICTED TO CHEMICALS?

The truth is that nobody really knows why some people become drug addicts.
Nobody has been able to say exactly how or why people progress from the
experimental use of chemicals to heavy use, and then on to substance abuse,
or even further to the point of drug addiction.

Goodwin (1989), drawing on the American Psychiatric Association's *Diagnostic and Statistical Manual of Mental Disorders*, identifies the following
nine criteria by which people are classified as addicted to chemicals:

1. preoccupation with use of the chemical between periods of use;
2. use of larger or more frequent doses of the chemical than had been anticipated;
3. the development of tolerance to the chemical;
4. a characteristic withdrawal syndrome from the chemical when it is discontinued;
5. use of the chemical to avoid or control withdrawal symptoms;
6. repeated efforts to cut back or stop drug use;
7. intoxication at inappropriate times (such as at work), or inability to function on a daily basis because of withdrawal symptoms;
8. a reduction in social, occupational, or recreational activities to accommodate further substance use; and
9. continuation of chemical use despite having suffered drug-related social, emotional, or physical problems.

Any combination of *four or more* of these signs would identify an individual as suffering from the "disease" of addiction. The "disease model" of substance abuse, or the "medical model" as it is also known, holds that (1) addiction is a medical disorder, just as cardiovascular disease or a hernia are medical disorders; (2) that there is a biological predisposition towards addiction; and (3) that the disease of addiction is progressive.

The medical model of addiction is a difficult aspect of drug abuse to write about. Although substance-abuse professionals often speak of *the* disease model of addiction, in reality there is no single, universally accepted disease model. Rather, there is a group of loosely allied researchers who believe that drug addiction is the outcome of a biomedical or psychobiological process. On the basis of this belief, they argue that chemical dependency should be classified as a "disease."

But there are also those who argue with equal fervor that alcohol and drug addiction in no sense meet the criteria for a "disease." Goodwin and Warnock (1991) refer to this basic disagreement between the mental health and medical professions as a "turf battle" (p. 485). The final victor in this war of words has yet to be declared.

At present, however, the treatment of chemical addiction in the United States is considered to fall within the realm of medicine. In this section, we will discuss the disease model of addiction along with some of the research that, according to proponents of this treatment model, supports the belief that the compulsive use of chemicals is a true "disease."

Jellinek's Model of Alcoholism

The work of E. M. Jellinek (1952, 1960) has had a profound impact on the evolution of the medical model of addiction. Jellinek concentrated on the prototypical addiction—alcoholism. Prior to the American Medical Association's decision to classify alcoholism as a formal "disease" in 1956, it was viewed as immoral behavior. Alcoholics were viewed as immoral individuals both by society at large and by the majority of physicians.

Jellinek (1952, 1960), like others before him, argued that alcoholism was actually a disease, like cancer or pneumonia. The disease of alcoholism had specific symptoms and a progressive course, according to Jellinek. The key elements in the Jellinek (1960) model are (a) a loss of control over one's drinking, (b) a progression through distinct phases or stages, and (c) if left untreated, the alcoholic's ultimate death.

In an early work on alcoholism, Jellinek (1952) describes the progression of alcohol addiction through four different stages. The first of these stages, which he terms the *prealcoholic phase*, is marked by the individual's use of alcohol for relief from social tensions. In the prealcoholic stage, the roots of the individual's loss of control are apparent. He or she is no longer drinking on a social basis, but has started to drink for relief from stress and anxiety.

As the individual uses more and more alcohol, he or she enters the second phase of alcoholism, or the *prodromal stage*. This second stage is marked by the development of memory blackouts, secret drinking (also known as hidden drinking), a preoccupation with alcohol use, and guilt over inappropriate behavior while intoxicated.

With continued use, the individual eventually becomes physically dependent on alcohol, a hallmark of what Jellinek terms the *crucial phase*. Other symptoms of this third stage are a loss of self-esteem, a loss of control over one's drinking, social withdrawal to accommodate alcohol use, self-pity, and a neglect of proper nutrition. During this phase, the individual attempts to reassert his or her control by entering into short periods of abstinence, only to return to the use of alcohol.

Eventually, the alcoholic enters the *chronic phase*. Symptoms of this phase include a deterioration of morality, drinking with social inferiors, the development of motor tremors, an obsession with drinking, and, for some, the use of "substitutes" when alcohol is not available (for example, rubbing alcohol). In Figure 16-3, these four stages of alcoholism are graphically depicted.

In 1960, Jellinek presented a theoretical model of alcoholism that was both an extension and a revision of his earlier work. According to Jellinek (1960), the alcoholic is unable to consistently predict how much he or she will drink at any given time. This model also refers to specific symptoms of alcoholism, including the physical, social, vocational, and emotional complications often experienced by the compulsive drinker. As before, Jellinek views alcoholism as having a progressive course that results in the individual's death, in the absence of medical intervention.

In his 1960 work, Jellinek went further than he had previously by attempting to classify different patterns of addictive drinking. As Dr. William Carpenter did in 1850, Jellinek came to view alcoholism as a disease that could take on a number of different forms (Lender, 1981). Dr. Carpenter thought that there were three types of alcoholics, but Jellinek identified five. He used the first five letters of the Greek alphabet for his designations, and admitted that other subtypes of alcoholism were possible in different parts of the world.

The first of Jellinek's (1960) subtypes of alcoholics is the *alpha* drinker.

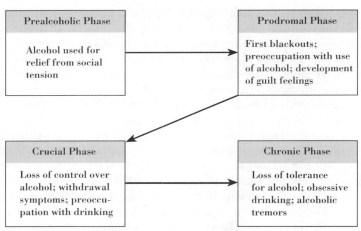

FIGURE 16-3 The four stages of alcoholism.

This individual is psychologically dependent on alcohol, but does not suffer from any of the physical complications caused by chronic alcohol use. According to Jellinek, the alpha drinker can actually abstain from alcohol use for short periods of time, but only under pressing circumstances. An example of the alpha drinker would be the business executive who "needs" a martini or two before dinner to unwind from the day's troubles.

As stated previously, Jellinek (1960) did not view the alpha pattern of drinking as reflecting a physical dependency on alcohol. Further, he did not believe that the alpha pattern of drinking was *automatically* progressive. Indeed, he felt that the pattern was likely to be quite stable for an extended period of time, as exemplified by the executive who confines alcohol intake to two (and only two!) martinis after work over the course of many years.

If the alpha drinking pattern were to evolve into another form of alcoholism, Jellinek believed that it would evolve into what he terms the *gamma* form of alcoholism. We will discuss the gamma pattern in more detail shortly. The point to remember here is that Jellinek (1960) viewed the alpha form as relatively stable, rarely progressing to more serious forms of alcohol use.

Jellinek (1960) also classifies some drinkers as *beta* alcoholics. The beta drinking pattern is very similar to the alpha pattern, but in addition to the psychological dependency on alcohol, the beta drinker also has physical complications from his or her alcohol use. These complications could include alcoholic gastritis and cirrhosis of the liver, both of which develop after extended periods of alcohol use. If the beta alcoholic progressed, it would also be to the gamma form of drinking, according to Jellinek.

Jellinek describes the *delta* drinker as one who demonstrates a physical dependence on alcohol, including the development of alcohol tolerance, "craving" when he or she cannot drink, and a loss of control over alcohol. However, the delta alcoholic would have few physical complications from alcohol use, or possibly none at all. By contrast, the gamma alcoholic demonstrates physical withdrawal symptoms, "craving," and medical complications caused by alcohol use. The gamma alcoholic also demonstrates a progressive loss of control over alcohol use, according to Jellinek. As we have noted, both the alpha and, less frequently, beta alcohol-use patterns could progress to the gamma pattern over time.

Finally, the *epsilon* alcoholic may best be classifed as the binge drinker. Jellinek states that this form of alcoholism is the one least frequently encountered in the United States, where the alpha and the gamma patterns are most common. Jellinek also refers to other culturally related patterns of drinking (for example, "fiesta drinking") that are worthy of study, but possibly not true forms of alcoholism.

Jellinek's (1960) model of alcoholism offers a number of advantages to physicians. First, it provides a diagnostic framework within which they can classify different patterns of drinking. This framework is considerably less restrictive than the simple yes/no distinction as to whether individuals are or are not alcoholics. Secondly, one should recall that prior to Jellinek's (1960) work alcoholism was viewed as a moral weakness. His model of alcoholism as a physical disease allowed for "unprejudiced access" to medical treatment (Vaillant, 1990, p. 5).

Surprisingly, Jellinek's (1952, 1960) theoretical model has become the standard model for alcoholism in the United States. It has been used, without significant modification, since the time that it was introduced. Further, although Jellinek's model was developed as a theory for alcoholism, it has been applied to the use of other drugs.

The Genetic Inheritance Theories

In the years that have passed since Jellinek's work, researchers have started to explore the genetics of alcoholism and other forms of drug addiction. Researchers have long been aware that alcoholism appears to run in families. But it has only been in the past 50 years that they have had research tools necessary to explore the genetics of alcoholism. Proponents of the disease model of addiction often point to these studies as evidence that alcoholism (and, by extension, the other forms of addiction) are actually biomedical disorders.

One of the most extensive research studies exploring the genetics of alcoholism was conducted by Cloninger, Gohman, and Sigvardsson (1981). They used the adoption records of some 3,000 individuals from Sweden, where extensive records are kept on all parties in adoption cases. The reseachers found that the children of alcoholic parents were likely to grow up to be alcoholic themselves, even in cases where they were reared by nonalcoholic adoptive parents almost from birth.

It was also found that the children of alcoholic parents fell into two groups. The first group generally began to drink in moderation. It was only later in life that their drinking progressed to the point where they could be classified as alcoholic. Even so, Cloninger et al. found that these individuals tended to function within society, and only rarely demonstrated antisocial behaviors. These individuals have come to be known as "Type 1" alcoholics (Goodwin & Warnock, 1991).

Further, Cloninger et al. found that for this group, there was a strong environmetal impact. Even in cases where genetic inheritance seemed to predispose the child to alcoholism, if he or she had been adopted by a middle-class family in infancy, the chances of actually being alcoholic in adulthood were no greater than chance. However, if the child had been adopted into a poor family, it was more likely that he or she would grow up to be an alcoholic. These findings suggest a strong environmental influence on the evolution of alcoholism in this subgroup, despite an individual's genetic inheritance.

According to Cloninger et al., the second, smaller, group of alcoholics (all males) were more violent. These individuals, who are now known as "Type 2" alcoholics (Goodwin & Warnock, 1991), tended to be involved in criminal behavior. A male child born to a "violent" alcoholic ran almost a 20% chance of himself becoming alcoholic, no matter what the social status of his adoptive parents. This suggests a strong genetic influence for this subgroup of alcoholics.

Over the past 50 years, a virtual flood of research has appeared in which various theories have been offered to the effect that alcoholics (or other addicts) are somehow different from nonaddicts. This research is far too extensive to review in this chapter, but the general themes are that alcoholics and nonalcoholics metabolize alcohol differently and at different sites, and that alcoholics react differently than nonalcoholics to the effects of the drug.

The general thrust of these research articles is that there is a biological difference between alcoholics and nonalcoholics. Recently, Blum et al. (1990) explored the possibility that a specific gene, known as the dopmanine D_2 receptor gene, was involved in the predisposition towards alcoholism.

Dopamine is one of the neurotransmitters affected by alcohol, and researchers have identified two different subtypes of receptors in the brain that respond to dopamine—the "D_1" and "D_2" receptors. In the Blum et al. (1990) study, samples of brain tissue from 70 cadavers were obtained. Half of the brain-tissue samples were from known alcoholics; the other half were from nonalcoholics. It was found that 77% of the alcoholics, but only 28% of the nonalcoholics, possessed the dopmanine D_2 receptor gene. These findings suggest a genetic basis for alcohol use, according to Blum et al.

In an extension of the original research, Noble, Blum, Ritchie, Montgomery, and Sheridan, (1991) used tissue samples from the brains of 33 known alcoholics and a matched group of 33 nonalcoholic controls. On the basis of their "blind" study of the genetic makeup of the tissue samples, there appeared to be strong evidence of a genetic foundation for severe alcoholism involving the D_2 dopamine receptor.[1]

---

[1]This study was "blind" in that the researchers conducted their experiments of the tissue samples without knowing whether any given sample was from the experimental (alcoholic) or control (nonalcoholic) group. In this way, the possibility that they would treat the samples differently was avoided.

As we will discuss in the next chapter, both the Blum et al. (1990) and the Noble et al. (1991) studies have been challenged by other researchers. Thus, the controversy over whether there are measurable biochemical or biophysical differences between alcoholics and nonalcoholics remains unanswered. At this point, clinical research points to such a difference, but no unequivocal biochemical or biophysical difference has been identified by researchers. The discovery of such a unique difference would provide a basis for the identification of the biological foundation of alcoholism, and, by extension, the other forms of drug addiction. For now, research in this area continues.

The Personality Predisposition Theories

Many researchers believe that substance abuse has its roots in the individual's personality. Indeed, many researchers have come to believe that there are personality patterns that predict subsequent chemical use. For example, a psychoanalytic therapist might view substance abuse as

> the behavioral manifestation of psychic imbalance arising from frustration, deprivation and emotional pain. (Smith, 1990, p. 62)

Within this broad definition, Horney (1964) views substance abuse as a reflection of emotional pain, where the individual attempts to blot out the anxiety that he or she has experienced in life. Khantzian (1985) suggests that some are drawn to narcotics because these drugs help to control internal feelings of rage and aggression. Others seem to be drawn to cocaine in their attempt to relieve feelings of depression (Kandel & Raveis, 1989).

Most certainly, there is evidence to suggest that individuals who abuse chemicals have suffered significant psychological trauma in their lives. Estimates of the numbers of female alcoholics who have either been neglected or sexually abused range from 40% to 70% (Coleman, 1988b). Fossum and Mason (1986) suggest an even higher figure, noting that some adolescent treatment centers have indicated that 75% of their female clients attest to having been sexually abused.

Clinical evidence would strongly suggest that sexual or physical abuse on the part of parents or significant others can leave deep emotional scars on a child. In adult life, these battered children may very well turn to drugs to help them deal with the emotional pain of having been physically, emotionally, and/or sexually abused (Kaufman, 1989).

Bradshaw (1988a) suggests that *all* compulsive behavior, including the compulsive use of chemicals, reflects an individual's attempt to escape the shame experienced in the family of origin. In response to the shame and pain of growing up in his own family, Bradshaw states: "I felt sane only when I was drunk" (p. 89). However, when a person compulsively uses one, and only one, method of escaping from the experience of shame, he or she becomes addicted to that system of control.

It should be noted, too, that compulsive behaviors are effective only in the short term. As Beattie (1989) observes, "compulsive behaviors may help us temporarily avoid feelings or problems, [but] they don't really stop the pain"

(p. 14). Thus, the individual is faced with the problem of how to cope with this pain time and time again.

Rapoport (1989) relates how a young adult male suffering from an obsessive-compulsive disorder (OCD) used drugs in order to self-medicate. Obsessive-compulsive disorder is a neurological disorder marked by unwelcome thoughts ("obsessions") and behaviors ("compulsions") that cause extreme distress, in many cases. The individual described by Rapoport found relief only through drugs that impacted on those neurons utilizing serotonin as the major neurotransmitter—especially LSD. The current treatment of choice for OCD is a group of antidepressants that increase the amount of serotonin available in the brain.

Rapoport goes on to suggest that many of those who use chemicals might be doing so in an attempt to self-medicate their distress, especially the distress caused by undiagnosed and untreated OCD. Indeed, alcohol and many of the drugs of abuse impact on those neurons that utilize serotonin as a neurotransmitter, lending support to Rapoport's suggestion. However, research to support this hypothesis is lacking.

In a series of research projects attempting to identify a pre-existing "alcoholic personality" (Hoffman, Loper, & Kammeier, 1974; Loper, Kammeier, & Hoffman, 1973), the researchers examined the Minnesota Multiphasic Personality Inventory (MMPI) profiles of 38 males who had taken the MMPI while they were students in college. These scores were then compared with MMPI profiles obtained from these same individuals following their admission to a chemical-dependency treatment program.

The two sets of profiles did reveal a tendency toward impulsive behavior, but they did not reveal any other sign of significant pathology. Despite findings, the authors hold that certain personality patterns predate the development of alcoholism and that these patterns can be uncovered by personality instruments such as the MMPI.

According to Weiss, Mirin, Griffin and Michael (1988), the psychiatric diagnoses of 149 cocaine abusers admitted to a private hospital from 1982 to 1986 reveal a shift in the personality types of those abusing cocaine. They noted that their sample of cocaine abusers were less likely to have mood disorders, but were more likely to suffer from personality disorders, especially the antisocial personality disorder. Thus, these cocaine users were unlikely to be attempting to self-medicate depressive feelings, as may have been true in the late 1970s and early 1980s. The current cocaine user is more likely to have a personality disorder than cocaine users in the past two decades, according to Weiss et al.

While at first glance the results obtained from the Weiss et al. (1988) study might seem to contradict the self-medication hypothesis advanced by Khantzian (1985), these results actually support Khantzian's theory. The antisocial personality is marked by a sense of inner emptiness (Ansevics & Doweiko, 1983). Given this fact, it is not surprising that those who suffer from the antisocial personality disorder might seek to fill this emptiness through the use of chemicals.

Addressing the treatment of alcoholism, S. Brown (1985) notes that the chemical a person uses provides *an illusion of control* over the harsh, painful feelings encountered in life. Franklin (1987) makes a similar observation, noting the opiates' ability to lift the addict from an ongoing depression. Franklin postulates that before drug use, this lifelong depression is perceived by the individual as a normal emotional state.

After being introduced to drugs, however, the individual comes to learn that their distress was not "normal." The narcotics provide at least the illusion of control over the depression that he or she has known throughout life. However, ultimately, the method of "control" comes to dominate the individual's life, and the person becomes addicted.

Alcohol is occasionally used in an attempt to self-medicate depression. However, because alcohol is itself a depressant, it can bring about a drug-induced depression through chronic use. Research findings suggest that the feelings of depression reported by alcoholics are alcohol-induced in the vast majority of cases (Willenbring, 1986). However, in about 5% of the cases, there is a primary depression that the person may be attempting to self-medicate through alcohol.

A concluding note   Research into whether there are certain personality characteristics that predispose a person to alcoholism or other forms of chemical abuse is quite suggestive. Although certain personality traits appear to be associated with chemical use or dependency, it is difficult to ascertain whether these personality traits precede the development of the drug dependency or if they are a result of the frequent use of chemicals. To date, no causal factor has been clearly identified, and research into possible personality factors that might predispose an individual to alcohol or substance abuse continues.

SUMMARY

In the past century, and most certainly in the last generation, researchers have approached the problem of alcohol and substance abuse from a range of different perspectives, collectively termed the "medical model." Many research studies have attemped to uncover differences between the psychological or biological predisposition of those who have become addicted to chemicals and those who have not. Different researchers have suggested that alcoholics differ from nonalcoholics along one dimension or another; however, to date, no universally accepted psychological or biological "marker" for alcoholism or drug abuse has been identified.

Chapter 17

ARE PEOPLE PREDESTINED
TO BECOME ADDICTS?

In the past century, researchers have approached the problem of alcohol and substance abuse from a number of different perspectives. As we discussed in the last chapter, there are those who believe that individuals who abuse chemicals do so because of a biological or psychological predisposition. As such, these theories are often said to reflect a "disease" model of chemical abuse. The individual is thought to abuse alcohol or drugs because of a flaw in their genetic or psychological makeup that is beyond their control. In a sense, the individual is viewed as predestined to abuse chemicals by his or her biological or psychological heritage.

The second school of thought maintains that there are *no* biological or psychological traits that predispose an individual to abuse chemicals. Advocates of this school argue that much of what we believe to be true about substance abuse is based on false assumptions. In this chapter, some of the arguments against the disease model of substance abuse will be examined.

REFLECTIONS ON THE DISEASE MODEL OF ADDICTION

One must always remember that the American concept of disease is viewed from the framework of medicine as practiced in the Western world. There are often subtle (and sometimes not so subtle) philosophical differences between the Western concept of disease and concepts that prevail in other parts of the world. Thus, to understand illness, one needs to understand the diagnostic system—the "yardstick," so to speak—by which disease is measured.

Within the framework of American medical practice, a "disease" has a biophysical base. In infectious diseases, this is the bacteria, virus, or fungus that invades the host organism. Another class of diseases are caused by genetic disorders, resulting in abnormal growth or functioning of the organism. In still a third class of diseases, the optimum functioning of the organism is disrupted by acquired trauma. In each case, the disease process prevents the organism from functioning as well as it could.

As noted in previous chapters, there are those who believe that there is a genetic "loading" for alcoholism, although the exact nature of predisposition has not been clearly identified (Goodwin & Warnock, 1991). The case for

190

a genetic predisposition to other forms of addiction is even weaker. But if a genetic predisposition exists for alcoholism, it is logical to assume that such a predisposition also exists for all forms of addiction. If it is true that there is a genetic predisposition for addictive behaviors, then chemical dependency is very much like a number of other physical disorders where there is a genetic predisposition. In this sense, substance abuse might be said to be a "disease."

Shortcomings of the Jellinek Model

In the 30 years since Jellinek advanced his theory, a number of flaws in his model have come to light. First, Jellinek (1960) based his work on mail surveys conducted with members of Alcoholics Anonymous (AA). But, of the many hundreds of surveys mailed out, only 98 reponses were received. Thus, Jellinek received a response from only a minority of those individuals he contacted. Yet it was on this data that he based his comprehensive theory of alcoholism.

As we will discuss in Chapter 30, members of AA are self-selected, and there is little evidence that they are representative of the majority of alcoholics. Further, Jellinek assumed that those individuals who responded to his survey did not differ in any way from those who failed to return the questionnaire. One must never assume that volunteers for a research project are representative of all those who were possible participants. One group of individuals agreed to participate in the study, whereas another group did not. If the two groups exhibit this important distinction, there may be other significant differences as well.

Despite a sample that was possibly nonrepresentative of the alcoholic population, Jellinek generalized his findings to build a model for *all* alcoholics. Since its introduction, his model has been used as the basis for planning treatment programs for untold thousands of alcoholics who have entered treatment in the years since he first advanced his theory.

Further, as Vaillant (1983) observes, the Jellinek model fails to account for the fact that drinking patterns often change over time. The steady, heavy drinker may, in response to internal or external pressure, cut back to the occasional social use of alcohol. The rare social drinker may, in a period of stress, drink to excess day after day for a period of time, and then return to a pattern of only occasional alcohol use. As a generation of researchers have discovered, when used in longitudinal research, the Jellinek (1960) model begins to break down.

Although Jellinek advanced the theory that alcoholism is a progressive disorder, research has challenged the idea that alcoholism is *automatically* progressive (Peele, 1989; Vaillant, 1983). Indeed, it has been postulated that alcoholism does not reflect a total loss of control. There is strong evidence that alcoholics tend to regulate their drinking to achieve a desired emotional state (Peele, 1989). At best, then, the alcoholic might be said to demonstrate *inconsistent* control over his or her drinking (Vaillant, 1990). There objections raise further doubt as to the validity of Jellinek's (1960) model of alcoholism.

To be fair, Jellinek did not claim that his model represented the perfect theory of alcoholism. Rather, he proposed it as a *preliminary theory* of alcoholism. Nevertheless, and in spite of its subsequently identified short-comings, it has become "virtually gospel in the field of alcohol studies" (Lender, 1981, p. 25). Moreover, Jellinek most certainly did not intend his model to be applied to addictions other than alcoholism. Thus, one of the cornerstones of the medical model of addiction appears, on close examination, to be seriously flawed.

Is Alcoholism Purely a Genetically Mediated Disorder?

We have already described several studies suggesting a possible genetic predisposition to addiction. However, in spite of continued research, the nature and impact of this genetic loading remains unclear. For example, the research of Cloninger et al. (1981) was briefly reviewed in the previous chapter. Their work is often used by proponents of the medical model to support the contention that there is a biological predisposition for alcoholism. Although the original intent of Cloninger et al. was to explore the genetic basis of alcoholism, they were surprised to also find evidence suggesting a strong environmental impact on the development of this disorder. Even in cases where genetic inheritance seemed to predispose a child to alcoholism, if that child had been adopted by a middle-class family in infancy, his or her chances of actually being alcoholic in adulthood were found to be no greater than chance.

If, on the other hand, the child was adopted by a poor family, the chances were greater that he or she would grow up to be an alcoholic. These findings suggest a strong environmental influence on the evolution of alcoholism, in spite of the individual's genetic inheritance for "Type 1" alcoholism.

Type 1 alcoholism has also been termed *milieu-limited* alcoholism, and it was the most common form of alcoholism encountered by Cloninger et al. The "typical" Type 1 alcoholic could be either male or female and engaged in nonproblematic alcohol use until around the age of 25. In the average case, the researchers found that the individual did not begin to drink to excess until after the age of 25. Further, even when the individual's drinking became a problem, it was often not recognized, and usually went untreated.

As you might recall, a second, smaller, group of alcoholics identified by Cloninger et al. were more violent and tended to be involved in criminal behavior. Alcoholics in this group tended to be all male and were classified as "Type 2" alcoholics. Type 2 alcoholism is often called *male-limited* alcohol-ism. The adopted male offspring of a "violent alcoholic" was found to run almost a 20% risk of himself becoming alcoholic, regardless of the social status of his adoptive parents.

However, here again, the statistics are misleading. Even though almost 20% of the male children born to a violent alcoholic themselves become alcoholic, over 80% do not follow this pattern. This would suggest that other factors (for example, environmental) could play a role in the evolution of alcoholism for Type 2 alcoholics, as well as for Type 1 alcoholics.

Murray, Clifford, and Gurling (1983) compared the drinking status of identical and fraternal twins on the assumption that the identical twins, who are by definition genetically the same, would demonstrate more consistent rates of alcoholism than the fraternal twins. However, findings were not as anticipated, casting doubt on the hypothesis that alcoholism is purely a genetically mediated disorder.

Pickens et al. (1991) attempted to isolate the impact of genetic inheritance on the development of alcoholism for pairs of both male and female twins. According to their analysis, "the influence of genetic factors appears to be somewhat weaker than the influence of shared environmental factors, especially for female subjects" (p. 25). Thus, while they did find evidence supporting a biological predisposition to alcoholism for both male and female pairs of twins, the data also suggested that environmental factors play a significant role in the development of alcohol-use patterns.

Indeed, in the case of identical twins, one of whom is alcoholic, the concordance rate for alcoholism in both twins is only 58% (Schuckit, 1987). In other words, when one identical twin is alcoholic, there is only a 58% chance that the other twin will be alcoholic, too. If alcoholism were mediated *only* by an individual's genetic inheritance, then one would expect that identical twins would have a concordance rate of nearly 100%, given their identical genetic makeup. Clearly, while there is a possible genetic component to alcoholism, there are also other factors that influence its development.

These findings are very similar to those of Swinson (1980), who explored the question of genetic and environmental factors in the development of substance abuse. According to Swinson, genetic inheritance appears to be stronger in men than in women, whereas the environmental factors are stronger in women than in men. Pickens et al. (1991) also report that the impact of genetic inheritance and environmental factors is not the same for both sexes.

According to Schuckit (1987), certain environmental forces play a strong role in the development of alcoholism. These factors may include an unstable home environment in the early years, the father's relatively low-status occupation, and an extended neonatal hospital stay for the infant who would later grow up to become an alcoholic.

The Dopamine D_2 Connection

In the previous chapter, the association between alcoholism and the presence of the D_2 receptor gene within the brain was discussed (Blum et al., 1990; Noble et al., 1991). This line of research, while suggestive of a possible biological foundation for alcoholism, has not been supported by subsequent research (Bolos et al., 1991; Parsian & Cloninger, 1991).

For example, Bolos et al. used a different, more extensive methodology than did Blum et al. In the Bolos et al. study, subjects were subtyped according to the age of onset of alcoholism, severity of alcoholism, evidence of antisocial personality disorder, and family history. According to the findings, there is apparently no widespread association between the D$_2$ receptor gene and alcoholism.

Parsian et al. (1991) also explored the genetics of alcoholism, concluding that "[no] specific gene influencing the risk or expression of alcoholism has been identified" (p. 655). Although they acknowledge that there may be several possible biological factors, according to their findings the D$_2$ dopamine receptor gene does not appear to be the biological foundation for alcoholism.

Further Criticism of the Disease Model of Addiction

No matter how you look at it, addiction remains a most curious "disease." Even Vaillant (1983), who has long been a champion of the disease model of alcoholism, concedes that to make alcoholism fit into the disease model it must be "shoehorned" (p. 4). Further, according to Vaillant, even if alcoholism is a disease, "both its etiology and its treatment are largely social" (p. 4).

Dreger (1986) agrees that alcoholism is not easily explained by the medical model. He states that alcoholism is a rather unusual "disease" in that it is foisted on the public:

[It is] promoted by every Madison Avenue technique and by every type of peer pressure one can imagine. No other disease is thus promoted. (p. 322)

This observation raises an interesting point. If addiction is indeed a "disease," why then is drinking encouraged by commercial means?

The role of individual responsibility   Modern medicine "always gives the credit to the disease rather than the person" (B. S. Siegel, 1989, p. 12), and this is certainly true for the addictive disorders (Peele, 1989; Tavris, 1990). For example, Pratt (1990) argues that "activation of the disease of addiction, once an individual is exposed to activating agents, is genetically predetermined" (p. 18). From this perspective, once an individual has been exposed to the "activating agents," he or she ceases to exist, except as a genetically preprogrammed disease process!

According to Dole and Nyswander (1965), *even a single dose* of narcotics forever changes an addict's brain structure, making the addict crave further narcotics use. But if narcotics are so incredibly potent, then one must account for the thousands of patients who receive doses of narcotics for the control of pain for extended periods of time without developing a "craving" for narcotics after their treatment ends. Further, Dole and Nyswander's (1965) theory fails to account for the many individuals who "chip" (occasionally use) narcotics for years, without becoming addicted to these drugs.

The concept on which methadone maintenance is based is the belief that narcotics are so powerful that just a single dose takes away all of the individual's power of self-determination. This tendency of the medical model to devalue individual's power is also evident in Blum and Payne's (1991) contention that alcohol causes an "irresistible craving" (p. 237). Yet, alcoholics are in agreement that they can resist the craving for alcohol, *if the reward for doing so is high enough.* Many alcoholics successfully resist the desire to drink for weeks, months, years, or decades, casting doubt on the concept of an "irresistible" craving. Indeed, in reviewing the problem of relapse, one is left with the impression that it is not so much a matter of this craving that causes a return to chemicals as it is a combination of other factors.

It goes without saying that once a person has been diagnosed as having a certain "disease," he or she is expected to take certain steps toward recovery. According to the medical model, the "proper way to do this is through following the advice of experts (e.g., doctors) in solving the problem" (Maisto & Conners, 1988, p. 425). Unfortunately, as we noted in Chapter 1, *physicians are not required to be trained in either the identification or the treatment of the addictions.* The medical model of addiction thus lacks internal consistency. While medicine claims that addiction is a "disease," it does not train its practitioners in how to treat this ailment.

Problems in defining the addictive disorders   At this point, nobody seems to know what the addictive disorders actually are. In his classic (1972) paper, Szasz concluded that alcoholism was simply a "bad habit" (p. 84). Admittedly, the individual should attempt to overcome bad habits, but this does not make them diseases. Szasz warned that "if we choose to call bad habits 'diseases,' there is no limit to what we may define as a disease" (p. 84). Twenty years later, Szasz's warning seems particularly relevant. Leo (1990) states:

> As addictions have been converted into diseases (alcoholism), bad habits have been upgraded and transformed into addictions (yesterday's hard-to-break smoking habit is today's nicotine addiction). (p. 16)

Leo contends that the outcome of this transformation has been the birth of a multitude of "pseudo ailments" through which people have been able to avoid responsibility for a variety of socially unacceptable behaviors. Indeed, so pervasive has this process become that Leo refers to the current generation as the "golden age of exoneration" (p. 16). Further, although we don't have a cure for every disease, as Ehrenreich (1992) observes, one of the benefits of modern medicine is that "there's no reason we can't have a disease for every cure" (p. 88). Thus, the "disease" label is applicable to a wide range of conditions. We have the cure, now all we need is the proper disease to apply it to.

In a later essay, Szasz (1988) suggests that drug abuse is a "mythical disease" (p. 319). He points out that, in terms of value, drugs are essentially neutral. It does not matter whether the specific drug in question is a natural agent, such as morphine, or the product of human ingenuity, such as fentanyl. According to Szasz, *by themselves, drugs are neither good nor bad.* It is the *way in which the drugs are used* that determines their worth.

Szasz (1988) further notes that society's decision to classify some drugs as "dangerous" and others as socially acceptable is arbitrary, based not on scientific studies, but on "religious or political (ritual, social) considerations" (p. 316). He also charges that the current "war" on drugs is really a "war on human desire" (p. 322). The problem is not so much that people use chemicals, according to Szasz, but that people desire to use them for personal pleasure.

The unique nature of addictive disorders   In spite of all the research that has been conducted over the years, an important fact continues to be overlooked. Unlike the other diseases, drug abuse and addiction requires the *active participation* of the "victim." The addictive disorders do not force themselves on the individual in the same sense that an infection might. Alcohol or drugs do not magically appear in an individual's bloodstream, despite what some would have us believe.

Rather, the "victim" of addiction must go through several steps to introduce a chemical into his or her body. Consider heroin addiction, for example. The addict must obtain the money necessary to buy the drug. Then, he or she must find somebody who is selling herion and actually buy some for use. Next, the "victim" must prepare the heroin for injection (mixing the powder with water, heating the mixture, pouring it into a syringe), find a vein to inject the drug into, and then insert the needle into the vein. Finally, after all of these steps, the individual must then actively inject the heroin into his or her body.

This is a rather complicated chain of events, each of which involves the active participation of the individual—the so-called victim of the process. If it took as much time and energy to "catch" a cold, pneumonia, or cancer, it is doubtful that *any* of us would ever be sick a day in our lives!

Another, indirect, challenge to the disease model of alcoholism comes from Viktor Frankl (1978), a psychiatrist interested in the issue of psychosis. Psychosis is another disorder in which there appears to be a strong genetic component, as is the case with drug addiction. Frankl (1978) describes psychosis as

> a matter of the bodily system's biochemistry. However, what the patient makes of his psychosis is entirely the property of his human personality. The psychosis that afflicts him is biochemical, but how he reacts to it, what he invests in it, the content with which he fills it—all this is his personal creation, the human work into which he has molded his suffering (p. 60).

Thus, in Frankl's (1978) opinion, the individual retains responsibility and the power of choice in the face of a genetically influenced disorder such as psychosis.

Much the same might be said of chemical addiction. Evidence suggests a possible biological predisposition toward alcoholism. However, the individual's reaction to the addiction—what he or she invests in the addiction—is the personal creation of the addict. Thus, the individual retains responsibility for personal behavior, even if he or she has a "disease" such as addiction (Vaillant, 1983, 1990).

In the past 50 years, proponents of the medical model of alcoholism have attempted to identify the biological foundation for abusive drinking. Over the years, there has been a virtual flood of research articles, many of which report findings that alcoholics (a) seem to metabolize alcohol differently than nonalcoholics or (b) seem to be relatively insensitive (or, depending on the research study, more sensitive) to the effects of alcohol as compared with nonalcoholics. Proponents of the medical model of addiction often point to these studies as evidence of a biological predisposition toward alcoholism.

However, despite the fact that it is more than a decade old, Nathan's (1980) observation continues to ring true for researchers in the field of addiction, namely:

> No differences have been found in the rate of metabolism, route of metabolism, site of metabolism, or susceptibility to the effects of drugs, between people who become addicts and those who do not. (p. 243)

Thus, at this point, it does not appear that the disease model of addiction *as it now stands* provides the ultimate answer to the question of why people become addicted to drugs of abuse.

The disease model as theory   Treadway (1990) suggests that the disease model can serve as a useful frame of reference to help patients understand their compulsion. He notes, however, that mental health professionals tend to become uncomfortable when it is presented as scientific fact. Indeed, proponents of the disease model of addiction do tend to speak of it not as a theoretical model, but as an established fact.

Further, proponents of the disease model tend to be quite zealous in defending it against criticism. Indeed, many seem to have adopted a "cultlike" philosophy, in which dissenters are viewed as unenlightened savages. It is not uncommon for those who question the disease model to be met with such comments as "If you *really* understood alcoholism, you would see that it *is* a disease," or "Obviously, you do not really understand alcoholism."

An unfortunate tendency within science is that once a certain theoretical viewpoint has become established, proponents of that position work to protect it from both internal and external criticism (Astrachan & Tischler, 1984). This tendency is all too apparent in the case of the disease model of addiction. The current atmosphere is one in which legitimate debate over strengths and weaknesses of the different models of addiction is discouraged. There is only one "true" path to enlightenment, according to proponents of the disease model, and its wisdom should not be questioned.

The tendency for proponents of the disease model to turn a deaf ear to other viewpoints is exacerbated by political and economic forces. According to Fingarette (1988), in the United States the disease model has become "big politics and big business" (p. 64). In fact, it has formed the basis of a massive "treatment" industry, into which many billions of dollars and untold amounts of human energy have been invested. Thus, the medical model has taken on a life of its own. Peele (1988) states:

> [The] disease model has been so profitable and politically successful that it has spread to include problems of eating, child abuse, gambling, shopping, premenstrual tension, compulsive love affairs, and almost every other form of self-destructive behavior. (p. 67)

What is surprising is not that the disease model exists, but that it has become so politically successful in the United States despite evidence showing that current treatment methods for the addictions are possibly *less effective than doing nothing* for the individual (Peele, 1989). Vaillant (1983), in his exploration of the disease of alcoholism, concludes that there is no significant difference in "recovery" rates between those who are treated for alcoholism and those who are not. A number of other studies have reached similar conclusions.

After some 50 years of claiming that the addictions are diseases, proponents of the medical model are hardly likely to admit to insurance companies or to the public that they were wrong, or that their methods fail to work. Rather, as Peele (1989) points out, when the "treatment" of an addictive disorder is unsuccessful, the blame is put on the patient. He or she "did not want to quit," or "was still in denial" of having an addictive disorder, or any of a thousand other excuses. The blame is *never* placed on the "disease" model, despite all the evidence that it has not been successful as applied to the addictive disorders.

SOME TENTATIVE CONCLUSIONS CONCERNING THE DISEASE MODEL OF ADDICTION

In exploring the interaction between environmental factors and genetic heritage, Loranger and Tulis (1985) acknowledge evidence of a genetic predisposition to either mild or severe alcohol abuse. But, they conclude, "environmental factors largely determine the severity of the abuse" (p. 156). Tarter (1988) agrees that there are "inherited behavioral traits" (p. 189) that predispose an individual to substance abuse, including alcoholism. But he, too, notes that research has not been able to identify the specific environmental factor, nutritional deficit, or genetic pattern that will bring about addiction.

In their summary of the current state of the research attempting to identify a biological predisposition toward addictive behavior, Goodwin and Warnock (1991), state that while alcoholism is known to run in certain families, "we do not believe that alcoholism definitely has been shown to be genetic" (p. 485). Finally, according to the University of California, Berkeley (1990d), in spite of significant efforts to identify a psychological or biological predisposition toward addiction, "there's no proof that anyone is chemically, genetically or psychologically doomed" (p. 2).

Thus, although the disease model of chemical dependency has dominated the treatment of substance abuse in the United States, it is not without its critics. Interestingly, the medical model of addiction has not found wide acceptance beyond the borders of the United States.

Variations on the Personality Predisposition Theories of Substance Abuse

Personality factors have long been thought to play a role in the development of addiction (Jenike, 1989; Butcher, 1988). There are a number of variations on this "predisposing personality" theme. For example, Tarter (1988) notes that the personality characteristics of the antisocial personality disorder and certain neurotic traits might increase the risk of subsequent addiction. Along these same lines, Jenike (1989) identifies a history of antisocial behavior as being one factor that predicted whether or not American servicemen who had used opiates in Vietnam would continue to use them after returning home.

The predisposing personality position is strongly deterministic and seeks to find factors that might predict vulnerability toward addiction. However, such theoretical models do not allow for more than a general statement that certain personality characteristics might increase the long-term risk that a person will become addicted.

In the previous chapter, we discussed a series of research projects that tried to identify a pre-existing "alcoholic personality" (Hoffman et al., 1974; Loper et al., 1973). The Minnesota Multiphasic Personality Inventory (MMPI) profiles of 38 males who had taken the MMPI while they were college students were compared with MMPI profiles obtained from these same individuals following their admission to a chemical-dependency treatment program.

You may recall that although the two sets of profiles did reveal a tendency toward impulsive behavior on the part of the students, they failed to reveal any other sign of significant pathology. In spite of this fact, it was concluded that there were personality patterns that predated the development of alcoholism and that these factors could be measured by such personality instruments as the MMPI.

What these research projects did not attempt to ascertain, however, was how many students who had the supposedly predisposing personality characteristics when they first took the MMPI while in college subsequently displayed no evidence of ever becoming addicted to chemicals. Thus, it is not known whether the personality patterns identified in the studies were a significant indicator of future addiction for the majority of the alcoholics studied, or only a pattern that was common both to addicted and nonaddicted individuals for reasons that had nothing to do with a predisposition toward alcoholism.

There are those who challenge the deterministic viewpoint that there are pre-existing personality characteristics that predict addiction (Blume, 1989; Nathan, 1988). These researchers point to the fact that there are no consistent psychometric patterns that reliably differentiate future alcoholics from those who will not become alcoholic. Further, Nathan (1988) postulates that the characteristics of the so-called addictive personality found by earlier researchers actually might reflect a misdiagnosis. He suggests that previous research confuses the antisocial personality disorder with a prealcoholic personality pattern.

Admittedly, there is a distinct tendency for those diagnosed as having an antisocial personality disorder to use chemicals. Indeed, it has been suggested that substance abuse might be an unrecognized aspect of the APD, given society's tendency to separate antisocial behavior from chemical use. Peele (1989) states:

> Those arrested for drunk driving frequently also have arrest records for traffic violations *when they aren't drunk*. . . . In other words, people who get drunk and go out on the road are frequently the same people who drive recklessly when they're sober. (p. 154)

However, in American society, an individual who commits a criminal act while under the influence of chemicals is viewed by the public as *controlled by the chemical*, despite what that individual's behavior might have been when not under the influence of drugs.

Thus, the fact that reckless behavior is a characteristic of individuals with the antisocial personality disorder is overlooked when the person is arrested for driving while under the influence of alcohol or chemicals. This individual is not viewed as being responsible for yet another display of reckless behavior. Rather, the drug is to blame. The individual's past record of reckless driving is conveniently overlooked and he or she is forced into treatment for a "drug problem."

According to Fingarette (1988), the disease model of alcoholism has been misused by some to avoid dealing with social problems they feel they can't handle. He states:

> Judges, legislators, and bureaucrats . . . can now with clear consciences get the intractable social problems caused by heavy drinkers off their agenda by compelling or persuading these unmanageable people to go elsewhere—that is, to get "treatment." (p. 66)

Thus, as we will discuss in Chapter 26 on intervention, the boundaries marking where the addictive disorders end and the personality disorders begin are blurred. In part, this is because the so-called alcoholic personality is similar in many respects to the personality disorders, especially the antisocial personality disorder.

A number of researchers have examined the issue of whether or not there is such a thing as the "alcoholic personality." According to Bean-Bayog (1988), for example, the so-called alcoholic personality emerges as a result of the impact of chronic alcoholism on the personality pattern—not as a precondition of the addiction. In other words, Bean-Bayog suggests that the personality characteristics often pointed to in the alcoholic are a *result* of the disease process, not a contributing factor to the initial development of the disease.

Bean-Bayog holds that much of the research conducted to date on identified addicts has been based on the mistaken assumption that certain of their personality characteristics precede addiction, when, in fact these characteristics are actually a result of the addictive process. It would be as if researchers had thought for years that the pain of a broken leg *caused* the injury to the bone, rather than that the pain was a signal of a broken limb.

Thus, at this point in time, there is little conclusive evidence that there are personality characteristics that predispose an individual to addiction. However, the study of the whole area of personality growth and development (not to mention the study of those forces that initially shape and later maintain addiction) is still so poorly defined that we cannot yet resolve this issue with certainty.

THE FINAL COMMON PATHWAY THEORY OF ADDICTION

As should be evident by now, there have been strong challenges to the medical model of substance abuse. At the same time, the psychological models of drug use also have been challenged as being too narrow in scope. Another theory to consider is called the *final common pathway* theory of chemical dependency. Actually it is a nontheory, in the sense that it is not supported by any single group or profession. The final common pathway theory holds that there is an element of truth in each of the other theories of drug addiction previously reviewed, but that *none* of them is able to fully account for the phenomenon of drug abuse.

Depending on the individual, the "cause" of an addictive disorder might involve social forces, psychological conditioning, an attempt to come to terms with internal pain, or some combination of these or other factors. Indeed, proponents of the final common pathway model are willing to acknowledge the possibility of genetic predisposition toward substance abuse. But, they are also willing to accept that there may not be. In the final analysis, the final common pathway model requires a professional to develop a comprehensive picture of the individual in order to answer the question, *What caused this individual to become addicted to chemicals?*

The final common pathway theory of addiction holds that chemical dependency is a common endpoint that can be reached by any number of different paths. The addicted individual may use alcohol or drugs because he or she finds that they fill an internal need. Somehow, for the addict, chemical use feels "right."

At first, the individual uses chemicals simply for the good feelings they produce. The drugs provide an enjoyable experience that the user wants to repeat over and over again. But, for one reason or another, the addict-to-be starts to use chemicals more and more compulsively, whereas others from the same environment, perhaps even the same family, do not.

Did some biological predisposition bring about the addiction? Were there close relatives who were also addicted, suggesting a genetic predisposition to chemical dependency? Was the person raised in an environment in which drug use was perhaps expected? Did the social forces of the environment allow the individual to excell, or was he or she locked into a lifetime of frustration and failure? Is there a history of psychological suffering the person is attempting to treat through self-medication?

This, then, is the core element of addiction according to the final common pathway theory of addiction: Addiction is the *common end point* for each individual who suffers from the compulsion to use chemicals. In order to treat the addiction, the chemical-dependency counselor must identify the unique set of factors that led to the individual's addiction and supported it. On the basis of this understanding, the chemical-dependency counselor can then establish a treatment program that will help the individual achieve and maintain sobriety.

SUMMARY

Although the medical model of drug dependency has dominated the treatment industry in the United States, this model is not without its critics. For each study claiming to have identified a biophysical basis for alcoholism or other forms of addiction, there are other studies failing to document such a difference. For each study claiming to have isolated personality characteristics that seem to predispose one toward addiction, there are other studies failing to corroborate these findings, or perhaps concluding that the personality characteristic in question is brought about by the addiction, instead of predating it.

It was suggested that the medical model of addiction can serve as a metaphor to help people better understand their problem behavior. However, the medical model of addiction is a *theoretical* model, one that has not been proven, and one that does not easily accommodate the concept of "disease" as the American medical establishment understands the term. Indeed, it has been suggested that drugs are themselves valueless. The use to which people put them determines whether they are good or bad.

Chapter 18

ADDICTION AS A DISEASE
OF THE HUMAN SPIRIT

Modern society, especially in the practice of medicine, tends to disparage matters of the spirit. We turn away, as if embarrassed by a subject so "primitive." Yet, in so doing, we deny that which makes us unique—for humans are first of all spiritual beings. To some, addiction is a disease of the "spirit"; and from this perspective, to understand the reality of addiction is ultimately to understand something of human nature.

The word "spirit" is derived from the Latin *spiritus*, which means the divine living force within each of us. In humanity, life has become aware of itself (Fromm, 1956). With this self-awareness, however, comes the painful understanding that each of us is forever isolated from all others. Fromm likens this awareness of one's basic isolation to an "unbearable prison" (p. 7), in which are found the roots of anxiety and shame. "The awareness of human separation," he states, "without reunion by love—is the source of shame. It is at the same time the source of guilt and anxiety" (p. 8).

The flowers, the birds, and the trees cannot help but be themselves, for that is their nature. A bird does not think about being a bird, and a tree does not think about being a tree. Each behaves according to its gifts, as either a bird or a tree. But humans possess the twin gifts of *self-awareness* and *self-determination*. We may, within certain limits, be aware of ourselves and decide our fate. These gifts, however, carry a price. Fromm (1956, 1968) views our awareness of our fundamental aloneness as the price we had to pay for the power of self-determination.

Through self-awareness, we have come to know that we are different from other animals. This awareness of "self" gives us the power of self-determination. But, in becoming aware of ourselves, we also came to feel isolated from the rest of the universe. Humankind became aware of "self," and in so doing came to know loneliness. It is only through the giving of "self" to another through love that Fromm (1956, 1968) envisioned humanity as transcending its isolation to become part of a greater whole.

Merton (1978) came to adopt a similar view on the nature of human existence. He clearly understood, on the basis of personal experience, that one could not derive happiness through the compulsive use of chemicals. Rather, happiness could be achieved through love shared openly and honestly with others. Martin Buber (1970) takes an even more extreme view, holding that it is only through our relationships that our life has definition. Each person stands "in relation" to another. The degree of relation—the relationship—is defined by how much of the "self" one offers to another and what one receives in return.

At this point, you might question what relevance this material has to a text on chemical dependency. It is relevant in that the early members of Alcoholics Anonymous came to view alcoholism (and, by extension, the other forms of addiction) as a "disease"—not only as a disease of the body, *but also as one of the spirit.* This insight enabled them to transform themselves from helpless victims of alcoholism into active participants in the healing process of sobriety.

Out of this struggle, the early members of AA came to share an intimate knowledge of the nature of addiction. They came to view addiction not as a phenomenon to be dispassionately studied, but as an elusive enemy that held each member's life in its hands. The early members of AA struggled not to find the smallest common element that might "cause" addiction, but to understand and share in the healing process of sobriety. In so doing, these pioneers of AA came to understand that recovery is a spiritual process through which an individual recovers the spiritual unity that cannot be found through chemicals.

Such self-help groups as Alcoholics Anonymous and Narcotics Anonymous do not postulate any specific theory of how chemical addiction comes about.[1] According to Herman (1988), unlike either medical or mental health professionals, "twelve-step programs do not dwell on the causes of addiction" (p. 52). Rather, it is simply assumed that any person whose chemical use interferes with his or her life has an addiction problem. The need to attend AA was, to its founders, self-evident: Either you were addicted to alcohol or you were not.

Addiction itself was viewed as a spiritual flaw. Drugs do not bring about addiction, but rather an individual comes to abuse drugs because of what he or she believes and holds to be important (Peele, 1989). Such spiritual flaws are not uncommon and usually pass unnoticed in the average person. For the addict, however, his or her spiritual foundation is such that chemicals are deemed acceptable, appropriate, and desirable.

According to Peele (1989), this spiritual flaw is expressed in people's tendency to try to escape responsibility for their lives. Personal suffering is, in a sense, a way of taking responsibility for one's life. One of the core beliefs of Buddhism holds that suffering is an inescapable fact of life (G. G. May, 1988; B. S. Siegel, 1989). If we are alive, we will encounter problems and suffering. However, Peck (1978) states:

> Some of us will go to quite extraordinary lengths to avoid our problems and the suffering they cause, proceeding far afield from all that is clearly good and sensible in order to find an easy way out, building the most elaborate fantasies in which to live, sometimes to the total exclusion of reality. (p. 17)

[1]Although they share many common elements, AA and NA are not affiliated. The two organizations cooperate on many matters, but are not associated with each other.

In this, the addict is not unique; it is difficult for anyone to accept the pain and suffering inherent in life. We all must come to terms with personal responsibility and with the pain of our existence. But the addict chooses a different path. Addiction might be viewed as an outcome of a process through which an individual comes to use chemicals to avoid recognition and acceptance of life's problems. Chemicals come to lead the individual away from what is real in return for the promise of comfort and relief.

DISEASES OF THE MIND, DISEASES OF THE SPIRIT: THE MIND/BODY QUESTION

As B. S. Siegel (1986) and many others have observed, modern medicine has come to enforce an artificial dichotomy between an individual's "mind" and "body." As a result of this dichotomy, modern medicine has taken on a mechanical quality, with the physician treating "symptoms" or "diseases," rather than the patient as a whole (Cousins, 1989; B. S. Siegel, 1989).

In a sense, the modern physician might be said to be highly skilled technician, but one who often fails to appreciate the unique *person*, now in the role of a patient. Diseases of the body are within the province of physical medicine, whereas diseases of the mind fall to the psychological sciences. Diseases of the human spirit, according to this scheme, are the specialty of the clergy (Reiser, 1984).

The problem is that the patient is not a "spiritual being" *or* a "psychosocial being" *or* a "physical being." The patient is a unified whole. When, as Adams (1988) notes, a person abuses chemicals, that person is affected "physically, emotionally, socially, and spiritually" (p. 20). Unfortunately, society has difficulty accepting that a disease of the spirit, such as addiction, is just as real as a disease of the physical body.

But humans are indeed spiritual beings, and self-help programs such as AA and NA view addiction to chemicals as a spiritual illness. Their success in helping people achieve and maintain sobriety would suggest that their view makes sense. However, society continues to cling to the artificial mind/body dichotomy. In the process, people struggle to come to terms with the disease of addiction, which is neither totally a physical illness, nor exclusively one of the mind.

THE GROWTH OF ADDICTION: THE CIRCLE NARROWS

According to S. Brown (1985), as the disease of alcoholism progresses, the alcoholic comes to center his or her life around drinking. Indeed, Brown speaks of alcohol as the "axis" on which the alcoholic's life turns. Alcohol comes to assume a central role both for the alcoholic and his or her family. Peele (1989) contends that one reason this process takes place is because the individual's value system tolerates chemical use as an acceptable behavioral alternative.

It is difficult for those who have never been addicted to chemicals to understand the importance the addict attaches to a chemical. The addicted person will be preoccupied with chemical use and will fiercely protect his or her source of chemicals. It is not uncommon for cocaine addicts to admit that, if pressed to decide, they would choose cocaine over friends, lovers, or even family.

This reality is hard for the nonaddict to comprehend. The grim truth is that the active addict is, in a sense, morally insane. The drug has become all-important, at the expense of other people and other commitments. Addicts, in a very real sense "never seem to outgrow the self-centeredness of the child" (*Triangle of Self-Obsession*, 1983, p. 1). The following passage from the book *Narcotics Anonymous* (1982) highlights this point:

> *Before coming to the fellowship of N.A. we could not manage our own lives. We could not live and enjoy life as other people do. We had to have something different and we thought we found it in drugs. We placed their use ahead of the welfare of our families, our wives, husbands, and our children. We had to have drugs at all costs.* (p. 11)

Walter Kaufmann, in his elegant introduction to Buber's (1970) text, speaks of those whose all-consuming interest is themselves. In this sense, chemical addiction might be viewed as a form of self-love, or perhaps as a perversion of self-love. Through the use of chemicals, addicts seek to avoid the experience of reality—to replace it with their distorted desires.

In their ongoing preoccupation with chemical use, addicts demonstrate an exaggerated concern about maintaining their supply of the drug. Moreover, they avoid those who might threaten further drug use. For example, the alcoholic who, with six or seven cases of beer in storage in the basement, goes out to buy six more "just in case," is obviously preoccupied with maintaining an "adequate" supply.

Addicts tend to view other people as either useful in maintaining their habit or as possible threats to further drug use. That is, if the existence of others is acknowledged at all. Nothing is allowed to come between the addict and his or her drug. That relationship takes precedence over all.

THE CIRCLE OF ADDICTION: ADDICTED PRIORITIES

The authors of *Narcotics Anonymous* conclude that addiction is a disease composed of three elements: (1) a compulsive use of chemicals, (2) an obsession with further chemical use, and (3) a total self-centeredness on the part of the addict. It is this total self-centeredness—the spiritual illness that causes the person to demand "what I want when I want it" that makes the individual vulnerable to addiction.

As we have noted, the addict comes to center his or her life around continued use of the chemical. Chemical-dependency professionals will often speak of the addict's *preoccupation with drug use*. But, for the addict to admit to this would be to accept the reality of personal addiction. So, those who are addicted to chemicals will begin to use the defense mechanisms of denial, rationalization, projection, and minimization to justify their increasingly narrow range of interests both to themselves and to significant others.

To support his or her addiction, the individual must renounce more and more "self" in favor of new beliefs and behaviors that make it possible to continue to use chemicals. This is the spiritual illness that defines addiction. No price is too high, nor is any behavior unthinkable, if it allows for further drug use. As Peele (1989) points out, this is a value judgment made by the individual.

As the economic, personal, and social costs of continued drug use mount, the individual will often come to lie, cheat, and steal. Addicted persons have been known to sell prized possessions, steal money from trust accounts, misdirect medications prescribed for patients, and deny their feelings for family members in order to continue their drug use. In a sense, all vestiges of their humanity gradually slip away.

Some addicts, on considering the costs demanded by drug use, turn away from chemicals with or without formal treatment. But others accept the costs willingly. Many addicts will go to great pains to hide evidence of their drug addiction. More than one "hidden" alcoholic has described, for example, how he or she would "take the dog for a walk" at night to hide empty bottles in neighbors' trash cans. Addicts have been known to hide drug supplies under rocks in the countryside, behind books in the study, under the kitchen sink, behind the headboard of the bed, and in a multitude of other places. All this to maintain the illusion that they are not using chemicals.

Addicts themselves are confused as to what caused their change in personality. When you ask them why they use drugs, they have trouble answering. At the same time, they are often envious of, and mystified by, the normal individual's ability to say no to chemical use. Addicts are, in a very real sense, spiritually blind.

As the addiction comes to exert increasing control, more and more effort must be expended by the addict to maintain the illusion of normalcy. Gallagher (1986) relates how one physician, addicted to the synthetic narcotic fentanyl, ultimately bought drugs from the street because it was no longer possible to divert enough drugs from hospital sources to maintain his habit. When the telltale scars from repeated injections of street drugs began to form on his arms, this physician intentionally burned himself with a spoon to hide the scars.

The addict also must find new ways to meet the ever-growing monetary demands associated with drug use. More than one cocaine or heroin addict has turned to prostitution to finance his or her habit. Everything is sacrificed in order to obtain and maintain what the addict perceives as an "adequate" supply of chemicals.

Both AA and NA place a heavy emphasis on honesty. Drug dependency hides behind a wall of deception, and honesty is the way to break down this wall—to bring addicts face to face with their addiction.

SOME GAMES OF ADDICTION

Jenike (1989) speaks at length of the manipulative games that addicts often engage in to maintain their drug habits. To manipulate others, they are likely to use such ploys as "outrage, tears, accusations of abandonment, abject pleading, promises of cooperation, and seduction" (p. 13). Physicians and other professionals who work with addicts must be aware of these ploys if they are to succeed in their treatment programs.

According to Klass (1989), narcotics addicts have been known to visit hospital emergency rooms and doctors' offices in an attempt to obtain medication. Sometimes they complain of "kidney stones" or other painful conditions, describing how desperate they are for relief. They may say they are spitting up blood, or that they have noticed blood in their urine or stool (Cunnien, 1988). The object of these "games" is to obtain a prescription for narcotics from a sympathetic doctor.

When asked for urine samples, which would show traces of blood if the person was suffering from a real kidney stone, addicts have been known to surreptitiously prick their finger with a needle to sqeeze a few drops of blood into the urine. Another common practice is for an addict to insert a foreign object (for example, a darning needle) into the urethra to irritate the urethral lining. This will cause a small amount of blood to be released by the injured tissues, thus enabling a sample of bloody urine.

Addicts also have been known to visit many different physicians for the same illness to acquire multiple prescriptions for drugs. The cunning addict may be quite knowledgeable about various medical conditions. Addicts need to know what symptoms to fake and how to put on a convincing show for health care professionals. Again, the object of the game is to convince the physician to prescribe the drug that they desire. Salloway, Southwick, and Sadowsky (1990) describe the case of a 39-year-old Vietnam War veteran who feigned the symptoms of a posttraumatic stress disorder allegedly triggered by an industrial accident. Ultimately, it was discovered that the patient's story was simply an elaborate charade designed to obtain narcotics and shelter from the attending physicians of an inpatient psychiatric unit.

Addicts have been known to have "conned" psychiatrists into keeping their supplies of cocaine. They would profess an interest in therapy, but actually what they wanted was a safe "stash" for their drug. In this way, they avoided the fear of being caught with cocaine by the police or having it stolen by other addicts.

The only price the addicts had to pay for this deception was to show up a few days a week, confess their latest transgression of having purchased more cocaine, and then allow the therapists to take possession of all but the immediate day's supply of the drug as an incentive to come back. The addicts were then "safe" from police searches or from other addicts looking for drugs. The therapists apparently thought that they could out-manipulate the addicts into staying in therapy.

What the therapists perhaps failed to realize was that they were putting themselves in jeopardy. If the police were to search their offices, the therapists (not the addicts) would be in possession of a controlled substance. The addicts could even deny all knowledge of the cocaine being there in the first place. The therapists could then quite possibly face criminal charges, while the addicts would look for other places to stash their drugs.

A Thought on Playing the Games of Addiction

A friend of mine, who worked in a maximum security penitentiary for men, was warned by older, more experienced corrections workers not to try to "outcon a con." Which is to say that the person was warned not to try to outmanipulate a person whose entire life centered on the ability to manipulate others. This advice is worth remembering: When you are at home watching the evening news, or out enjoying a movie, con artists are busy at work on perfecting their "game." It is *their* game, *their* rules, and in a sense *their whole life.*

This is also a good rule to keep in mind when working with addicts. Addiction is a *lifestyle*—one that largely involves the manipulation of others into supporting the addiction. This is not to deny that addicts are capable of "changing their spots." They can remain sober, at least for a short time, especially early in the addiction process or during the early stages of treatment.

Often, addicts will go "on the wagon" for a few days, or perhaps even a few weeks, in order to prove both to themselves and to others that they can "still control it." Stuart (1980) comments on this trait:

> The alcohol-prone individual who passes up a drink so that he or she can later boast to a spouse about this major feat of self-management demonstrates not self-control but a choice between a lesser (alcohol) and a major (attention by a significant other) reinforcement. (p. 31)

Unfortunately, addicts who go on the wagon attempting to prove they are in control, are actually deluding themselves. They might be able to give up the drug for a short time, *if the reward is large enough.* However, as the addiction progresses, it takes more and more to motivate the addict to give up the drug. And even "a short time" becomes too long.

V. E. Johnson (1980) speaks at length of how addicts will even use compliance as a defense against treatment. Overt compliance is often used as a defense against owning up to one's own spiritual, emotional, and physical weaknesses. Johnson notes that compliance is marked by a subtle defiance. The individual appears just to be "going through the motions" to avoid further confrontation. In the struggle to avoid facing the reality of addiction, addicts will use a small portion of the truth as a defense against having to face the whole truth.

HONESTY AS A PART OF THE RECOVERY PROCESS

The authors of *Narcotics Anonymous* (1982) warn that progression toward acceptance of the fact of one's addiction is not easy. Indeed, self-deception is part of the price the addict pays for addiction, according to NA. As the "big book" puts it: "Only in desperation did we ask ourselves, 'Could it be the drugs?'" (pp. 1–2).

Addicts will often speak with pride about how they have been more or less "drug free" for various periods of time. The list of "reasons" why the individual is drug-free is virtually endless. This person is drug-free because his or her spouse threatened divorce if the drug use continued. (But the individual secretly longs to resume chemical use, and will if he or she can find a way to do so.) Another person is drug-free because his or her probation officer has a reputation for being tough on those whose urine sample tests positive for chemicals. (But this individual is counting the days until probation ends, and possibly sneaking an occasional pill when he or she can get away with it.)

In each instance, the person is drug-free only because of an external threat. In virtually every case, as soon as the external threat is removed, the individual will drift back to chemicals. It is simply impossible for one person to continue to provide motivation for another person to remain drug-free. As Peele (1989) points out, an individual must personally commit to sobriety if he or she is to achieve and maintain it. Personal choice, or *commitment* to sobriety, is a necessary ingredient to recovery.

After strong confrontation, many addicts admit to having simply switched chemicals to give the appearance of being "drug free." It is not uncommon for an opiate addict in a methadone maintenance program to be using alcohol, marijuana, or cocaine. The methadone does not block the euphoric effects of these drugs as it does the euphoria of narcotics. Thus, the addict maintains the appearance of complete cooperation, appearing each day to take his or her methadone without protest, while still freely using cocaine, marijuana or alcohol.

In a very real sense, the addicted person has lost touch with reality. Over time, those who are addicted to chemicals come to share many common personality traits. As we discussed in the previous chapter, there is some question whether the so-called addicted personality predates addiction or evolves as a result of the addiction (Bean-Bayog, 1988; Nathan, 1988). However, this chicken-or-egg question does not alter the fact that, for the addict, the addiction *always* comes first. The addict centers his or her life around the chemical use.

Some addicts describe going without food for days on end, but few willingly go without chemicals for even a short period. Cocaine addicts admit that they would give up sexual relations in favor of using their drug of choice. Just as the alcoholic will often sleep with an "eye opener" (alcoholic drink) already mixed by the side of the bed, addicts speak of having a "rig" (hypodermic needle) loaded and ready for use, so that they can inject the drug even before getting out of bed in the morning.

Many physicians boast that the patients they work with would not lie to them. One physician "knew" a certain patient did not have prescriptions from other doctors because, as he put it, "the patient told me so"! The chemical-dependency professional needs to keep in mind at all times these two realities: (1) for the person who is addicted, the chemical comes first and (2) the addicted person centers his or her life around the chemical. To lose sight of these realities is to run the risk of being trapped in the addict's web of lies, half-truths, and manipulations.

Recovering addicts openly acknowledge their manipulative ways, often admitting that they were their own worst enemy. As they move along the road to recovery, addicts come to recognize that self-deception is part of the addiction process. One inmate remarked: "Before I can run a game on somebody else, I have to believe it myself." As the addiction progresses, addicts do not question their perception, but come to believe what they need to believe in order to maintain the addiction.

It is for this reason that self-help groups such as AA and NA place such heavy emphasis on honesty. Recovering addicts recognize that honesty is their best defense against the self-deception they used in the past to support their addiction.

FALSE PRIDE: THE DISEASE OF THE SPIRIT

In the final analysis, every addiction is a disease of the spirit. Edmeades (1985) recounts a story about Carl Jung, who was treating an American, Rowland H., for alcoholism in 1931. Immediately after treatment Rowland H. relapsed, but was not accepted back into analysis by Jung. His only hope of recovery, according to Jung, lay in a spiritual awakening, which he later found through a religious group in America.

Carl Jung thought of alcoholism (and by implication all forms of addiction) as a disease of the spirit (Peluso & Peluso, 1988). The Alcoholics Anonymous publication, *Twelve Steps and Twelve Traditions* (1981), speaks of addiction as a sickness of the soul. Kandel and Raveis (1989) point to a "lack of religiosity" (p. 113) as a significant predictor of continued use of cocaine and/or marijuana for young adults having previous experience with these drugs. Peluso and Peluso note that for addicts who achieve sobriety, a spiritual awakening appears to be an essential element of their recovery.

In speaking with addicts, one is impressed by how much they have suffered. It is almost as if a path could be traced from the emotional trauma to the addiction. Yet the addict's spirit is not crushed at birth, nor does the trauma that precedes addiction come about overnight. The individual's spirit comes to be diseased over time, as the addict-to-be loses his or her way in life.

According to Fromm (1968), "we all start out with hope, faith and fortitude" (p. 20). However, the assorted insults of life often join forces to bring about disappointment and a loss of faith. The individual comes to feel an empty void within. B. Graham (1988) alludes to a turning point. If the spiritual void is not filled, the individual may turn to drugs. Few of us escape this moment of ultimate disappointment or ultimate awareness, according to Fromm. It is at this moment that individuals must decide to "reduce their demands to what they can get and . . . not dream of that which seems to be out of their reach" (p. 21). The NA pamphlet *The Triangle of Self-Obsession* (1983) notes that this process is, for most, a natural part of growing up.

But the person in danger of addiction refuses to reduce his or her demands. Rather, the addict-to-be comes to demand "What I want when *I* want it!" Addicts refuse to accept the fact that they will not be given everything. They are childlike in their self-obsession. And they are seldom able to achieve sustained contentment.

Despair comes to exist when an individual experiences true powerlessness. Existentialists speak of this void as awareness of one's nonexistence. In this sense, individuals come to feel the utter futility of existence. When a person faces the ultimate experience of powerlessness, there is still a choice to be made: either accept one's true place in the universe or distort one's perceptions to maintain the illusion of being more than what one actually is.

Peck (1978) identifies the acceptance of one's true place in the universe, and the pain and suffering that life might offer, as an essential ingredient of spiritual growth. When people reach this point of ultimate disappointment, many choose to turn away from reality, for it does not offer them what they think they are entitled to. In so doing, these people become somewhat grandiose, and exhibit the characteristic *false pride* so frequently encountered in addiction.

It is impossible to maintain the illusion of being more than what one is without an increasingly large investment of time, energy, and emotional resources. Merton (1961) suggests that it is the lack of true humility that allows despair to grow within. Humility implies an honest, realistic view of self-worth. Despair comes about through a distorted view of one's place in the universe. This despair grows with each passing day, as reality threatens time and again to force on the individual an awareness of the ultimate measure of his or her existence.

In time, external supports are necessary to maintain false pride. S. Brown (1985) points out that alcohol is able to offer an individual an *illusion of control* over his or her feelings. This is a common characteristic of every drug of abuse. If life does not provide the pleasure that one feels entitled to, at least this pleasure is available in drug form. Drugs offer an escape from life's pain and misery—at least for awhile.

When faced with the unwanted awareness of their true place in the universe, addicts increasingly distort their perception to maintain an illusion of superiority. Chemicals help them do this. Only too late do they realize that the chemicals offer an illusion only. There is no substance to the self-selected feelings produced by the chemical—only a mockery of peace. The deeper feelings that result from acceptance of one's lot in life are a mystery to addicts. "How can you be happy?" they ask. "You are nothing like *me!* You don't use!"

Humility, as we have noted, is the honest acceptance of one's place in the universe (Merton, 1961). This includes the honest and open acceptance of one's strengths and weaknesses. When individuals become aware of the nature of their being, they may come to accept their lot in life or they may choose to struggle against existence itself.

When one struggles against the reality of existence, one in effect places oneself above all else to say "Not as it is, but as I want it!" It is a cry against the ultimate knowledge of being lost that Fromm (1968) spoke of. This despair is often so all-encompassing that, ultimately, the "self" is unable to withstand its attack. Addicts have described this despair as an empty, black void within. As B. Graham (1988) notes, they attempt to fill this void with the chemicals they find around them.

As we have mentioned, *Twelve Steps and Twelve Traditions* (1981) speaks of false pride as a sickness of the soul. In this light, chemical use might be viewed as a reaction against the ultimate despair of encountering one's lot in life: the false sense of being that says "not as it is, but as *I* want it" in response to one's discovery of personal powerlessness.

Andrew Weil (cited in Perrin & Coleman, 1988), suggests that the addict is essentially "seeking wholeness" (p. 58). But, in place of the spiritual struggle that Peck (1978) speaks of as being necessary to achieve this ultimate awareness, the addict seeks a shortcut. According to G. G. May (1988), addiction sidetracks "our deepest, truest desire for love and goodness" (p. 14). Drugs come to dominate the individual's life until, finally, the person believes that he or she cannot live without them.

In a sense, the false pride that characterizes drug addiction is a form of narcissism. Narcissism is a reaction against perceived worthlessness, loss of control, and emotional pain so intense that it almost seems physical. Millon (1981) describes narcissistic personalities as having an exaggerated view of their own self-worth. They tend to "place few restraints on either their fantasies or rationalizations, and their imagination is left to run free" (p. 167).

While addicts are not usually narcissistic personalities in the true sense of the term, they do have narcissistic traits. Narcissism, or false pride, is based on lack of humility. Addicts come to distort not only their perceptions of "self," but also of "other," in the service of their pride. People whose entire life centers on themselves

> imagine that they can only find themselves by asserting their own desires and ambitions and appetites in a struggle with the rest of the world. (Merton, 1961, p. 47)

Here lie the seeds of addiction. The addicts' chemical of choice allows them to assert their own desires and ambitions to rise above the rest of the world. S. Brown (1985) speaks at length of the illusion of control over one's feelings that alcohol gives an individual. G. G. May (1988) speaks of how chemical addiction reflects a misguided attempt to also achieve complete control over one's life. Drugs of abuse allow individuals to harbor the dangerous illusion that they can dominate the external world. In reality they are losing their will to the chemicals.

Addicts often speak with pride of the horrors that they have suffered in the service of their addiction. V. E. Johnson (1980) describes this "euphoric recall," as a process whereby addicts recall only the pleasant aspects of their drug use. For example, more than one addict has expounded on the quasi-sexual thrill that cocaine or heroin provides. In the process, the addict dismisses the fact that this same drug has cost him or her a spouse, a family, and tens of thousands of dollars.

There is a name for the distorted view of one's self and one's world that comes with chronic chemical use. It is called the insanity of addiction.

DENIAL, RATIONALIZATION, PROJECTION, AND MINIMIZATION: THE FOUR MUSKETEERS OF ADDICTION

Addiction, like all forms of insanity, rests in no small part on characteristic psychological defenses. In this case, these are the defenses of *denial, rationalization,* and *projection.* These defense mechanisms, like all psychological defenses, operate unconsciously in both the intrapersonal and interpersonal spheres. They operate as unconscious, automatic defense systems to protect the individual from the conscious awareness of anxiety.

Often without knowing it, addicts will use these defense mechanisms in an effort to avoid confronting the reality of their addiction. Once the reality of the addiction has been recognized, there is an implicit social expectation that they will deal with it. Thus, to understand addiction, one must also understand each of these characteristic defense mechanisms.

Denial   This most commonly encountered defense mechanism is defined by Kaplan and Sadock (1988) as

> a mechanism in which the existence of unpleasant realities is disavowed. The term refers to keeping out of consciousness any aspects of reality that, if acknowledged, would produce anxiety. (p. 312)

In a sense, denial is a catch-22 for addicts. To avoid anxiety, the danger signs of the growing addiction are shut out. But, while avoiding the experience of anxiety, the individual also avoids coming to terms with the evidence of the addiction to chemicals.[2]

The defense mechanism of denial involves selective perception on the part of the addict. Those familiar with the AA steps would term this "tunnel vision." Further, it is interesting to note that Perry and Cooper (1989) identify denial as being a rather immature defense mechanism, usually demonstrated

---

[2]It should be noted at this point that denial is not *necessarily* a symptom of addiction. Peele (1989) describes at length how treatment centers often view an individual's refusal to admit to his or her addiction as confirmation of the fact that the individual is addicted. The possibility that the individual is *not* addicted is all too often not considered. An individual's refusal to admit to being addicted might be a reflection of reality—not an expression of denial.

by addicts who are experiencing significant internal and interpersonal distress.

Projection   This defense mechanism is defined by Kaplan and Sadock (1988) as an "unconscious mechanism in which a person attributes to another . . . ideas, thoughts, feelings and impulses that are . . . undesirable or unacceptable" (p. 312). V. E. Johnson (1980) defines projection differently, noting that the act of projection is the act of "unloading *self*-hatred onto others" (p. 31).

The defense mechanism of projection forms the basis of *scapegoating* (Cameron, 1963), a common defensive "game" used by addicts to justify their behavior. Young children will often cry out "See what you made me do!" when they have misbehaved. Addicts will often do this as well, blaming their addiction on others.

Rationalization   This third defense mechanism has been defined as "a mechanism in which irrational or unacceptable behavior, motives, or feelings are logically justified or made consciously tolerable" (Kaplan & Sadock, 1988, p. 312). Cameron (1963) goes further in his definition, as follows:

> [Rationalization is] the justification of [an] otherwise unacceptable, ego-alien thought feeling or action, through the misuse and distortion of facts and through employing a pseudo-logic. [It] is a common device . . . where people explain away their own defects, failures and misdeeds. (p. 243)

Anybody who has ever worked with addicts will attest to the fact that rationalization is one of the most important of the defense mechanisms.

Minimization   This defense mechanism works in a different way than the three we have just discussed. In a sense, minimization is like rationalization, but it is more specific. The addicted individual who uses minimization as a defense will actively seek to give the impression that the amount of chemical he or she is using is less than it actually is.

The alcoholic, for example, might drink his or her drinks out of an oversized container, perhaps with the volume of three or four regular glasses, and then admit to having "just three drinks a night!" Or the addict might claim to use "only once a day," hoping that the interviewer will not think to ask whether a "day" means a full 24-hour day or just when it is light outside. Another trick is for addicts to point to the time when they were in treatment, in jail, or in the hospital as "straight time," neglecting to mention that they were unable to get drugs.

Some of the specifics of the various defense mechanisms can be quite farfetched. For example, there is the rationalization, offered to this author by a number of different addicts, that marijuana use did not constitute addiction, since marijuana was "a herb," and thus a natural substance. You could only, or so the rationalization went, become addicted to *artificial* chemicals, such as alcohol, amphetamines, or heroin. Another popular rationalization is that it is "better to be an alcoholic than a needle freak. After all, alcohol is legal!" Countless numbers of alcoholics deny their addiction, despite compelling evidence to the contrary, through one or more of these common defense mechanisms.

SUMMARY

Many professionals in the field of human services who have had limited contact with addicts tend to have a distorted view of the nature of drug addiction. Having heard the term *disease* applied to chemical dependency, the inexperienced human-service worker tends to think in terms of more traditional illnesses, and is often rudely surprised at the deception inherent in drug addiction.

While chemical dependency is a disease, it is a disease like no other. As noted earlier, it is a disease that requires the active participation of the patient. Further, self-help groups such as AA and NA, view addiction as a disease of the spirit, and offer a spiritual program to help members achieve and maintain sobriety.

In a sense, addiction is a form of insanity. The insanity of addiction rests on the psychological defense mechanisms of rationalization, denial, and projection. These three defense mechanisms, plus minimization, shield the addict from an awareness of the reality of the addiction until the disease has progressed quite far. To combat this deception, AA emphasizes honesty. Honesty, both with oneself and with others, is the central feature of the AA program.

Chapter 19

CHEMICALS AND THE NEONATE: THE CONSEQUENCES OF DRUG ABUSE DURING PREGNANCY

With the exception of heroin use during pregnancy, medical research has not paid much attention to maternal drug abuse (Chasnoff & Schnoll, 1987). As a result, very little is known about the long-term consequences of maternal drug abuse on the fetus (Chasnoff, 1991; Zuckerman & Bresnahan, 1991).

Although maternal drug use during pregnancy is not uncommon, the social user of chemicals responds differently to the knowledge that she is pregnant than the addict. When a social user learns that she is pregnant, she will usually stop using chemicals. Unfortunately, a woman who is addicted to chemicals often finds herself unable to avoid the use of alcohol or drugs (Haller, 1991). Nationally, 8% to 14% of women of childbearing age are addicted to chemicals (Lewis, Bennet, & Schmeder, 1989). Research findings also indicate that in some parts of the country, up to 38% of expectant mothers either admit to, or test positive for, alcohol, cocaine, or other drugs of abuse (*Alcoholism & Drug Abuse Week*, 1990b).

THE NATURE OF THE PROBLEM

Maternal drug abuse during pregnancy is associated with such complications as preterm labor, early separation of the placenta, fetal growth retardation, and a number of congenital abnormalities. Since most drugs taken during pregnancy easily cross the placenta and enter the blood of the fetus, the developing child is usually exposed to the same chemicals that the mother uses (Chasnoff, 1988; Chasnoff & Schnoll, 1987).

But the consequences of the drug use for the fetus are often quite different from those suffered by the mother. Because the fetus lacks the fully developed liver and excretory systems of the mother (Chasnoff, 1988), the drugs may remain in the circulatory system of the fetus longer and have a more devastating impact.

At its most extreme, if the mother is addicted at the time of delivery, the child will share in the mother's addiction. According to Peluso and Peluso (1988), 80 of every 10,000 children born in New York City are addicted to chemicals at birth. Nationally, more than 1,000 children a day are born to

217

mothers who are addicted to chemicals (Byrne, 1989a). But, even if the child
is not addicted at the time of birth, maternal drug use may have had other
effects on the child. For example, Dominguez et al. (1991) conclude that fetal
exposure to chemicals during pregnancy is one cause of subsequent brain and
vision abnormalities in children.

The consequences of maternal drug use during pregnancy do not stop with
the child's birth. With the birth of the child, the mother's chemical abuse
during pregnancy might first be recognized; however, the child might continue
to suffer consequences for the rest of his or her life. According to Chasnoff
(1991), the median cost of care for children born to mothers who had used
illicit chemicals during pregnancy was between $1,100 and $4,100 higher
than for children whose mothers were drug-free. When one considers that
between 350,000 and 739,000 children are exposed to illicit chemicals before
birth, these costs translate into an expenditure of between $385 million and
$3 billion in additional medical costs each year for treatment of drug-induced
neonatal health problems.

When children born addicted to drugs reach school age, they will require
further specialized services that are an additional expense for society. Whereas the average educational cost for the normal child is approximately $3,000 a
year, the cost of the special education classes often required by children born
addicted to drugs might be as high as $15,000 a year per child (Barden,
1991). This is in addition to the extra medical costs, costs for social services,
and so on, that such children often require. Thus, the problem of drug use
during pregnancy is often not immediately recognized, and the children
become lifelong "hidden" victims.

FETAL ALCOHOL SYNDROME

Women who drink on a regular basis while pregnant run the risk of causing
alcohol-induced birth defects, a condition known as *fetal alcohol syndrome*
(FAS). Although this condition is not evident in every child of an alcoholic
mother who drank during pregnancy (Chasnoff, 1988), there is a known
association between maternal alcohol use and developmental abnormalities in
their children. When some, but not all, of the symptoms of FAS are apparent
in a child, the condition is referred to as *fetal alcohol effects* (Charness et al.,
1989; Streissguth et al., 1991).

Fetal alcohol syndrome is thought to be at the most severe end of a
continuum of disabilities brought on by maternal alcohol use during pregnancy (Streissguth et al., 1991). According to Charness et al. (1989), two
factors play a role in determining whether or not the child will develop FAS:
(1) the pattern and extent of the mother's drinking during pregnancy and (2)
the genetic vulnerability of the fetus to maternal alcohol use. If the mother
drinks heavily throughout pregnancy, and the fetus is especially vulnerable to
the effects of the alcohol in the mother's system, then there is a very real

danger that the fetus will develop to be born with the full fetal alcohol syndrome.

It is estimated that perhaps as many as 6% of the children of alcoholic mothers will be born with the full fetal alcohol syndrome (Charness et al., 1989). An unknown percentage of children whose mothers used alcohol during pregnancy will suffer lesser effects from their exposure to this drug. Alcohol quickly crosses the placenta into the bloodstream of the fetus, and when a pregnant woman drinks, the blood alcohol level of the fetus reaches the same level as the mother's in only 15 minutes (Rose, 1988). Indeed, if the mother drank just prior to childbirth, the smell of alcohol might be detected on the breath of the newborn, according to Rose. Fetal alcohol syndrome is thought to be the leading cause of mental retardation in the United States (Charness et al., 1989; Streissguth et al., 1991) and is also the only cause of birth defects that is *totally* preventable (Beasley, 1987).

Infants who suffer from the full fetal alcohol syndrome usually have a lower than normal birth weight, characteristic facial abnormalities, and a smaller than average brain size at birth (Charness et al., 1989). Such children also exhibit slow growth patterns following birth and are more likely to be retarded than normal children. Generally, they are mildly to moderately retarded following birth, with an average IQ of 68 (Bays, 1990; Chasnoff, 1988).[1]

However, some 40% of children with FAS will have measured IQs above 70, a score that is often used to determine which children qualify for special services (Streissguth et al., 1991). This is not to say that these children have not suffered from the mother's use of alcohol during pregnancy. Rather, these children do not qualify for special support services because their measured IQ happens to be higher than the cutoff score of 70 typically used to determine who qualifies for these remedial services.

Gold and Sherry (1984) explored the impact of alcohol consumption during pregnancy on childrens' subsequent school performance. The authors found that children whose mother consumed alcohol during pregnancy were likely to suffer from learning disabilities, short attention span, emotional problems, or hyperactivity during their school years.

Research findings to date suggest that the fetus is especially vulnerable to FAS during the first trimester of pregnancy (Chasnoff, 1988). Mirin et al. (1991) note that seriously affected children might never achieve normal growth or intelligence, in spite of an optimal postnatal environment. Once the damage has been done during pregnancy, the child appears to be unlikely to recover, even if special efforts are made to help him or her following birth. Streissguth et al. (1991) examined the lives of adolescent and young adult victims of FAS and found that only 6% of those students in school could function in regular classes without special help. The average reading level for these victims was fourth grade, while the average arithmetic skill level for their sample was second grade. Such scores highlight the lifelong con-

---

[1]An IQ of 68 falls in the mildly retarded range of intellectual function. The average IQ is 100, with a standard deviation of 15 points.

sequences of maternal alcohol use on the child's subsequent growth and development.

It was also found that "major psychosocial problems and lifelong adjustment problems were characteristic of most of these patients" (Streissguth et al., 1991, pp. 1965–1966). Although the low-birth-weight characteristic of FAS seemed at least partially to resolve itself by adolescence, at the time of their study "none of [the] patients were known to be independent in terms of both housing and income" (p. 1966). These findings again underscore the lifelong impact of maternal alcohol use during pregnancy on the child.

Breast feeding and alcohol use   Animal research suggests that even if the mother does not drink during pregnancy, if she drinks during the time that she is breast feeding, the infant may still absorb alcohol through her milk (Little, Anderson, Ervin, Worthington-Roberts, & Clarren, 1989). Little et al. found a direct relationship between the level of exposure to alcohol through the mother's milk and developmental delays exhibited by the infant. The more the mother drank while she was breast feeding, the greater the developmental delay in the infant.

Thus, it would seem that alcohol use by the mother during breast feeding is a risk factor for the infant. The exact mechanism through which the infant's motor development is affected was not clear, but Little et al. hypothesized that the infant's brain may be "exquisitely sensitive" to even small amounts of alcohol. Alternatively, the infant's body may store up the alcohol ingested through breast milk, so that the accumulated intake impacts motor development through some unknown mechanism within the first year of life.

COCAINE USE DURING PREGNANCY

Peters and Theorell (1991) estimate that approximately 15% to 17% of all cocaine users are women of childbearing age. Even more frightening is the fact that cocaine is the illicit chemical pregnant women most commonly abuse (American Academy of Family Physicians, 1990b; Ney, Dooley, Keith, Chasnoff, & Socol, 1990).[2] In this country, between 240,000 (Phibbs, Bateman, & Schwartz (1991) and 300,000 (Bays, 1990) babies are exposed to cocaine prior to birth each year. In some communities, 10% of all babies test positive for cocaine at birth (Revkin, 1989).

As recently as 1982, some medical textbooks claimed that maternal cocaine use did not have a harmful effect on the fetus (Revkin, 1989). It is now known that women who use cocaine during pregnancy suffer a higher than average incidence of complications of pregnancy that might prove fatal to the infant and possibly to the mother as well (Sbriglio & Millman, 1987).

Maternal cocaine use during pregnancy may result in early separation of the placenta and spontaneous abortions (Chasnoff, 1988; Peters and Theorell,

---

[2]The classification of *illicit* chemicals does not include alcohol, since this chemical may be legally purchased.

1991; Revkin, 1989). It also may result in low birth weight, poor fetal growth, and small head circumference (Zuckerman & Bresnahan, 1991). There is a known association between maternal cocaine use and preterm labor, often resulting in premature birth. Perhaps as many as 17% of the women who experience preterm labor have measurable amounts of cocaine in their urine (Cordero, 1990; Ney et al., 1990), and some physicians now advocate routine urine toxicology testing for any woman who experiences preterm labor (Peters & Theorell, 1991).

The mother's use of cocaine during the first trimester may result in congenital abnormalities in the urinary tract of the child (Chavez, Mulinare, & Cordero, 1989; Peters & Theorell, 1991). According to Peters and Theorell (1991), maternal cocaine use, especially early in pregnancy, has been implicated in fetal skull abnormalities, low birth weights, short body lengths, and small head circumferences at birth. Cocaine use by the mother results in constriction of the blood vessels in the placenta and uterine bed, reducing blood flow to the fetus for a period of time.

In adults, blood or urine toxicology tests will detect cocaine only for 24 to 48 hours following the drug use. In newborn children, the mebabolites of cocaine require 4 to 6 days to clear the body (Lewis et al., 1989), underscoring the fact that cocaine remains in the infant's body longer than it does in the mother's. This is because the infant's liver is unable to produce normal amounts of the enzyme *pseudo-cholinesterase*, which is necessary to metabolize cocaine (House, 1990; Peters & Theorell, 1991).

If the mother is addicted to cocaine at the time that she gives birth, the infant will also be addicted to cocaine. Thus, the infant will have to go through cocaine withdrawal at the same time that he or she is recovering from the trauma of birth. According to the *Mayo Clinic Health Letter* (1989), whereas the average hospital stay for a normal infant following birth averages 3 days, the average "crack baby" (an infant who was addicted to crack cocaine at birth) requires an average hospital stay of 42 days.

This prolonged hospitalization places a strain on health care resources. Since many of these children are born to parents who have no health insurance, this cost is ultimately passed on to those who are insured in the form of higher costs. Furthermore, many of these women receive little or no medical care during their pregnancy, adding still another risk. The mother's cocaine use may prevent the fetus from receiving adequate nutrition during pregnancy, with lifelong consequences for the baby.

There is evidence to suggest that infants born to mothers who use cocaine during pregnancy might suffer from small strokes prior to birth (Chasnoff, 1988; Peluso & Peluso, 1988; Phibbs et al., 1991). Research suggests that over a third of the infants who are exposed to cocaine during pregnancy have structural abnormalities of the brain that may be detected by CAT scans or ultrasound examination (Bays, 1990; Zuckerman & Bresnahan, 1991).

These small strokes are thought to be a result of the rapid changes in the mother's blood pressure brought on by cocaine use. Chasnoff (1988) contends that such strokes are similar to those occasionally seen in adults who use cocaine, noting that there is evidence that cocaine use during pregnancy may result in cardiac and central nervous system abnormalities in the fetus.

In an investigation of the problems of children born to mothers addicted to crack cocaine, Byrne concludes:

> [They] are susceptible to a long list of problems, including small size, small heads and brains, neurological abnormalities, kidney malformations, damage to the small intestine, strokes, and crib death. (p. 4A)

This last conclusion—that crack babies are susceptible to "crib death" or "sudden infant death syndrome" (SIDS)—is not to be underestimated. Fully 15% of these babies suffer from SIDS, a potentially fatal condition that is extremely rare in babies whose mothers did not use cocaine during pregnancy (Lewis et al., 1989; Peters & Theorell, 1991).

To compound the problem, crack has been implicated as a contributing factor to child neglect. The addicted parents invest all their energy in maintaining their habit, rather than caring for the child (Byrne, 1989a; Revkin, 1989). Children who are born addicted to cocaine often demonstrate poor interactive skills during the first weeks of life—a time when the all-important "bonding" with the mother should be taking place.

Breast feeding and cocaine use Cocaine may be stored in the mother's milk, and thus passed on to the infant by the mother through breast feeding (Peters & Theorell, 1991; Revkin, 1989). However, the cocaine levels in the maternal milk may be eight times as high as those in the mother's blood (Revkin, 1989). Thus, the infant may be exposed to extremely high levels of cocaine even if the mother had used even a modest amount.

THE USE OF NARCOTICS DURING PREGNANCY

The narcotics, like a large number of other drugs, cross the placenta in the pregnant woman. Thus, both the mother and the fetus are exposed to these drugs if they are used during pregnancy. Each year, approximately 10,000 babies are born to narcotics users in the United States (Bays, 1990; Zuckerman & Bresnahan, 1991). After cocaine, heroin is the second most commonly abused illicit drug by expectant mothers, accounting for almost 25% of all cases of fetal exposure to illegal drugs (American Academy of Family Physicians, 1990b).

According to Chasnoff (1988), complications associated with narcotic use during pregnancy include spontaneous abortions, premature delivery, the potentially fatal neonatal meconium aspiration syndrome, neonatal infections acquired through the mother, low birth weight, and neonatal narcotic addiction.

Chronic use of narcotics during pregnancy results in a state of chronic exposure to opiates for the fetus. At birth, the infants are themselves physically dependent on narcotics because of their passive exposure to the drug.

Following birth, as they are no longer able to absorb drugs from the mother's blood, these infants go through drug withdrawal. Depending on the specific narcotics being abused by the mother, this withdrawal process may last for weeks, or even months, in the newborn (Bays, 1990). The half-life for heroin in the newborn is 4 hours; for methadone, it is 23 hours (Zuckerman & Bresnahan (1991).

In years past, opiate withdrawal in the newborn resulted in almost a 90% mortality rate. The mortality rate has dropped significantly in recent years, largely as a result of increased medical awareness of the special needs of the addicted infant (Mirin et al., 1991). However, infants born addicted to narcotics are in a precarious state. It is a great struggle for them to survive the first few days of life. For example, there is evidence to suggest that infants exposed to narcotics during pregnancy are at risk for sudden infant death syndrome (Lewis et al., 1989).

Breast feeding and narcotics use   The narcotics user who is nursing her child will pass some of the drug on to the infant through the milk (Lourwood & Riedlinger, 1989). While the effects of a single dose of narcotics have only a minimal impact on the child, prolonged use may cause the child to be groggy, eat poorly, and possibly develop respiratory depression.

According to Lourwood and Riedlinger (1989), because the liver-metabolizing functions of the infant are not well developed, there is a danger that narcotics will accumulate in the child's body if the mother uses them for a prolonged period of time while breast feeding. Indeed, the baby who is breast fed by an opiate-abusing mother might actually obtain sufficient amounts of narcotics through breast milk to remain addicted to narcotics, according to Zuckerman and Bresnahan (1991).

MARIJUANA AND PREGNANCY

It has been estimated that 6 million women of childbearing age in this country use marijuana on a regular basis (Bays, 1990). Research findings suggest that marijuana use during pregnancy might contribute to "intrauterine growth retardation, poor weight gain, prolonged labor, and behavioral abnormalities in the newborn" (Nahas, 1986, p. 83).

Roffman and George (1988) report that several research studies have found significant evidence that marijuana use by the pregnant woman might result in developmental problems in the fetus, such as lowered birth weight and possible central nervous system abnormalities. According to Bays (1990), women who use marijuana at least once a month during pregnancy have a higher than average risk of premature delivery and their babies tend to be smaller than normal for their gestational age.

Breast feeding and marijuana use: The active agent of marijuana, THC, will pass into human milk and be passed on to the infant during breast feeding. The journal *Pediatrics for Parents* (1990) reports that breast feeding by mothers who smoke marijuana results in slower than average motor development for the child in the first year of life. Although this finding is based on a preliminary study of the effects of the mother's use of marijuana on the infant's development, it does suggest a potential hazard that should be avoided if at all possible.

THE USE OF BENZODIAZEPINES DURING PREGNANCY

Graedon (1980) warns that women who are pregnant, especially those in the first trimester of pregnancy, should not use any of the benzodiazepines. The benzodiazepines were once thought to contribute to the formation of cleft palates in children, a conclusion that has not been supported by further research (L. S. Cohen, 1989). However, benzodiazepine use during pregnancy is not recommended (L. S. Cohen, 1989; Graedon, 1980).

Breast feeding and benzodiazepine use   Since the benzodiazepines are found in the nursing mother's milk, Graedon (1980) suggests that nursing mothers also not use benzodiazepines. Lourwood and Riedlinger (1989) recommend that since these drugs are metabolized mainly by the liver, an organ that may not be fully developed in the infant, nursing mothers not use any of the benzodiazepines.

SMOKING AND PREGNANCY

A significant percentage of pregnant women smoke cigarettes. Unfortunately, pregnant women who smoke have a 30% higher risk of stillbirth and a 26% higher risk of having the infant die within the first few days of life than nonsmoking pregnant women (*Consumer Reports*, 1989). Furthermore, it is also possible that passive smoking (inhaling smoke from the cigarettes of others) may impact on fetal development, as noted in *Consumer Reports*.

THE USE OF OVER-THE-COUNTER ANALGESICS DURING PREGNANCY

Aspirin

Women who are pregnant, or who suspect they might be, should not use aspirin except under the supervision of a physician (Govoni & Hayes, 1988). Aspirin has been implicated as a cause of low birth weight in babies born to women who use it during pregnancy. There is also evidence pointing to aspirin as a cause of stillbirth and increased risk of perinatal mortality (United States Pharmacopeial Convention, 1990a).

Briggs, Freeman, and Yaffe (1986) explored the impact of maternal aspirin use on the fetus, and on breast-fed infants. They report that the use of aspirin by the mother during pregnancy might produce "anemia, antepartum and/or postpartum hemorrhage, prolonged gestation and prolonged labor" (p. 26a). They also state that aspirin has been implicated in significantly higher perinatal mortality and retardation of intrauterine growth when used at high doses by pregnant women.

Briggs et al. note that maternal use of aspirin in the week before delivery may cause delayed clotting of the infant's blood following birth. The United States Pharmacopeial Convention (1990a) goes further than this, warning that women should not use aspirin in the last *two* weeks of pregnancy. Aspirin has been found to cross the placenta, and research has suggested that maternal aspirin use during pregnancy may result in higher levels of aspirin in the fetus than in the mother.

Chasnoff (1988) notes that since the liver of the fetus is not fully developed, it is often difficult to predict the consequences of any drug in the fetus's body. Furthermore, since the fetus lacks the highly developed renal function of the mother, it would be difficult for a drug to be excreted even if the fetus could metabolize the drug into an excretable form. Govoni and Hayes (1988) do not recommend *any* use of aspirin by pregnant women, especially those *in the last trimester* of pregnancy.

According to Briggs et al. (1986), in addition to the more traditional forms of aspirin, many "hidden" forms of this drug are also consumed during pregnancy. Chasnoff (1988) reports that between 50% and 60% of pregnant women use some form of analgesic during their pregnancy. Such a large number of women using various chemicals under poorly contolled conditions makes it most difficult to assess the impact of aspirin use on the fetus or nursing mother, according to Briggs et al. They warn, however, that pregnant women should not use aspirin or products that contain aspirin on the grounds that the benefit/risk ratio of such drug use has not been established.

Although there have been no *proven* problems associated with the use of aspirin in women who choose to breast feed, this practice is also not recommended (Briggs et al., 1986; United States Pharmacopeial Convention, 1990a). Lourwood and Riedlinger (1989) suggest that mothers who are taking high doses of aspirin on a regular basis refrain from breast feeding, although they do not point to any risk from occasional use of aspirin.

Acetaminophen

Acetaminophen is considered "safe for short-term use" at recommended dosage levels by pregnant women (Briggs et al., 1986, p. 2a). There have been no reports of serious problems in women who hae used this drug during pregnancy. Briggs et al. note, however, that the death of one infant from kidney disease shortly after birth has been attributed to the mother's continuous use of acetaminophen at high dosage levels during pregnancy. Thus, there is a need for further research into the effects of this analgesic by women who are pregnant.

Although acetaminophen is excreted in low concentrations in the mother's milk, Briggs et al. (1986) found no evidence to suggest that this might have effects on the nursing infant. However, because acetaminophen is metabolized mainly by the liver, which is still quite immature in the newborn child, Lourwood and Riedlinger (1989) recommend that the mother who is breast feeding immediately after giving birth not use this drug. However, the authors do not warn against the occasional use of acetaminophen in women who are nursing their babies after the postpartum period.

Ibuprofen

When used at therapeutic dosage levels, ibuprofen has not been reported to cause congenital birth defects (Briggs et al., 1986). However, similar drugs have been known to inhibit labor, prolong pregnancy, and possibly cause other problems for the developing child; hence, use of ibuprofen should be avoided during pregnancy. Research would suggest that ibuprofen does not enter into human milk in significant quantities when used at normal dosage levels (Briggs et al., 1986), and is considered "compatible with breast feeding" (p. 217 i). Indeed, Lourwood and Riedlinger (1989) report that ibuprofen is "felt to be the safest" or the nonsteroidal anti-inflammatory drugs for the woman who is breast feeding her child.

BLOOD INFECTIONS ACQUIRED DURING PREGNANCY

A woman who abuses injected drugs, such as narcotics or cocaine, and who shares intravenous needles, runs the risk of contracting any of a number of infections from other addicts. If a pregnant woman becomes infected, the fetus may be exposed to the same infection. Indeed, babies born to women who use intravenously administered drugs may develop *any* of the blood infections commonly found in addicts.

It is quite possible for the fetus to acquire AIDS through the mother's blood. Indeed, Pope and Morin (1990) report that 2% of the babies born in New York City have HIV antibodies in their blood at the time of birth. However, Revkin (1989) estimates that only 30% to 50% of the babies who test positive for AIDS at birth actually are infected. The others are "false positives" as a result of maternal antibodies that normally circulate in the blood of the fetus before delivery.

These antibodies from the mother's blood may remain in the child's system for up to a year following delivery (McCutchan, 1990). In this time frame, the mother does not know whether she has a healthy baby or one who is infected wih HIV. This makes it difficult for her to "bond" with the child because she is uncertain whether or not the child will survive.

The transmission of blood-borne infections from mother to child is usually not considered a common problem. Yet, in some populations, a significant percentage of infants have been exposed to one or more infections as a result of the mother's use of intravenous drugs. These children are indeed hidden victims of drug addiction.

SUMMARY

In the past decade, the first steps toward an understanding of how drug addiction impacts a woman's life have been taken. There is evidence to suggest that women come to use chemicals for different reasons than men and that they support their addiction through different means than men. Despite this evidence, there has been relatively little research on the problem of drug dependency in women

Infants born to women who have used chemicals of abuse during pregnancy represent a special subpopulation. These children are often born addicted to the drugs. In many cases, the mother's use of chemicals during pregnancy causes the child to experience physical complications that may include low birth weight, stroke, retardation, and a host of other drug-specific complications. The over-the-counter analgesics represent a special area of risk because their effects on fetal growth and development are not well understood. However, the available research findings suggest that the OTC analgesics should be used with caution by pregnant or nursing women. Finally, the developing fetus is also at risk for blood infections transmitted by the addicted mother-to-be who shares hypodermic needles.

Chapter 20

OTHER HIDDEN VICTIMS OF CHEMICAL DEPENDENCY

A ll too often, addiction involves not only the addict but a host of others as well. Even when we limit consideration to just the addict, the disease is often hidden from view. It is the purpose of this chapter to explore this hidden aspect of chemical dependency and to sensitize the reader to the many forms that substance abuse can take.

WOMEN AND ADDICTION—AN OFTEN UNRECOGNIZED PROBLEM

It has been only in the past decade that researchers have begun to explore the relationship between women and chemical use (Rerucha, 1986). Recent findings suggest that addiction to chemicals finds different expression in women than it does in men. Further, it would seem that women who are addicted to chemicals are "underserved in terms of both numbers . . . and of quality of service" by treatment programs (Levers & Hawes, 1990, p. 528). In a study by Wilsnack (1991), fewer than a third of the treatment programs investigated had specialized treatment components for women.

Few women fit the popular stereotype of the drug user (Joyce, 1989). Women usually obtain their drug of choice in different ways than men; moreover, they tend to use drugs for different reasons and to experience them differently than their male counterparts. However, although they appear to have unique drug-use patterns, the literature "has paid relatively little attention to women" (Griffin, Weiss, Mirin, & Lang, 1989, p. 122), a point also attested to by Peluso and Peluso (1988), Blume (1985), and Rerucha (1986).

Peluso and Peluso (1988) offer some shocking statistics on the relationship between chemical use and gender. It is their contention that sedatives and "diet pills" have become "women's drugs" (p. 10), and they point out that 70% of sedative prescriptions and 80% of diet pill prescriptions are for women. Further, fully two-thirds of the prescriptions written for mood-altering chemicals are for women, leading Peluso and Peluso to conclude that for "millions of women . . . dependence on prescription chemicals has been rendered invisible" (p. 9). These women receive their drug of choice through strictly legal channels.

In their study of gender-related differences in drug-use patterns, Griffin et al. (1989) found that addicted females are more likely to start using opiates later in life than males and to use drugs more heavily. At the same time, women addicted to narcotics were found to be approximately the same age as men at the time of their first admission into drug treatment. This would suggest that, for women, narcotics addiction follows a different course than it does for men.

With cocaine, the picture is somewhat different. According to Griffin et al. (1989), female cocaine abusers start drug use at an earlier age than male cocaine abusers and are significantly younger at the time of their first admission to a drug treatment program. Kolodny (1985) observes that for many women a gift of cocaine has much the same meaning as a gift of flowers might have had generations ago. Again, these findings suggest that there are gender-related differences surrounding cocaine abuse. Again, however, research into narcotic and cocaine addiction has failed to address the different impact of chemicals on women as compared to men.

In a comparison of male and female alcoholics, Blume (1985) states that alcoholic females tend to display more varied responses to alcohol. Also, the woman's menstrual cycle will influence her response to alcohol. Finally, according to Blume, female alcoholics drink less alcohol in the average day than alcoholic males. Despite these differences, Blume reports that females first enter treatment for alcoholism at about the same age as males.

The 1976 publication *Alcoholics Anonymous* reported that nearly 25% of the members of AA were women, and that for newer members the percentage of women was closer to a third. According to Peluso and Peluso (1988), in a recent year some 42% of those who called the "800-COCAINE" telephone hotline were women. These figures suggest that women are as deeply involved in drug use as men.

Women who enter the workforce are thought to be two to three times as likely to develop problems with alcohol as those who do not (Kruzicki, 1987). However, according to Pape (1988), it is generally more difficult to detect addiction in the working woman than in the working man. As Kruzicki points out, many women in the workforce are working below their potential capacity, often in low-status positions where their chemical use may not interfere with their job performance.

Kruzicki also states that the addicted female is generally less threatened by possible job termination than the addicted male. Many women in the workforce work only to supplement their husband's income. Thus, it is often easier for an addicted woman to simply quit her job than to give in to a threatened loss of employment if she does not seek treatment (Pape, 1988).

It has been suggested (Hoard, 1988; Rerucha, 1986) that as many as 64% of female alcoholics suffer from premenstrual syndrome (PMS). This condition involves feelings of anxiety, tension, insomnia, and mood swings. In many cases, alcohol or other psychoactive chemicals are used by women with PMS to obtain relief from their symptoms. When PMS again places significant stress on the woman, a relapse to drug or alcohol use is likely (Schaefer & Evans, 1988).

To address this special problem, Schaefer and Evans suggest that women who suffer from PMS need to learn how to cope with the symptoms without resorting to chemicals. Such nondrug coping methods might include dietary changes, appropriate use of certain forms of birth-control medications, and individual counseling.

Women are indeed hidden victims of addiction. Peluso and Peluso (1988) hypothesize that addiction in women has gone largely unrecognized because of the important role women play in society. Rather than face the problem and deal with its realities, it is easier for society to close its eyes.

ADDICTION AND THE ELDERLY

The problem of alcoholism in the elderly has only recently begun to receive attention and presents an underrecognized challenge to mental health professionals (Ehlert, 1989; Wade, 1988). Research findings suggest that heavy drinking peaks in the age range of 40 to 50, after which it declines until about age 70 (Abrams & Alexopoulos, 1987). However, it is estimated that problem drinking still might be found in 5% to 12% of males and 1% to 2% of females aged 60 to 70 (Blake, 1990; Hurt, Finlayson, Morse, & Davis, 1988).

A small number of individuals become addicted to alcohol late in life, without having demonstrated earlier problem drinking. These individuals are referred to as "reactive alcoholics" by Peluso and Peluso (1989). The phenomenon has been termed "late onset alcoholism" by Hurt et al. (1988). According to Peluso and Peluso, about one-third of the elderly who drink to excess are reactive alcoholics, with the rest being long-term alcoholics.

It has been suggested that alcoholism is less likely to be detected in the elderly than in younger individuals (Anderson, 1989b; Rains, 1990). Moreover, the number of drinks consumed is a poor indicator of alcoholism in the elderly since "three beers at age 60 may have the same effect as 12 at age 21" (Anderson, 1989b, p. 7 ex). Further, the "impairments in social and occupational functioning attributable to alcoholism in younger people are not as obvious [in the elderly]" (Abrams & Alexopoulos, 1987, p. 1285).

Peluso and Peluso (1989) note that alcohol-related blackouts, financial problems, and job loss are often more difficult to identify in the elderly because of medical or age-related problems. Because of the physical effects of aging, older alcoholics are less able to withstand the physical impact of drinking than their younger counterparts (Blake, 1990; Rains, 1990). Further, alcohol's effects on an individual's cognitive abilities mimic those changes associated with normal aging, and even physicians find it difficult to differentiate between late-onset Korsakoff's syndrome and different forms of senile dementia, such as Alzheimer's disease (Anderson, 1989b; Blake, 1990; Reins, 1990).

The elderly, in particular, are at risk for alcohol-induced drug interactions. As a group, they use 25% of all prescriptions and over-the-counter medications, and their bodies require more time to metabolize many drugs. In spite of the fact that between 7% and 10% of those over 55 years of age have an alcohol-abuse problem placing them at risk for alcohol-drug interactions, few health care providers make the effort to explore possible alcohol use in the elderly (Ehlert, 1989). All too often, this results in potentially deadly combinations of medications and alcohol for these people (Ehlert, 1989; Peluso & Peluso, 1989).

Even social drinking has been found to be associated with cognitive deterioration in the elderly (Abrams & Alexopoulos, 1987; Rains, 1990). Alcoholism has been identified as the cause for psychiatric hospitalization in more than one-third of the cases studied (Abrams & Alexopoulos, 1987). On the bright side, however, there is evidence suggesting that elderly alcoholics respond better to treatment than do younger alcoholics (Blake, 1990; Rains, 1990).

Elderly alcoholics are more likely to present medical complications as a result of their drinking than younger adults (Hurt et al., 1988; Rains, 1990). Rains (1990) suggests that physicians carry out a comprehensive medical evaluation of all elderly patients to rule out hidden alcoholism. According to Ehlert (1989), "between 12% and 14% of older people hospitalized for *any* reason have a significant problem with alcohol. Alcoholics seem to use more health-care resources" (p. 10, italics added).

According to Vandeputte (1989), between 5% and 15% of the elderly seeking medical treatment for one reason or another are thought to have a drug-related problem. Blake (1990) estimates this percentage as 49%. As Vandeputte points out, alcohol may either complicate the treatment of existing diseases, or even cause the individual to develop various new medical problems. But, he goes on to state, few elderly alcoholics receive treatment for their addiction, resulting in increased medical costs for both the individual, and ultimately society, to treat these alcohol-induced problems.

Zimberg (1978) classifies older alcoholics into three subgroups. First are those individuals who develop drinking problems only late in life. Next are those individuals who have a history of intermittent problem drinking, but who develop a more chronic alcohol problem in late adulthood. Finally, there are those whose alcohol problems begin in young adulthood and continue into the later years.

Zimberg groups the second and third classes together to form a classification of what he terms "early onset" alcoholism. This subgroup is thought to include about two-thirds of the older alcoholics. Those individuals who demonstrate alcohol problems only in the later phases of life are said to have "late onset" alcoholism and are thought to compose about one-third of the elderly alcoholic population.

According to Zimberg, each subgroup presents different needs to treatment centers and each has a different prognosis. Further, early-onset alcoholics are more likely to have developed medical complications as a result of their alcohol use. Both early- and late-onset alcoholics are thought to be reacting to stresses of retirement, bereavement, loneliness, and physical illness common to the later stages of life (Dunlop, Manghelli & Tolson, 1989; Zimberg, 1978). Group therapy approaches that include a problem-solving and social-support component are thought to be useful in working with the older alcoholic, especially if such programs include Alcoholics Anonymous (Dunlop et al., 1989; Rains, 1990; Zimberg, 1978).

Dunlop et al. (1989) recommend that treatment programs for the elderly include the following components:

- A *primary prevention program* to warn about the dangers of using alcohol as a coping mechanism for life's problems;
- An *outreach program* to identify and serve older alcoholics who might be overlooked by more traditional treatment services;
- *Detoxification services* staffed by personnel experienced in working with the elderly, who frequently require longer detoxification periods than younger addicted persons;
- *Protective environments,* which is to say structured living environments that allow the elderly to take part in treatment while being protected from the temptation of further alcohol use;
- *Primary treatment programs* for those who could benefit from either inpatient or outpatient short-term care;
- *Aftercare programs* to help the older alcoholic with the transition from primary care to independent living;
- *Long-term residential care* for those who suffer from severe medical and/or psychiatric complications from alcoholism; and
- Access to *social work support services.*

Drinking patterns in the elderly are often different from those of younger adults (Peluso & Peluso, 1989; Vandeputte, 1989). Older alcoholics are more likely to be steady drinkers than binge drinkers. They rarely are involved in such alcohol-related altercations as barroom brawls, and the blackouts they may experience from excessive drinking are often attributed to nonalcohol-related medical problems by physicians or concerned individuals (Peluso & Peluso, 1989).

Vandeputte (1989) notes that the depression often seen in older individuals could be secondary to the use of alcohol, although this possibility is often overlooked by mental health professionals. The older alcoholic may require weeks or months to detoxify from alcohol or drugs (Anderson, 1989b). Indeed, according to Rains (1990), they may require up to 18 months of abstinence in order to fully recover from the effects of drinking. Further, older alcoholics may need help in building a nonalcoholic support structure to enable them to break the bonds of their drinking.

According to Zimberg (1978), elderly widowers are more likely to be alcoholic than elderly widows, with a rate of 105 alcoholic widowers per 1,000 population. He states further that between 10% and 15% of the elderly could be diagnosed as being alcoholic. Dunlop et al. (1989) suggest that an even higher percentage of the elderly population—perhaps as high as 25%—may be suffering from alcohol-related problems.

Abrams and Alexopoulos (1987), in a study that included other drugs besides alcohol, found that "more than 20 percent of patients over 65 years old admitted to a psychiatric hospital in one year could be considered drug dependent" (p. 1286). Hurt et al. (1988) also note that the elderly have a significant chemical-dependency problem. In their findings, some 10% of the patients admitted to a chemical-dependency treatment unit were over 65 years of age.

In their discussion of drug misuse in the elderly, Abrams and Alexopoulos (1987) point to (1) intentional overuse of medication, (2) underuse of medication, and (3) erratic use of prescribed medication. They also attribute drug misuse to the failure of physicians to obtain *complete* drug histories from their elderly patients. Intentional misuse of prescribed medications was found to be the largest category of drug abuse in the elderly by Abrams and Alexopoulos. The elderly were found to underuse prescribed medication often because of financial limitations.

It has been suggested that family members may experience shame or guilt over drug-addiction problems in their grandparents or great-grandparents (Peluso & Peluso, 1989; Vandeputte, 1989; Wade, 1988). For this reason, the family may hesitate to report the addicted person's problem. According to Wade (1988), only 15% of those elderly persons with a drug or alcohol problem are currently receiving help for that dependency.

The elderly often are slower to respond both physically and mentally than younger individuals. Furthermore, they are often offended by profane language or crude behavior commonly associated with younger individuals in alcoholic treatment programs (Dunlop et al., 1989). Unless their special needs are addressed, the elderly are unlikely to be motivated to participate in treatment. However, as we have noted, when their needs are met the elderly alcoholic often will respond to treatment better than younger alcoholics.

THE HOMOSEXUAL AND SUBSTANCE ABUSE

The homosexual male, or the lesbian woman, constitute part of what Fassinger (1991) terms a "hidden minority" within American society. However, the gay population is sizable, accounting for perhaps 10% to 15% of the total population. Society's response to individuals who have adopted a nontraditional form of sexuality has frequently been less than supportive, and many gay/lesbian individuals feel ostracized by a culture that neither understands nor tolerates their lifestyle. Thus, the homosexual may live on the fringes of society.

Within the gay community the bar assumes a role of central importance, for it is here that homosexuals can socialize without fear of ridicule or harassment. Further, the gay bar provides a safe haven for both gay men and lesbian women in the process of discovering their sexuality. While the gay bar no doubt serves a useful function, the fact that it is so important in the gay community is unfortunate for a number of reasons.

First, the alcoholism rate for gay men and lesbian women is higher than that of the heterosexual population. Indeed, it has been estimated that 18% to 38% of gay men and 27% to 35% of lesbian women would meet diagnostic criteria for a formal diagnosis of alcohol abuse or alcoholism (Hellman, Stanton, Lee, Tytun, & Vachon, 1989). Further, research has found that, as a group, lesbians suffer from higher rates of substance abuse than nonlesbians of the same age (Browning, Reynolds, & Dworkin, 1991).

Secondly, research has shown that homosexuals who abuse alcohol or drugs are not likely to practice "safe sex" (Linn et al., 1989). This contributes to the spread of AIDS and other sexually transmitted diseases. (We will discuss AIDS in more detail in Appendix 3.)

There is very little research into the special health care needs of the gay/lesbian client, and virtually no research into what treatment methods are effective for the substance-abusing gay/lesbian individual. However, considering Fassinger's (1991) estimate that gay/lesbian individuals make up 10% to 15% of the population and the estimate that approximately one-third of the gay/lesbian community abuses chemicals, it would appear that a significant percentage of those in treatment for substance-abuse problems live a nontraditional lifestyle.

The vast majority of substance-abuse professionals believe that their training in meeting the needs of gay/lesbian clients is "fair" at best. Indeed, almost 40% of the time, substance-abuse counselors receive *no* formal training in how to effectively work with the gay/lesbian client (Hellman et al., 1989). There are only a small number of specialized treatment programs to meet the needs of the gay/lesbian community, according to Hellman et al., and these programs are usually located in major metropolitan areas. There is thus a significant need for substance-abuse counselors to become aware of the special treatment needs of gays and lesbians and for treatment professionals to arrange for the specialized training necessary to effectively meet these needs.

SUBSTANCE ABUSE AND THE DISABLED

Very little research has been conducted in the area of substance-use patterns among the disabled. Nelipovich and Buss (1991) suggest that between 15% and 30% of the 33 to 45 million Americans with disabilities abuse alcohol or drugs. However, they report what appears to be an interaction effect between the specific form of disability and substance abuse. Specifically, Nelipovich and Buss found that individuals with visual impairments, orthopedic problems, or spinal cord injuries are more likely to abuse alcohol or drugs than those with other types of disabilities.

In their review of the available treatment resources in the state of Wisconsin, Nelipovich and Buss (1991) report that this population is "highly underserved" (p. 344). Rather than being identified as a special-needs subgroup, the disabled are often viewed "as isolated occasional cases, only remembered because of the difficulty and frustration they present to the professionals trying to serve them" (p. 344). The authors call for "creativity" on the part of rehabilitation staff who are attempting to meet the needs of disabled substance-abusing clients. Needless to say, cooperation among various rehabilitation professionals is also needed to work effectively with this unrecognized special-needs population.

SUBSTANCE ABUSE AND ETHNIC MINORITIES

Very little is known about the natural history of substance abuse in the various minority groups in the United States. J. E. Franklin (1989), for example, found that 16,000 articles on alcoholism published between 1934 and 1974, only 11 specifically deal with blacks (p. 1120). Virtually no research has been done on the subject of alcoholism and black females. Franklin notes that black alcoholics are more likely to suffer from medical complications of alcoholism than white alcoholics. Further, within the black community, AA has become a significant part of the treatment and recovery process, according to Franklin.

It should be noted, too, that there is virtually no research on the subject of alcohol/substance abuse among American Indians, Chinese-Americans, Japanese-Americans, or other Asian-Americans. What little is known about alcohol- or substance-abuse patterns within these subgroups is based on studies involving mostly white sample populations. Obviously, there is a need for research into the impact of substance use in these subgroups, including treatment methods that might prove valuable in working with them.

SUMMARY

We all have stereotypic images of the "typical" addict. Some may imagine a "skid-row" alcoholic drinking cheap wine out of a bottle. Others may think of a heroin addict in the ruins of an abandoned building, ready to inject a drug into his or her vein. While these images of addiction may be based in reality, they are isolated images only. Each fails to reflect the many hidden faces of addiction.

For example, there is the grandfather who is quietly drinking himself to death. There is the expectant mother who is exposing her unborn child to staggering amounts of cocaine, heroin, or alcohol. There is the career woman whose chemical addiction is hidden behind a veil of productivity. And there is the addict whose drug use is sanctioned by unsuspecting physicians who are trying to provide relief for feelings of depression or anxiety. There are faces of addiction so well hidden that, even today, they go unrecognized. As professionals, we must learn to look for and identify the hidden victims of addiction.

Chapter 21

CHILD AND ADOLESCENT
SUBSTANCE ABUSE

Although chemical use by children and adolescents has received a great deal of media attention in the past 20 years, it is by no means a new phenomenon. Children and adolescents have been using alcohol at least since the time of Charles Dickens, when alcoholism was rampant among the youth of England (Wheeler & Malmquist, 1987). The social changes that took place in the late 1800s and early 1900s drove child and adolescent alcohol use underground, and changes in the laws made it difficult for many children and adolescents to obtain alcohol. However, there has always been at least a small percentage of alcohol- or drug-using adolescents in the United States, although society for the most part has denied the existence of a significant problem.

Adolescent drug use did not become widespread again until the late 1960s and early 1970s. It was during this time that society went through a period of rapid evolution. Large numbers of adolescents rebelled against society's standards and the use of chemicals was viewed as a legitimate part of this rebellion. Although a phase of drug experimentation has long been accepted as part of the normal growth sequence of adolescents (Newcomb & Bentler, 1989), only in the last two generations have younger adolescents and even children been experimenting with chemical use on the scale we see today.

DRUG-USE PATTERNS IN CHILDREN AND ADOLESCENTS

Little is known about drug use and addiction among children and adolescents (Evans & Sullivan, 1990). Further, little is known about the distinguishing characteristics of those youngsters who abstain from drug use, those who use chemicals only as part of a phase of experimentation, and those individuals will go on to develop a problem with drug addiction.

Lack of information on possible chemical-use patterns in children makes it quite difficult to identify criteria by which to distinguish between normal and abnormal chemical use during the first decade of life. Further, this lack of information makes it difficult to identify which chemicals are likely to be used by children and what the implications of their drug use might be for their subsequent growth and development.

236

On a similar note, there has been only limited research into teenage drug-use patterns (Evans & Sullivan, 1990; Kaminer, 1991; Newcomb & Bentler, 1989). Thus, it is difficult to determine current drug-abuse trends or identify the factors that might motivate an adolescent to experiment with chemicals. We cannot say with certainty whether drug use in a given individual is part of a normal phase of experimentation or a symptom of a serious problem. We also do not know the impact that drug use might have on the adolescent's emotional adjustment.

Another factor that contributes to the confusion surrounding child and adolescent drug use is the tendency for some to equate virtually *any* use of chemicals during adolescent with a serious drug-abuse problem (Newcomb & Bentler, 1989; Peele, 1989). This viewpoint confounds the question of exactly what constitutes "drug abuse" and ignores the fact that many adolescents use drugs only in an experimentation or exploration phase (Shedler & Block, 1990).

During this phase of experimentation, an adolescent might use one or more chemicals repeatedly, only to settle down in young adulthood to a more acceptable pattern of chemical use (Evans & Sullivan, 1990; Peele, 1989). A recent study, for example, found that of identified adolescent "problem drinkers," 53% of the males and 70% of the females were *not* judged to still be problem drinkers 7 years later (Zarek, Hawkins, & Rogers, 1987). Thus, the adolescent who uses chemicals on a regular basis may or may not go on to develop a problem with chemicals in young adulthood.

Finally, drug-use patterns among children and adolescents fluctuate rapidly. Moreover, they may vary according to geographic location and current drug-use "trends." For example, the phenomenon of inhalant abuse represents a drug-use fad that rapidly waxes and wanes in a given geographic area.

THE SCOPE OF THE PROBLEM

As we have already mentioned, there is a paucity of research on drug use in children, which is to say alcohol or drug use before the age of 12 or 13. The available research on adolescent drug use suggests that it peaked around 1981 and has been slowly declining since then (Oetting & Beauvais, 1990). There is some limited drug use in the 4th and 5th grades, with the greatest increase in the numbers of adolescents using chemicals appearing in the 6th through 9th grades. This is followed by a decline in the number of school-aged drug users in grades 10 through 12 (Oetting & Beauvais, 1990).

According to Newcomb and Bentler (1989), inhalants are likely to be the first chemicals used by children to alter their state of consciousness. As to the epidemiology of childhood drug use no statistics are provided. Johnston et al. (1989) report that over 17% of the high school seniors in the class of 1989 admitted to using inhalants at least once in their lives. Approximately two-thirds of those who admitted to using inhalants at some point did so on fewer than six occasions.

As noted in Chapter 11, inhalant abuse usually is a phase that lasts for 1 to 2 years at most; however, about a third of the children who abuse inhalants will move on to more traditional forms of drug abuse (Brunswick, 1989). Thus, for some, inhalants serve as a "gateway" chemical that leads to other forms of drug abuse.

Alcohol is the most common mood-altering chemical used by adolescents. Although many parents worry about possible alcohol use by their adolescent children, when questioned they tend to underestimate how much their teenagers actually drink (Rogers, Harris, & Jarmuskewicz, 1987; Zarek et al., 1987). It is for this reason that much of what is known about adolescent drug-use patterns is based on information gathered through anonymous surveys of adolescents.

According to Rogers et al. (1987), the average age of the first drink of alcohol is 11.9 years for boys, and 12.7 years for girls. Despite isolated reports of alcohol-abuse problems in children as young as 11 years of age, they conclude that problem drinking is quite rare in preadolescence. The most popular form of alcohol for the adolescents surveyed by Rogers et al. was beer, although the recently introduced wine coolers were increasing in popularity. Those individuals who admit to even occasional experimentation with vodka, gin, whiskey, or bourbon should be considered as having an alcohol-abuse problem in the opinion of Rogers et al.

In a study by Johnston et al. (1988), by the time of high school graduation, 92% of the adolescents sampled had used alcohol at least once, while approximately 18% of high school seniors of the class of 1988 smoked cigarettes on a regular basis. Newcomb and Bentler (1989) report that by the time of early adolescence, approximately 30% of the adolescents they surveyed had used at least one illicit drug (usually marijuana). By the time of high school graduation, this percentage increases to 54%, according to Johnston et al. Zarek et al., (1987) report that about two-thirds of the adolescents in grades 7 through 12 have used alcohol at least once and conclude that "most adolescents become drinkers before entering high school" (p. 484).

By the time of graduation from high school, 43.7% of the 17,000 high school seniors questioned by Johnston et al. admitted to having used marijuana at least once, while almost 91% admitted to having used alcohol at least once. Further, on the basis of their data, Johnston et al. conclude that by the time of graduation, 50.9% of high school seniors will have tried at least one illicit chemical (again, usually marijuana).

The findings of Newcomb and Bentler (1989) are very similar to those reported by Johnson et al. Newcomb and Bentler report that 92% of the high school seniors studied admitted to having used alcohol at least once, while 66% admitted to the use of alcohol in the preceding month. In Newcomb and Bentler's survey, 57% of the high school seniors admitted to the use of an illicit drug at least once, and more than one-third admitted to the use of an illicit drug other than marijuana. Although cocaine use in general appears to be decreasing, the use of crack cocaine seems to be growing in popularity (Johnston et al., 1989).

It should be noted that adolescent drug-use surveys focus on the greatest concentration of adolescents—those who are in school. However, as Oetting and Beauvais (1990) point out, there may be a self-selection process at work in the schools, in the sense that those adolescents who use narcotics or inhalants on a regular basis may very well drop out of school.

Children who encounter academic problems in the middle to late elementary school grades are more likely to engage in alcohol and/or drug abuse than are those students who achieve higher grades (Board of Trustees, 1991). Furthermore, those adolescents who are not interested in academic achievement are more likely to turn to chemicals and are also at high risk for dropping out of school. Thus, surveys of adolescent drug use that are based on student responses may underestimate the extent of adolescent drug use.

Another shortcoming of national surveys is that they frequently fail to account for regional variations on drug-use patterns (Oetting & Beauvais, 1990). For example, Moncher, Holden, and Trimble (1990) conclude that adolescent Native Americans are two to three times as likely to be at least moderately involved with alcohol as their non-Native-American counterparts. Consequently, it should be kept in mind that national drug-use patterns among adolescents may or may not reflect local adolescent substance-abuse behaviors.

Smoking Patterns in Children and Adolescents

Although cigarettes and other tobacco products cannot be legally purchased by minors in the United States, the fact remains that nicotine addiction is *not* limited to adults. Within the past few years, there has been a growing awareness that a significant number of children and adolescents also use tobacco products. Indeed, the very roots of nicotine addiction may lie in childhood or adolescence, as evidenced by the fact that between 80% (Roper, 1991) and 90% (Pierce et al., 1991) of adult cigarette smokers began to smoke before the age of 21.

Tobacco use by children and adolescents is hardly an insignificant problem. Johnston et al. (1989) state that almost 19% of high school seniors in the class of 1989 admitted that they smoked on a regular basis. This was a slight increase from the year before, when slightly over 18% of the class of 1988 admitted to smoking. These figures are similar to those obtained by DiFranza and Tye (1990), who report that 18.1% of the high school seniors they surveyed admitted to smoking cigarettes on a daily basis. Thus, there is agreement among researchers that approximately one in five high school seniors are habitual cigarette smokers.

According to some, it is not by accident that children and adolescents turn to the use of cigarettes. Indeed, according to Waxman (1991), given the high mortality rates associated with tobacco smoking, "the success of the tobacco industry is dependent on recruiting people who don't believe that smoking kills" (p. 3185). Because smokers who either stop or who die for one reason or another must be replaced, it has been suggested that tobacco advertising techniques are designed to specifically target children and adolescents (Di-Franza et al., 1991; Pierce et al., 1991), as well as those who are economically disadvantaged or who live in the Third World (Waxman, 1991).

According to DiFranza and Tye (1990), if sales to children account for 3.3% of cigarette sales, "six companies share an annual $703 million in revenues and $221 million in profits from the sales of cigarettes to children" (p. 2786).

DiFranza and Tye also note that many of the children and adolescents who begin to use tobacco before the age of 21 will go on to become addicted, thus providing the tobacco companies dividends in the form of new generations of smokers.

According to Holland and Fitzsimons (1991), the transition from a non-smoker to smoker in childhood or adolescence appears to take place in four stages, as follows:

1. the *preparatory* phase, during which the youngster will form attitudes accepting of cigarette smoking;
2. the *initiation* phase, in which he or she will smoke for the first time;
3. the *experimentation* phase, in which the child or adolescent learns how to smoke; and
4. the *transition* to regular smoking.

Given that the attitudes supportive of, or at least accepting of, smoking are formed prior to the initiation of actual smoking behaviors, Holland and Fitzsimons suggest that attempts at intervention need to be aimed at children who have not started to form these attitudes. Such attempts at intervention should focus on helping children learn social skills that will enable them to resist smoking. If the adolescent reaches the age of 18 without having initiated smoking, he or she is unlikely to do so, according to Holland and Fitzsimons.

WHY DO ADOLESCENTS USE CHEMICALS?

The initial factor that influences adolescent experimentation appears to be either curiosity or peer pressure (Joshi & Scott, 1988) coupled with an inability to perceive oneself as vulnerable to the negative effects of alcohol or the other drugs of abuse (Alexander, 1991). In time, however, many adolescents find that their chemical use offers some relief from feelings of depression (Joshi & Scott, 1988) or conflict (Evans & Sullivan, 1990), or that it serves as a means of coping with stress (Rhodes & Jason, 1990). The reasons for any given individual's chemical use is often influenced by his or her emotional maturity, available resources, and social support systems.

During childhood, parental influence on subsequent drug-use behavior is the strongest. During this period of life, the child will accept parental guidance as to how to behave, but will also be very aware of the unspoken "guidance" of their parents' behavior (Rogers et al., 1987). Thus, if the parents use chemicals, they may be modeling drug-use behaviors for their children. Kaminer (1991) notes that there is evidence that parental substance use is associated with subsequent use of chemicals by the adolescent. He points out, however, that the relationship between parental chemical abuse and drug use by the teenaged children is quite complex, involving other factors than simply whether or not the parents use chemicals.

During adolescence, peer influences play an increasingly important role in shaping the individual's drug-use pattern. Some adolescents find that using chemicals causes them to be accepted by other drug-using teens. Others find that the drugs offer relief from internal distress, and they again drift towards those who also use drugs. Still other adolescents find that drug use is consistent with a risk-taking, sensation-seeking lifestyle often associated with social delinquency (Kaminer, 1991).

The early adolescent years are a time of special vulnerability for later drug abuse. It is during this stage that many begin to experiment with various gateway chemicals that open the door to drug-abuse problems in adulthood (Pentz et al., 1989). Such gateway drugs include tobacco, alcohol, and marijuana. As previously mentioned, inhalants also serve as gateway drugs (Brunswick, 1989).

THE ADOLESCENT ABUSE/ADDICTION DILEMMA: HOW MUCH IS TOO MUCH?

Unfortunately, because very little is known about adolescent drug use, it is quite difficult to distinguish between experimental drug use, an early drug-use problem, a chronic drug-abuse problem, and drug addiction in adolescents (Wheeler & Malmquist, 1987). Further, little is known about the personality characteristics of those who abstain from chemical use as opposed to those who experiment with chemicals or those who ultimately go on the develop some form of addiction.

Newcomb and Bentler (1989) report that such social variables as low socioeconomic status, lack of religious commitment, low self-esteem, and disturbed families all tend to influence adolescent drug-use patterns. As we have noted, peer pressure has been found to be one of the strongest immediate influences on adolescent drug use (Joshi & Scott, 1988; Newcomb & Bentler, 1989).

However, according to Shedler and Block (1990), certain personality traits seem to predispose individuals to abstain from recreational chemical use or drug abuse during adolescence. In their longitudinal study of a group of adolescents tracked from early childhood, Shedler and Block found that extremes of behavior (that is, total abstinence or serious drug abuse) characterized those adolescents who were most maladjusted. The healthiest group were those who had occasionally experimented with chemicals.

These findings, although surprising at first glance, do seem to make clinical sense. The emotionally healthy adolescent might experiment with drugs on occasion, but ultimately would have the interpersonal and intrapersonal skills necessary to cope with life. However, as Shedler and Block report, those adolescents who used drugs on a frequent basis demonstrated poor impulse control, a pattern of social alienation, and emotional distress—all signs that they lacked the emotional resources of the first group.

Further, those individuals who totally abstained from chemical use were found to be anxious, emotionally constricted, and lacking in social skills. These individuals seem to lack the self-confidence to allow them to explore their environments, which includes an exploration of the possibility of recreational drug use. According to Shedler and Block, an individual's chemical-use pattern (abstinence, experimental drug use, or frequent drug abuse) can be interpreted only in light of the individual's emotional adjustment.

Robert Haggarty (quoted in Kirn, 1989) suggests that "problem behavior" in adolescents might reflect economic problems and a rather pessimistic view of the future. Such problem behavior includes teen pregnancies, delinquency, and drug abuse. According to Mikkelsen (1985), such acute stressors as a geographic move, a major psychological loss, an increase in family conflict, or increased pressure to perform in school all are predictors of the initial, usually transient, use of chemicals by adolescents.

The Stages of Adolescent Chemical Use

R. L. Jones (1990) identifies four distinct stages of drug abuse in adolescents. In the first of these stages, which Jones refers to as "learning the mood swing," the young drug user is exposed to and learns what to expect from substance use. For those individuals who continue to abuse chemicals, many will reach the second stage of drug abuse, "seeking the mood swing." This stage is marked by a change in friendship patterns, erratic school performance, unpredictable mood swings, and manipulative behaviors in the service of continued substance abuse.

According to Jones, the third stage of substance abuse is marked by a preoccupation with the mood swing. Those friends who do not use drugs are dropped and family confrontations develop. The adolescent will lie constantly and may be expelled from school or be fired from his or her job. At this stage, the use of mood-altering chemicals will be on a daily basis. Ultimately, some individuals will continue to the final stage, in which drugs are used not to get high but just to feel normal. At this point, the individual will experience physical complications from the drug use, including memory loss and/or flashback experiences, paranoia, and anger.

Jones believes that certain adolescents should be evaluated for possible substance abuse, including "runaways," those showing signs of depression, and those demonstrating behavioral problems at school. Further, those adolescents in trouble with the law because of substance abuse and those exhibiting delinquency problems or experiencing recurrent accidents should be considered drug abusers until proven otherwise, according to Jones.

It was once thought that adolescents were unlikely to actually become addicted to chemicals, if only because they did not have the opportunity to abuse chemicals for an extended period of time. According to Morrison (1990), because adolescents are unlikely to have developed physical dependence and withdrawal symptoms, the first sign of a drug-abuse problem in the adolescent might be a drug-related visit to the local emergency room.

Can Adolescents Actually Become Addicted to Chemicals?

Adolescents may indeed become addicted to chemicals, even though their drug use usually has not been of long duration. Hoffmann, Belille, and Harrison (1987) found, for example, that over three-quarters of their sample of 1,000 adolescents in treatment for drug abuse reported having developed tolerance to alcohol or other drugs. Further, one-third of their sample reported withdrawal symptoms from drugs or alcohol.

In a study by Evans and Sullivan (1990), adolescents also reported having experienced withdrawal symptoms from chemicals. In this case, however, these symtoms appeared to be the exception rather than the rule. Thus, although there is evidence that adolescents can become physically addicted to chemicals, the extensiveness of adolescent addiction is not clear.

There are some researchers who challenge the concept of adolescent addiction. For example, Farrow (1990) states that "the number of teenagers who are *truly* chemically dependent is less than 1% of all users" (p. 1268, italics added). Another 10% to 15% might meet diagnostic criteria for alcohol/drug abuse, while a full 10% to 15% of all teenagers have little or no experience with alcohol or drugs. The remainder are occasional users, and will likely adjust their use in "nonproblematic ways" as they grow older (p. 1268).

The key point to remember is that there is a difference between adolescent drug use and drug abuse. According to Newcomb and Bentler (1990), individuals who start to use drugs in response to social pressure may continue to use them in response to internal emotional states. However, there is significant evidence suggesting that the majority of those adolescents who use chemicals will not go on to develop dependency on them (R. L. Jones, 1990). Rather, one phase of development that many adolescents go through seems to involve experimental drug use. Of those adolescents who enter into this phase, only a small percentage will go on to develop a more serious drug-abuse problem.

Problems in Diagnosis and Treatment of Adolescent Drug Abuse

The diagnosis of adolescent drug abuse is a complicated task, requiring an extensive data base (Evans & Sullivan, 1990; Wheeler & Malmquist, 1987).

In the opinion of Newcomb and Benler, 1989), the occasional use of alcohol or marijuana at a party does not necessarily reflect drug abuse. The treatment professional must keep in mind the possibility that the adolescent has not developed a drug-abuse problem, but that he or she is merely going through a period of experimentation in which drug use is limited to isolated episodes.

Referrals for a chemical dependency evaluation on an adolescent will come from many sources. The juvenile court system will frequently refer an offender for an evaluation, especially when that individual was shown to be under the influence of chemicals at the time of his or her arrest. School officials may request an evaluation on a student suspected of abusing chemicals. Treatment-center admissions officers will frequently recommend an evaluation, although this is usually referred to in-house staff rather than to an independent professional. Some parents also will request an evaluation and/or treatment for their teenager after the first known episode of alcohol or drug use.

Because adolescent drug abusers have not had time in which to develop an extensive history of chemical use, such "traditional" symptoms of a drug-abuse problem as tolerance, craving, and withdrawal are not commonly encountered according to Kaminer and Frances (1991). Moreover, when these symptoms are encountered in the adolescent, they are usually much less severe than the same symptoms in the adult.

Kaminer and Frances also note that the adolescent's developmental stage may preclude his or her being able to understand the implications of drug use. Adolescents frequently feel that they are invulnerable; they are unconcerned with the long-term consequences of their destructive behavior. The adolescent will not have had time to "hit bottom" and may have a rather immature view of life. This simplistic outlook may mistakenly be interpreted by treatment staff as a sign of resistance. Thus, Kaminer and Frances recommend a multidisciplinary team approach to assessment in cases of suspected adolescent substance abuse to ensure the accurate appraisal of the individual's adaptive style.

Even when a legitimate need for treatment has been identified, several factors may interfere with the treatment process. As cited by Kaminer and Frances, these include (a) unrealistic parental expectations for treatment, (b) hidden agendas for treatment by both the adolescent and the parents, (c) parental psychopathology, and (d) parental drug or alcohol abuse. These factors often combine to inhibit treatment of the adolescent drug or alcohol abuser.

The financial incentive for overdiagnosis   The admissions officers of many treatment centers hold that chemical use by adolescents absolutely points to a drug-abuse problem. Such treatment professionals, perhaps with an eye more on the balance sheet than on the individual's needs, frequently recommend treatment on the basis of any adolescent drug use. As Newcomb and Bentler (1989) comment, there is growing concern that for various reasons, not the least of which is the profit motive, treatment programs are purposefully blurring the distinction between use and abuse (any use equals abuse) and preying on the national drug hysteria to scare parents into putting their teenager in treatment with as little provocation as having a beer or smoking a joint. (p. 246)

According to Dr. Norman Hoffmann (quoted in Turbo, 1989), the annual bonus for the director of many inpatient treatment programs is based on the average daily census. Thus, there is a financial incentive for the clinical staff to keep as many beds occupied as possible. In such a situation, it is to the financial advantage of the treatment center staff to find as many cases of "addiction" as they can. One must wonder, given this situation, how much effort the treatment center staff is likely to invest in excluding the possibility of drug abuse in an adolescent (or even an adult) being evaluated for possible admission.

Forcing an individual—even if "only" an adolescent—into treatment when he or she does not have a chemical addiction may have lifelong consequences (Peele, 1989). Furthermore, such action may violate the rights of the individual. Indeed, in some states it is illegal to force adolescents into treatment against their will, even with parental permission (Evans & Sullivan, 1990).

It is important to keep in mind that there are no diagnostic criteria by which to determine accurately whether or not an adolescent is addicted to chemicals. Nevertheless, drug rehabilitation programs continue to try to instill the belief in children that they are perpetually debilitated. Peele (1989) notes:

Only *after* making this concession, treatment personnel contend, can children begin to make progress through life, albeit now convinced that they can never really be whole or lead a normal existence. (pp. 103–104)

The risks of underdiagnosis   A diagnosis of adolescent drug/alcohol abuse is not easily arrived at. Moreover, as Wheeler and Malmquist (1987) point out, such a diagnosis is further complicated by the fact that adolescents, as a general rule, do not develop the hallmark symptoms of adult forms of drug addiction. However, there are also risks associated with failing to treat those adolescents for whom drug use is a serious problem (Evans & Sullivan, 1990). When an individual's drug use *has* resulted in serious physical changes, or when he or she has acquired a blood infection such as AIDS from dirty needles, the individual is scarred not just for the rest of adolescence, but for life.

The work of Crumley (1990) underscores yet another aspect of adolescent drug abuse: the possibility that it may lead to attempted suicide. Crumley posits that adolescent substance abuse and suicide attempts are significantly related, although the exact nature of this relationship is not clear. He states:

Psychoactive substance abuse appears to have become an addition to the list of risk factors for adolescent suicidal behavior. (p. 3055)

Indeed, drug abuse has been associated with an astounding 70% of all suicides in adolescents and young adults (Group for the Advancement of Psychiatry, 1991).

The chemical dependency treatment professional who works with adolescents must attempt to find the middle ground between underdiagnosis, with all of its attendant dangers, and overdiagnosis, which may burden individuals for life with the mistaken notion that they are forever impaired.

DIAGNOSTIC CRITERIA FOR ADOLESCENT DRUG/ALCOHOL PROBLEMS

In light of the preceding discussion, one may wonder whether or not there are indicators of adolescent chemical problems. Zarek et al. (1987) identify the following criteria by which to diagnose adolescent drug abuse: (a) using chemicals to get "smashed"; (b) attending parties at which drugs other than alcohol are used; (c) refusing to attend parties at which drugs are not available; (d) drinking liquor, as opposed to beer or wine; (e) using marijuana, and (f) being drunk at school. Zarek et al. describe the adolescent with a drug-abuse problem as likely to be experiencing behavior problems at school.

According to Evans and Sullivan (1990), adolescents who are using drugs will often demonstrate such school-related problems as tardiness, absenteeism, apathy, drowsiness in class, moodiness, negativity towards school, loss of interest in extracurricular activities, and failure to complete class assignments. These adolescents may abandon old friends in favor of a different crowd and start to dress differently. Evans and Sullivan go on to note that adolescent drug-use patterns are different from adult patterns. Teenagers more often exhibit bingelike patterns rather than gradual increases in their drug use.

The adolescent who is becoming more and more preoccupied with chemical use, or who demonstrates an interest in an expanding variety of chemicals, might be demonstrating the adolescent equivalent of the progression of chemical use characteristic of adults. They will also demonstrate a loss of control, which is expressed through violations of personal rules about drug use. Thus, Evans and Sullivan argue that those adolescents with drug-abuse problems may be identified and should be treated for chemical dependency.

According to Newcomb and Bentler (1989), a teenager with a drug-abuse problem is (a) repeatedly using chemicals; (b) using chemicals at inappropriate times; or (c) experiencing legal, social, or school-related problems as a result of chemical use. This drug-abuse problem may be acute, episodic, or chronic.

SUMMARY

Clearly, children and adolescents are often hidden victims of drug addiction. Yet there is a serious lack of research into the problem of child or adolescent drug use/abuse. While mental health professionals acknowledge that peer pressure and family environment influence the adolescent's chemical use pattern, the exact role that these forces (or the media) play in shaping the adolescent's behavior is still not known. There are many unanswered questions surrounding the issue of child and adolescent drug use, and in the years to come we might see significant breakthroughs in our understanding of the forces that shape chemical use beliefs and patterns of use in the young.

In the face of this dearth of clinical research, the treatment professional must steer a cautious path between underdiagnosis and overdiagnosis of chemical dependency in the younger client. Just as surgery performed during childhood or adolescence will have lifelong consequences, so will the traumatic experience of being forced into treatment for a problem that may or *may not* exist. As with surgery, the treatment professional should carefully weigh the potential benefits of treatment against the potential harm to the individual.

Chapter 22

THE DUAL-DIAGNOSIS CLIENT: ADDICTION AND MENTAL ILLNESS

It is now known that alcohol or chemical abuse is involved in at least one-third of psychiatric cases seen by mental health professionals (Galanter, Casteneda, & Ferman, 1988) and fully 60% of all first-time adult psychiatric admissions to inpatient treatment (Willoughby, 1984). Yet, until quite recently the problem of drug abuse or addiction among the mentally ill was all but ignored.

In past years, drug abuse or addiction in the mentally ill was thought to be quite rare. This may be because health care professionals often did not even bother to look for it. If it *was* discovered that the client had been abusing chemicals, or that he or she was addicted, the drug use was assumed to be secondary to the "primary" disease of mental illness. Mental health professionals were taught to believe that the substance abuse or addiction would automatically go away once the "primary" psychiatric problem had been resolved.

In the past decade, as health care professionals have come to understand more about the nature of mental illness and substance abuse, they have discovered that the so-called dual-diagnosis client is not as rare as was once thought (Minkoff, 1989). Indeed, drug abuse is seven times as prevalent in the mentally ill as in the general population. Further, researchers have discovered that alcohol abuse or addiction is ten times as prevalent in the mentally ill as in the general population (Kivlahan, Heiman, Wright, Mundt, & Shupe, 1991).

However, for all that we now know about the substance-abuse problem in the mentally ill, there is much left to discover. Health care professionals have reached the point where they may acknowledge the existence of a drug-abuse problem in clients who suffer from one form or another of mental illness. But, beyond this vague acknowledgement that a problem does indeed exist, little is known about how best to deal with it.

WHAT IS MEANT BY "DUAL DIAGNOSIS"?

The term *dual diagnosis* has been applied to a wide range of coexisting problems, including combinations of substance abuse and a variety of other disorders, such as anorexia, bulimia, gambling, spouse abuse, and AIDS. For the purpose of this text, *dual diagnosis*, or *MI/CD*, will be used in reference to those individuals with a coexisting psychiatric disorder and substance-abuse problem.

Protracted chemical use may result in the client developing any of a wide range of psychiatric syndromes, depending on the specific agents being used. The chronic cocaine user, for example, may experience a postcocaine depression of suicidal proportions, while the amphetamine addict may develop an amphetamine-related paranoia closely resembling paranoid schizophrenia. As you may recall from Chapter 4, there is a strong relationship between alcohol use and depression. This depression usually resolves within a few days after abstinence has been achieved.

Distinguishing a primary psychiatric dysfunction from a drug-induced disorder is quite difficult (Galanter et al., 1988). While drug-induced disorders can be serious problems, they are not *primary* psychiatric dysfunctions. Rather, these psychiatric disorders are secondary to the individual's chemical use. On a diagnostic summary form, such problems are noted as being secondary to the individual's cocaine abuse, amphetamine abuse, or other chemical abuse.

Dual-diagnosis clients, as we have indicated, are those clients who not only suffer from mental illness, but who also abuse chemicals. Such clients are a subpopulation of those who abuse drugs or who are addicted to them. In the dual-diagnosis client, the mental illness and the substance abuse/addiction are *separate* chronic disorders. The chemical abuse/addiction problem and the mental illness have independent courses, yet each is able to influence the progression of the other (Carey, 1989).

One should keep in mind that the label "mentally ill" is, itself, quite vague. There are a range of different conditions, each with a different etiology, that are lumped together under the heading of "mental illness" (Weiss, Mirin, & Frances, 1992). The classification "dual-diagnosis client," while serving to identify a subset of substance abusers, is, unfortunately, only a vague classification that fails to communicate much information about the client's unique strengths or needs.

For example, consider the following dual-diagnosis clients. The first suffers from schizophrenia and uses marijuana and alcohol. The second has a personality disorder and is addicted to alcohol. The third struggles with a phobic disorder and is addicted to benzodiazepines. Finally, a fourth client suffers from a major depressive disorder and is addicted to heroin. Each of these clients would be classified as "mentally ill." Each one is also either abusing or is addicted to chemicals. As such, each qualifies as a dual-diagnosis client.

The preceding clients, although all classified as dual-diagnosis, would receive different treatment. The treatment approach for the depressed individual would be far different from that used for the client suffering from schizophrenia. And both approaches would be far different from the treatment approach used in working with the personality-disordered client. Further, all three treatment approaches would be far different from the one used for the client with the phobia.

Much of the literature that addressed the dual-diagnosis client focuses on the problem of psychosis (usually schizophrenia) and substance abuse. There is virtually no information available on the phobic patient, for example, who also is abusing chemicals. Thus, much remains to be discovered about the multitude of ways in which substance abuse and the various forms of mental illness might interact.

DUAL-DIAGNOSIS CLIENTS: A DIAGNOSTIC CHALLENGE

Dual-diagnosis clients represent a special challenge to treatment professionals. First of all, until the client is drug-free it is not possible to accurately diagnose the primary psychiatric dysfunction (Carey, 1989; Evans & Sullivan, 1990; Rado, 1988; Wallen & Weiner, 1989). According to Nathan (1991), it is necessary for the patient to be drug-free for 4 to 6 weeks before an accurate diagnosis can be made.

To further complicate the diagnostic picture, MI/CD clients are often unable to discuss their chemical use because of their ongoing psychiatric problems (Kanwischer & Hundley, 1990). The schizophrenic client might be too disorganized to discuss his or her chemical use, while the client suffering from a phobia might be unwilling to give up what he or she feels is an essential coping mechanism for drug-related anxiety.

Also, treatment professionals must keep in mind that dual-diagnosis clients may also actively attempt to hide their drug use from mental health professionals. Direct questions about alcohol or drug use may contribute to their feelings of defensiveness or shame (Pristach & Smith, 1990). This factor, along with the others we have mentioned, makes the dual-diagnosis client particularly hard to identify. It is not uncommon for treatment professionals to require a period of weeks, or even months, in which to gather sufficient information to make an accurate diagnosis.

Why Worry About the Dual-Diagnosis Client?

Once, while talking to a psychiatrist about a specific client, a clinical psychologist mentioned his concern about the patient's use of alcohol. The patient, who had been institutionalized for chronic schizophrenia for many years, would visit a local bar once or twice a month for a few drinks. The staff at the state hospital would tolerate this patient's drinking while on an occasional unsupervised "pass" from the campus, on the grounds that he was an adult and that drinking was on of his few remaining pleasures.

Unfortunately, research now suggests that even limited drug use by a mentally ill client may exacerbate a separate psychiatric disorder, complicating the individual's treatment (Evans & Sullivan, 1990; Drake, Osher, & Wallach, 1989; Pristach & Smith, 1990; Ries & Ellingson, 1990; Rubinstein, Campbell, & Daley, 1990).

For example, Drake et al. (1989) found that even minimal use of alcohol by schizophrenic patients—drinking in amounts clearly not abusive by traditional standards—was one factor that predicted those clients who would require rehospitalization within a year. Alcohol may easily contribute to feelings of depression, intensifying the client's distress. Use of chemicals by clients with psychiatric disorders often complicates the treatment of their mental illness.

Drug abuse traditionally has been viewed by mental health professionals as a negative influence on the course of psychiatric disorders (Kivlahan et al., 1991; Miller & Tanenbaum, 1989; Rubinstein et al., 1990; Stoffelmayr, Benishek, Humphreys, Lee, & Mavis, 1989). For example, it has been found that substance abuse by schizophrenic patients may contribute to family conflicts. As the family withdraws from the patient as a result of the increased level of conflict, his or her available social support base becomes smaller. This, in turn, makes it harder for the patient to be able to cope with the demands of life. Given the fact that psychiatric patients with weaker social support systems tend to require longer and more frequent periods of hospitalization, the negative impact of substance abuse on the individual's psychiatric condition becomes more clear.

Thus, evidence suggests that drug use by a psychiatric patient will complicate the treatment of his or her psychiatric condition (Kay, Kalathara, & Meinzer, 1989). Kanwischer and Hundley (1990), for example, found that the hospitalization rates of psychiatric patients who abused chemicals on a regular basis were 250% higher than those of individuals who rarely or never abused chemicals.

When one stops to consider the level of pain experienced by the mentally ill, the cost of lost productivity, and the cost of hospitalization and treatment, and then adds on the financial, social, and personal cost brought on by substance abuse in these clients, the need to address this problem becomes clear.

THE SCOPE OF THE PROBLEM

Substance abuse is thought to be at least twice as common in the mentally ill as in the general population (Brown, Ridgely, Pepper, Levine, & Ryglewicz, 1989; Regier et al., 1990). Indeed, there is evidence to suggest that between one-third and one-half of psychiatric patients also have an alcohol or drug-abuse problem (Carey, 1989; Evans & Sullivan, 1990; Regier et al., 1990).

The tendency to abuse alcohol or chemicals appears to be strongest in young mentally ill clients (Drake et al., 1989), especially in young adult *male* psychiatric clients (Szuster, Schanbacher, & McCann, 1990). Brown et al. (1989) estimate that in the young mentally ill population "the substance abuse rate approaches or exceeds 50%" (p. 566), a conclusion supported by Miller and Tanenbaum (1989), Kanwischer and Hundley (1990), and Evans and Sullivan (1990).

These clients are hidden victims of drug dependency. One reason why they remain hidden is that physicians are often not trained to detect substance-abuse problems, especially in the mentally ill (Goodwin, 1989). Further, dual-diagnosis clients are heterogeneous in terms of psychiatric diagnosis, the drug(s) abused, and the impact that this drug use has had on their lives (Kanwischer & Hundley, 1990; Osher & Kofoed, 1989). Lacking a pattern to look for, mental health professionals often fail to recognize the possibility that a mentally ill client might also have a substance-abuse problem (Peyser, 1989).

In a study by Ananth et al. (1989), a sample of 75 psychiatric patients, each of whom had been seen and diagnosed by mental health professionals, were reevaluated after having been admitted to a center for psychiatric treatment. None of these patients had been diagnosed as having an alcohol- or drug-abuse problem at the time of admission. Yet, Ananth et al. concluded that 54 of the 75 subjects should also have received a diagnosis of either drug abuse or drug dependence, in addition to their psychiatric diagnosis. Ten of the 54 subjects found to be using were also found to be either abusing alcohol or to be addicted to alcohol, while 2 additional subjects were found to meet the diagnostic criteria only for alcohol abuse/dependence. Thus, of the 75 patients who had been admitted for psychiatric treatment, three-quarters had an undiagnosed alcohol- or drug-abuse problem.

According to Rado (1988), the number of dual-diagnosis clients is increasing, possibly because professionals are becoming more aware of the existence of drug addiction in many psychiatric patients. However, despite this fact, "fewer and fewer clinics are accepting clients with this profile" (p. 5). Unfortunately, dual-diagnosis clients are often refused treatment at either psychiatric or chemical dependency treatment centers, at the very time when treatment professionals are beginning to recognize the need for their treatment as inpatients (Kofoed, Kania, Walsh, & Atkinson, 1986; Penick et al., 1990).

CHARACTERISTICS OF DUAL-DIAGNOSIS CLIENTS

As previously mentioned, relatively little is known about psychiatric patients who also abuse chemicals (Lehman, Myers, & Corty, 1989; Minkoff, 1989; Osher & Kofoed, 1989; Penick et al., 1990; Wallen & Weiner, 1989). It has been suggested, however, that dual-diagnosis clients are extremely vulnerable to the effects of chemicals (Brown et al., 1989; Drake et al., 1989). As we have mentioned, the available evidence suggests that both mental illness and chemical dependency are chronic disorders, each of which may influence the course of the other (Carey, 1988). This makes it difficult for such clients to benefit from traditional chemical dependency treatment (Kofoed & Keys, 1988). To further complicate matters, dual-diagnosis clients are thought to be a high-risk group for suicide (Brent et al., 1988; Ries & Ellington, 1990).

Psychiatric patients who abuse alcohol are more likely to be hospitalized a second time following their initial hospitalization as general psychiatric patients (Drake et al., 1989; Lyons & McGovern, 1989). Further, dual-diagnosis clients are viewed as being less impaired than general psychiatric patients, but as tending to exhibit more frequent suicidal, homicidal, and impulsive behaviors (Kay et al., 1989; Szuster et al., 1990). Some researchers (for example, Mueser, Yarnold, & Bellack, 1992), suggest that the dual-diagnosis client is less severely psychotic and more intelligent than other psychiatric patients.

In contrast to this conclusion, however, Drake and Wallach (1989) described their sample of dual-diagnosis clients (who were mainly schizophrenic) as

> less able to care for themselves, in terms of maintaining regular meals, steady finances, stable housing, and regular activities, and . . . therefore highly vulnerable to homelessness . . . They were clinically characterized by hostility, suicidality, and disorganized speech. (p. 1044)

Like their nonpsychiatric addicted counterparts, dual-diagnosis clients tend to exhibit sociopathic behaviors more often than psychiatric patients in general (Kay et al., 1989). Stoffelmayr et al. (1989) suggest that dual-diagnosis clients may suffer from more generalized problems in living than clients who do not suffer from both a psychiatric and chemical dependency problem.

Psychopathology and Drug of Choice

One popular theory regarding dual-diagnosis patients is that they are attempting to "self-medicate." That is, there are those who believe that these individuals use chemicals in an attempt to treat, or at least control, their psychiatric condition. In support of this theory, it should be noted that Test, Wallisch, Allness, and Ripp (1990) found that of those patients with schizophrenia who admitted to using drugs, the majority used only alcohol. Marijuana was the second most frequently abused drug, while only about 3% admitted to the use of cocaine. Schizophrenic patients who admitted to the abuse of drugs or alcohol reported that these chemicals helped them deal with anxiety, insomnia, boredom, depression, and the side effects of prescribed antipsychotic medications.

In a study by Kivlahan et al. (1991), 71% of their sample of 60 volunteers being treated at an outpatient community support program for schizophrenia would have qualified for a diagnosis of a "substance-abuse disorder" at some point in their lives. Surprisingly, Kivlahan et al. found that marijuana, not alcohol, was the most frequently abused drug in their sample population. Eighty-eight percent of their sample used marijuana at least occasionally. As for the other drugs being abused, 30% had used amphetamines at some point, 22% had used alcohol, 18% had used hallucinogens, and 13% had used either cocaine or narcotics at some point in their lives.

According to Putnam (1989), perhaps a third of those who suffer from multiple personality disorder (MPD) also abuse chemicals. These individuals

tend to use CNS depressants and alcohol, although stimulants are also frequently abused by this subgroup of mentally ill drug users. Hallucinogens,
possibly because of the nature of MPD, do not seem to be a popular drug of
abuse within this subgroup. The exact reason why certain drugs are popular
with those who suffer from MPD is not clear; however, Putnam does suggest
that MPD clients may use chemicals in an attempt to medicate their internal
distress.

Although there appears to be a tendency for individuals with MPD to avoid
the use of hallucinogens, Rapoport (1989) describes a single case in which a
young adult male suffering from an obsessive-conpulsive disorder used drugs
in order to self-medicate. (This case was previously mentioned in Chapter 16
on hallucinogens.) The individual found relief only through drugs that impacted on those neurons that utilize serotonin as the major neurotransmitter—
especially LSD. This case, while suggestive, involves only one case of OCD,
and thus may or may not reflect a tendency within this subgroup of mentally ill
individuals to attempt to self-medicate with chemicals.

In contrast to the research suggesting a tendency for different subgroups of
dual-diagnosis patients to favor different kinds of drugs, Mueser et al. (1992)
failed to find any significant pattern between the drugs abused and the
patient's diagnosis. They did find a weak trend for patients with a diagnosis of
bipolar affective disorder (once called a "manic-depressive psychosis") to
abuse alcohol. However, they failed to identify other patterns for drug use
among the mentally ill patients they studied.

The results of the research to date suggest that mentally ill patients who do
use chemicals tend to abuse the full range of substances. However, whether
specific subgroups of patients might be drawn to specific chemicals is not
clear at this time.

PROBLEMS IN WORKING WITH DUAL-DIAGNOSIS CLIENTS

The first step for the substance abuse specialist who works with MI/CD clients
is to examine his or her personal attitudes toward psychopharmacology. For
example, recovering addicts are often uncomfortable with patients' use of
medications to control their psychiatric disorder. Many recovering addicts
believe that *any* use of drugs serves only to substitute one addiction for
another, despite the legitimate function of prescribed medications. Further,
recovering addicts may feel uncomfortable around individuals who use prescribed medications (Evans & Sullivan, 1990; Fariello & Scheidt, 1989;
Penick et al., 1990). If substance abuse professionals are unable to accept the
prescribed use of psychotropic medications, they should refrain from working
with MI/CD clients.

The outlook for dual-diagnosis clients traditionally has been thought to be
quite poor. In part, this is because the treatment philosophies of substance

abuse counselors and mental health professionals often conflict (Carey, 1989; Howland, 1990; Osher & Kofoed, 1989; Wallen & Weiner, 1989). In addition, the dual-diagnosis client is often unlikely either to recognize that substance abuse is a problem or to accept abstinence as a viable treatment goal. These factors may bring about a significant degree of confusion and frustration for both clients and treatment professionals.

Kofoed et al. (1986) note that more severe levels of psychopathology have been associated with an unfavorable outcome for substance abusers, in part because "coexisting thought or affective disorders may exacerbate denial of substance abuse" (p. 1209). As we have mentioned, denial of substance abuse is a significant problem in the dual-diagnosis client—a problem that makes their treatment more difficult. In many cases, the dual-diagnosis client will focus almost exclusively on his or her psychiatric disorder to avoid confronting the drug dependency. Once the psychiatric condition is controlled, such a client is likely to drop out of treatment.

In the process of "interchangeable" or "free-floating" denial, clients will tell the mental health professional that most of their problems are drug related. At the same time, they will tell the substance abuse counselor that most of their problems are caused by the mental illness. In a sense, it is not uncommon for these clients to use one disorder as a shield against intervention for the other disorder. For example, as we noted in Chapter 4, individuals who suffer from multiple personality disorder often will attribute their loss of memory (experienced when one personality is forced out of consciousness and another takes over) to the use of chemicals. This is far less threatening to the individual than accepting that he or she is mentally ill.

Dual-diagnosis clients tend to be "crisis users" of medical and chemical dependency services (Rubinstein et al., 1990). Because they will frequently drop out of treatment after the crisis has been stabilized, treatment staff are often not motivated to invest a great deal of time and energy into working with them. To complicate this problem of treatment dropout, dual-diagnosis patients are often viewed as primarily psychiatric patients by chemical dependency professionals, while mental health professionals often view them as primarily substance-abuse cases.

As Layne (1990) points out, this state of affairs evolved out of a political climate in which the treatment of substance-abuse cases became separated from traditional psychiatric care. This division in treatment philosophy is apparent in the case of dual-diagnosis clients. When they *do* come into contact with a treatment center, the staff frequently views them as "not our problem," and will refer them elsewhere. All too often, the outcome of this refusal-to-treat policy is that clients are bounced between psychiatric and chemical dependency treatment programs, much in the manner of ping-pong balls (Osher & Kofoed, 1989; Wallen & Weiner, 1989).

Furthermore, dual-diagnosis patients often find themselves in a catch-22 situation. Their behavioral difficulties frequently make them unattractive to many chemical dependency treatment programs. At the same time, traditional psychiatric hospitals often refuse to accept them until their chemical dependency problems have been addressed (Fariello & Scheidt, 1989; Penick, et al., 1990). Unfortunately, staff psychiatrists in traditional psychiatric hospitals usually lack training and experience in working with addicted individuals (Howland, 1990). So, when such patients are admitted to a psychiatric facility, they may receive potentially addictive substances as part of their psychiatric care, prescribed by a psychiatrist who is more experienced in working with the "traditional" client.

The MI/CD Client and Medication Compliance

To further complicate matters, medication noncompliance is a significant problem with dual-diagnosis clients (Drake & Wallach, 1989). According to Kashner et al. (1991), these clients are 12.8 times as likely not to follow doctors' prescriptions as psychiatric patients who do not use drugs. Not only may they refuse to take prescribed medications, they may also continue to use drugs of abuse even after admission to inpatient psychiatric treatment facilities (Alterman, Erdlan, La Porte, & Erdlen, 1982).

As we have noted previously, psychiatric patients have been known to abuse drugs in an attempt at self-medication (Caton, Gralnick, Bender, & Simon, 1989; Rubinstein et al., 1990). This may be because they do not trust prescribed medication (Evans & Sullivan, 1990) or because some psychiatric medications have a significant abuse potential of their own.

For example, it is not uncommon for patients to abuse anticholinergic medications. These are often prescribed to help control the side effects of prescribed antipsychotic agents. The anticholinergics may potentiate the effects of alcohol or the amphetamines (Land, Pinsky, & Salzman, 1991), and the "buzz" that may be obtained from such drugs often serves as a substitute for the effects of other chemicals when supplies run short. As we will discuss in a later section, urine toxicology samples are useful in determining whether a patient is taking antipsychotic medications as prescribed.

Because of poor medication compliance, Fariello and Scheidt (1989) recommend the use of long-term injectable phenothiazines rather than the more traditioal short-term preparations for control of the thought disorder and agitation often suffered by dual-diagnosis clients. Frequent urine toxicology screenings will also allow treatment staff to verify medication compliance or noncompliance in the dual-diagnosis client.

Considering the pain and suffering inherent in many forms of mental illness, it is understandable that mentally ill individuals often strive to maintain external structure and predictability as a way to cope with their lack of internal structure and predictability. Self-administered drugs are a means of controlling internal chaos in that they provide an illusion of control over one's feelings (S. Brown, 1985). Even if the drugs cause the schizophrenic patient to experience additional hallucinations, at least he or she can exert some degree of control by deciding whether or not to take the chemical.

TREATMENT APPROACHES FOR
DUAL-DIAGNOSIS CLIENTS

Although it is becoming increasingly apparent that dual-diagnosis clients require specialized treatment programs to meet their needs, few such programs exist (Howland, 1990). The traditional approach has been to address the client's mental illness first, then, after psychiatric stabilization has been achieved, to begin to explore the client's chemical-use pattern (Rado, 1988).

The decision as to which to treat first—the psychiatric condition or the drug dependency—is often quite arbitrary (Howland, 1990; Kofoed, et al., 1986) and there is little research data to support either approach (Osher & Kofoed, 1989). Layne (1990) suggests treating both disorders concurrently, an alternative to the either/or approach used by most treatment centers.

For a treatment program to meet the needs of dual-diagnosis clients, a team approach must be employed. A comprehensive program in which the different treatment philosophies of psychiatric and chemical dependency professionals are synthesized and geared toward the individual client seems to work best (Evans & Sullivan, 1990; Osher & Kofoed, 1989).

Chemical detoxification is a necessary first step in treating a dual-diagnosis client (Layne, 1990; Wallen & Weiner, 1989). This requires psychiatric support from professionals who are knowledgable in both the fields of psychiatry and chemical dependency (Evans & Sullivan, 1990). Once detoxification has been achieved, the treatment team can set about determining which problems are a result of the client's chemical use and which are manifestations of his or her psychiatric disorder. At this point, the team would decide on the sequence of treatment.

As part of the evaluation process, urine toxicology screening should be conducted. There are two advantages to the use of urine toxicology screens from the time of admission for the dual-diagnosis client. First, when properly supervised, urine samples may yield information on the specific illicit chemicals the client had been using in the recent past. This information is of value during the diagnostic process. Secondly, the urine toxicology screen can verify whether the client had taken prescribed medications according to the orders of a physician.

The Treatment Setting

The general psychiatric unit is usually not structured to the needs of a dual-diagnosis client (Howland, 1990). Kofoed and Keys (1988) suggest that psychiatric units should consider limiting treatment goals to (a) detoxification from drugs of abuse, (b) psychiatric stabilization, and (c) persuasion of the client to pursue chemical dependency treatment. The clinician must be patient, often waiting years until conditions are right to finally persuade a dual-diagnosis client to enter treatment.

Dual-diagnosis clients may be treated either on an outpatient (Kofoed et al., 1986) or inpatient (Pursch, 1987) basis, depending on the client's needs and available resources. Long-term inpatient treatment may be necessary in more dififcult cases, according to Caton et al. (1989). The ideal program for a dual-diagnosis client would have facilities for working with both psychiatric and addicted clients. This would allow the dual-diagnosis patient to be shifted from one program to another as his or her needs change during treatment. The unified treatment team suggested by Osher and Kofoed (1989) would allow for the same flexibility of treatment approaches.

Treatment Stages

The dual-diagnosis client usually will come to the attention of mental health or chemical dependency professionals as a result of repeated hospitalizations, legal problems, psychiatric decompensation, or eviction from his or her apartment (Fariello & Scheidt, 1989; Rubinstein et al., 1990). It is at this point that treatment might be initiated.

Lehman et al. (1989) identify the first phase of treatment as "acute treatment and stabilization" (p. 1020). Minkoff (1989) terms this phase *acute stabilization*. It is during this phase of treatment that the client's psychiatric condition is stabilized and detoxification carried out. The possibility of a dual diagnosis is also considered by the clinician during this phase of evaluation and treatment. If the symptoms of a psychiatric disorder completely clear during detoxification, then the possibility that the client is not a dual-diagnosis patient should be considered (Layne, 1990). However, if the symptoms persist after detoxification, then the dual-diagnosis designation is more likely to be appropriate (Lehman et al., 1989). In either case, during this phase of treatment staff should focus on helping the individual understand the relationship between the current crisis and his or her untreated problem(s).

Once the patient is sober and psychiatrically stable, money-management programs, psychoeducational materials or lectures, and social support may be introduced to the treatment program. It is at this point that treatment staff attempt to break through the denial that surrounds both the individual's mental illness and his or her addiction. This phase of treatment has been termed *engagement* (Kofoed, 1989; Minkoff, 1989) or *early engagement* (Layne, 1990). The goals are for the professional staff to establish a therapeutic relationship, arrive at an accurate diagnosis, and convince the client that treatment has something to offer. Staff members should attempt to work with family members or legal representatives to bring the client into treatment on an involuntary basis if this should become necessary. Although the client might be seen on an outpatient basis, Carey (1989) recommends transfer to an inpatient psychiatric treatment center should the client's condition warrant such a transfer.

This second phase of treatment has also been termed *maintenance and rehabilitation* (Lehman et al., 1989). The clinician works toward the goal of preventing a recurrence of both the chemical abuse and the psychiatric disorder. This is the same process that Fariello and Scheidt (1989) identify as *breaking the cycle*. Group therapy may be an important element of this phase.

According to Kofoed and Keyes (1988) and Layne (1990), this should take place in the psychiatric unit rather than in the substance abuse unit.

Osher and Kofoed (1989) refer to this second phase of treatment as *persuasion.* The treatment staff will attempt to convince the client to accept the need for abstinence. According to Kofoed and Keys (1988), the therapeutic goals are to (a) persuade clients to accept the reality of their drug dependency and (b) persuade them to seek continued treatment for the drug dependency.

The third phase of treatment—that of *active treatment* (Osher & Kofoed, 1989)—attempts to help the client learn "the attitudes and skills necessary to remain sober" (p. 1027). Many of the techniques used in general drug-addiction treatment are also useful in working with dual-diagnosis clients. Osher and Kofoed (1989) argue against lower treatment expectations or the acceptance of the inevitability of relapse for dual-diagnosis clients. Layne (1990) suggests that treatment staff might need to teach clients specific *life skills* in order to help them learn how to function in society without the use of drugs of abuse, despite ongoing delusions.

However, it should be noted that the very nature of the dual-diagnosis client population presents unique challenges to the treatment staff and requires modification of the techniques used in traditional treatment of chemical dependency. When confrontation is used with dual-diagnosis clients, for example, it has been suggested that it be less intense than the confrontation used with traditional personality-disordered clients (Carey, 1989; Penick et al., 1990).

As is the case with the nonpsychiatric addict, dual-diagnosis clients will use denial as a major defense. The danger is that once the psychiatric condition is controlled, the client's drug-related defenses again begin to operate (Kofoed & Keys, 1988). Dual-diagnosis clients often argue that once their psychiatric symptoms are under control, they no longer will be in danger of chemical addiction. These clients are often unable to see the relationship between their chemical abuse and the psychiatric symptoms they experience.

Dropping out of treatment for such clients is the ultimate expression of denial. Another form of denial—one that frequently characterizes traditional clients—is evident when the client informs the treatment specialist that all drug or alcohol use has been discontinued. In effect, the client is telling the counselor what he or she wants to hear in order to avoid confrontation.

Another problem for dual-diagnosis clients is that they are often unable to take advantage of such traditional support systems as Alcoholics Anonymous or Narcotics Anonymous because they feel out of place in self-help meetings (Fariello & Scheidt, 1989; Wallen & Weiner, 1989). It is for this reason that peer groups are most effective in working with the dual-diagnosis client (Kofoed & Keys, 1988). The peer group provides an avenue through which clients may share their experiences with even limited recreational drug use and discusss the need for the support of a twelve-step group (Fariello & Scheidt, 1989; Kofoed & Keys, 1988; Rado, 1988). When such groups are effective, dual-diagnosis clients tend to be rehospitalized less often (Kofoed & Keys, 1988) and function better in society.

SUMMARY

The dual-diagnosis client presents a special challenge to the health care professional. Such clients often use an interchangable system of denial. With drug-addiction counselors, they speak of their psychiatric problems; with mental health professionals, they focus on their drug use. Obviously, then, working with them is difficult.

Traditional treatment methods require some modification in working with dual-diagnosis clients. For example, the degree of confrontation that may be appropriate in working with a personality-disordered client is likely to be far too strong for a dual-diagnosis client suffering from schizophrenia or some other form of mental illness. However, gentle confrontation will often work with the client who is mentally ill and drug dependent, but not personality disordered.

Chapter 23

CODEPENDENCY AND ENABLING

For each identified addict, there are many hidden victims. Some of these people might be total strangers to the addict; for example, victims of drug-related burglaries or alcohol-related automobile accidents. While these occurences are unfortunate, and possibly tragic, the victims are not usually involved in an ongoing relationship with the addicted individuals. Rather, the drug-related burglary or the alcohol-related accident is an isolated incident—not a part of an ongoing relationship.

As substance abuse professionals have started to explore the interpersonal relationships that surround the addict, they have found there are those who, while sickened by the addict's behavior, actually behave in ways that *enable* the individual to continue to abuse drugs. Further, researchers have found that some family members seem to be *codependent* with the addict. Codependency and enabling—arguably, themes of the current generation—will be the focus of this chapter.

ENABLING

In the context of chemical dependency, to *enable* someone means to knowingly do something that makes it possible for that person to continue to use chemicals without having to suffer the natural consequences of substance abuse. In a very real sense, one who enables an addict protects that person from the consequences of his or her behavior. Armed with the best of intentions, the enabler becomes part of the problem, not the solution. The enabler prevents the addict from taking advantage of the many opportunities to discover first-hand the cost of his or her addiction.

A common misconception is that only family members enable addicts. The truth is that enablers may be friends, co-workers, supervisors, teachers, therapists, or even drug-rehabilitation workers. Any person who *knowingly* acts in such a way as to protect an addicted person from the natural consequences of his or her behavior may be said to be an enabler.

The booklet *The Family Enablers* (Johnson Institute, 1987) defines an enabler as *any* person who "reacts to an alcoholic in such a way as to shield the alcoholic from experiencing the full impact of the harmful consequences of alcoholism" (p. 5). The same criterion might be applied to those who enable people who are addicted to other drugs of abuse. By knowingly shielding the user from the harmful consequences of her or his behavior, one enables.

One does not have to be involved in an ongoing relationship with an addict to enable him or her. A person who refuses to provide testimony about a crime that he or she witnessed out of a wish not to become involved, or perhaps out of fear, may be said to have enabled the perpetrator of that crime to escape. But sometimes the enabler *is* involved in an ongoing relationship with an addicted person, as in the case of co-workers. Then, one person might be manipulated into enabling another's addiction on an ongoing basis.

Enabling Behaviors in the Workplace

It is difficult to understand the multitude of ways in which one person might enable an addict to continue the compulsive use of chemicals. Hyde (1989) speaks of how operating-room staff hesitate to confront a surgeon suspected to be under the influence of chemicals for reasons of denial, fear of reprisal, or a wish not to become involved. Although cases in which a surgeon would attempt to operate under the influence of chemicals are perhaps quite rare, medical professionals who hesitate to confront or report an impaired surgical colleague might be called enablers of that surgeon's continued use of chemicals.

According to Hyde (1989), characteristic behaviors of the enabler in the workplace include the following:

- doing work for the addicted individual when that person is unable to do his or her own required work;
- "covering" for the impaired individual's poor performance;
- accepting excuses or making special arrangement for the impaired individual;
- overlooking frequent absenteeism or tardiness; and
- overlooking evidence of chemical use.

Admittedly, it is difficult to deal with an addicted person in the workplace, especially if the addict happens to be a supervisor or administrator. To further complicate matters, the addict will actively try to manipulate the interpersonal environment to force others to continue to enable his or her continued chemical use. Not uncommonly, the alcoholic will treat enablers as if they should be grateful for being granted the "privilege" of assuming responsibility for his or her life! The temptation here is for the enabler to go along with this myth rather than confront the addict and risk retaliation.

For example, when confronted by his or her supervisor for being late again, the addicted employee might respond, "You're lucky that I work here in the first place!" perhaps out of a fear of legal action or some other form or retribution, the supervisor may agree that the company is indeed lucky to have the addict as an employee. The supervisor may warn the addict not to be late again, but not take any firm action.

Styles of Enabling

Ellis et al. (1988) identify three subtypes of enablers, classified according to behavioral style. The first of these subtypes, the *joiner*, will work to support the addict's use of chemicals and may even use drugs with the addict in an attempt to control the addict's habit. A classic example of a "joiner" is the woman who seeks marital counseling because her husband will not limit his cocaine use to the $100 a week that she sets aside in the family budget for his drug use! Another example of a joiner is the spouse who drinks or uses chemicals along with his or her addicted mate in the hope of exercising some measure of control over the mate's chemical use. It is quite common for a spouse to go to a bar with the alcoholic in the hope that he or she will learn "responsible" drinking by example.

A second type of enabler, according to Ellis et al., is the *messiah*. The messiah fights against the addict's chemical use, but does so in such a way that the addict is never forced to experience the consequences of his or her behavior. For example, in a social support group, the father of a narcotics addict admitted that he had taken out personal loans more than once to pay off his daughter's drug debts. One of the addicts in the group who had been in recovery for some time asked why the father would do this. "After all," this addict said, "if you pay off her debts for her, she won't have to worry about paying them off herself." Indeed, several group members suggested to this parent that his daughter might have to suffer some consequences on her own in order to "hit bottom" and come to terms with her addiction. After a period of silence, the father responded, "Oh, I couldn't let that happen. She isn't ready to assume responsibility for herself!"

Finally, Ellis et al. describe the *silent sufferer*. This enabler seems to live by the motto, As long as I suffer, I *am* somebody. In a very real sense, the silent sufferer is a martyr, living with the alcoholic despite the pain this person causes; unhappy, yet unwilling to leave. It is as if the silent sufferer derives meaning from life only through a relationship with the addict.

As Ellis et al. point out, the silent sufferer prevents the addict from suffering the consequences of his or her behavior by "always being there and pretending that nothing is wrong" (p. 109). Rather than risk the loss of what little emotional security the addict might offer, silent sufferers try not to rock the boat. They keep family conflict from breaking out and seem to act as lightning rods, drawing all of the pain and suffering away from the addict to themselves.

The Relationship Between Enabling and Codependency

The key concept to remember is that an enabler *knowingly* behaves so as to protect the addict from the consequences of his or her behavior. We all behave in ways that, in retrospect, may have enabled an addict to avoid some consequences that he or she would otherwise have suffered as a result of drug use.

This is a point that is often quite confusing to the student of addiction.

Codependency and enabling may be, and often are, found in the same person. However, one may also enable an addicted person without being codependent on that person. Enabling refers to *specific behaviors,* whereas codependency refers to *a relationship pattern.* Thus, one may enable addiction without being codependent. But the codependent individual, because he or she is in an ongoing relationship with the addict, will frequently enable the addict.

The wife who calls in to work to say that her husband is "sick" when he is actually hung over from the night before is an example of a spouse who is both codependent and an enabler. Another example is the husband who calls to tell the parole officer that his wife cannot keep today's appointment because she is ill. The husband knows full well that his wife had been drinking the night before, and that if the parole officer were to ask for a urine sample she would fail it and be sent to prison. Thus, the husband is both codependent and is enabling his wife's continued drinking.

A diagram of the relationship between codependency and enabling is shown in Figure 23-1. The area of overlap represents how codependents may enable addicts—a very common occurrence. As many rehabilitation professionals can attest to, this enabling is often carried out in the name of "love." Helping the codependent see the difference between love and enabling is often a difficult task.

CODEPENDENCY

The concept of codependency has emerged in the past decade to become one of the cornerstones of rehabilitation. Surprisingly, in spite of all that has been said and written about it, there is no standard definition of codependency (Heimel, 1990; Tavris, 1990). Indeed, mental health professionals have yet to agree on such a basic issue as whether the word is hyphenated (co-dependency) or not (codependency) (Beattie, 1989).

Even without a standard definition for the concept, however, many families and friends of addicted persons have begun to become aware that they have suffered, and often continue to suffer, as a result of their "relationship with a dysfunctional person" (Beattie, 1989, p. 7).

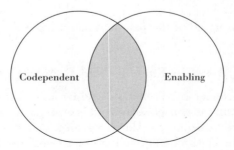

FIGURE 23-1 The overlapping relationship of codependency and enabling.

Proposed Definitions of Codependency

According to Wegscheider-Cruse (1985), codependency is

> a specific condition that is characterized by preoccupation and extreme dependence (emotionally, socially, and sometimes physically) on a person or object. Eventually, this dependence . . . becomes a pathological condition that affects the co-dependent in all other relationships. (p. 2)

In a later work, Wegscheider-Cruse and Cruse redefined codependency as

> [a] pattern of painful dependency on compulsive behaviors and on approval from others in an attempt to find safety, self-worth and identity. (Wegscheider-Cruse and Cruse, 1990, p. 8)

These definitions of codependency identify different aspects of the condition: (a) *overinvolvement* with a dysfunctional person; (b) *obsessive attempts to control* the dysfunctional person's behavior; (c) a strong *reliance on external sources of self-worth* (that is, approval from others); and (d) a *tendency to make personal sacrifices* in an attempt to "cure" the dysfunctional person of his or her problem behavior.

The Dynamics of Codependency

In an early paper on the subject, Beattie (1987) spoke of codependency as a process in which the individual's life becomes unmanageable. This is because he or she is involved in a committed relationship with an addict and is thus unable to simply walk away.

Often, codependents come to believe that the addict's behavior somehow reflects themselves. In response to this threat to self-esteem (*your* behavior is a reflection of *me*) the codependent person becomes obsessed with the need to control the addict's behavior (Beattie, 1987). Gradually, the codependent will assume increasing responsibility for decisions and events not actually under his or her control, such as the significant other's drinking or drug use. For example, more than one codependent spouse has accepted the blame for "causing" the alcoholic to go out on a binge after having a fight. "It's all my fault that he (or "she") went out drinking" is a common theme for the codependent.

As we have noted, one symptom of codependency is a *preoccupation* (Wegscheider-Cruse, 1985) or an *obsession* (Beattie, 1989) with controlling the significant other's behavior. This obsession may extend to the point where the codependent will try to control not only the addict's drug use, but all of the addict's life. For example, consider the case of the elderly mother of an inmate in a Midwest maximum security penitentiary for men. She telephoned a staff psychologist, telling him to make sure the man who shared her son's cell was a good influence. As she put it, "There are a lot of bad men in that prison, and I don't want him falling in with a bad crowd!"

The mother in this case overlooked the grim reality that her son was not simply in prison for singing off-key in choir practice but had been to prison on several different occasions for various crimes. Rather than let him live his life and try to get on with hers, she continued to worry about how to "cure" him of his behavior problem. She continued to treat him as a child and to be overly involved in his life. She was quite upset at the suggestion that it might be time to let her son learn to *suffer* (and perhaps learn from) *the consequences of his own behavior.*

The rules of codependency   Although the codependent often feels as if he or she is going crazy, an outside observer will notice that there are certain patterns or "rules" to codependent behavior. Beattie (1989) notes the following unspoken rules of codependency:

- It's not OK for me to feel.
- It's not OK for me to have problems.
- It's not OK for me to have fun.
- I'm not lovable.
- I'm not good enough.
- If people act bad or crazy, I'm responsible.

These rules are actively transmitted from one partner in the relationship to the other, setting the pattern for codependency.

Are Codependents Born or Made?

Codependency seems to be a *learned behavior.* It is often passed from one generation to another. In a real-life example of how one unhealthy generation trains another to be codependent—one that (unfortunately) is repeated time and time again—a parent confronts a child who wants to go to college with the taunt, "You're too dumb to go to college. The best that you can hope for is that somebody will be stupid enough to marry you and take care of you!"

Scarf (1980) points out that we all try to resolve "unfinished business" with our parents by re-creating all-important early relationships in our adult lives. Frequently, especially for the individual who struggles with feelings of low self-esteem as a result of having been raised in a dysfunctional home, this means being drawn to unhealthy partners as part of the process of trying to resolve parent–child conflicts early in life.

In other words, we tend to re-create our original families through our adult relationships. Further, we then attempt to resolve any unresolved conflicts through surrogates. Depending on how healthy or unhealthy these surrogates may be, this process might benefit the individual or trap him or her into unhealthy cycles. For example, Heimel (1991) vividly describes how she realized that she was reacting to a boyfriend's rejection with the same depression she experienced when she was growing up:

> This is how I felt as a kid when my mother turned her back and wouldn't speak to me, when my father, my beloved father, shook his head and said, "After all we've done for you." This is how I felt when I was turning myself inside out trying to get my parents to love me, something they couldn't quite manage. (p. 42)

Because of this earlier rejection, Heimel (1991) saw herself as being vulnerable to being rejected again, in adulthood. She lacked sufficient self-esteem to weather the crisis of being rejected, although on one level she understood that there was never a serious relationship with the young man in question.

Children who have been exposed to physical, sexual, or emotional abuse are frequently left with significant feelings of low self-esteem. These individuals are unable to affirm the "self," possibly because they do no believe they are valuable or capable individuals. Such victims are vulnerable to being drawn time after time to unhealthy partners in an attempt to resolve past trauma through current relationships. It is almost as if they are trapped in a never-ending cycle.

Further, as the dysfunctional elements in the relationship develop, the codependent will frequently come to also feel "trapped" in the relationship. All relationships have some dysfunctional elements. In a healthy relationship, however, the partners will confront these unhealthy components, and work on resolving them to the satisfaction of both partners.

For example, one partner might express an opinion to the other that their finances are getting a little tight and suggest that perhaps they should look at cutting back on unnecessary spending for a couple of weeks. But, in the codependent relationship, this "working through" process is stalled. If one partner does express some concern over a possible problem, the other partner will move to prevent the problem from being clearly identified. Or, if it is identified, he or she will try to keep it from being resolved.

As part of the attempt to avoid displeasing the addict, the codependent will restrict communications—avoiding people or topics of conversation that might anger the significant other. Eventually, a self-fulfilling cycle will be established, in which the codependent is afraid to say the wrong thing, talk to the wrong people, and, in short, assert selfhood. The codependent is afraid to leave, believing that he or she has nobody to turn to but the significant other. Yet, the codependent is often miserable in the relationship with the addicted individual.

Codependency and Self-Esteem

In an attempt to live up to the unspoken rules of codependency, the codependent experiences a great deal of emotional pain. The core of codependency, as viewed by Zerwekh and Michaels (1989), is related to low self-esteem on the part of the codependent person:

> Co-dependents frequently appear normal, which in our culture is associated with a healthy ego. Nevertheless, they also describe themselves as "dying on the inside," which is indicative of low self-worth or esteem. (p. 111)

Lacking sufficient self-esteem to withstand the demands of the dysfunctional partner, the codependent often comes to measure personal worth by how well he or she can take care of the addicted individual. Another way that codependents often measure self-worth is through the sacrifices they make for the addicted individual, the family, or significant others (Miller, 1988). In this way, the codependent individual substitutes an external measure of personal worth for an inability to generate *self*-worth.

Drug-rehabilitation workers are often surprised at the amount of suffering and pain that codependent family members suffer, but confused as to why they do not do something to end the pain. There is a reward for enduring this pain! As Shapiro (1981) points out, there is a certain moral victory to be achieved through suffering: "It keeps alive in the mind's record an injustice committed, a score unsettled" (p. 115).

According to Shapiro (1981), suffering is, for the martyr,

> a necessity, a principled act of will, from which he cannot release himself without losing his self-respect and feeling more deeply and finally defeated, humiliated, and powerless. (p. 115)

Thus, for some, trials and suffering become a defense against the admission of powerlessness or worthlessness. The codependent person, in many cases, comes to affirm personal worth by being willing to "carry the cross" of another person's addiction of dysfunctional behavior.

Codependency and Emotional Health

There is a very real tendency for some to *overidentify* with the codependency concept. As Beattie (quoted in Tavris, 1990) points out, there are those who believe that codependency exists in all relationships—that "everyone is codependent." This is an extreme position that overlooks the fact that many of the characteristics that define the codependent are also found in healthy human relationships. Only a few "saints and hermits" (Tavris, 1990, p. 21A) fail to demonstrate at least some of the characteristics of the so-called codependent individual. Even Wegscheder-Cruse and Cruse (1990), strong advocates of the codependency movement, admit that "co-dependency is an exaggeration of normal personality traits" (p. 28). Thus, codependency is a matter of degree.

Whereas certain personality types tend to isolate themselves from interpersonal feedback, the codependent individual tends to be extremely dependent on feedback from the significant other. The whole goal of the codependent seems to be that of winning love, approval, and acceptance from the object of his or her affection. Unable to affirm the "self," the codependent seeks to win affirmation from the significant other.

The danger is that the significant other might withdraw even the little love and affirmation sometimes offered. The codependent becomes exquisitely sensitive to the slightest sign of disapproval or rejection from the significant other, to the point where he or she might come to lose touch with feelings of his or her own. Thus, on the one hand, there is a total insensitivity toward interpersonal feedback, while on the other there is a supersensitivity to this feedback. In between these two extremes is an *interdependency* that is the hallmark of healthy relationships. The extremes between codependency and isolation are graphically depicted in Figure 23-2.

Thus, codependency is not an all-or-nothing phenomenon. Admittedly,

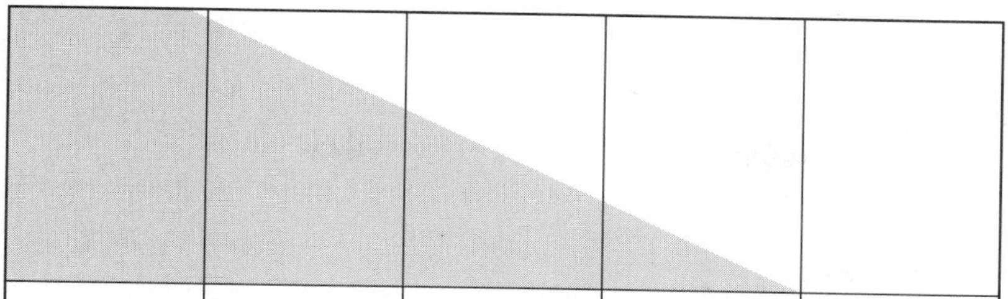

0	1	2	3	4
Codependent: Totally dependent on external feedback for self-worth	Strong codependent traits	Interdependent: Balances own feelings with external feedback	Strong tendency to isolate self from feedback from others	Totally discounts external feedback in favor of own desires

FIGURE 23-2 From codependency to isolation.

codependency does exist, and there are those who do seem to be codependent. But there are degrees of codependency, just as there are degrees of isolation from interpersonal feedback. Few of us are at either extreme, and most of us tend to fall somewhere in the middle. We exhibit tendencies both to behave in codependent ways and to be overly isolated from feedback from others.

How to Build a Codependent

Substance abuse professionals often speak of a "cycle" of codependency that takes on a life of its own. Figure 23-3 graphically depicts this cycle, in which there are two necessary components. The first is that one partner, the codependent, must suffer from low self-esteem. Otherwise, he or she would be able to affirm "self," and thus would back away from a dysfunctional partner; consequently, no codependent relationship would evolve.

Secondly, the significant other must prove to be dysfunctional. If the partner were emotionally healthy, he or she would affirm the codependent. Such an atmosphere would enhance the psychological growth of the codependent, who in time would be able to affirm "self" without the need for external supports. Thus, codependency rests on an interaction between the "pathology" of the two partners.

Challenges to the Codependency Concept

Since the concept of codependency was first introduced, it has been a controversial issue. For example, some argue that the concept of codependency serves to promote feelings of helplessness in individuals. The codependent is told that the "disease" is progressive, and that he or she is powerless to reverse it (Tavris, 1990). Thus, the concept of codependency diminishes the individual's incentive to try to exert control over his or her life.

Much of the literature on codependency communicates to the individual

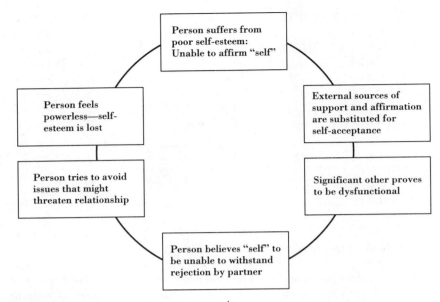

FIGURE 23-3   The cycle of codependency.

that he or she is "doomed to suffer as a result of the trauma of childhood travails" (Japenga, 1991, p. 174). Such a viewpoint totally discounts the possibility that the individual might have successfully weathered the storm of childhood trauma. It suggests that people who have been raised in dysfunctional homes inevitably have deep-seated, permanent emotional scars.

However, recent research findings suggest that many of those who are exposed to extreme adverse conditions in childhood somehow find a way to adjust, survive, and fulfill life goals, despite their early trauma. Werner (1989) found that some children, even when faced with extreme psychological trauma, appear to develop a natural resilience that helps them weather the emotional storms not only of childhood, but of adult life as well.

Codependency has also been criticized on the grounds that it excuses the addicted individual from responsibility for his or her behavior (Tavris, 1990). The blame is shifted from the abusive spouse, sibling, or parent to the codependent individual who "enables" this abusive, violent, or destructive behavior. In this manner, the disease model as applied to codependency shifts the blame from the abuser to the abused.

In discussing the shortcomings of the concept of codependency, the University of California, Berkeley (1990a) concluded:

> According to adherents of this theory, families of alcoholics cannot. . . . hold them responsible for the abuse. Somehow the victim must get well by dint of pure self-analysis, meditation and prayer, without reference to the social, economic, legal and psychological forces that create dysfunctional families in the first place. (p. 7).

The fact that the word *codependent* is an outgrowth of the 1950s term *co-alcoholic* represents an additional challenge to the concept of codependency. *Co-alcoholic* was a term used to refer to people who were involved in a relationship with an alcoholic on the assumption that they were as much in need of treatment as was the alcoholic for the role they played in helping to bring about and support the alcoholism (Simmons, 1991). The concept of the co-alcoholic has been discredited by health care professionals, but it has found new life in the codependency movement.

Still another weakness of the concept of codependency stems from the fact that it has been broadened to the extent that it is no longer useful. Now, the codependent can be "anyone who has ever been involved with anyone who has ever had a problem around which a twelve-step program has been, is being, or should be built" (Simmons, 1991, p. 26A). Indeed, Simmons calls codependency a catchword of "recoveryspeak," which he defines as a form of secret handshake that is used to bring a sense of security to people in an insane, overpowering world.

Finally, the concept of codependency appears to be vague, without foundation. Wegecheder-Cruse and Cruse (1990) argue that codependency is a disease of the brain. According to their hypothesis, the individual engages in self-defeating behaviors in an attempt to bring on the "excessive rush" provided by his or her own "brain chemicals" (pp. 12–13). However, there is no scientific evidence to support this hypothesis. Indeed, if human beings as a species engaged in self-defeating behaviors simply for the "rush," how would we have survived long enough to become predominant?

There is a need for balance in considering the concept of codependency. Admittedly, there are those people who experience significant hardship because of their involvement in an ongoing relationship with an addict. But not every person who is in such a relationship is necessarily codependent. Thus, when attempting to identify and treat a codependent, several rules should be observed:

1. The diagnosis should be applied only to a small minority of those in an ongoing relationship with an addicted person—those who have *suffered significant hardship* as a result of the relationship.
2. The diagnosis should not become an excuse for continued dysfunctional behaviors. Many codependents hide behind the label, often with the excuse that they cannot help themselves.
3. Finally, the therapist should help the client learn how to regain power to escape the trap of codependency. This will often require the client to hold those who have abused him or her responsible for their actions.

SUMMARY

The concepts of codependency and enabling have evolved over the past decade to become cornerstones of our understanding of the interpersonal dynamics of alcoholism. However, both *codependency* and *enabling* are poorly defined terms. As these concepts have gained greater acceptance within the treatment industry, significant confusion has developed over the exact nature of codependency and the specific behaviors that constitute enabling. In this chapter, we have explored some of the current definitions of codependency and enabling and some of the challenges to these concepts.

Chapter 24

ADDICTION AND THE FAMILY

Individuals who are addicted to chemicals, or who eventually will become addicted, are often married. Sometimes they marry first and then start down the road toward addiction. In such cases, family members are suddenly faced with the unwelcome addiction of an additive disorder within their ranks. Sometimes the addict begins to use drugs compulsively while still single, and then marries. The choice of a spouse may be another addict—a marriage of convenience that brings with it a "using partner," an additional source of chemicals, and sometimes money for drugs. Some individuals enter marriage with full knowledge of the spouse's addiction, but with hopes of "saving" the addict from his or her behavior. However, in many cases, the individual is unaware of the chosen mate's addiction prior to the marriage, and subsequently is faced with the sudden reality of an addicted spouse.

Clearly, then, the problems of substance abuse and addiction are not confined to the individual user or addict. His or her spouse, children, and other family members are also affected. Considering that over 10% of the U.S. population was raised in an alcoholic home (Ackerman, 1983), this problem assumes major proportions.

Data are not available on what percentage of the population was raised in a home where other forms of addiction prevailed. But it is safe to say that children are indeed being raised in homes that harbor some form of addiction. In this chapter, we will begin to explore the impact of substance abuse on the family—hidden victims of the addict's drug use.

ADDICTION AND MARRIAGE

Very little is known about the role that chemicals play in the marital relationship. The little information that is available deals almost exclusively with the "alcoholic marriage." In this type of marriage, there is often a "role reversal" between the marital partners (Ackerman, 1983). The alcoholic will often assume a "sick dependency" (Phillips, 1979, p. 3) on other family members, who in turn will have a codependent relationship with the alcoholic.

The Evolution of Codependency

Bowen (1985) observes that people generally tend to marry those who have achieved similar levels of "differentiation of self" (p. 263). He states that the concept of differentiation is more or less equivalent to that of emotional maturity. A primary developmental task is for the individual to separate from his or her parents (or *individuate*) and resolve the various emotional attachments to the parents that evolved during childhood.

We all develop different relationship patterns with our parents. Usually when we are quite young we believe that we cannot possibly survive without our parents' care and support. Normally, we outgrow this belief during adolescence and young adulthood. Inherent in Bowen's (1985) theory is the belief that it is possible for a person to fail to learn to resolve the multiple conflicts that exist in childhood and adolescence. That is to say, the person can fail to individuate or to become emotionally mature.

This might possibly come about in a home where one or both of the parents are dysfunctional, such as the alcoholic home. The child requires parental support and guidance during his or her emotional growth. If the parents are unable to provide the proper guidance and support to the child, he or she might fail to make the appropriate emotional break necessary to individuate. The child would continue to be emotionally dependent on the parents. In adulthood, this person would have low self-esteem and be quite dependent on external sources of feedback and support. This might be obtained either from continued dependency on the parents or from reliance on a parental substitute.

In searching for a marital partner, we each seek someone with a similar level of emotional independence. The child who failed to individuate may grow up to be an emotionally dependent adult looking for a mate to meet the residual dependency needs from childhood and adolescence.

The marriage that results from a union of two emotionally vulnerable individuals is one in which each looks to the other to meet his or her dependency needs, according to Bowen (1985). While the marriage might bring with it the potential for further emotional growth for both partners, it also brings with it the risk inherent in emotional growth. For some, this risk is too great. They turn not to another person for emotional support, but instead to chemicals.

The dance of codependency is now complete. On the one hand, there is the person who is addicted to chemicals—a person who seeks as little responsibility as possible in order to devote full attention to drug use. On the other hand, the codependent person seeks to fuse with the marital partner, in order to find the emotional strength in the partner that is lacking in the "self." The stage is then set for the sick interdependency known as codependency.

The therapeutic task in working with a codependent is to teach the person how to detach from the addict and to meet his or her own needs. This is a difficult task, for the therapist is seeking to foster emotional independence that should have been achieved in childhood and adolescence. The dependent person will struggle to hold on to what he or she views as a source of emotional security—the partner. Further, premature separation of the dependent person from the object of attachment (in this case, the addicted spouse) will result in the former "feeling useless, immobilized, and hurt" (Dyer, 1989, p. 178).

Conditional love is an important means of control within the alcoholic marriage. It is not uncommon for the alcoholic spouse to threaten withholding love or financial support, or even to threaten physical abuse to control others within the family and make sure that they do not stray too far from the alcoholic fold.

Detachment becomes both an expression of *un*conditional love and a vehicle to free the individual from the enmeshment of the alcoholic home. The detached expression of love is one in which each partner allows the other the freedom to make his or her decisions without conditions. It is often necessary to teach codependents the difference between *concern* for another person and *responsibility* for that person; that is, I might have feelings for another person, but I am not responsible for living that person's life.

It is also necessary to help the codependent learn appropriate interpersonal boundaries. The alcoholic home, resting as it does on the unstable sands of addiction, is in constant danger of being washed away. Each family member develops an unnatural involvement in the lives of the others. As part of the natural growth process that results in individuation, the child learns to establish boundaries between "self" and "other." But in the alcoholic home, the child learns to become *enmeshed* in the lives of others. Each person is trained to believe that he or she is responsible for every other member of the family.

In a very real sense, the codependent person has been "trained" to be codependent in the process of being raised in a disturbed home environment. The individual never has had the opportunity to differentiate from the family of origin. Such families are frequently so enmeshed in each other's lives that personal growth is virtually impossible.

The codependent person does not learn during childhood that he or she has the right to set limits within relationships—even in the marital relationship. In many cases, the codependent will tolerate violations of personal boundaries in an attempt to win the approval and love of any person who offers even the remote promise of accepting him or her. In other cases, codependents will have had their boundaries violated so often in the past that they do not even recognize appropriate limits to begin with.

Armed with distorted perceptions of family life, the child grows up to join the world of adults, and perhaps to marry. The potential partner who most closely matches the home environment of the codependent is, quite often, another addict. Thus, between the addicted person and the codependent person, there is an interaction of pathologies. Addicts often attempt to foster the impression that they are in need of somebody to take care of them because they cannot face the demands of daily living alone. They are actually looking for somebody who will relieve them of some of the responsibilities of daily living so that they can invest all that energy in supporting their drug use.

In other words, addicts look for a spouse who will become part of their addictive support system. Once they have found such a person, they strive to keep the spouse in a supportive role in order to remain addicted. On the other hand, the codependent is looking for somebody to take care of because of a weakened sense of self-esteem and a distorted picture of what family life is all about.

THE ALCOHOLIC HOME

According to Bowen (1985), the treatment of addiction involves identifying and ultimately modifying whatever dysfunctional family system allowed the development and maintenance of the addiction in the first place. In the alcoholic marriage, for example, it has long been known that the alcoholism becomes a "secret partner," first of the marriage and ultimately of the family. In time, this "family secret" becomes the dominating force around which the family's rules and rituals are centered (S. Brown, 1985).

Parents, because of their special role in the family, often set the tone or themes around which family members center their lives. They do this through parental injunctions. In the dysfunctional family system, unspoken injunctions often include (1) there is no addiction in this home and (2) don't you dare talk about it!

According to Ackerman (1983), "the key to surviving an alcoholic home is adaptation" (p. 16). The family will attempt to adapt to meet the demands of an addicted parent within the atmosphere established by the parental injunctions. For example, as Dulfano (1978) states, once addiction to alcohol has developed, family members often take on additional responsibility so that the addict "may maintain his drinking behavior" (p. 120).

Rather than fight with the alcoholic—to force the person to continue to carry out his or her traditional role, it becomes easier just to redistribute power and responsibilities within the family unit. The family system changes to accommodate the alcoholic, and in so doing some members may find themselves holding important positions for the first time. Thus, maintaining the alcoholic's behavior may actually carry a reward.

The adaptation that accommodates the alcoholic's drinking is often based on a fear of his or her behavior, especially when intoxicated. According to Deutsch (quoted in Freiberg, 1991), family members in the alcoholic family are constantly on guard:

> [They live] in a hypervigilant state, metaphorically walking through life on emotional eggshells, never knowing when the alcoholic will act out in an intoxicated and uncontrolled fashion. (p. 30)

This fear, often in combination with real or imagined threats, is used by the alcoholic to exert control over the family. Further, in order to facilitate the further use of alcohol, the addict will either give up, or never assume, responsibilities within the family that would normally be his or hers.

As the other family members come to assume responsibilities formerly held by the addict, he or she becomes less and less involved in family life. An older brother may assume responsibility for discipline of the children, or a daughter may assume responsibility for making sure the children are fed each night before they go to bed. The children, then, assume the parental responsibility of their addicted father or mother.

In adapting to parental alcoholism, the family achieves a new (if rather unstable) "balance." Family members may cling to this delicate balance in order to maintain stability in their lives. However,

> if the dysfunctional parent starts to get better or enters a treatment program, this can severely threaten the family balance. The rest of the family (especially the other parent) may unconsciously find ways to sabotage the dysfunctional parent's progress so that everyone can return to his or her familiar role. (Forward & Buck, 1989, p. 180)

Thus, within the alcoholic family a paradox often comes to exist. The family is uncomfortable with the addiction but may be quite happy with the current distribution of power and responsibility. However, if the family allows the alcoholism to continue, they may rather quickly fall into the trap of actually becoming a part of the addict's support system, making it easier for the alcoholic to drink. In so doing, the family members enable the addict's sick behavior to continue, as they "feed into" the addict's dependency.

Further, within the new family constellation, some individuals might assume responsibilities they are not emotionally ready to handle, creating a dysfunctional environment that will, in turn, impede the emotional growth of the family members. The child who assumes the role of caretaker may automatically assume this same role in adulthood, seeking as a spouse one who needs to be taken care of—the addict! In this way, pathology passes from one generation to another.

It is for this reason that many professionals who work with chemical dependency view addiction as a family-centered disorder. Bowen (1985), in his essay on the role of the family in the development of alcoholism, notes that "every important family member plays a part in the dysfunction of the dysfunctional member" (p. 262). Forward and Buck (1989) suggest that family members assume the role of caretaker in the alcoholic home to create a "comfortable balance of weak/strong, bad/good, or sick/healthy" (p. 180). In other words, when one parent is alcoholic, the other family members redistribute parental duties to again achieve a sense of balance. Often, this is done without guidance or external support. In fact, family members come to use the very same defense mechanisms so characteristic of addicts: denial, rationalization, and projection.

Without professional intervention, the dysfunctional family is unlikely to learn that it might actually be far more healthy to distance itself from the addict—to let the addict suffer the natural consequences of his or her behavior (Johnson Institute, 1987). Rather, the entire family assumes responsibility for the pathology of a single member, restructuring in an attempt to somehow "cure" the disturbed family member. In this way, the addict is relieved of the responsibility for his or her addiction or its cure.

As the individual's drug use progresses, the addiction assumes increasing importance in his or her life. Family commitments that interfere with drug use are dropped in favor of drug-centered activities. A son's long-anticipated trip to the ball park is postponed because dad is still too hung over from last night to be able to stand the heat and noise of the city. The long-awaited camping trip is cancelled at the last minute because mom went on another drinking spree last night, and is in no condition to go camping.

As part of this process of family accommodation, the son keeps silent when the teacher asks for volunteer drivers for an upcoming school trip, knowing that mom is unlikely to be sober enough to drive that day. The children stop bringing friends over to visit any more to avoid the embarrassment of having their alcoholic, or otherwise addicted parent, seen by their friends. The family struggles to accommodate itself to the addiction, and in the process may enable the addict. The addict knows that he or she will not have to face co-workers, PTA members, or friends of the children. The family "secret" is protected for another day.

The process of family accommodation to parental addiction develops over time, and often it is not fully apparent until after the addiction is full-blown. The point to be kept in mind, however, is that addiction does not spring into being overnight. Rather, the addiction, be it to alcohol or any other drug, *evolves* over a period of time. Furthermore, the addict does not stand alone, but has a family "support system" that he or she has helped to mold and shape. In turn, this family support system helps him or her to become and *remain* an addict.

Family accomodation to parental alcoholism is not without its costs. Until recently, the children were not thought to suffer significant damage from their parent's alcoholism. Current theory holds that parental alcoholism will create a disturbed home environment (Miller & Hester, 1989) that is thought to be quite similar to the home in which there is physical, emotional, or sexual abuse (Treadway, 1990). Thus, in theory, it would appear that children raised by alcoholic parents are at risk for the development of various forms of psychopathology (Miller & Hester, 1989; Owings-West & Prinz, 1987).

It has even been suggested that damage caused by parental alcoholism might extend beyond the children—to the *grandchildren* of the alcoholic (Beattie, 1989; Kohr, 1988). Even if we limit consideration to the immediate consequences of addiction, the suspected impact of parental drug dependency is staggering.

In their review of the impact of parental alcoholism on the psychological development of children, Owings-West and Prinz (1987) conclude that parental alcoholism contributes to a number of behavioral problems, including poor academic performance and inattentiveness. Silverman (1989) suggests that parental alcoholism is one element in the development of an antisocial personality disorder, or even an addictive disorder in the child.

Research into the impact of parental alcoholism has revealed that children who are raised in a home with at least one alcoholic parent do indeed seem to suffer some psychological harm. Puig-Antich et al. (1989) conclude that "the effects of living with an alcoholic parent may precipitate very early depression in children with loaded familial aggregation for affective disorders" (p. 413). Which is to say that there is a positive correlation between depressive disorders and alcoholism in certain families. When the potential for both conditions are present as a result of biological and environmental factors, children of families with an alcoholic parent are themselves more likely to suffer from a major depressive disorder, according to Puig-Antich et al.

Adult children of alcoholic parents often do not trust their perceptions and have difficulty understanding feelings (both their own and those of other people) (Black 1987; Deutsch [quoted in Freiberg, 1991]). Such children grow up to have trouble understanding interpersonal boundaries. They also may be impulsive and lack trust in their relationships.

As mentioned previously, children who are raised in an alcoholic home are often required to assume responsibilities far beyond their abilities or maturity. More than one 5-year-old has learned, for example, how to make sure that a parent is sleeping in such a position so as not to choke on vomit after a night's heavy drinking. Children or adolescents raised in the alcoholic home will often spend a lot of time "worrying about the safety of the whole [family] system" (Webb, 1989, p. 47).

Adolescents may learn to stay awake while the alcoholic parent is out drinking and check on the safety of sleeping siblings. They may develop elaborate fire-escape plans that involve returning time and time again to the burning house to rescue siblings, pets, and valuables (Webb, 1989). In response to the distorted family system, many adolescents will become overly mature, serious, and well organized—all in an attempt to maintain control of the home environment.

Some children and adolescents will become addicted to the excitement and unpredictability of living with an alcoholic parent and will possibly become involved in fire-setting behaviors (Webb, 1989). This addiction to excitement is thought to be one element that sets the foundation for future development of the antisocial personality disorder, according to Ansevics and Doweiko (1983). The antisocial personality disorder is thought to help the individual come to terms with an inconsistent home environment by helping him or her gain control of feelings of vulnerability.

It is Webb's (1989) contention that the adolescent raised in an alcoholic home spends so much time and energy meeting basic survival needs that he or she does not have the opportunity to establish a firm sense of personal identity. This is not to say that *every* child raised in an alcoholic home necessarily suffers this psychological trauma, but rather that these children are more likely to experience long-lasting emotional injuries as a result of their home environment than children raised in a more normal home.

CHILDREN OF ADDICTION: THE ACOA MOVEMENT

As more light has been cast on the dynamics of parental addiction in families, older victims of dysfunctional families have started to join together to form a self-help movement known as Adult Children of Alcoholics. (ACOA). This self-help movement, which has experienced phenomenal growth in the past 15 years, has borrowed heavily from the twelve-step program of Alcoholics Anonymous, although it is not affiliated with AA.

The Impact of Parental Alcoholism on the Family

Ackerman (1983) notes several interrelated factors that influence the impact of parental alcoholism on the growing child. The first of these factors is the sex of the addicted parent. Each parent plays a different role within the family. Obviously, the impact of an alcoholic mother will be far different from that of an alcoholic father.

A second factor that influences the impact of parental alcoholism on the family is the length of time that the alcoholic parent has actively been addicted. An alcoholic parent who has used chemicals for "only" 3 years will not have the same impact on the family as that of an alcoholic parent who has used chemicals for 17 years.

Third, the sex of the child plays a role in the impact parental alcoholism exerts. A daughter is affected differently by an alcoholic father than a son (Ackerman, 1983). Finally, the specific family constellation plays a role in how parental alcoholism will impact each individual child.

Consider, for example, the case in which the father has a 3-month relapse when the third boy in a family of six children is 9 years old. Contrast this child's experience with that of the oldest boy in a family of six children whose father relapses for 3 months when he is 9 years old. Both of these children would experience a far different family constellation than the only child, a girl, whose father relapses for 3 months when she is 9 years old.

All three children would have a far different experience in life than the third boy in a family of six children whose mother constantly drank until he turned 14 years of age.

The Role of Parental Surrogates

The oldest boy of a family of six children whose father was actively addicted for the first 14 years of the boy's life might possibly protect himself from the full impact of his father's alcoholism. It has been found that, *if* the child is able to find a parental substitute (uncle, neighbor, real or imagined hero, and so forth), it may be possible for that child to find a way to avoid the worst of his father's alcoholic parenting (Ackerman, 1983).

In a study of "resilient" children—those at risk because of social or biological trauma but who went on to succeed in life—Werner (1989) found these children "to be particularly adept at recruiting . . . surrogate parents when a biological parent was unavailable . . . or incapacitated (p. 108 D). Werner's work provides partial support for Ackerman's (1983) conclusion that it is possible for a child to find a substitute parent, and thus escape the full consequences of parental alcoholism.

Later in Life: The Adult Child of Alcoholic Parents

The child who is raised by an alcoholic parent or parents will eventually grow up. Indeed, the baby-boom generation, those middle-aged adults whose parents fought World War II, were not, as Collette (1990) pointed out, the first to grow up in alcoholic homes. However, the baby boomers were the first to view those in their ranks who had grown up in an alcoholic home as victims of parental alcoholism.

The baby boomers were also the first generation to form self-help groups to help adults face the trauma of being raised in an alcoholic home. It is estimated that there are between 22 million (Collette, 1990) and 27 million (Ackerman, 1983) adult children of alcoholics in the United States.

As we stated earlier, the alcoholic home has much in common with other dysfunctional home environments. Researchers have started to discover that the effects of growing up in an alcoholic home often last beyond the individual's childhood years. Indeed, childhood trauma often will continue to exert its influence through adolescence, into adulthood. Berkowitz and Perkins (1988) found, for example, that ACOAs are more critical of themselves and think less of themselves than adult children of nonalcoholic parents.

Woititz (1983), an early pioneer in the field of therapeutic intervention with ACOAs, lists a number of their characteristics, including the following:

- having to "guess" at what normal adult behavior is like, including the tendency to have trouble in intimate relationships;
- a tendency to have difficulty following a project through to completion;
- a tendency to lie in situations where it is just as easy to tell the truth;
- a tendency not to be able to "relax"; and
- a tendency to feel uncomfortable with themselves and to constantly seek affirmation from significant others.

Hunter and Kellogg (1990) agreed that ACOAs suffer from being raised in dysfunctional homes, but argue that traditional views of these individuals are too narrow. In their view, ACOAs often have personality characteristics *opposite* to those that would be expected of children raised in a dysfunctional home.

For example, as we have noted, ACOAs are thought to have trouble following a project through to completion. Yet, Hunter and Kellogg (1990) suggest that some ACOAs actually are compulsive workaholics, who struggle to carry out a project despite feedback that further work is no longer necessary or that the work is actually counterproductive.

In a study exploring the differences between young adults who had been raised by alcoholic parents and their counterparts who had not, Sher, Walitzer, Wood, and Brent (1991), conducted extensive interviews with college students to determine the drinking status of their parents. The following findings were reported:

1. College freshmen with an alcoholic father tended to drink more and to have more symptoms of alcoholism than those freshmen who were not raised by an alcoholic father.

2. Women raised by an alcoholic parent or parents and who drank themselves reported more extensive alcohol-related consequences than their nondrinking counterparts.
3. Children of alcoholic parents were more likely to use other drugs of abuse in addition to alcohol than children raised by nonalcoholic parents.
4. Adolescents of alcoholic parents had more positive expectancies for alcohol than adolescents of nonalcoholic parents.
5. As adults, children raised by alcoholic parents tended to have higher scores on test items suggesting "behavioral undercontrol" than those individuals who were not raised by alcoholic parents.
6. As college students, children raised by alcoholic parents tended to score lower on academic achievement tests than their non-ACOA counterparts.

Sher et al. thus identify several areas where parental drinking status appears to affect college students' adjustment and academic performance. While a causal relationship is not clearly identified, nor is the exact mechanism by which parents' drinking status might impact on the child's adjustment as a college student, this study does suggest that parental alcoholism has a strong impact on the subsequent growth and adjustment of the children.

Of ACOAs and guilt   Adult children of alcoholic parents often blame themselves for their parents' drinking (Freiberg, 1991). Collette (1988, 1990), for example, speaks of how she blamed herself for her father's pain and describes how she was close to the point of suicide until she became involved in an ACOA self-help group. Sanders (1990) states that he felt responsible for his father's drinking and tells of how he "paid the price" for this drinking through nights of fear and dread when his father threatened to leave or argued with his mother.

Obviously, in a survey text it is not possible to examine the self-help movement for adult children of alcoholic parents in great detail. However, as we have mentioned, the growth of ACOA groups has been phenomenal. Although the movement started in earnest only in the 1980s, there are now thought to be between 1,900 (Collette, 1990) and 4,000 (Blau, 1990) active self-help groups for adult children of alcoholics. This is a reflection of the great numbers of people who have been hurt by a parent's alcoholism and of the desire of these hidden victims of addiction to find peace by working through the shame and guilt that is left over from childhood (Collette, 1990).

Criticism of the ACOA Movement

While the ultimate goal of the ACOA movement is to provide a format for self-help for those who believe they have been hurt by being raised in a dysfunctional environment, the movement is not without its critics. For example, Elkin (quoted in Collette, 1990), points out that "we all want to feel like victims" and that "self-righteous indignation is the hardest drug to beat" (p. 30). However, he goes on to state:

> If you identify yourself as a survivor of incest or abuse, you are making an existential and self-hypnotic statement that defines you by the most destructive thing that ever happened to you. In the short term, it's important to say it, but you can get stuck there. (p. 30)

Treadway (1990) echoes this warning and notes that the process of attaching a label to a victim can "perpetuate the process of blaming in a new language" (p. 40). In a sense, like many medications, the ACOA movement may be either a tool or itself a form of compulsive behavior. It all depends on whether the individual uses the ACOA group as a means to grow or as a means to remain fixated in the past.

Further, the whole concept of ACOA limits the individual by keeping the focus *on the previous generation* (Peele et al., 1991). Admittedly, some children are raised in terrible, abusive environments. But, the central thesis of the ACOA movement rests on the impact of past parental behavior (often, years past) on the individual's *current* life problems. In a very real sense, the ACOA movement tends to encourage individuals to define "self" on the basis of their parents' problems and choices, according to Peele et al.

Other critics point out that although ACOA has never been recognized as a separate diagnostic category, some substance abuse counselors use it as such. "Adult Child of Alcoholics" is not listed by the American Psychiatric Association in the *Diagnostic and Statistical Manual of Mental Disorders* (3rd edition, revised). Nor is it listed in the World Health Organization's *International Classification of Diseases*, 9th edition. However, it is not unusual to see this diagnosis on an intake evaluation form as if it were a legitimate diagnostic category.

Thus, there is the tendency to assume that being an ACOA necessarily means that one has suffered as a result of parental addiction. However, as Peele et al. (1991) point out, there are those individuals who are able to grow up relatively healthy, in spite of a "dysfunctional" environment. The individual who resists the label of an ACOA might be in "denial," or he or she actually may not have suffered as a result of the parent's addiction. But a third possibility (frequently overlooked by many) is that the individual may very well have resolved any conflict(s) he or she suffered as a result of parental alcoholism *without professional intervention.* For these reasons, the ACOA label should be used with caution.

Further, the purpose of a diagnostic classification is to allow for easier communications through a common nomenclature system. The diagnosis of "adult child of alcoholic parents" fails to communicate anything about the specifics of a given individual's disorder. Rather, it assumes that *all* ACOAs are carbon copies of each other.

The ACOA movement has become something of a growth industry in this country (Blau, 1990). When it began in the early 1980s, it focused on the survivors of extreme abuse, according to Blau. However, over the years, the definition of what constitutes "abuse" has become so blurred that the tendency to blame parents for everything has become "a national obsession—and big business" (p. 61).

According to Peele et al. (1991), by current standards, 96% of the U.S. population may be said to have been raised in a "dysfunctional" family. One wonders, then, to what degree the characteristics identified by the proponents of the ACOA movement reflect not some form of pathology, but simply the problems of living in today's society for which we now have found language to blame our parents for.

In reality, there has been very little research into the psychological dynamics of families of alcoholics, or of other addicts (Goodwin & Warnock, 1991; University of California, Berkeley, 1990a). Indeed, very little is known about what constitutes a "normal" family, or the limits of unhealthy behavior that may be tolerated in an otherwise "normal" family. Moreover, while the limited research to date does suggest that children of alcoholic parents are more likely to experience psychological problems such as depression than children raised in nonalcoholic homes, these reports are inconclusive and often cannot be replicated in follow-up studies (Goodwin & Warnock, 1991).

Blau (1990) contends that the entire concept of the "adult child" is a reflection of the baby boomers' reluctance to accept that they are now entering middle adulthood. They are no longer the children of their parents in the same sense that they were two decades ago. They are now adults who, upon entering middle age, are discovering that they will not fulfill all their dreams of late adolescence and young adulthood. Thus, the implication of Blau's (1990) work is that the force behind the ACOA movement is a rebellion against aging by the baby-boom generation, reminiscent of the rebellion against the demands of the Vietnam conflict when that generation entered young adulthood.

SUMMARY

Within the past generation, substance abuse professionals have started to explore the family dynamics that both challenge and support an individual's alcoholism. As more has become known about the impact of alcoholism in a spouse or a parent on other members of the family, there has been a virtual explosion in the number of self-help groups for individuals raised within alcoholic homes and for those whose marriages have been affected by alcoholism. Some of these self-help groups, such as Adult Children of Alcoholics, have been challenged on a number of grounds.

Chapter 25

THE ASSESSMENT OF
CHEMICAL DEPENDENCY

F or many who are addicted to chemicals, the first step toward
rehabilitation is a drug-use assessment (Donovan, 1992). Through the
chemical dependency assessment, a substance abuse or mental health
professional attempts first to determine whether or not the client is an abuser
of chemicals. Secondly, the assessor seeks to determine whether or not the
client is addicted to chemicals. Finally, if there *is* evidence that the client is
either an abuser of chemicals or is addicted to them, the assessor attempts to
provide an overview of the client's chemical-use pattern and make the appropriate referrals.

THE THEORY BEHIND
DRUG-USE ASSESSMENTS

As Cohen and Marcos (1989) state, mental health professionals are increasingly being called upon to determine those individuals "whose criminal
('bad') behavior is not necessarily attributable to being mentally ill ('mad')" (p.
677). Chemical dependency professionals are being asked to make the same
determination for those thought to be addicted to chemicals. In addressing this
issue, Lewis et al., (1988) warn that

> merely walking into a substance abuse treatment facility does not in and of
> itself, warrant a diagnosis of "chemical dependency" or "alcoholism." Rather,
> clinicians must carefully evaluate the client and only then make decisions
> concerning diagnosis and treatment. (p. 75)

This is a timely warning for a number of reasons. First, there are those who
would like to excuse antisocial behavior on the grounds that it is an "illness,"
such as chemical dependency. Thus, the first duty of the assessor should be to
establish a firm basis for either making a diagnosis of chemical dependency or
for not making such a diagnosis. It is only after the diagnosis has been
established (*if it is established*) that the need for treatment should be considered. Treatment centers that assume the client *must* have a problem with
chemicals simply because he or she walked in do not serve the client's
interests—only their own. *The need for treatment must be established and well
documented.*

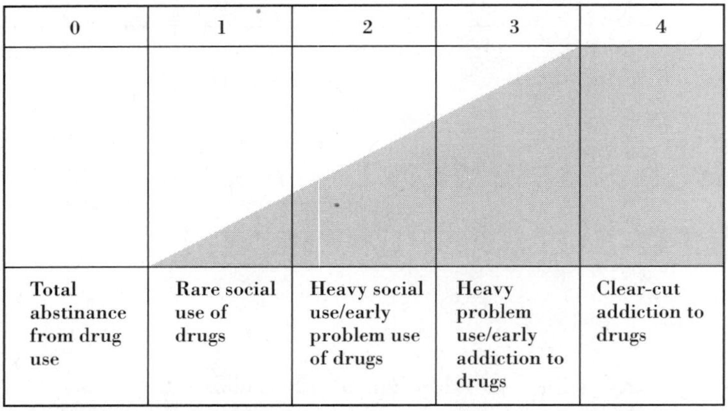

0	1	2	3	4
Total abstinance from drug use	Rare social use of drugs	Heavy social use/early problem use of drugs	Heavy problem use/early addiction to drugs	Clear-cut addiction to drugs

FIGURE 25-1   The drug-use continuum.

Secondly, as Kerr (1988) notes, "effective therapy depends on assessment; if the assessment is too narrow in scope, the therapy will probably be ineffective" (p. 35). The assessment process allows the therapist to identify the client's strengths, needs, areas of weakness, and priorities. The central goal of this evaluation process is to design a treatment plan that will be most beneficial to the client. If, as Kerr observes, the assessment fails to identify significant areas of need, the therapeutic intervention will be unlikely to succeed.

The reverse is also true. If the assessment incorrectly identifies specific problems, which is to say if the assessment process reveals a need that is not there, therapy also will be unlikely to benefit the client. Thus, it is essential for the therapist to identify as many potential areas of strength, support, and need as is possible during assessment.

In Chapter 2, the concept of addiction as a continuum was introduced. We used a chart to illustrate the continuum of drug use/abuse, ranging from the extreme of total abstinence from chemicals to that of chronic addiction (see Figure 2-1). For the reader's convenience we repeat this chart as Figure 25-1.

Quite simply, the assessment process involves a professional evaluation of where on the drug-use continuum the individual being assessed might fall. For example, the person might exhibit strong evidence of a drug-dependency problem. However, it might also be determined that he or she has not progressed past the stage of heavy social use of chemicals. In some cases, the assessment process will reveal that the client only uses chemicals socially.

DRUG ABUSE AND DRUG DEPENDENCE DEFINED

Kamback (1978) states that two elements necessary to define an addiction to chemicals are *dependence* on the chemical, and *tolerance* to the drug's effects. As the individual's body adapts to the continuous use of the one or more chemicals, there is a declining effect from the initial dosage levels. In order to achieve the effect once achieved with a relatively low dose, larger and larger doses must be administered. This is tolerance.

Dependence on a chemical is diagnosed by the presence of a characteristic *withdrawal syndrome* when the drug is discontinued. The body, as it adapts to the continued presence of the drug(s) being used, alters its normal biological activities. When the drug is discontinued, there is a period of time during which the body must again adapt, this time to the absence of the chemical. During this period of readaptation to the absence of the chemical, the individual will experience the characteristic withdrawal syndrome for that chemical.

Abel (1982), in addressing the difference between abuse of a drug and dependence on it, identifies four elements as necessary for the diagnosis of addiction: (1) a compulsion to continue use of the drug, (2) the development of tolerance, (3) major withdrawal symptoms following withdrawal from the drug, and (4) adverse effects from drug use, both for the individual and for society.

The diagnosis of chemical dependency is, unfortunately, retrospective. Furthermore, even after the disorder is fully developed, all four of Abel's (1982) elements are not clearly demonstrated in each and every case. The existence of one symptom of addiction is often taken as evidence by health care professionals that the other symptoms also exist.

When a patient goes through major withdrawal symptoms from alcohol, benzodiazepines, barbiturates, or narcotics, for example, it may be safely assumed that he or she is also tolerant to the drug's effects. Tolerance usually is apparent before the development or physical withdrawal symptoms from these chemicals. The withdrawal symptoms also imply the compulsive use of one or more drugs in the patient who had to use the drug(s) frequently for a long period of time for physical dependency to develop. Further, the withdrawal process would suggest that the drug has affected the individual adversely if only in the form of the withdrawal process itself.

The exact nature of the withdrawal syndrome will reflect the specific drugs that were used and the length of time the individual used them. It will also reflect whether the individual discontinued the chemical use all at once or gradually. Both tolerance and dependence must be present in order to diagnose an addiction to one or more chemicals.

However, there also is a phenomenon known as *psychological dependence* on a chemical. The psychologically dependent individual will habitually use one or more drugs in an attempt to deal with anxiety or stress. The term *habituation* has also been applied to this phenomenon. In such a case, there is no physical adaptation to use of the drug (the body does not incorporate the drug into its normal function), but there is a *psychological adaptation* in the sense that the person comes to believe that they *need* the drug.

Consider, for example, the individual whose only alcohol use is a "nightcap" each and every night just before going to bed to "unwind." This individual has very likely developed a psychological dependence on the alcohol to help him or her deal with the stress and frustration of daily living. As such, he or she could be said to have become habituated to alcohol.

It is the assessor's responsibility to determine if the client's chemical-use pattern might best be classified as "social use," "abuse," or "addiction" to one or more drugs. This process is a complicated one and involves gathering information from a wide variety of sources. In so doing, the assessor must work within the data privacy laws.

THE ASSESSOR AND DATA PRIVACY

The client *always* has a right to privacy; that is, the assessor does not automatically have access to personal information about the client. The client may refuse to answer a specific question or refuse to permit another person to reveal specific information to the assessor. The assessor must respect the client's right to control access to information about him or her.

Both federal and state data-privacy laws often apply when working with individuals who are thought to be addicted to drugs or alcohol. If the client agrees to the assessment, he or she is then willingly providing personal information during the assessment process. However, the client still retains the right to refuse to answer any question. If information is required from individuals other than the client, *the assessor should always obtain written permission* from the client authorizing the assessor to contact specific individuals to obtain information about the client's chemical use or any other aspect of his or her life. This written permission is recorded on a *release-of-information authorization form.*

Occasionally, a client will refuse such permission. The client retains this right and can refuse to allow the assessor to speak with *any* other person. This refusal, in itself, might say a great deal about how open and honest the client has been with the assessor, especially if the assessor has explained to the client exactly what information will be requested.

One possible solution, which some professionals advocate, is to have the client sit in on the collateral interview. One drawback to this solution is that the client's presence might inhibit the freedom of the collateral information source in discussing his or her perception of the client. In this case, a potentially valuable source of information about the client would be unavailable to the assessor. Thus, it is rarely productive to have the client, or the client's representative, sit in on collateral interviews.

When a client is being referred for an evaluation by the court system, the court will often provide referral information about his or her previous legal history. The courts will often also include a detailed social history of the client, obtained during the presentence investigation. If asked, the assessor should acknowledge having read this information but should not discuss the contents of referral information provided by the courts. Such discussions are to be avoided for two reasons.

First, the purpose of the clinical interview is to assess the client's chemical-use patterns. A discussion of what information was or was not provided by the court does nothing to further this evaluation. Secondly, the client, or his or her attorney, has access to this information through established channels. Thus, if the client wishes to review the information provided by the court, he or she is free to do so.

Clients will occasionally ask to see the records provided by the court during the clinical interview. Frequently, these clients are checking to see what information has been provided by the courts in order to decide how much and what to reveal during the interview period. Here we have the philosophy, Let me know how much *you* know about me, so that I'll know how "honest" I should be.

A simple statement to the effect that the client may obtain a copy of the court record through established legal channels often suffices in this situation. Those clients who persist in demanding to see their court records should be reminded that the purpose of the interview is to explore the client's drug-use patterns—not to review court records. Under no circumstances should the chemical dependency/mental health professional let the client read his or her referral records. To do so would be a violation of the data-privacy laws because the referral information was released to the professional, *not* to the client.

When the final evaluation is written, the assessor should identify the source of the information. Collateral information sources should be advised that the client, or his or her attorney, has a right to request a copy of the final report before the interview. It is *extremely* rare for a client to request a copy of the final report, although technically the client does have the right to do so after the proper release-of-information authorization forms have been signed.

DIAGNOSTIC RULES

Washton (1990) notes that many clients will resist a diagnosis of chemical dependency, at least at first. For this reason, two diagnostic rules should be followed as closely as possible in the evaluation and diagnosis of a possible drug addiction, even in special cases. If either of these rules cannot be adhered to, the assessor making the diagnosis should state the reason for this situation to avoid missing important information.

Rule 1: Gather collateral information   A fundamental aspect of chemical dependency is deception. Thus in attempting to make a diagnosis of addiction, the assessor should *use as many sources of information as possible*. Evans and Sullivan (1990), in discussing the need for a wide data base, caution, "Never, ever diagnose using information based only on the client's presentation at the time of assessment" (p. 54).

To underscore the importance of collateral information, every chemical dependency professional has encountered cases in which the individual being evaluated claims "I drink only once a week" or "no more than a couple of beers after work." The spouse of this person often reports, however, that the client is drunk almost every night.

Using as many sources of information as possible minimizes danger of deception and enables the development of as comprehensive a history of the client as possible. Slaby et al. (1981) recommend that such collateral information sources include the following:

- the client's family and friends;
- the client's employer or co-workers;
- clergy members;
- local law enforcement authorities;
- the client's primary-care physician; and
- the client's psychotherapist (if any).

Obviously, the time restrictions of the assessment process might prevent using some of these collateral sources. For example, if the assessment must be completed by the end of the week and the assessor is unable to contact the client's mother, it may be necessary to write the final report without benefit of her input. In addition, other potential sources may simply refuse to provide any information whatsoever. It is the assessor's responsibility, however, to *attempt* to contact as many of these individuals as possible and to include their views in the final evaluation report.

Rule 2: *Always* assume deception until proven otherwise Not all addicts automatically lie. Indeed, there is evidence to suggest that, *as a group*, alcoholics are quite accurate in their self-report as to the amount of alcohol consumed and the frequency of their alcohol use (Donovan, 1992). But, as noted earlier, the nature of addiction is deception. According to Sierles (1984), substance abusers are one of the two groups of patients most likely to attempt to deceive assessors (the other group being those with a history of sociopathic behaviors). Cunnien (1988) states that the addict will be persistent in his or her attempts to deceive others.

At times, alcoholics will minimize the amount of alcohol they drink so as to hide the full extent of their drinking. Opiate addicts who are admitted for detoxification, on the other hand, will often exaggerate the amount of drugs they use in the hope of obtaining more drugs from detoxification center staffs. Cocaine addicts may also exaggerate their drug use, although this finding is not consistent. Some cocaine addicts may initially deny or minimize their use of the drug.

When evaluating a person's drug use it is also not unusual for the assessor to encounter a client who claims to be using a certain amount of heroin or cocaine, only to later find out from friends of the client that the person had *never* used opiates or cocaine. The client was just attempting to impress the assessor, the courts, or drug-using "friends."

Alcoholics may claim to drink only a couple of times a week, until reminded that their medical problems are unlikely to have been caused by such moderate drinking levels. At this point, they sometimes admit to more frequent drinking episodes. However, even when confronted with evidence of serious, continual alcohol use, many alcoholics still deny the reality of their alcoholism.

Clients have been known to admit to "one" arrest for driving under the influence of alcohol or to possession of a controlled substance. However, records provided by the court at the time of admission into treatment often reveal that the person in question had been arrested in two or three different states for similar charges. When confronted, these clients may respond that they thought the assessor "only meant in *this* state," or that since the arrest occurred in another state it didn't apply. It bears repeating that the assessor must use as many different sources of information as possible to minimize the risk of deception.

THE EVALUATION FORMAT

Although, ultimately, each individual is unique, there is a general assessment format that may be used when confronted by either known or suspected chemical addiction. This assessment format is modified as necessary to take into account individual differences. In the balance of this chapter, our discussion will build on this format.

Area I: Circumstances of Referral

The first step in the diagnostic process is to examine the circumstances under which the client is seen. The client who is in a hospital alcohol detoxification (or "detox") unit for the first time is far different from the one who has been in the detox unit 10 times in the last 3 years. Thus, the first piece of data for the chemical dependency assessment is a review of the circumstances surrounding the individual's referral.

The manner in which the client responds to the question "What brings you here today?" can provide valuable information about how willing a participant the individual will be in the evaluation process. If he or she responds, "I don't know, they told me to come here," or "You should know, you've read the report," this client is obviously less than cooperative. The rare client who responds, "I think I have a drug problem," is demonstrating some degree of cooperativeness. In each case, the manner in which the client identifies the circumstances surrounding his or her referral for evaluation provides the assessor with a valuable piece of information.

Area II: Drug-Use Patterns

The next step is for the assessor to explore the individual's drug- and alcohol-use patterns *both past and present*. As mentioned previously, clients will often claim to drink "only once a week," or to have had "nothing to drink in the last 6 months." Treatment center staff are not surprised to find out that this drinking pattern has been the rule *only* since the person's last arrest for an alcohol-related offense.

From time to time, the assessor will encounter a person who proudly claims not to have had a drink or not to have used chemicals in the last 6 to 12 months, or perhaps even longer. This person may "forget" to report that he or she was locked up in the county jail awaiting trial during that time, or under strict supervision after being released from jail on bail, and had little or no access to chemicals. This is in sharp contrast to the client who reports that he or she has not had a drink or used chemicals in the past year, is not on probation or parole, and has no charges pending.

Thus, the assessor should explore the client's living situation to determine if any environmental conditions restricted the individual's drug use. Obviously, a person who is incarcerated, in treatment, or whose probation officer requires both frequent and unannounced supervised urine screens to detect drug/alcohol use, will have an environmental restriction imposed on him or her. Although a report of having "not used drugs in 6 months" may be the literal truth, it may be designed to mislead.

The individual's chemical-use pattern and *beliefs about his or her drug use* should then be compared with the circumstances surrounding referral. For example, consider the person who states that he or she does not have a problem with chemicals. Earlier in the interview, he or she may also have admitted to an arrest for possession of a controlled substance for the second time in 4 years. In this situation, the client has provided two important, but discrepant, pieces of information to the assessor.

Several important areas should be explored at this point in the evaluation process. The evaluator needs to consider whether the client has ever been in a treatment program for chemical dependency and whether his or her drug or alcohol use has ever resulted in legal, financial, social, or medical problems. The assessor also needs to consider whether the client has ever demonstrated any signs of either psychological dependency or physical addiction to drugs or alcohol.

To understand this point, one need only contrast the cases of two clients who are seen following an arrest for driving a motor vehicle while under the influence of chemicals. The first person claims (and the collateral information agrees) that he or she only drinks in moderation once every few weeks. Furthermore, the background check conducted by the courts reveals that this client never had any previous legal problems of any kind. However, after receiving a long-awaited promotion, the client celebrated with some friends. The client was a rare drinker, who drank heavily with friends to celebrate the promotion and subsequently misjudged the amount of alcohol that had been consumed.

In contrast to this person is the second client, whose collateral information sources seem to indicate a more extensive chemical-use pattern to the assessor than he admitted to during the interview. A background check conducted by the police at the time of this individual's arrest reveals several prior arrests for the same offense.

In the first case, one might argue that the client simply made a mistake. Admittedly, he was driving under the influence of alcohol. However, he had *never* done so in the past, and does not fit the criteria even for a diagnosis of heavy social drinking. The report to the court should outline the sources of the data examined and in this case provide a firm foundation for the conclusion that this individual had made a mistake in driving after drinking.

In the second case, the individual's drunk driving arrest was the tip of a larger problem, which was outlined in the report to the court. The assessor detailed the sources of information that supported this conclusion, including information provided by family members, the individual's physician, the patient, the county sheriff's department, as well as friends of the client. The final report concluded that the client had a significant addiction problem that required treatment in a formal chemical dependency treatment program.

Area III: Legal History

Part of the assessment process should include an examination of the client's legal history. This information might be based on the individual's self-report or on a review of his or her police record as provided by the court, the probation/parole officer, or some other source. *It is always important to identify the source of the information on which the report is based.* Information pertaining to the client's legal record should include the following:

- charges that have been brought against the client in the past by the local authorities, and their disposition;
- charges that have been brought against the client in the past by authorities in other localities, and their disposition; and
- the nature of current charges (if any) against the individual.

There are many cases on record in which an individual was finally convicted of a misdemeanor charge for possession of less than an ounce of marijuana. However, all too often, a review of the client's police record reveals that the individual had been arrested for a felony drug-possession charge, and that the charges had been reduced through plea-bargaining agreements. In some states, it is possible for the charge of driving a motor vehicle under the influence of alcohol (a felony in many states) to be reduced to a misdemeanor charge, such as public intoxication, by plea-bargaining agreements.

The assessor needs to determine both the *initial charges,* and the *ultimate disposition* by the court of these charges. The assessor should specifically inquire as to whether or not the client has had charges brought against him or her in other states or by federal authorities. Individuals may admit to *one* charge for possession of a controlled substance, only for the staff to later find out that this same client has had several arrests (and also convictions) for the same charge in other states. Or the client may admit to an *arrest* for possession charges in other states, but may not mention that he or she had left the state before the charges could be brought to trial.

Since he or she was never *convicted* of the charges, the client may rationalize that they need not be mentioned during the assessment. The fact that the charges were never proven in court because he or she was a fugitive from justice (as well as the fact that interstate flight to avoid prosecution is a possible federal offense) may well be overlooked by the client.

Past military record   An important (and often overlooked) source of information is the client's *military history*, if any. Many clients with military history will report only on their civilian legal history, unless specifically asked about their military legal record. Clients who may have denied any drug or alcohol legal charges whatsoever may, upon inquiry, admit to having been reprimanded or brought before a superior officer on charges of chemical use while serving in the military.

The assessor must specifically inquire as to whether or not the individual has ever been in the service. If the client has not served, it might be useful to determine the reason. Often, the client will respond, "I wanted to join, but I had a felony arrest record," or "I had a DWI (driving while under the influence of alcohol) on my record, and couldn't join." These responses provide valuable information to the assessor, and open new areas for investigation.

If the client has served in the military, was his or her discharge status honorable, a general discharge under honorable conditions, a general discharge under dishonorable conditions, or a dishonorable discharge? Was the client ever brought up on charges while in the service? If so, what was the disposition of these charges? Was the client ever referred for drug treatment while in the service? Was the client ever denied a transfer or promotion because of drug or alcohol use? Finally, was the client ever transferred because of his or her drug or alcohol use?

The client's legal history should be verified, if possible, by contacting the court or probation/parole officer, especially if the client was referred for evaluation for an alcohol- or drug-related offense. The legal history will often provide significant information about the client's life-style and the extent to which his or her drug use has (or has not) resulted in conflict with social rules and expectations.

Area IV: Educational/Vocational History

The next step in the assessment process is to determine the individual's educational and vocational history. This information, which might be based on the individual's self-report or on school or employment records, provides information on the client's level of function and on whether or not chemical use has interfered with his or her education or vocation. As before, the evaluator should identify the source of this information.

For example, the client who says that she dropped out of school in the 10th grade because she was "into drugs" presents a different picture than does the client who obtained a bachelor of science degree from a well-known university. The individual who has had five jobs in the past 2 years might present a far different picture than the individual who has held a series of responsible positions with the same company for the past 10 years. Thus, the assessor should attempt to determine the client's educational/vocational history to determine his or her educational level, potential, and the degree to which chemical use has affected his or her educational or work life.

Area V: Developmental/Family History

The assessor can often uncover significant material through an examination of the client's developmental and family history. For example, a client might reveal that her father was "a problem drinker" upon being asked "Were either of your parents chemically dependent?" but she may hesitate to call that parent an alcoholic. How a client describes the chemical use of a parent or sibling might reveal how the client thinks about his or her own chemical use.

The client who says "My mother had a problem with alcohol" might have a different attitude about drinking than the client who says "My mother was an alcoholic." The client who hesitates to use the term *alcoholic*, but who is comfortable with "problem drinker" might be hinting that he is also uncomfortable with *alcoholic* as it applies to him. But he may also have accepted the rationalization that he is a "problem drinker," just like his brother or sister.

Information about either parental or sibling chemical use is important for still another reason. As will be recalled from Chapter 4 on alcohol, there is significant evidence suggesting a genetic predisposition toward alcoholism. By extension, one might expect that future research will uncover a genetic link toward the other forms of drug addiction, as well.

In addition to this, the assessor will be able to explore the client's attitudes about parental alcohol or drug use in the home while he or she was growing up. Did the client view this chemical use as normal? Was the client angry or ashamed about the parents' chemical use? Does the client view chemical use as a problem for the family or not?

Thus, it is important for the assessor to examine the possibility of either past or present parental or sibling chemical use. Such information will offer insights into the client's possible genetic inheritance, especially as to whether he or she might be at risk to develop an addiction. Furthermore, an overview of the family environment provides clues as to how the client views drug or alcohol use.

Family environments differ. The client whose parents were rare social drinkers would have been raised in a far different environment than the client whose parents were drug addicts. Clients who report that they never knew their mother because she was a heroin addict who put them up for adoption when they were little would view drugs far differently than those who report that they were raised to believe that hard work would see a person through troubled times and whose parents never drank at all.

Area VI: Psychiatric History

Chemical use will often result in either outpatient or inpatient psychiatric treatment. A natural part of the assessment process should be to discuss with the client whether or not he or she has ever been treated for psychiatric problems on either an inpatient or an outpatient basis. For example, clients have been known to admit to having been hospitalized for observation because of hallucinations, attempted suicide, violence, or depression.

Perhaps months or even years after admission to chemical dependency treatment, a client may reveal that he or she had been using drugs at the time of admission. Often, when asked, the client reveals that he or she had not mentioned this fact to the staff of the psychiatric hospital. It might be that the client had lied to the hospital staff or that the psychiatric admissions staff had simply failed to ask the appropriate questions. It is important, then, that the assessor inquire as to whether the client has ever been hospitalized for psychiatric treatment or been treated for a psychiatric disorder on an out-patient basis.

If possible, the assessor should obtain a release-of-information form from the client and send for the discharge summary from the treatment center where the client was hospitalized. The possibility that drugs contributed to the psychiatric hospitalization or outpatient treatment should be either confirmed or ruled out, if possible. This information will allow the asssessor to determine whether or not the client's drug use ever resulted in psychiatric problems serious enough to warrant professional help.

As noted in Chapter 7 the CNS stimulants, it is not uncommon for chronic use of amphetamines or cocaine to cause a drug-induced psychosis that, at least in its early stages, is very similar to paranoid schizophrenia. A client who reports having spent a short time in a psychiatric hospital for a "brief psychosis" may well have developed such a drug-related problem, whether or not it was recognized as such by the hospital staff.

Area VII: Medical History

Clients who are chemically dependent will often have a history of numerous hospitalizations for the treatment of accidents or injuries that may have been drug-related. For example, one client reported having been hospitalized many times after rival drug dealers had tried to kill him. He had accumulated an impressive assortment of knife wounds, gunshot wounds, and fractured bones from these "business transactions" that had, in his words, "gone bad" over the years.

However, this client had never been hospitalized for a drug overdose. An assessor who asked, "Have you ever been hospitalized because of a drug overdose?" would have missed out on the details of these hospitalizations because the client viewed them as being related to "business transactions," not to personal drug use. On a similar note, alcoholics who drive while under the influence of alcohol are often hospitalized following "accidents" that may or may not be alcohol-related in their eyes.

The assessor should inquire about periods of hospitalization *for any reason*. Then, he or she should explore whether or not these were drug-related. A client who is hospitalized following an automobile accident may contract hepatitis B (a viral liver infection, transmitted through the blood) following a blood transfusion. If that accident was caused by the person's drinking, then indirectly the client may be said to have contracted hepatitis B as a result of drinking.

The client who admits to the use of intravenous drugs and who is hospitalized for the treatment of the infection of the heart valves known as endocarditis may have shared needles with other addicts. Or, he or she may have developed the infection only after being malnourished after a protracted period of drug use. It is up to the assessor to try to determine whether the person's chemical use was a causal agent in the client's hospitalization. Such information will often help the assessor gain a better understanding of the client's chemical use and its consequences.

Area VIII: Previous Treatment History

In working with a person who may be addicted to chemicals, it is helpful for the assessor to determine whether or not the client was ever in a treatment program for chemical dependency. This information, which may be based on the client's self-report or on information provided by the court system, sheds light on the client's past and on his or her potential to benefit from treatment.

The person who has been hospitalized three times for a heart condition, but who continues to deny having any heart problems, is denying the reality of his condition. The same is true for the client who says that she does not think she has a problem with chemicals, but who has been in drug treatment three times. The problem then becomes one of making a recommendation for the client in light of his or her previous treatment history and current status.

The assessor should pay attention to the discharge status from previous treatment programs, noting how long after the discharge the person maintained sobriety. Clients often claim to have been sober for 3 months. But on close questioning they may admit that they were in treatment for these 3 months and that they started to use drugs shortly after they were discharged, if not before. Unfortunately, the client who reports having used chemicals on the way home following treatment is well known to chemical dependency treatment professionals.

A client who admits to having used chemicals during a previous treatment period is providing valuable information about his or her attitude toward the current treatment exposure, as well. This client would have a different prognosis than would a client who had maintained total sobriety for 3 years following the last treatment exposure, and who had then relapsed. Clients should be asked specific questions as to *when they entered treatment, how long they were there, and when they started to use chemicals following treatment.*

THE CLINICAL INTERVIEW

The clinical interview forms the cornerstone of chemical dependency assessment. Information provided by the client should shed considerable light on his or her previous chemical use. But, as we have noted, since clients will either consciously or unconsciously distort the information they provide, other sources of data should also be used in evaluating suspected addiction to chemicals.

The first part of the interview process is an introduction by the assessor. It is explained that the assessor will be asking questions about the client's possible chemical-use patterns and that *specific* responses would be most helpful. It is explained that although many of the questions may have been asked by others in the past, this information is important. The client is asked if he or she has any questions, after which the interview will begin.

The assessor should attempt to review the diagnostic criteria for chemical dependency outlined by the American Psychiatric Association's (1987) *Diagnostic and Statistical Manual of Mental Disorders* (third edition, revised), also known as the *DSM-III-R*. This manual provides a framework within which to diagnose chemical dependency.

Many of the questions used in the clinical interview are designed to explore the same piece of information from different perspectives. For example, at one point in the interview process the client may be asked, "In the *average* week, how many nights would you say that you use drugs or alcohol?" At a later point, this same client may be asked, "How much would you say, on the average, that you spend for drugs or alcohol in a week?"

The purpose is not to "trap" the client so much as to provide different perspectives on the client's chemical-use pattern. For example, the client who claims to use alcohol one or two nights a week might admit to spending $50 per week on chemicals. The assessor might then inquire how it can be that the client drinks only once or twice weekly, but that this costs approximately $50 a week. The client may respond that he or she drinks at a bar and she often buys drinks for friends. This information reveals more about the client's chemical-use pattern, helping the assessor form a clearer picture.

OTHER SOURCES OF DATA: MEDICAL INFORMATION

The importance of information provided by medical professionals was discussed in the section on collateral information. However, medical tests and medical personnel can often shed further light on the client's chemical-use pattern at the time of the evaluation by either confirming or negating the client's claims to be using certain drugs.

Clients sometimes claim to be using a certain amount of heroin on a daily basis; however, blood or urine tests may fail to reveal *any* trace of narcotics whatsoever. In more than one case, when confronted, the client admits to such deception in the hope of being put on methadone for a few days' "withdrawal." The reverse is also true. Clients have been known to deny the use of certain drugs, such as marijuana, only to have a supervised urine toxicology test detect THC in their urine.

Medical tests can often

- confirm the *presence* of certain chemicals in the client's blood or urine sample;
- identify the *amount* of certain chemicals present in the blood or urine sample; and
- determine whether the drug levels in the blood or urine sample have *increased* since the last test (suggesting further drug use), *remained the same* (which also might suggest further drug use), or *decreased* (suggesting no further drug use since the last test).

The detection of chemical use by laboratory testing is a complex technical art (Verebey & Turner, 1991). This testing may prove invaluable in certain situations. For example, it is not uncommon for a client involved in an automobile accident to claim to have had only two beers. However, a laboratory test conducted within an hour of the accident may reveal a blood-alcohol level far higher than two beers would produce. Thus, some distortion on the client's part would be apparent.

Clients who test negative for marijuana on one occasion may very well test positive for this same chemical only a few days later. Subsequent inquiry will often reveal that they used drugs sometime after the first test, thinking that they were "safe" and would not be tested for drugs again for a long time. Such drug use would be detected by *frequent* and *unannounced* urine tests that are *closely supervised* to detect illicit drug use.

Thus, medical tests data is often a valuable source of objective information about a client's drug use. Clients may appear sleepy simply because they did not sleep well the night before—or perhaps because they used drugs or alcohol in the past few hours. Laboratory test data can reveal which is the case. The assessor should always attempt to use such data to further establish a foundation for the diagnosis of chemical dependency.

PSYCHOLOGICAL TEST DATA

A number of psychological tests may be useful in diagnosing chemical dependency. Many of the assessment tools available today are paper-and-pencil tests. These instruments are either filled out by the client (and as such are known as *self-report* instruments) or by the assessor, as he or she asks questions of the person being evaluated. Self-report instruments offer the advantage of being inexpensive; moreover, they are usually inoffensive to the client (Stuart, 1980).

One of the most popular assessment instruments is the Michigan Alcoholism Screening Test (MAST) (Selzer, 1971). This test is composed of 24 questions which may be answered either yes or no, depending on whether the item applies to the respondent. Test items are weighted with a value of 1, 2, or in some cases 5, points. A score of 5 points or more suggests alcoholism. The effectiveness of this test has been demonstrated in clinical literature (Miller, 1976), but because it addresses *only* alcoholism (Lewis et al., 1988), it is of limited value in cases where the person uses other chemicals.

There are other assessment tools available. For example, Roffman and George (1988) provide examples of a self-report instrument used in the evaluation of marijuana-use patterns. Washton, Stone, and Hendrickson (1988) discuss the use of the Cocaine Abuse Assessment Profile in their essay on the evaluation of cocaine users. These tests, while useful, are also of limited value in the assessment of polydrug users.

The original Minnesota Multiphasic Personality Inventory (MMPI) was introduced 50 years ago. In 1965, the MacAndrew Alcoholism Scale (also known as the Mac Scale) was introduced, after an item analysis suggested that alcoholics tended to answer 49 of the 566 items of the MMPI differently than nonalcoholics. A cutoff score of 24 items out of 49 answered in the "scorable" direction correctly identified 82% of the alcoholic and nonalcoholic clients in a sample of 400 male psychiatric patients. Subsequent research has suggested, however, that this scale might measure a general tendency toward addiction rather than the specific behavior of alcoholism (J.R. Graham, 1990).

After 7 years of research, an updated version of the MMPI, the Minnesota Multiphasic Personality Inventory-2 (or, MMPI-2) was introduced in 1989. The Mac scale was essentially retained, with minor modifications. However, in the time since it was first introduced, research has revealed that black clients tend to score higher on the Mac scale than white clients. Further, clients who are assertive, extroverted, or exhibitionistic, or those who experience "blackouts" for *any* reason or who enjoy risk-taking behaviors, all tend to score higher on the Mac scale, even if they are not addicted (J.R. Graham, 1990).

Although the Mac scale was designed to detect alcoholics, Otto, Lang, Megargee, and Rosenblatt (1989) report that alcoholics may be able to "conceal their drinking problems even when the relatively subtle special alcohol scales of the [original] MMPI are applied" (p 7). Thus, the MMPI Mac scale could yield either false positive or false negative results. Until proven otherwise, counselors should assume that the revised Mac scale of the MMPI-2 shares this same weakness with the original Mac scale.

Unlike many of the other assessment tools, the MMPI offers the advantage of having five "truth" scales built into it. These scales are discussed in detail by J. R. Graham (1990). A major disadvantage of the MMPI is that it is possible for the individual taking the test to "intentionally diminish . . . the level of pathology evident in overall MMPI profiles" (Otto et al., 1989, p. 7). Furthermore, in spite of the truth scales that are built into the MMPI, individuals who are attempting to project an image of themselves as being well adjusted may still accomplish their goal and reduce measured levels of distress.

Overall, a major disadvantage of paper-and-pencil tests is that they are best suited to situations in which the client will be unlikely to "fake" (the technical term is "positively dissimulate") answers on the test in order to appear less disturbed (Evans & Sullivan, 1990). A common problem, well known to chemical dependency professionals, is that these instruments are subject to the same problems of denial, distortion, and outright misrepresentation often encountered in the clinical interview setting.

Clients have been known to initially deny the use of a chemical only to subsequently test positive for it on a urine toxicology test conducted at the time of admission to a treatment center. Clients have also been known to either overestimate or underestimate the amount or frequency of their drug use. Such distortion might be unintentional, as in a case where the person simply forgets an episode of chemical use, or it might be quite intentional.

Roffman and George (1988) point out that distortion in self-report inventories also may occur because the client may not be aware of the drug's potency. How did the drug interfere with the individual's ability to evaluate its effects? A client might honestly believe that he or she was only mildly intoxicated, whereas an outside observer might express the belief that the client was "dead drunk."

One technique that may be useful in the detection of intentional dissimulation is to review the test results with the client, in the presence of his or her spouse or significant other. Often, the spouse or significant other will contradict the client's response to one or more test items, providing valuable new data for the assessment process.

For example, on the Michigan Alcoholism Screening Test, clients often answer no to the question of ever having been involved in an alcohol-related accident. The client's wife, if present, may speak up at this point, asking "What about the time you drove off the road into the ditch a couple of years ago?" When the client points out that the police had ruled the cause of the accident to be ice on the road, the wife may respond, "But you told me that you had been drinking earlier that night."

Another technique frequently used by this author is to administer the same test, or ask the same questions, twice during the assessment process. For example, the Michigan Alcoholism Screening Test may be administered during the initial interview, and again at the follow-up interview a week or so later. If there are significant discrepancies, this is explored with the client in order to determine the reason.

Clients have been known to score perhaps 13 points on the initial administration of the MAST, a score well above the cutoff score necessary to suggest alcoholism. At follow-up, a week later, the same client may score only 9 points on the same test. The latter score, while lower, is still above the cutoff score necessary to suggest alcoholism, but difference in the two test scores would suggest some degree of deception on the client's part. When the test is later reviewed with the client's spouse present, several other items may be found to apply to the client, suggesting a final score of perhaps 24 points.

Psychological test data can often provide valuable insights into the client's personality pattern and chemical use. Many such tests require a trained professional to administer them and interpret the results to the client. However, when used properly, psychological test data can add an important dimension to the diagnostic process.

OUTCOME OF THE ASSESSMENT PROCESS

At the end of the assessment, the chemical dependency professional should be in a position to state his or her opinion as to whether the client is (a) addicted to one of more chemicals, (b) a serious abuser of one or more chemicals, or (c) not involved with chemicals so as to cause problems. Based on this assessment, the professional should then be able to decide whether treatment is necessary, and make some recommendations as to the disposition of the client's case. Figure 25-2 is a flowchart outlining the assessment process.

Obviously, if the client is found to be addicted to one or more chemicals, a recommendation that he or she enter treatment would be appropriate. Such a recommendation might be for inpatient or for outpatient treatment, depending on the client's needs. However, if the client is found to be only an abuser of chemicals, the decision must be made whether to recommend chemical dependency treatment or not. Other recommendations might include participation in self-help groups, such as Alcoholics Anonymous or Narcotics

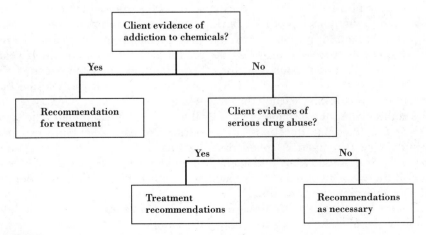

FIGURE 25-2   A flowchart of the assessment process.

Anonymous, a referral to a mental health center for evaluation and treatment, and so forth.

It is possible that the client will be found not to present a drug abuse/addiction problem, but still be in need of professional support. A referral for marital counseling, for example, might be made if there is evidence of a marital problem in a client who does not seem to be addicted to chemicals. The assessor may still make an appropriate referral, even if he or she has not found evidence of addiction.

SUMMARY

The assessment process should include information from a number of sources in order to provide the most comprehensive picture of the client's chemical-use pattern. Information from the client is collected during one or more clinical interviews through which the assessor attempts to obtain accurate data on the individual's chemical use. Information should also be obtained from collateral sources whenever possible, as such collateral information may be more revealing than the client's own data.

Information from medical personnel, who would be in a position to evaluate the client's physical status, can often prove valuable in understanding a client and the role drugs have played in his or her life. Finally, psychological test data may reveal much about the client's personality profile and drug-use pattern. However, psychological test data suffers from the drawback that it is easily manipulated by a client who wishes to dissimulate.

The outcome of the assessment process should be a formal report in which evidence supporting the conclusion that the client is or is not chemically dependent is outlined. Recommendations for further treatment may be made at this time, even if the client is found not to be addicted to chemicals.

Chapter 26

THE PROCESS OF
INTERVENTION

V. E. Johnson (1980) notes that alcoholics, like all addicts, "[are] not in touch with reality"; however, "[they are] capable of accepting some useful portion of reality, *if that reality is presented in forms they can receive*" (p. 49). The first step in attempting to break through their system of denial is to get them to recognize and accept the fact that they are in need of help. This is done through the process known as *intervention*.

It is not easy to obtain a commitment from an addict to enter a treatment program and *remain in it*. More than one addicted person enters treatment one day, only to leave shortly afterward, having satisfied the demands of parents, judges, or family to enter a treatment program. "After all," many seem to reason, "nobody said anything about my having to *stay* there."

Addicts will often openly admit "that they are addicted to chemicals not because of a desire to achieve or maintain sobriety, but because this admission offers an excuse to *continue* to use chemicals. The addict embraces a circular pattern of logic—an elaborate rationalization—in which "addicted" comes to mean "hopelessly addicted." Since they are "hopelessly addicted," at least in their own mind's eye, they give themselves permission to go on using chemicals.

This bizzare justification for chemical use overlooks the fact that addiction is a treatable disease. The first part of the "treatment" is convincing the addicted person that he or she is indeed addicted and in need of help for the drug dependency that has come to dominate his or her life. This awareness, and the commitment to enter into treatment, is often achieved through the intervention process.

A DEFINITION OF INTERVENTION

It was once thought that addicts had to "hit bottom," as it is called in AA, before they could accept the need for help. At this point, addicts have no choice but to admit utter and total defeat. V.E. Johnson (1980), a pioneer in the intervention process, challenges this notion that the addict must "hit bottom." Instead, he suggests that the addict can learn to accept the reality of addiction, *if it is explained in language that he or she can understand.*

304

Because of the physical and emotional damage that uncontrolled addiction can cause, Johnson advocates *early intervention* in cases of drug addiction. He identifies intervention as

> [a] process by which the harmful, progressive and destructive effects of chemical dependency are interrupted and the chemically dependent person is helped to stop using mood-altering chemicals, and to develop new, healthier ways of coping with his or her needs and problems. (Johnson Institute, 1987, p. 61)

Twerski (1983), who also advocates early intervention in cases of drug addiction, defines intervention as

> a collective, guided effort by the significant persons in the patient's environment to precipitate a crisis through confrontation, and thereby to remove the patient's defensive obstructions to recovery . . . (p. 1028)

Rothenberg (1988), who explored the legal ramifications of intervention, describes the intervention process for alcoholism as

> talking to the alcoholic, confronting his or her denials, and breaking down defenses so as to secure agreement to seek treatment. (p. 22)

These three statements refer to various components of the intervention process. First, intervention is an (a) *organized effort* on the part of (b) *significant others* in the addict's environment to (c) *break through the wall of denial, rationalization, and projection* by which the addict seeks to protect his or her addiction. The purpose of this collective effort, which is (d) *usually supervised* by a chemical dependency professional, is to (e) secure an agreement to *immediately seek treatment*.

CHARACTERISTICS OF THE INTERVENTION PROCESS

One significant characteristic of the intervention process is the absence of any malice. Rather, the intervention process is seen as a "profound act of caring" (Johnson Institute, 1987, p. 65). In intervention sessions, significant others in the addict's social circle break the rule of silence surrounding the addiction. Each person confronts the addicted person with specific evidence that he or she has lost control of drug use in language the addict understands.

The participants also express their desire for the addict to seek professional help for the drug problem (Williams, 1989). In the process, they affirm their concern for the addict, but they also are very straightforward in offering hard data to indicate that the addict is no longer in control. The goal is to break through the addict's denial and have him or her accept the need for help. This is the central theme around which an intervention session is planned.

According to V.E. Johnson (1986), effective intervention sessions are *planned in advance*. In addition, intervention sessions are *rehearsed* by the participants to ensure that the information presented is appropriate for an intervention session. Williams (1989) agrees on the need for rehearsal sessions, emphasizing that participants should be informed as to the goal of intervention:

> Diagnosing chemical dependency is not part of an intervention. The goal is to elicit an agreement from the person to be evaluated for possible chemical dependency and to follow the resulting recommendations. (p. 99)

Thus, the goal of intervention is not to get individuals to admit that they have a problem with chemicals, or that their behavior has hurt others. Rather, the goal is to convince them of the need to be evaluated immediately and, if treatment is recommended, to follow through.

THE MECHANICS OF INTERVENTION

As noted, the intervention process is planned and should be rehearsed beforehand by the participants. It should involve every person in the addict's life who might have something to add, including the addict's spouse, siblings, and children, Friends, supervisors or employers, ministers, and co-workers could participate. V.E. Johnson (1986) suggests that the supervisor be included because addicts often will use their perception of their job performance as an excuse not to listen to others in an intervention session. Each individual is advised to bring forward *specific incidents* in which the addict's behavior, especially the chemical use, has interfered with his or her life in some manner.

One-on-one confrontation with an addicted person is difficult at best, and in most cases is an exercise in futility (V.E. Johnson, 1986). Any person who has tried to talk to an addict will attest to the fact that the addict will deny, rationalize, threaten, or simply try to avoid any confrontation that threatens continued drug use. If the spouse of an alcoholic individually questions whether the alcoholic was physically able to drive the car home the previous night, he or she may meet with the response, "No, but Joe drove the car home for me, then walked home after he parked the car in the driveway." However, if Joe is present, too, he might then confront the alcoholic about how he did *not* drive the car home that night, or any other night for that matter.

Before the group has assembled for an intervention session, it is unlikely that isolated lies, rationalizations, or episodes of denial have been checked out. The addict's denial, projection, and rationalization will often crumble under scrutiny of all the significant people in his or her environment. This is why a collective intervention session is most powerful in working with the addict.

Twerski (1983) notes that it is common for addicts to promise to change their behavior. Although these promises might be made in good faith, or simply to avoid further confrontation, the fact remains that they are not likely to be kept:

[since addiction] responds to treatment and not to manipulation, it is unlikely that any of these promises will work, and the counselor must recommend treatment as the optimum course. (p. 1029)

If the addict refuses to acknowledge the addiction or refuses to enter treatment, each participant in the intervention session should be prepared to detach from the addict. This is *not* an attempt to manipulate the addict through empty threats. Rather, each person should be prepared to follow through with a specific action to begin to detach from the addict should he or she refuse to enter treatment.

If the employer or supervisor has decided that the company can no longer tolerate the addict's behavior, then as soon as it is the employer/supervisor's turn to speak at the intervention session, he or she needs to clearly state that if the addict does not seek treatment, his or her position will be terminated. Then, if the addict refuses treatment, the employer/supervisor should follow through with this action.

Family members should also have thought about and discussed possible options through which they might begin to detach from the addict prior to the start of the intervention session. If the addict should refuse treatment (possibly by leaving the session before it ends) they should follow through with their plan. The options should be discussed with the other participants in the intervention project, and during the rehearsal each participant should practice informing the addicted person what he or she will do if the addict does not accept treatment.

There is, again, no malice in this. The participants are not engaging in threats to force the addicted person into treatment. Rather, each participant is exercising his or her right to respond in a certain manner, should the addict choose not to accept treatment. The addicted person is still able to exercise freedom of choice by either accepting the need for treatment or not, as he or she sees fit. But, now the addict will have a clear understanding of the consequences of not going into treatment.

Family Intervention

Family intervention is a specialized intervention process in which all concerned family members gather together under the supervision of a trained professional and plan a joint confrontation of the individual. The family intervention session, like all other forms of intervention, is carried out in order to break through the addict's denial and obtain a commitment to enter treatment. The focus is on the individual's drug-using behaviors and on the concern the participants have for the addict.

Family intervention sessions help individual family members detach from the addict. For this reason, R. Meyer (1988) describes them as an "opportunity for healing" (p. 7). Twerski (1983) observes that the intervention session also allows family and significant others to deal with their feelings about the addict's chemical use, including their own mismanagement of the disease of addiction. The participants in the intervention session can express their love and concern for the addicted person and at the same time reject the addict's drug-centered behaviors.

The family intervention process allows the various members of the addict's social circle to compare notes and come forward to express their concern for the individual's life-style. Family members, friends, employers, or whoever is involved in the intervention process, may prepare detailed lists of specific incidents. The information reviewed during an intervention session should be highly specific so as to avoid confusion. Sometimes family members will bring in a personal diary to use as a reference in the intervention session.

The planning period helps participants to focus on the specific information they want to bring to the intervention session. During rehearsal, the professional who will coordinate the intervention session decides who will present information, and the order of the presentation. This planned sequence is adhered to as closely as possible. Again, the information is presented to the addict in a calm, nonthreatening manner.

An Example of a Family Intervention Session

In this hypothetical intervention session, the central character is a patient named Jim. Also involved are his parents, his two sisters, and a chemical dependency counselor. The intervention session is held at the home of Jim's parents, where Jim has been living. During the early part of the session, Jim claims that he never has drunk to the point of passing out. He also claims that he always drinks at home so that he won't be out on the roads while intoxicated. He does not believe that his drinking is as bad as everybody said it is for these reasons, and he adds that he sees no reason why everybody is so concerned.

Jim's sister Sara also lives at home. She immediately describes how just three weeks ago Jim had run out of vodka early in the evening, after having had four or five mixed drinks. She points out that Jim had hopped into the car to drive down to the liquor store to buy a new bottle or two after having consumed the last of the vodka in the house.

Sara states that she is not calling Jim a liar, but that she *knows* he had driven a car after drinking on this occasion. She was concerned about the possibility of his getting involved in an accident, and still feels uncomfortable about this incident. She is afraid he might do it again, and that the next time he might not be so lucky as to make it back home again in one piece.

Jim's mother then speaks. She points out that she found her son unconscious on the living room floor twice in the past month. She states the exact dates of the occurrences, describing her discomfort at seeing Jim sleeping on the floor, surrounded by empty beer bottles. She picked up the empty bottles to keep them from being broken by accident and covered Jim up with a blanket while he slept. But she, too, is concerned, and believes that her son is drinking more than he thinks.

After Jim's mother finishes, his sister Gloria presents her information and concerns. She states that she asked Jim to leave her house last week, which is news to the rest of the family. She took this step, she explains, because Jim was intoxicated, loud, and abusive toward his nephew. She adds that everybody who was present, including her son's friend who happened to be visiting at the time, smelled the alcohol on Jim's breath and was repulsed by his behavior. Gloria concludes by stating that Jim is no longer welcome in her home, unless he goes through treatment.

At this point, the chemical dependency counselor tells Jim that his behavior is not so different from that of thousands of other addicts. The counselor also points out that at this point in the intervention session many addicts begin to make promises to cut back or totally eliminate the drug use, an observation that catches Jim by surprise because he was just about to make such promises. They die in his throat, even before he opens his mouth.

Before Jim can think of something else to say, the counselor goes on to state that Jim exhibits every sign of having a significant alcohol problem. The counselor lists the symptoms of alcohol addiction one by one, and points out how Jim's family has identified different symptoms of addiction in their presentations. "So now," the counselor concludes, "we have reached a point where you must make a decision. Will you accept help for your alcohol problem?"

If Jim says yes, family members will explain that they have contacted the admissions officers of two or three nearby treatment centers and that these centers have agreed to hold a bed for him until after the intervention session has ended. Jim will be given a choice of which treatment center to enter and will be told that travel arrangements have been taken care of. His luggage is packed in the car, and if he wishes the family will escort him to treatment as a show of support.

If Jim says no, the family members will then confront him about the steps they are prepared to take to separate from his addiction. His wife may inform him that she has arranged for a marital separation and present him with the papers that her attorney has drawn up. His sister may reinforce the injunction that Jim is no longer welcome in her home because of his chemical use. If his employer is present, Jim may be told that his job is no longer there for him if he does not enter treatment.

Jim may be told that, no matter what he may think, these steps are not being taken as punishment. Each person will inform Jim that he or she finds it necessary to detach from him until such time as he chooses to get his life in order. Each person then will affirm his or her concern for Jim, but will also start to detach from him—no longer protecting him from his addiction.

These decisions were all made in advance of the intervention session. Which option the participants exercise rests largely on Jim's response to the question, Will you accept help for your alcohol problem?

Intervention and Other Forms of Chemical Addiction

The Johnson Institute (1987) addresses the issue of intervention when the drug-of-choice is not alcohol, but any of a wide range of other chemicals. The same techniques used in alcoholism also apply to cases involving cocaine, benzodiazepines, marijuana, amphetamines, or virtually any other drug of abuse. Significant others will gather, discuss the problem, and review their data about the addict's behavior. Practice intervention sessions are held in which problems are addressed as they are uncovered.

Finally, when everything is ready, the formal intervention session is held, with the addicted person in attendance. There is no malice in the attempt to help him or her see how serious the addiction has become. Rather, there is a calm, caring review of the facts by person after person, until the addict is unable to defend against the realization that he or she is addicted to chemicals and in need of professional help.

Arrangements are made in advance for the individual's admission into treatment. This may be accomplished by a simple telephone call to the admissions officer of a treatment center. The caller may explain the situation and ask if the center would be willing to accept the target person as a client. Usually, the treatment center staff will want to carry out their own chemical dependency evaluation to confirm that the person is an appropriate referral to treatment. But most treatment centers are more than willing to consider a referral from a family intervention project.

THE ETHICS OF INTERVENTION

As humane as the goal of intervention is, questions have been raised concerning the ethics of this practice. Rothenberg (1988) notes that there is some concern as to the necessity of validating the diagnosis of chemical dependency before an attempt at intervention is made. In other words, should there be an independent verification of the diagnosis of drug addiction before an attempt at intervention is carried out? If there is not, what are the legal sanctions that can be brought against a chemical dependency professional who, in good faith, has supervised an attempt at intervention?

Furthermore, the question of whether chemical dependency professionals involved in an intervention project should tell the client that he or she is free to leave at any time has not been answered (Rothenberg, 1988). It has been suggested that current intervention methods may be in violation of either state or federal law in that failing to inform clients that they are free to leave might be interpreted as a violation of the laws against kidnapping or unlawful detention.

Rothenberg's (1988) warning raises some interesting questions for the chemical dependency professional in both the moral and legal areas. In future years, the courts may rule that the professional is legally obligated to inform clients that they are free to leave the intervention session at any time.

Furthermore, the courts may rule that the professional can make no move to hold the clients, either by physical force or by threats, should they express a desire to leave.

The courts may also rule that intervention is a legitimate treatment technique when used by trained professionals. No legal precedent has been established in this area. Chemical dependency professionals are advised to consult with an attorney to discuss specific laws that may apply in their area of practice.

LEGAL INTERVENTION

Sometimes "intervention" comes in a much simpler form: through the courts. An individual may be arrested for driving while under the influence of alcohol (a "DWI," as it is called in some states); for possession of chemicals; or on some other drug-related charge. The judge may offer an alternative to incarceration: *Either* you successfully complete a drug-treatment program, *or* you will be incarcerated.

Exactly how much time the individual spends in jail would depend on the specific nature of the charge brought against him or her. However, either/or treatment situations are unique in that individuals are offered a choice. They may elect to spend time in jail to fulfill their obligation to the courts or they may elect to accept the treatment option. In so doing, they are not *ordered* into treatment. Rather, they have chosen to enter treatment. The individual always has the choice of incarceration if he or she does not believe that treatment is necessary.

"Either/or" treatment admissions usually are easier to work with than voluntary admissions to treatment. Indeed, court-sponsored intervention is a powerful incentive to treatment (Moylan, 1990). The very fact that there is a legal hold means that it is that much less likely that the person will leave treatment when his or her denial system is confronted. Also, the very fact that he or she was admitted on an either/or basis is information that can be used to confront the individual about the nature of the addiction problem. After all, it is difficult for someone who has just been arrested for a second or third drug-related charge to deny that chemicals are a problem, although this is known to happen.

In a study by Collins and Alison (1983), when the treatment programs of some 2,200 addicts who were "legally induced to seek treatment" were reviewed, those who chose treatment as an alternative to incarceration did as well in treatment as those who were there voluntarily. Furthermore, it was found that those who were in treatment at the court's invitation were likely to stay in treatment longer than those who had no restrictions placed on them. Collins and Alison conclude:

> The use of legal threat to pressure individuals into drug treatment is a valid approach for dealing with drug abusers and their undesirable behaviors. Legal threat apparently helps keep these individuals constructively involved in treatment and does not adversely affect long-term treatment goals. (p. 1148)

According to E. Matuschka (1985), treatment in which there is a coercive element is more likely to be effective than treatment in which no coercion is involved. Thus, those who accept treatment as an alternative to incarceration seem to do better than individuals who enter treatment on a voluntary basis (Collins & Alison, 1983; E. Matuschka, 1985). It would seem that legal intervention is a viable alternative for those who would not accept the need for treatment if left to their own devices.

Peele (1989), on the other hand, views such either/or referrals as intrusive and counterproductive. He states that individuals convicted of driving a motor vehicle while under the influence of chemicals respond better to legal sanctions (for example, jail or probation) than to being forced into treatment. Peele (1989) argues strongly that individuals be held responsible for their actions, *including the initial decision to use chemicals*, and that chemical use or abuse does not excuse individuals from responsibility for their behavior.

Treatment or Incarceration: When Is Treatment Appropriate?

As previously mentioned, the courts may offer those individuals convicted of drug-related charges the opportunity to enter drug-treatment programs rather than go to jail or prison. While many individuals have taken advantage of this "last chance" to begin serious work on their recovery from drug addiction, in many cases the individual uses "treatment" merely to avoid jail or prison.

Participation in a treatment program should not be substituted for incarceration when the latter is deserved. Unfortunately, however, individuals are often given the opportunity to enter treatment without consideration for their motives. For example, one must question the motives of the alleged drug pusher who is arrested with several pounds marijuana and who then enters "treatment" prior to going to court.

The motives of the person arrested for the fifth time while driving under the influence of alcohol who enters "treatment" on the advice of an attorney prior to going to court also must be questioned. Some chronic drinkers are quite open about the fact that they plan to continue to drink, and that their only motive for entering "treatment" is to try to avoid the legal consequences brought on by their alcohol use. "I'm here because my lawyer said it would look good in court" is a common refrain heard by treatment center staff.

Chemical dependency treatment professionals frequently encounter individuals who "suddenly remember" that they have to go to court for drug-related charges. This revelation often comes within the first or second week following admission to the treatment center. Treatment personnel are then placed in the uncomfortable position of having to allow the client to briefly leave treatment in order to go to court, secure in the knowledge that they have been used. Some addicts go so far as to openly boast that they entered "treatment" to make a good impression on the judge and jury.

Another situation in which treatment is abused involves individuals who enter a program to stop their personal drug use, but who openly admit that they plan to continue to sell drugs to others. How seriously are these individuals going to participate in the program? How cost effective is treatment going to be under these circumstances? Unfortunately, the courts seldom ask these questions. It is easier for the overworked legal system to accept "treatment" as an option, without examination of whether or not it is likely to be effective in helping the addict come to terms with his or her drug use.

A physician who indiscriminately prescribes antibiotics for every patient who walks through the door would quickly be brought up on charges of incompetence. The decision to use one medication or another is not one that should be taken lightly. Obviously, physicians must first examine their patients and then weigh the potential benefits of each treatment approach against the anticipated risk.

The same is true for chemical dependency treatment. While the option of treatment in place of incarceration should certainly be considered by the courts, it must be remembered at all times that a treatment program is *not* the answer to every drug-related problem. In deciding whether or not a treatment option would be appropriate, professionals should keep in mind that *treatment should never stand between the individual* and *the natural consequences of his or her behavior.*

OTHER FORMS OF INTERVENTION

Another form of "either/or" situation arises when an addict's spouse or employer sets down the law: *Either* you stop drinking, *or* I will file for divorce, terminate your position here, or whatever. Often, the physician is the one who establishes the either/or situation by threatening to file commitment papers on the addict unless he or she enters treatment. One individual, in treatment shortly after his wife had filed for divorce, said simply, "I didn't think that she meant it. . . . I guess she did!"

Adelman and Weiss (1989) found that "employees coerced into treatment by their employers had better treatment outcomes than employees who volunteered for treatment" for alcoholism (p. 515). They concluded that treatment programs that use such "constructive coercion" may actually be more effective for alcoholics than programs that do not.

This is not to say that the intervention process will meet with success, or even that a court-ordered treatment exposure will result in sobriety. As noted earlier, alcoholics may reach a point where they will sacrifice just about everything in order to support the addiction. In this sense, alcoholism is not very different from the other forms of chemical addiction. There are documented cases in which addicts have accepted the loss of a job, a family, and a spouse as part of the price to be paid for their addiction.

Court-Ordered Involuntary Commitment

In some states, individuals can be committed to treatment against their will, if the courts have sufficient evidence to conclude that they are in imminent danger of harming themselves or others. "Harm to self" may include neglect, and more than one alcoholic who fell asleep in the snow while walking home is surprised to learn that he or she has been found to be a danger to "self" on the basis of this fact.

The exact provisions of court-ordered involuntary commitments vary from state to state, in those states where they apply. Obviously, chemical dependency professionals must consult with an attorney to review the exact legal statutes that apply in each case. However, the reader should be aware that the laws of many states allow for the courts to intervene should a person's chemical use put his or her life or the lives of others in danger.

Occasionally, an individual will enter treatment on a voluntary basis. It is more common, however, for addicts to continue to use chemicals if they can do so without having to pay one or more consequences. It is for this reason that external pressure of some kind—be it family, legal, medical, or professional penalties—is often necessary to help the addicted person see the need to enter treatment.

SUMMARY

At one time it was thought that alcoholics had to "hit bottom" before they would accept the need for help. By extension, this same expectation was thought to apply to the other forms of addiction. However, within the past 30 years, treatment professionals have come to accept that addicts are able to appreciate the need for treatment *if they are confronted in terms they can understand*. It is on the basis that the process known as intervention is carried out.

In this chapter, we discussed some of the many forms of intervention. We reviewed the advantages and disadvantages of each and pointed out some of the legal considerations that must be respected during the intervention process.

Chapter 27

THE TREATMENT OF
CHEMICAL DEPENDENCY

In this chapter we will explore the basic elements of the treatment process. The specific components of treatment may vary from one program to another. For example, a treatment program that specializes in working with alcoholic business people would have little use for a methadone maintenance component. Yet, there are also many common elements to the treatment process.

CHARACTERISTICS OF THE REHABILITATION PROFESSIONAL

Lewis et al. (1988) emphasize that counseling addicts is difficult and demanding work. Individuals who are working through chemical dependency or psychological problems of their own are discouraged from actively working with others until they have resolved these personal problems. If a counselor is preoccupied with personal problems, including those of chemical addiction, he or she probably could not help a client advance in terms of personal growth.

According to the well-known humanistic psychologist Carl Rogers, an important personality characteristic of human-service professionals is the ability to be empathetic; that is, to be able to understand the client's world, through the client's eyes. Other characteristics of human-service professionals that Rogers (1961) notes as essential are:

- warmth;
- dependability;
- consistency;
- the ability to care for and respect the client;
- the ability to be separate from the client (that is, to resist trying to "live through" him or her);
- the ability to avoid being perceived as a threat to the client;
- the ability to free oneself from the urge to judge or evaluate the client; and
- the ability to see the client as a person capable of growth.

In their discussion of the personality attributes of successful treatment staff members at an alcoholism treatment center, Adelman and Weiss (1989) conclude that those staff members who possess strong interpersonal skills are best equipped to help their clients. In their study, clients whose alcoholism counselors had weak interpersonal skills were twice as likely to relapse as clients whose counselors had strong interpersonal skills. Although Adelman and Weiss do not speak in the same terms as Rogers, the implication is clear that the most effective counselor is one who is well adjusted and accepting of others.

One point demands clarification at this point. The characteristics we have mentioned are *in no way related to permissiveness.* Human-service professionals occasionally confuse permissiveness with interpersonal warmth. Just as it is possible to be too confrontational, it is also possible to be too permissive. *Caring for clients does **not** mean protecting them from the consequences of their behavior.*

Clients, especially the addicted client, will often "test the limits" in order to determine whether or not the professional will act in accordance with the rules of the treatment program. The chemical dependency professional should be aware that "dependability" and "consistency" also apply to enforcement of the rules.

McCarthy and Borders (1985) explored the impact of limit-setting on further drug use on a group of patients in a methadone maintenance program. Patients were told that their urine would be tested to detect continued chemical abuse and that if their urine tested positive for other drugs four times in the next year, in place of the desired methadone maintenance they would be placed on a narcotic withdrawal program. It was found that patients in this structured program achieved significantly greater program compliance. They were less likely to use drugs than a matched control group of addicts who were not in a program that was so highly structured.

Treatment "Secrets"

A common scenario in the treatment center is for a client to ask for an individual conference with a staff member and then to confess to a rules infraction. Often, this admission of guilt is made to a student or intern at the agency rather than to a regular staff member. The confession might well be an admission of having used chemicals while in treatment. After having made this admission, the client will request that the staff member not tell the group, other staff members, or the program director about the rules infraction for fear of being discharged from treatment.

For the chemical dependency professional to honor the request not to tell other staff members would constitute entering into a partnership with the addict. Such a partnership, set up by the addict, would make the professional an "enabler." In some situations, to remain silent in this situation may make the professional vulnerable to later extortion by the client, who would be in the position of reporting the professional to his or her superior for not passing on the information to staff as he or she should have done.

The proper response in such a situation is to document the discussion *immediately.* Documentation may be in the form of a memo or an entry in the client's progress notes, as well as a discussion of the material revealed by the client with the professional's immediate supervisor. This is done without malice, in order to ensure uniform enforcement of the rules for all clients and to protect the professional reputation.

Confrontation and Other Treatment Techniques

According to Lewis, Dana, and Blevins (1988), confrontation is not the only technique that professionals need to master in working with addicts. Confrontation is often quite useful in breaking through the client's defenses, so that he or she can begin to understand the reality of the addiction and the need for treatment (Twerski, 1983). However, to effectively work with an addict, the professional needs a firm foundation in *all* of the skills of counseling, of which confrontation is but one.

Effective intervention with an addicted person requires the application and modification of therapeutic counseling skills to a specialized subpopulation— those who are chemically addicted. Confrontation is one skill that the professional needs in order to work with this subpopulation, but the skills outlined by Rogers (1961) are also necessary. The chemical dependency professional should be well trained in the theory and practice of individual and group counseling, as well as in the field of chemical dependency counseling, to be able to work in the field of addiction.

THE MINNESOTA MODEL OF CHEMICAL DEPENDENCY TREATMENT

The "Minnesota Model" of chemical dependency is attributed to Dr. Dan Anderson. Dr. Anderson worked as an attendent at the state hospital in Willmar, Minnesota, to earn money to finish his college degree (Larson, 1982). Following graduation, Anderson returned to the Willmar State Hospital as a recreational therapist. He was assigned to work with alcoholics, the least desirable position at that time.

Anderson was influenced by the work of Mr. Ralph Rossen, who was later to become the Minnesota state commissioner of health. At the same time, the growing influence of Alcoholics Anonymous, which had spread across Minnesota by the late 1940s, was used both by Anderson and staff psychologist Dr. Jean Rossi as a means of understanding and working with alcoholics. They were supported in this approach by the medical director of the hospital, Dr. Nelson Bradley (Larson, 1982).

Each person involved in this new approach contributed a different perspective on addiction. To the team was added the Reverend John Keller, who had been sent to Willmar State Hospital to learn about alcoholism in 1955. Thus, for this staff,

> knowledge of medicine, psychology, A. A. and theology [came] together under one roof to develop a new and innovative alcohol treatment program. (Larson, 1982, p. 35)

This new treatment approach, since called the Minnesota Model, was originally designed to work with alcoholics (*Alcoholism & Drug Abuse Week,* 1990). In the time since its introduction, it has also been used as a model for the treatment of other forms of chemical addiction besides alcoholism. The Minnesota Model uses a *treatment team* composed of chemical dependency counselors familiar with AA, psychologists, physicians, nurses, recreational therapists, and clergy, all of whom will work with the client during the course of treatment.

In the first stage of the Minnesota Model treatment approach, the *evaluation* phase, each member of the treatment team meets with the client to assess his or her needs from standpoint of the professional's area of expertise. Each professional will then make recommendations for the client's treatment plan.

In the second stage, the stage of *goal setting,* the professionals meet as a team to discuss the areas they feel should be the focus of treatment. This meeting is chaired by the individual who will be ultimately responsible for the execution of the treatment process. This is usually the chemical dependency counselor, who will function as the client's case manager. The assessments and the recommendations for treatment goals are reviewed and discussed by the treatment team. The members then select those recommendations that they agree are most appropriate in helping the client achieve and maintain sobriety.

The client, the parole/probation officer, and possibly interested family members, also participate in the treatment plan meeting. Both the client and family members are free to recommend additional areas of concern or to suggest specific goals they feel should be included in the treatment plan. The case manager reviews the treatment goals that were identified as being of value to the client and discusses the rationale for these recommendations.

On the basis of this meeting, the case manager and client enter the third stage of the treatment process, *developing a formal treatment plan.* The plan that emerges identifies specific problem areas, behavioral objectives, methods by which progress towards these objectives can be measured, and a target date for each goal. The treatment plan will be discussed in more detail in the next section of this chapter. A flowchart of the treatment plan process is presented in Figure 27-1.

The strength of the Minnesota Model lies in its redundancy and in its multimember concept. The information provided by the client is reviewed by many different professionals, each of whom may on the basis of his or her training identify a potential treatment problem that others may have overlooked. This allows for the greatest possible evaluation of the client's needs, strengths, and priorities.

Another advantage of the Minnesota Model is that it allows for different professionals to work together in the rehabilitation of the client. The team, with the combined training and experience of its individual members, offers a wider range of services than any single chemical dependency counselor ever could. In addition to multidisciplinary intake evaluations, each professional on the treatment team can work with the client, *if that client presents special needs.*

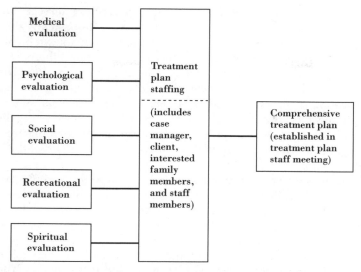

FIGURE 27-1   A flowchart of the Minnesota Model treatment plan.

Thus, the chemical dependency counselor does not have to be a jack of all trades. Rather, if the client presents a need that one staff member cannot fulfill, a referral to another member of the team for specialized treatment may be made. This feature has helped make the Minnesota Model one of the dominent treatment program models in the field of chemical dependency rehabilitation, although few people are aware of its roots.

Although it has become a standard within the treatment industry, the Minnesota Model is not without its critics. As mentioned previously, it was designed to work with cases of alcoholism, and there is no research available to support its application to other forms of substance addiction. Yet, the Minnesota Model has been used in treating virtually every known form of substance abuse (*Alcoholism & Drug Abuse Week*, 1990).

When it was developed, the client's length of stay at Willmar State Hospital was often arbitrarily set at 28 days. There is, however, little research data to support the need for a 28-day inpatient treatment stay (Turbo 1989). Although the 28-day treatment program has become an industry standard both for Minnesota model programs (Turbo, 1989) and as a guide for insurance reinbursement (Berg & Durbin, 1990), this length of stay may not be appropriate in all cases.

THE TREATMENT PLAN

As noted by Lewis et al. (1988), the treatment plan is "the foundation for success" of the treatment process (p. 118). It is a highly specific form, which in some states might be viewed as a legal document. Although different treatment centers may use different formats depending on specific state licensure requirements, the material covered tends to be basically the same.

First, the treatment plan provides a brief summary of the problem(s) that brought the client into treatment. In the second section, there is a brief summary of the client's physical and emotional state of health. The third section contains the individual's own input into the treatment process. The following section is the heart of the treatment plan. This is where the specific goals of treatment are reviewed. The discharge criteria follow, listing the steps that must be accomplished in order to discharge the client from treatment. Finally, there is a brief summary of those steps that will be part of the client's aftercare program.

The heart of the treatment plan, as noted, is where the specific treatment goals are outlined. This section of the treatment plan is often headed "Treatment Goals." These should include (a) a *problem statement*, or brief statement of the problem; (b) *long-term goals*; (c) *short-term objectives*; (d) *measurement criteria*; and (e) a *target date*.

The problem statement is a short statement, usually a sentence or two, identifying a *specific problem* that will be addressed in treatment. The long-term goal is the *ultimate objective*, and as such is a general statement of a hoped-for outcome. This statement is usually also only one or two sentences long.

The short-term objective is *a very specific behavior that can be measured*. The objective statement usually consists of one to three sentences, including measurement criteria, by which both client and staff will be able to assess whether progress toward the objective is being made. Finally, the target date is a simple statement naming *the date by which the hoped-for outcome will be achieved*.

A statement of treatment goals for a 24-year-old male polydrug addict (cocaine, alcohol, marijuana and occasionally benzodiazepines) who has used chemicals daily for the last 27 months might appear as follows:

PROBLEM: Client has used chemicals daily for at least the past two years and has been unable to abstain from drug use on his own.

LONG-TERM GOAL: That the client achieve and maintain sobriety.

SHORT-TERM OBJECTIVE: That the client not use mood-altering chemicals while in treatment.

METHOD OF MEASUREMENT: Random supervised urine toxicology screens to detect possible drug use.

TARGET DATE: Scheduled discharge date.

The typical treatment plan would identify perhaps five or six different problem areas. Each of these goals might be modified as the treatment program progresses, and each would provide a yardstick of the client's progress. Obviously, if the client is not making progress on *any* of the goals, it is time to question whether or not he or she is serious about treatment. The goals become the heart of the treatment program.

Aftercare

The *aftercare* program involves those elements of treatment that are carried out after the individual has been discharged from treatment. If, for example, the person enters into individual psychotherapy to address a problem that arose in treatment, it is entirely likely that this therapy will continue long after the individual is discharged from the typical 28- to 35-day inpatient rehabilitation program. Individual therapy on a once-a-week basis with a psychotherapist would then become a part of the aftercare program.

According to Downing (1990), an effective aftercare program (a) addresses chemical dependency issues that were identified in treatment, (b) addresses mistaken beliefs and interpersonal conflicts that might contribute to relapse, (c) helps the individual establish what Downing terms "the habit of sobriety," (d) helps the individual make the necessary life-style changes to maintain sobriety, and (e) "serve[s] as a monitor of sobriety" (p. 22).

Participation in Alcoholics Anonymous or Narcotics Anonymous might also be identified as part of an aftercare program. A medical problem that requires ongoing medical supervision and support should be a part of the aftercare program, as well as aftercare placement in a transitional living facility, such as a halfway house. If the individual presents any special needs, these should also be included as specialized elements of the aftercare program.

The aftercare program is designated and carried out on the assumption that treatment does not end with the individual's discharge from a formal treatment program. Rather, treatment is the first part of a recovery program that (it is hoped) will continue for the rest of the individual's life. The aftercare component of the treatment plan addressed those issues that should be addressed following the individual's discharge from the rehabilitation program.

Relapse

Even with the strongest legal or family pressure, there is no guarantee that an individual will actually accept treatment, or remain in treatment once he or she has started the program. Almost a generation ago, Baekeland and Lundwall (1975) found that a significant percentage of those admitted to either inpatient or outpatient chemical dependency treatment programs failed to "graduate" from treatment for one reason or another. Thus, treatment professionals now know that entry into a treatment program is no guarantee that the person will actually complete the program, or that he or she will benefit from treatment in any way.

The focus of treatment has shifted away from simply "getting them sober" to arming recovering addicts against the forces that may contribute to relapse. Even if an individual participates in the best of treatment programs and is highly motivated both during and after treatment, it is still possible for that person to resume the use of chemicals. Indeed, given the nature of drug addiction, it is to be expected that the individual will relapse from time to time.

For example, Niaura et al. (1988) found that "alcohol and tobacco abuse careers are quite variable, punctuated alternately by self-initiated periods of abstinence and controlled and uncontrolled use" (p. 133). Other studies have found that in the first 4 years following treatment, approximately 90% of those who "graduate" will relapse (National Institute on Alcohol Abuse and Alcoholism, 1989). Svanum and McAdoo (1989) state: "Few treated persons show a stable pattern of failure, and fewer still show a long-term pattern of a stable recovery. Most alternate between more or less favorable treatment outcomes" (p. 222). This does not imply that treatment programs seldom succeed; rather, it underscores the grim reality of addiction: It is a disease that can be *arrested*, but never entirely *cured*.

Relapse prevention   Recently, there has been a growing awareness that it is possible to block, or at least limit, the tendency towards relapse through a process termed *relapse prevention*. Despite evidence pointing to relapse as a very real risk, research into its causes and applied studies with at-risk individuals remains limited (Niaura et al., 1988).

According to Chiauzzi (1990), there are four elements common to those who relapse. First, they often have *personality traits* that interfere with continued sobriety. For example, many tend to be compulsive, not adjusting well to even minor changes in routine. Often, they are dependent, finding it difficult to assert their wish to maintain sobriety. Passive-aggressive personality traits place individuals at risk for relapse because they tend to blame others for their behavior. Narcissistic traits prevent many addicts from admitting to the need for help during weak moments. Finally, antisocial personality traits underscore the tendency to be impulsive and the desire to depart from the road taken by others.

A second factor advanced by Chiauzzi as contributing to relapse is a tendency for the individual to *substitute addictions*. Often, recovering addicts will substitute work, a new relationship, or other chemicals for the drug they are no longer using. The use of new drugs, a relationship in which the recovering addict is dependent on a partner, or an eating disorder could signal a high-risk situation for relapse.

Third, Chiauzzi found that a *narrow view of recovery* is often a factor in relapse. All too often, the recovering addict equates abstinence or simply attendance at a self-help group with "recovery." This limited view places addicts at risk for relapse because they are not working on the interpersonal problems that brought addiction on in the first place. They do not develop the self-awareness necessary to detect the personal drift toward relapse.

Finally, Chiauzzi found that what he terms *warning signals* of relapse are often overlooked by the recovering addict. Chiauzzi's concept of warning signals is very similar to the concept of mini-decisions first reported by

Cummings, Gordon, and Marlatt (1980). Cummings et al. presented a theoretical model in which drug relapse is viewed as evolving out of a series of "mini-decisions" (p. 297). According to this model, there is no major decision by which an individual returns to drug use. Rather, the road to relapse is lined with small decisions that, taken together, "begin a chain of behaviors which may set the stage for a relapse to occur" (p. 297).

For example, a mini-decision by the recovering addict may be to continue a friendship with an active addict or to go over to the local bar "just to play pool." Chiauzzi (1990) reports that individuals who relapse fail to notice negative thoughts. The desire to spend time with drug-using friends, or even signs of physical illness, are dismissed by the recovering addict. Cummings et al. (1980) point out that these seemingly innocent mini-decisions increase the chance that recovering addicts will encounter a situation where they are likely to relapse.

Addicts have been known to see if they could "just walk down the same street and not feel the urge to use anymore." Or they may describe how they stop off to pay a debt to a friend and "find drugs all over the place"—as if the drug-using behavior of the friend were a revelation. At such times, the newly recovering addict is at a decision point. He or she must either reaffirm the commitment to sobriety or start back on the path to the active use of chemicals. If they have adequate sober coping skills, recovering addicts will reaffirm the commitment to sobriety. However, if their sobriety-based coping skills are inadequate, they might relapse. At best, they would find the experience to be a frightening one, which may make them question whether they will *ever* be capable of self-sustained sobriety.

Often, such a mini-decision is the choice to stop going to regular AA or NA meetings. The initial decision might be to cut back from five meetings a week to four. Then, the next decision might be to cut back from four meetings to perhaps only one or two meetings a week. Eventually, the decision might be to go to meetings only every other week, then once a month. Finally, the individual no longer has any contact with his or her sober support system.

It is virtually guaranteed that every recovering addict will encounter at least one high-risk situation; that is, a situation in which the possibility of drug use is high. Cummings et al. (1980) group these high-risk situations into two categories. The first category centers on the acute period of drug withdrawal, when the individual is motivated to avoid further withdrawal discomfort through the ingestion of chemicals.

The second group of high-risk situations, according to Cummings et al., might be viewed as the social, environmental and emotional states that the individual perceives as stressful—those states in which drugs were used as a coping mechanism in the past. In this secong group of high-risk situations, cognitive evaluations of the social, environmental, or emotional stimuli mediate whether the individual considers the possibility of drug use or not. Such cognitive evaluations may then be interpreted by the individual as an "urge" or "craving" to use a substance.

Shiffman (1992) views the problem of relapse from a behavioral perspective, concluding that "stimulus factors" contribute to lapses in sobriety in the sense that environmental stimuli may trigger craving for drugs. To combat the influence of environmental triggers, Shiffman advocates the use of behavioral rehearsals to help the client learn skills that can be used to avoid relapse. A second area of emphasis is the identification of the client's feelings of demoralization and self-blame during the early phases of recovery, according to Shiffman. Such "cognitive" intervention has been shown to be at least as effective as behavioral training for environmental triggers toward relapse.

According to Lewis et al. (1988), the first step in relapse prevention is the identification of the high-risk situation for each individual. Self-monitoring and direct observation by treatment center staff are just two of the methods by which high-risk situations can be identified. The patient history may also underscore high-risk situations of particular significance for the individual. Treatment staff should pay particular attention to the client's self-report to identify possible high-risk factors.

Once the high-risk factors have been identified, specific coping responses for each high-risk situation must be devised by the treatment center staff. Niaura et al. (1988) report that when individuals are armed with cognitive and behavioral coping mechanisms that counteract feelings of helplessness in the face of cognitive, social, or environmental cues for drug use, they are unlikely to relapse. Lewis et al. (1988) recommend that a reminder card be carried in the wallet or purse, so that the individual who relapses will have written instructions on the steps to take to keep it within limits.

A Word on Controlled Drinking

The concept of helping the alcoholic to return to "social" or "controlled" drinking has been a controversial one for many years (Helzer et al., 1985; Schuckit, 1989). Unfortunately, ever since the first preliminary reports that it *might* be possible to train a percentage of alcoholics to return to a state of "controlled" drinking, many alcoholics have seized on the concept as justification for their continued drinking.

According to Helzer et al. (1985), research findings suggest that less than 2% of alcoholics are able to go back to a level of social drinking. While controlled drinking is a viable goal for individuals who are not clearly addicted and who have not experienced significant problems associated with addiction (Hester & Miller, 1989), it is not a goal for the vast majority of alcoholics. In other words, Hester and Miller suggest that it may be possible to teach many of those who *abuse* alcohol to control their drinking. But, only about 2% of those who are clearly *addicted* are able to go back to social drinking.

R. E. Meyer (1989a) is of the opinion that individuals who are moderately to severely addicted to alcohol will quickly return to abusive drinking if they attempt to try to drink on a "social" basis. *Every* alcoholic, however, would like to believe that he or she is among the 1% to 2% of alcoholics for whom controlled, or social, drinking is again a possibility.

Given that such a small percentage of alcoholics who have been tested to date have been able to return to social drinking patterns, one must argue against experimenting to find out if any given alcoholic falls within this category. In a negative sense, R. R. Miller (1989) opts for letting the alcoholic try. For individuals who maintain that they do not have an alcohol dependency problem, he recommends helping them to attempt "controlled drinking" for the following reason:

> An unsuccessful trial at "controlled drinking" may be a more persuasive confrontation of the need for abstinence than any amount of direct argumentation between therapist and client. (p. 77)

Thus, for Miller, a trial of "controlled drinking" may prove of value in helping the individual see the need for total abstinence. But the potential benefits of this trial must be weighed against the potential risks. Confirmed alcoholics who believe that they can return to social drinking and *maintain* a pattern of social drinking for the rest of their lives are taking a chance where the odds are at best 49 to 1 against them.

OPTIONAL ELEMENTS OF A CHEMICAL DEPENDENCY TREATMENT PROGRAM

In addition to the treatment plan, the various assessments conducted at the time of admission, the development of an aftercare plan, and relapse prevention, other elements of treatment might be included in a specific program, depending on the specific needs of the population served. Following is a brief exploration of some of the more important of these subcomponents of treatment.

Detoxification from Drugs

Many chemical dependency programs offer detoxification services, either as part of their regular treatment program or as a separate component of treatment. Such detoxification programs should meet the standards of state licensing boards, and detoxification should be carried out under the supervision of a physician who has both training and experience in this area.

As we noted in the chapters on alcohol and CNS depressants, withdrawal from these chemicals can often result in life-threatening seizures. While detoxification from *some* drugs is possible on an outpatient basis, detoxification from many of the chemicals of abuse is so dangerous that it should only be attempted on an inpatient basis. Miller, Frances, and Holmes (1988) recommend that each patient to be withdrawn from chemicals be evaluated by a trained physician to determine whether an inpatient or outpatient detoxification program would best meet the client's needs.

Outpatient detoxification requires daily follow-up from the detoxification staff to monitor the patient's progress and compliance with treatment (Miller et al., 1988). Inpatient detoxification programs should have adequate facilities for the medical support of clients, including on-duty medical personnel (nurses and physicians), as well as appropriate medications (anticonvulsants) and equipment to administer them.

Patients being withdrawn from drugs should be closely monitored by treatment staff to detect signs of drug overdose or seizures (Miller et al., 1988). Unfortunately, it is not uncommon for addicts to "help out" by administering drugs to themselves when they are supposedly being withdrawn from chemicals. Also, there are those addicted individuals who will go through detoxification dozens of times or perhaps even more often, to give themselves a place to live (Whitman et al., 1990). Thus, the chemical dependency professional should constantly be aware of the fact that detoxification services may be abused by addicted persons.

Narcotic withdrawal   Programs that specialize in the treatment of narcotic addiction often offer controlled withdrawal from opiates. Occasionally, a hospital will offer narcotic withdrawal programs even if long-term treatment for addicts is not available. The detoxification component in each center is very much the same.

Blood/urine toxicology screens   The testing of blood samples and/or urine samples to detect illicit drug use is a feature of many treatment programs. *Frequent, unannounced, random* drug toxicology screens should be used on *all* clients, not just on those suspected of using chemicals while in treatment. Treatment programs that conduct urine samples only on clients whose behavior has raised suspicions that they are using chemicals often do little more than teach clients not to act as if they were using chemicals.

Toxicology screening offers an additional measure of support during the initial period of sobriety and discourages chemical use during treatment. Each client knows that illicit drug use would likely be detected rather quickly, and thus would be less likely to use chemicals while in treatment. The toxicology sample would also serve as a measure of program compliance.

The fact that blood samples are drawn *directly* from the client is often an advantage, especially with an unconscious or uncooperative client. It is difficult for a client to substitute somebody else's blood sample for his or her own in order to hide illicit drug use—a common problem with urine toxicology testing. However, blood samples require that skilled professionals draw the blood under proper sterile techniques.

It is easier to run a urine sample through a toxicology screen to detect illicit drug use than it is to run a blood sample. Urine samples are more easily obtained than blood samples, and the collection of a urine sample does not require that a needle be used. Another advantage of urine toxicology screening is that drug levels are often higher in the urine than in the blood, making detection of illicit drug use easier.

However, it is not uncommon for clients to "fake" urine samples, either by substitution or by other means. One favorite trick is for the client to have a "clean" (drug-free) urine sample on hand, possibly hidden in a balloon or small bottle. When asked for a urine sample, the client may empty the container into the sample bottle, safe in the knowledge that the urine to be tested is "clean." Another trick is for the client to "accidentally" dip the bottle into the water in the toilet, diluting their urine so much that it is unlikely that the laboratory could detect any *urine*, never mind possible chemical traces! (One way to avoid this danger is to test the specific gravity and level of acidity of the urine sample, since water has a different specific gravity and acid level than urine.)

Another trick of many clients who are aware that they must provide a urine sample for toxicology testing is to force fluids to dilute whatever traces of chemicals might be found. For this reason, many laboratories recommend that urine samples submitted for testing be drawn from the client's first visit to the toilet in the morning, when urine is most concentrated.

Other tricks, according to *Playboy* (1991), include substituting a small sample of a certain diet soda for the requested urine. After being held under the arm for an hour to simulate the body's warmth, 2 ounces of this diet soda would be accepted as a valid urine sample 98% of the time. Obviously, this false sample will not detect any drugs or alcohol use. Further, although *Playboy* does not name the specific brand, adding eyedrops to the urine sample will camouflage any evidence of marijuana use. Also, bleach added to the urine sample will camoflage traces of cocaine.

Thus, *extremely close supervision of clients,* **both male and female,** *must be the rule when using urine samples for detection of illicit drug use.* This means that the person supervising the collection of the urine sample *must actually see the urine enter the bottle,* and not just stand outside the lavatories while the client is inside. Clients have been known to hide clean urine samples in the toilet area beforehand in order to substitute them for their own later that day.

If a staff person suspects that a client has "substituted" another person's urine for his or her own, there are several techniques that may be used to counter this. First, since urine is within 1 to 2 degrees of the core body temperature, one can detect a substitution by immediately taking the temperature of the sample. The client whose urine sample is 70°, for example, is likely to have substituted somebody else's and should be confronted with this fact.

Another technique is for the staff person to wait until the client is about to enter the lavatory, then to tell the client that he or she has been selected for another urine sample for drug testing. It is unlikely that clients will carry around a bottle of substitute urine all the time on the off chance that they will be asked for a sample. This procedure is likely to force the client to give a sample of his or her own urine, especially if care is taken to ensure that the client actually provides a valid sample.

Depending on the method used, laboratories can detect either the drugs, or metabolites produced by the body as the liver breaks down the drugs, for various periods of time. The chemical dependency professional should request a written summary from the laboratory, including:

- *methods* by which the laboratory attempts to detect illicit chemical use,
- the *accuracy* of the method used,
- *the specific chemicals that can be detected* by the laboratory,
- *the duration after the client has used chemicals over which the urine test may reveal such drug use,* and
- other drugs (including over-the-counter medications) that might yield false positive results.

According to Ravel (1989), a urine sample from a person who had used a *single* marijuana cigarette would be "positive" for 1 to 3 days at a cut-off level of 100 ng/ml; if a lower cut-off level of 20 ng/ml were used, the same individual would test positive for THC for 5 to 8 days ("ng" is the abbreviation for nanogram—one-billionth of a gram). Because the body stores THC and gradually releases it back into the blood, chronic marijuana users will test positive at the 20-ng/ml level for 30 to 40 days. Farrow (1990) provides an even higher estimate, stating that the daily marijuana user might continue to test positive for the THC for 6 to 81 days.

Thus, Ravel advocates the testing of new urine samples every 4 to 5 days for chronic users. If there has been no additional marijuana use, such serial urine samples should show "a progressive downward trend in the values" (p. 629).

Urine toxicology screening can detect other drugs of abuse besides marijuana. Depending on the route of administration and the amount of the drug utilized, it is possible to detect cocaine for 24 to 36 hours after the last drug use (House, 1990; Farrow, 1990; Schwartz, 1988). Ravel (1989) states that the period of time in which cocaine can be detected in urine samples depends on (a) the quantity ingested, (b) the number of times the individual used cocaine, (c) individual variation in the period of time necessary for the body to metabolize cocaine, and (d) the sensitivity of the test for cocaine. However, as a general rule, a large dose of cocaine can be detected for 2 to 3 days using enzyme immunoassay techniques, or for up to 7 days if more sensitive radioimmunoassay technique are utilized.

Ravel also states that PCP or its metabolites can be detected for up to a week following its use. However, as noted in Chapter 13 on hallucinogens, the speed at which PCP is excreted from the body depends on the acidity of the urine, and thus there will be some variation in the speed at which PCP is eliminated from the body. The amphetamines and narcotics, on the other hand, can be detected for only 24 to 48 hours after their last use, according to Ravel.

False positive test results and the need for retesting   There are a number of chemicals that may cause inaccurate test results. Poppy seeds, for example, which are used in baking certain kinds of bread, might produce a false positive result on a urine toxicology screen for narcotics (Ravel, 1980). Over-the-counter medications, such as pseudoephedrine hydrochloride (sold under the brand name "Sudafed") may cause the urine sample to test positive for amphetamines (Schwartz, 1988).

Once illicit drug use has been detected, it is necessary for the urine samples to be retested by another technique to rule out a false positive result. For example, Moyer and Ellefson (1987) report that when a pure urine specimen is utilized, the enzyme-mediated immunotechnique (EMIT) is able to detect marijuana use with better than 95% accuracy. When combined with other tests, such as gas chromatography/mass spectrometry (GC/MS), it is possible to obtain virtually 100% accuracy when testing urine specimens for evidence of marijuana.

Given the fact that the EMIT procedure has a 3% false positive rate, testing with another technique such as GC/MS is essential to rule out any possibility of error. Ravel (1989) also advocates the use of additional testing, such as mass spectrometry or gas chromatography, to confirm or deny the original positive test results for all drugs of abuse. These are highly specialized test procedures that essentially separate the constituents of a urine sample for identification. Multiple test procedures for all positive urine samples helps identify those individuals who have, in fact, used illicit chemicals and eliminates the danger of false positive test results (Schwartz, 1988).

Other uses of urine toxicology tests Urine toxicology testing may be used not only to detect illicit drug use, but also to check medication compliance. In other words, urine toxicology screening can be used to determine whether or not a client is taking medications as prescribed. Obviously, clients being detoxified from narcotics through methadone withdrawal should have methadone in their urine. Farrow (1990) reports that urine toxicology screening should be able to detect methadone for up to 56 hours after a dose of 40 mg. If the individual does not test positive for methadone, the staff should consider the possibility that this person has substituted another urine sample for his or her own.

Family and Marital Therapy

Many treatment programs include a family or marital therapy component. Williams (1989) notes that the defense systems of addicts and their families tend to be *inter*reinforcing. Family members come to develop defense mechanisms that reinforce those of the addicted person. In a family systems approach, the role that the drug-use behavior plays in the family is modified. This is often best carried out during the intervention session, according to Williams. Otherwise, the family *as a unit* will resist any change in the addict's behavior.

There are many theoretical models of family therapy, and this is rapidly becoming a specialized area of expertise (Bowen, 1985). Although it is beyond the scope of this chapter to provide a comprehensive overview of marital and family therapy, the chemical dependency professional should be aware that these specialized areas may serve as a useful component of the treatment program as a whole.

Group Therapy Approaches

Yalom (1985) notes that the therapy group offers a number of advantages over individual therapy. First, therapy groups allow one professional to work with a number of different individuals at once. Secondly, group members are able to learn from each other and to offer feedback to each other. Finally, because of the diverse nature of the therapy group, each individual can find members that reflect his or her family of origin, allowing the individual to work through problems from earlier stages of growth.

In some chemical dependency treatment programs, therapy groups are frequently the primary treatment approach offered to the client. While individual sessions might be used for special problems too sensitive to discuss in a group situation, clients are usually encouraged to bring their concerns to the group. It may meet daily, every other day, or two or three times a week, depending on the pace of the program.

According to Peele (1989), the harsh, confrontational-style groups commonly found in therapeutic communities have been found to be ineffective in working with recovering addicts. He suggests that therapy groups focus on helping the recovering addict learn effective coping skills through behavioral training and stress-management techniques.

The skills necessary for effective group leadership are quite complex and are beyond the scope of this text. However, the reader should be aware that groups are often the mainstay of both inpatient and outpatient treatment programs.

Assertiveness Training

Lewis et al. (1988) describe special training groups for assertiveness as useful in building self-esteem and self-confidence in interpersonal relationships. Individuals who are addicted to chemicals often lack the ability to assert themselves and can benefit from training in this interpersonal skill. Many programs offer an assertiveness-training component to certain of their clients.

Alcoholics Anonymous and Narcotics Anonymous

Although we have already discussed Alcoholics Anonymous and Narcotics Anonymous in some detail, brief mention of these groups should be made at this time. Participation in a self-help group such as AA is often a component of inpatient and outpatient treatment programs. Many community AA and NA groups encourage local treatment programs to allow their clients to participate in scheduled meetings. If the treatment program is large enough, an on-campus AA or NA meeting may be scheduled, which is limited to clients in treatment.

Both AA and NA offer opportunities for their members to model drug-free interpersonal interactions for clients in treatment. Each group also offers new members the opportunity to develop a drug-free support system to use in times of crisis following treatment. Members of AA or NA may also offer the newcomer insight into personal problems and suggest possible solutions based on their own experience.

Despite the usefulness of AA and NA to clients in treatment, Peele (1989) points out that many people recover without these groups, raising questions as to whether or not an individual *must* participate in a self-help group in order to succeed in treatment. Most professionals feel that treatment programs should provide for self-help group participation, as such groups have been found by many individuals to be quite helpful.

SUMMARY

In this chapter we described the Minnesota Model of treatment, which is one of the primary treatment models in the United States. We explored the concept of a comprehensive treatment plan, which serves as the heart of the treatment process. We also explored various pharmacological supports for recovering addicts in the early stages of sobriety and for those going through detoxification from chemicals.

We discussed the concept of relapse prevention and the use of blood and urine samples for toxicology screening to detect illicit drug use and medication compliance. We also briefly touched on some of the other components that are frequently included in treatment programs.

Chapter 28

Treatment Formats for Chemical Dependency Rehabilitation

Over the past quarter of a century, a debate has been going on within the chemical dependency treatment industry over the relative merits of outpatient versus inpatient program formats (Youngstrom, 1990b). This debate, while spirited, has remained without resolution. In this chapter we will review some of the characteristics of typical outpatient and inpatient programs, as well as some of the issues that have been raised about their relative advantages and disadvantages.

OUTPATIENT TREATMENT PROGRAMS

Outpatient treatment programs for addiction are many and varied. For the individual who is arrested for the first time while driving under the influence of chemicals, there is the "DWI school." The DWI school is an outpatient psycho-educational approach for first-time offenders who are assumed to have simply made a mistake by driving under the influence of chemicals, but who do not seem to be addicted to drugs. The main objective of the DWI school is to help the individual understand the dangers inherent in driving while under the influence of chemicals, in the hope that he or she will not repeat this mistake.

Many community mental health centers offer outpatient chemical dependency treatment. There are also numerous private clinics and therapists in private practice offering outpatient treatment for addiction. The mental health center or private clinic may use individual and/or group therapy as part of the treatment approach. Marital and family counseling may also be part of the rehabilitation effort.

Outpatient chemical dependency treatment programs usually adopt a twelve-step philosophy, similar to that used by Alcoholics Anonymous. Some programs include AA meetings in their schedule, although it is more common for the program to require client attendance at either AA or NA meetings in the community. Attendance may be verified by having two or more program participants attend the same meeting, or by having a member of AA sign an attendance verification form for the patient.

While the addict is in treatment, family members are encouraged to attend either Al-Anon or Alateen meetings while the client attends Alcoholics Anonymous. This is to introduce family members to the potential support available through Al-Anon or Alateen while the client is still in treatment. Resistance on the part of family members to participate in such self-help groups is explored during family night or at family group meetings. This is done to help members of the client's immediate family realize the benefits of community support systems as they learn how to support the client's sobriety.

Components of Outpatient Treatment Programs

Outpatient chemical dependency treatment may best be defined as a formal treatment program that (a) involves one or more professionals who are trained to work with individuals addicted to chemicals; (b) is designed specifically to work with the addicted person to help him or her achieve and maintain sobriety; (c) utilizes family, marital, individual and/or group therapy to help the addicted person come to terms with his or her problems; and (d) does so on an outpatient basis.

Outpatient treatment programs incorporate many of the components of treatment discussed in Chapter 27. Individual and group therapy formats are commonly used, as well as marital and family therapy. Most such programs will follow a twelve-step philosophy, and most require the individual to attend regular self-help group meetings as part of the treatment format.

The individual's treatment program is usually coordinated by a certified chemical dependency counselor (sometimes called an "addictions" or "substance abuse" counselor). A course of treatment will be established, review sessions will be scheduled on a regular basis, and the client's progress toward the established goals will be monitored by staff.

The general approach of individual and group therapy is the confrontation of the addict's system of denial, combined with counseling designed to help the client learn how to face the problems of daily living *without* using chemicals. This is accomplished, in part, through psycho-educational lectures in which the individual is presented with factual information about the disease of chemical addiction and its treatment.

Referrals to vocational counseling centers or to community mental health centers for individual, family, or marital counseling are made as necessary. Some programs provide a weekly or monthly "family night" during which family members are encouraged to participate and to discuss their concerns. Other programs feature a "family group" orientation in which couples participate together on a day-to-day basis. In such a format, the spouse of the addicted person will sit in on the group sessions and participate as an equal with the addicted person in the group therapy.

Whatever the general approach, the goal of any outpatient treatment program is to enhance the highest level of functioning possible for the addict, at the same time providing support. Some programs require the detoxification phase of treatment (when the individual is withdrawn from chemicals) to be carried out either at a detoxification center or in a general hospital. The individual is generally expected to have stopped all chemical use before starting any treatment program.

Abstinence from alcohol, as well as from other drug use, is expected. Many treatment programs will require the use of Antabuse, a common pharmacological treatment for alcoholism. Random urine tests to detect alcohol or drug use by the patient are also frequently required. Random urine testing allows the staff to determine if there is evidence of Antabuse in the urine sample, and if it is being taken as prescribed.

The goal of outpatient treatment is to afford the individual the opportunity to live at home, continue to work, and to continue family activities while participating in a rehabilitation program (Youngstrom, 1990b). This approach is helpful for some, although research suggests a high dropout rate for outpatient treatment programs (Baekeland & Lundwall, 1975).

Advantages of Outpatient Treatment

There is an obvious cost advantage in outpatient treatment as compared to inpatient treatment. A 28-day inpatient treatment program might cost between $7,000 and $30,000, depending on the daily fee for each specific treatment setting (*Alcoholism & Drug Abuse Week*, 1990; Tubo, 1989). By contrast, a 6-month outpatient treatment program might cost as little as $1,000, according to Turbo.

Surprisingly, although inpatient treatment might cost more, because of available insurance coverage, many clients actually pay *less* for inpatient treatment than for outpatient treatment. This is because outpatient treatment programs traditionally are not reinbursed at the same rate as the more expensive inpatient substance abuse program by health insurance carriers. This factor often fuels a tendency for health care providers to recommend inpatient over outpatient treatment programs, according to Berg and Dubin (1990).

Another advantage of the outpatient format is that the patient does not have to be removed from his or her environment. Unlike inpatient treatment programs, there is no community reorientation period needed after outpatient treatment (Bonstedt, Ulrich, Dolinar, & Johnson, 1984; Youngstrom, 1990b).

Nace (1987) recommends an outpatient treatment program of a year's duration. This, in itself, is an advantage over inpatient treatment programs, which tend to be shorter in duration. A 1-year treatment program offers long-term follow-up for the crucial first year of sobriety—a time when the individual is likely to relapse. The patient who knows that he or she may be subjected to random urine toxicology screening as part of a year-long outpatient program may be less likely to use drugs.

Berg and Dubin (1990) outline an intensive outpatient treatment program that is divided into four phases. Each of the first three phases—intensive, intermediate, and moderate treatment—is designed to last for 2 weeks. However, Berg and Dubin note that any given individual's placement is determined by "the severity of the patient's addiction, progress in treatment, financial resources, and ability to attend the program" (p. 1175). The final phase of treatment—the extended phase—involves an aftercare meeting once a week for an indefinite period of time.

Since outpatient treatment programs tend to last longer than inpatient programs, Lewis et al. (1988) point out that this rehabilitation format offers the counselor a longer period of time in which to help the client achieve the goals outlined in the treatment plan. The client also has an extended period of time in which to practice and perfect new behaviors that will support sobriety.

Outpatient treatment programs offer yet another advantage over inpatient treatment programs—flexibility (Turbo, 1989). Outpatient treatment participation may be through a *day-treatment* program, where activities are scheduled during normal working hours, or through an *evening-treatment* program. Finally, outpatient treatment programs offer the client the opportunity to practice sobriety while still living in the community. This is a significant advantage over traditional inpatient treatment programs, where the client is removed from the home community for the duration of treatment.

Drawbacks of the Outpatient Treatment Approach

Although statistical research has found no significant difference in the percentage of outpatient treatment program "graduates" who remain sober, as opposed to those who complete inpatient treatment programs for drug addiction, this is not to say that outpatient treatment is as effective as inpatient treatment. Rather, inpatient treatment programs tend to deal more effectively with a different clientele than outpatient treatment programs, making comparisons difficult.

Outpatient treatment programs occasionally have difficulty with clients whose detoxification from chemicals is quite complicated. Berg and Dubin (1990) report, however, that only approximately 10% of those individuals going through withdrawal will require hospitalization because of complications from their detoxification. Outpatient detoxification from alcohol, according to Berg and Dubin, is possible for the majority of those who are addicted to this chemical.

The outpatient treatment program does not offer the same degree of structure and support as an effective inpatient drug-addiction program offers. Outpatient treatment programs have less control over the client's environment and thus are of limited value for some patients who require a great deal of support during the early stages of sobriety. While outpatient treatment of substance abuse seems to work for many clients, it does not seem to be the ultimate answer to the problem of chemical dependency.

INPATIENT TREATMENT PROGRAMS

The client in an inpatient treatment program lives in a residential treatment facility while he or she participates in treatment. Such programs usually deal with the hard-core, the seriously ill, or the "difficult" patient. These are individuals for whom outpatient treatment has either not been successful, or for whom outpatient treatment has been ruled out due to the severity of the person's chemical use.

Residential treatment programs have evolved in order to provide the client with the greatest degree of support and help possible. Inpatient treatment also is "the most restrictive, structured, and protective of treatment settings" (Klar, 1987, p. 340). Moreover, it combines the greatest potential for positive change with high financial cost and the possibility of branding the patient for life. Thus, the decision to use inpatient treatment is one that should not be made lightly.

Often, the inpatient treatment program provides detoxification services as part of its services, and there is rapid access to medical support services for the seriously ill patient. Such programs are usually found in a hospital setting. Other forms of inpatient treatment may not provide the same degree of medical support, and may be associated with *therapeutic communities* or *halfway houses*, as well as other nonhospital-based facilities.

Varieties of Inpatient Treatment

Detoxification programs   Many chemical dependency programs offer general detoxification services as part of their regular treatment program, or perhaps as a separate component of treatment. Such detoxification programs should meet the standards of state licensing boards, and detoxification should be carried out only under the supervision of a physician who has both training and experience in this area.

Detoxification is not, in itself, a treatment for chemical dependency (Miller & Hester, 1986; National Academy of Sciences, 1990). Research has shown that simple detoxification from chemicals will usually fail to bring about a major change in drug-use behavior. Rather, detoxification is a necessary prelude to the treatment process. This may be carried out as part of a hospital-based service, or it may be carried out at a regional "crisis center." The main emphasis of detoxification programs is medically supervised detoxification from chemicals. These centers have, for the most part, replaced the "drunk tank," once so common in county jails.

While detoxification from chemicals is often carried out on an inpatient basis, there are those who question the need for inpatient detoxification from drugs on a routine basis (*Alcoholism & Drug Abuse Week*, 1990a; Berg & Dubin, 1990). It has been argued, for example, that only a minority of alcoholics actually require inpatient detoxification (Berg & Dubin, 1990; Miller & Hester, 1986). Other patients, perhaps a majority, could safely be detoxified from alcohol in a community setting, according to some experts in the field. Miller et al. (1988) advocate that each patient in withdrawal be evaluated by a trained physician to determine whether inpatient or outpatient detoxification is necessary.

In an evaluation of the merits of inpatient versus outpatient detoxification from chemicals, it was concluded, on purely technical grounds, that detoxification from illicit drugs does not automatically require inpatient hospitalization (National Academy of Sciences, 1990). What the National Academy of Sciences terms "ambulatory detox" results in a significant savings over the cost of inpatient detoxification, without an apparent reduction in the effectiveness of the withdrawal process. Further, if an individual patient does prove to be unable to complete detoxification on an outpatient basis, he or she can always be admitted to an inpatient detoxification center after the less restrictive process has been shown not to work.

As noted in the previous chapter, outpatient detoxification requires daily follow-up from the detoxification staff to monitor the patient's progress and compliance with the withdrawal process (Miller et al., 1988). Also, patients being withdrawn from drugs should be closely monitored to detect signs of drug overdose, or seizures.

Therapeutic communities   There is no generally recognized model of the therapeutic community (TC), according to the National Academy of Sciences (1990). Rather, there are a multitude of programs that differ as to recommended length of stay, client-to-staff ratio, and staff composition. In general, however, the TC might be viewed as a residential treatment program that "employs vigorous and forceful confrontation of addicts' attitudes and behavior" (Klein & Miller, 1986, p. 1083). Therapeutic communities usually require a commitment of between 1 and 3 years (DeLeon, 1989; Klein & Miller, 1986), although some programs have a minimal commitment of only 6 months.

The therapeutic community has a special place in the continuum of treatment. As noted by Lewis et al. (1988), the TC has gained prominence "particularly [for] those addicted to opiates" (p. 33). Such long-term residential treatment programs are thought to be quite effective for those individuals whose addiction is complicated by an antisocial personality disorder, or what *Alcoholism & Drug Abuse Week* (1990a) terms "social pathology."

Ellis et al. (1988) suggest that TC is particularly effective partly because it is based on a single therapeutic model. Such consistency is of value when working with the antisocial personality (Ansevics & Doweiko, 1983). Unfortunately, the TC model is followed only by a minority of treatment programs. DeLeon (1989) reports that of the estimated 500 drug-free residential treatment programs in the United States, under 25% follow the therapeutic community model.

DeLeon describes one central tenet of the TC model as "its perspective of drug abuse as a *whole person* disorder" (p. 177). Other characteristics of the TC include social and physical isolation, a structured living environment, a firm system of rewards and punishments, and an emphasis on self-examination and confession of past wrongdoing. Clients are expected to work outside the TC in an approved job or as part of the TC support staff. In many TCs, there is some potential mobility from the status of client to that of paraprofessional staff member (National Academy of Sciences, 1990). Former clients working as paraprofessional counselors are thought to be effective in breaking through denial and manipulation since "they have been there," and can draw on their experiences in working with newcomers.

The TC might offer an extended family for the individual—a "family" that the recovering addict may be encouraged never to leave. Indeed, according to Lewis et al. (1988), the original members of Synanon (one of the early therapeutic communities) were expected to remain there on a permanent basis.

Despite the emphasis on remaining in TCs, they tend to suffer from significant dropout rates. *The Addiction Letter* (1989b) reports that the highest dropout rate is within the first 15 days of treatment. According to Gelman et al. (1990), one TC, Phoenix House, experienced a 40% dropout rate in the first 90 days. Ultimately, according to Gelman et al., up to 80% of those who enter TCs either leave or are discharged for various rules infractions. Baekeland and Lundwall (1975) report that drug-free treatment programs (which would include TCs) suffer the highest dropout rates found in drug-treatment centers.

The National Academy of Sciences (1990) concludes that only 15% to 25% of those admitted to TCs will "graduate," and that the recovery rates of those who drop out in the earliest phases of treatment "basically cannot be distinguished from those . . . individuals who [do] not enter any treatment modality" (p. 167).

There is a great deal of controversy surrounding therapeutic communities. Some caution that the therapeutic community might not be a positive step for the individual, since many such programs use methods such as ego-stripping and unquestioned submission to the rules of the program (for example, Ansabel, 1983). Lewis et al. (1988) point out that the social isolation inherent in the TC prevents the client from going out into the community to try new social skills. The harsh confrontation and high relapse rates often associated with TCs have also drawn criticism from Lewis et al.

There are others, however, who note that the TC has proven effective where traditional methods often fail (for example, De Leon, 1989; Peele, 1989; Yablonsky, 1967). According to Peele (1989), the TC functions best when it strives to help the individual learn social skills and values inconsistent with drug-using behaviors. *Alcoholism & Drug Abuse Week* (1990a), in its review of the therapeutic community concept, concludes that such programs are quite effective, with upwards of 80% of those who complete the program remaining drug-free. The National Academy of Sciences (1990) concludes that those who remain in the program the longest are most likely to achieve a sober life-style.

Hospital-based inpatient treatment Traditional inpatient drug rehabilitation is often carried out either in a center that specializes in chemical dependency treatment or in a traditional hospital setting as part of a specialized drug-treatment unit. Many of these programs utilize the "Minnesota Model," which was explored in detail in the previous chapter. There is no standard treatment program under the Minnesota Model. Rather, it offers a great deal of flexibility to accommodate the various needs of different individuals. Residential treatment programs usually place strong emphasis on a twelve-step philosophy and use individual and group therapy extensively.

Inpatient rehabilitation programs, especially those in a hospital setting, will often include a detoxification component. Adelman and Weiss (1989) report that medically supervised withdrawal from alcohol dependency results in higher patient retention rates, improving the patient's chances of achieving and retaining sobriety. Whether part of a hospital or not, inpatient treatment programs use a variety of treatment methods and draw on the varied skills of the different members of the treatment team to best help the client.

The client's length of stay in treatment depends on several factors. Among them are the motivation of the client and the community resources available to the client to help him or her stay sober.

THE NEED FOR INPATIENT TREATMENT: IS IT LEGITIMATE?

Miller and Hester (1986), in discussing alcoholism treatment programs, note that "the relative merits of residential treatment are less than clear" (p. 794). Indeed, after a review of some 16 research studies, they conclude that there is no significant difference between inpatient and outpatient alcoholism rehabilitation programs on various measures of patient improvement.

Further, when Miller and Hester explored only the duration of inpatient treatment, they found no statistically significant improvement for long-term treatment programs as compared with programs of shorter duration. They admit, however, that their data suggest that inpatient treatment is possibly more advantageous for addicts of long standing. Outpatient treatment is probably more effective for clients who have not used chemicals for as long a period of time. However, aftercare programs play a more significant role in determining success or failure than the specific form of treatment used, according to Miller and Hester.

Although they are critics of inpatient treatment, Miller and Hester do not recommend that it be abolished:

> There may be subpopulations for whom more intensive treatment is justifiable. From the limited matching data available at present, it appears that intensive treatment may be better for severely addicted and socially unstable individuals. (p. 1246)

In response to Miller and Hester's original (1986) work, Adelman and Weiss (1989) conducted their own research into the merits of inpatient treatment. Adelman and Weiss report that 77% of those alcoholics treated for their alcoholism eventually require some form of inpatient treatment. They also found that treatment programs in "medically oriented facilities" have lower dropout rates than treatment programs in nonmedical centers. Furthermore, patients discharged after short inpatient treatment programs tend to relapse more frequently than those who remain in treatment longer, according to Adelman and Weiss.

According to Bonstedt et al. (1984), "aggressive outpatient treatment" of alcoholism is more cost-effective than inpatient treatment, in most cases. They point out that "the majority of alcoholics do not have to be hospitalized each time they present for treatment. . . ." (p. 1039). The issue of whether a prior history of chemical dependency treatment automatically excludes outpatient treatment thus remains one that is disputed among professionals.

In a study by Walsh et al. (1991), 227 factory workers who were known to be abusing alcohol were randomly assigned to one of three groups. The first required attendance at AA, the second required inpatient treatment, and the third offered a choice between the two alternatives. Findings revealed that while the referral to compulsory AA meetings initially was more cost-effective, in the long run inpatient treatment resulted in higher abstinence rates.

The Advantages of Inpatient Treatment

Although the case of outpatient treatment programs is a strong one, there are certain advantages to inpatient treatment programs. These advantages make inpatient treatment the method of choice in some cases, especially in more advanced cases of addiction.

Inpatient rehabilitation programs offer *more comprehensive treatment programming* than is possible in an outpatient treatment setting (Klar, 1987). This is an advantage in more advanced cases of drug dependency because the addicts often have centered their lives around the chemical for such a long period of time that they would be unable to benefit from a less restrictive treatment approach.

Inpatient treatment programs offer the advantage of an almost total control over the client's environment (Berg & Dubin, 1990). For clients used to a drug-centered life-style, the concept of a drug-free way of life is often quite foreign. The structured environment of inpatient treatment makes it easier for the addict to cope. Individual and group therapy sessions, meals, recreational opportunities, self-help group meetings, and spiritual counseling are all worked into the schedule.

Often, clients will report that they have not been eating on a regular basis prior to entering treatment. An inpatient rehabilitation setting allows staff to treat dietary disorders that may have been caused by the individual's addicted life-style. Supplementary vitamins or dietary supplements are often beneficial in such cases. Inpatient treatment also allows staff to closely monitor the client's recovery from the physical effects of addiction.

Many clients will attend their first AA meeting while in an inpatient setting. In some cases, the client will admit that he or she never would have attended such a meeting had it not been required by treatment staff. Adelman and Weiss (1989) contend that participation in AA is an essential component of an effective inpatient treatment program.

Another advantage of inpatient treatment is that it can provide *around-the-clock support during the earliest stages of sobriety*. It is not unusual to find a client sitting up at two o'clock in the morning, talking about personal problems with the staff member on duty. Nor is it uncommon to find a client pacing through the earliest stages of withdrawal in the middle of the night. When such clients are asked what they would do if they were not in treatment, they commonly respond, "I would go out and score [some drugs]"!

Because these clients are in treatment, they are able to draw on the support services of the staff on duty to help them through the pain of withdrawal. This support might come in the form of a sympathetic ear. Or support may be derived from the administration of previously prescribed medications to ease the discomfort. Staff members may offer suggestions to help the client. They may recommend walking around the ward or eating something. In short, they can "be there" for the client.

Inpatient treatment programs offer the additional advantage of *close supervision of clients*. Often, addicted clients live alone or lack close interpersonal support. In such cases, a medical emergency might go undetected for hours, or even days. In an inpatient treatment setting, medical emergencies may quickly be detected and the appropriate action taken by staff.

Close supervision by staff members also helps to discourage further drug use. Those clients with drug problems of long standing are often tempted to "help out" with the detoxification process by taking a few additional drugs or drinks during withdrawal. Narcotic addicts have been known to inject drugs that they brought into treatment with them, while alcoholics have been known to take a drink or two from a bottle that was thoughtfully tucked away in some hidden corner of a suitcase while packing to go to treatment.

Some inpatient treatment centers search the client's belongings on admission. Other treatment programs use the "honor system," in which other clients will confront the individual using chemicals in treatment. Most inpatient treatment centers use urine toxicology screenings to detect illicit drug use during treatment. The close supervision inherent in an inpatient treatment setting provides the opportunity for staff members to request a urine sample *immediately*, should they suspect drug use by clients.

According to Nace (1987), inpatient treatment is of value in cases where outpatient treatment has become a "revolving door" for the individual. It is also of value for individuals who have experienced repeated crisis situations while in outpatient treatment and for those who have been through several aborted attempts to use outpatient treatment or to establish an effective therapeutic alliance in a less restrictive setting. Individuals who are suffering from multiple problems (physical and psychiatric) while being treated drug addiction also benefit from inpatient treatment, according to Nace.

HOW TO DECIDE ON A TREATMENT SETTING

Deciding whether to use inpatient or outpatient treatment for a client is perhaps one of the most important decisions a treatment professional will make (Washton et al., 1988). It is often a difficult decision, as well. In recent years, questions have been raised as to whether inpatient treatment of chemical dependency is inherently better than outpatient treatment programs.

Outpatient treatment programs offer several advantages over inpatient programs. As we have mentioned, it is usually less expensive to participate in an outpatient treatment program than to enter an inpatient treatment program. A sad, rarely discussed, fact is that the restrictions on funding will play a role in deciding which treatment options are available for the individual. The person whose insurance will pay only for outpatient chemical dependency treatment will have certain financial restrictions placed on his or her treatment options. Thus, availability of funding is one factor that influences the decision whether to seek inpatient or outpatient treatment for substance abuse.

According to the Group for the Advancement of Psychiatry (1991), the following criteria are useful in deciding whether inpatient or outpatient treatment is best suited for a given client:

- the extent to which significant medical or psychiatric conditions or complications are involved in the client's condition;
- the severity of actual or anticipated withdrawal from the drug(s) being used;
- multiple failed attempts at outpatient treatment;
- the client's social support systems; and
- the severity of the client's addiction and the possibility of polysubstance abuse.

Outpatient rehabilitation is best suited to those clients who have not had an extensive prior treatment history (Nace, 1987). Also, the individual's motivation for treatment and the need for inpatient detoxification from chemicals should be considered in the decision whether to recommend inpatient or outpatient treatment. Another factor that should be considered is the patient's overall medical condition. Finally, the individual's psychiatric status and his or her social support systems should be evaluated when considering outpatient treatment as an option (Group for the Advancement of Psychiatry, 1991; Nace, 1987). Obviously, a deeply depressed individual who is recovering from an extended period of cocaine use might benefit more from the greater support offered by an inpatient treatment program, at least during the initial recovery period, when the depression is most severe.

Washton et al. (1988) state the following criteria by which the need for inpatient treatment for drug dependency may be evaluated. (The reader will note that some of the relevant factors are the same as those identified by Nace [1987].)

- concurrent dependence on different chemicals;
- serious medical or psychiatric illness;
- poor motivation for treatment;
- heavy involvement in dealing drugs;
- a past history of failure in outpatient treatment;

- severe psychosocial problems; and
- a proven inability to discontinue further drug use while in outpatient treatment.

By contrast, Miller and Foy (1981) emphasize only three factors for consideration by treatment professionals in working with addicts: (1) the client's physical condition, (2) the client's social support system, and (3) the client's expectations for treatment. Miller and Foy hold that these factors are most important in establishing a viable treatment plan with appropriate goals. These are also factors that should be evaluated when considering inpatient as opposed to outpatient treatment for an individual client.

Turbo (1989), echoing Nace's (1987) work, cites several criteria that would seem to indicate that an inpatient treatment program might be better for the client than the outpatient setting: (1) repeated failure to maintain sobriety in outpatient treatment, (2) an acutely suicidal state, (3) a seriously disturbed home environment, (4) serious medical problems, and (5) serious psychiatric problems.

As noted by Klar (1987), the final criterion for whether to suggest an inpatient or an outpatient treatment program is, *given the client's resources and needs, what is the **least restrictive treatment alternative**?* The treatment referral criteria advanced by Miller and Foy (1981), Nace (1987), and Turbo (1989) are useful guides to the selection of the least restrictive alternative that will meet the client's needs.

Although there are those who will argue that the inpatient treatment program sounds very similar to a concentration camp, one must recall that the dysfunction caused by drug addiction often requires drastic forms of intervention. Just as drastic intervention is often necessary in the practice of medicine (surgery, for example), inpatient treatment is necessary in more advanced cases of addiction to chemicals.

Partial Hospitalization Options

In recent years, several new treatment formats that combine elements of inpatient and outpatient rehabilitation programs have been explored. Each has its advantages and disadvantages, yet all of these programs should be considered viable treatment options for clients who present themselves for treatment. Depending on the client's needs, some of the new treatment formats might prove to be quite beneficial.

Two-by-four programs   One proposed solution to the dilemma of whether to recommend inpatient or outpatient treatment is the so-called two-by-four program. This program format, which borrows from both inpatient and outpatient treatment programs, is a two-phase rehabilitation system that seems to have some promise.

The individual is first hospitalized for a short period of time, usually 2 weeks, in order to achieve total detoxification from chemicals. Depending on the individual's needs, the initial period of hospitalization might be somewhat shorter than 2 weeks, or longer than the 2-week time span. The goal is to help the client reach the point of being able to participate in outpatient treatment as quickly as possible.

If the client is unable to function in the less restrictive outpatient rehabilitation program, as will occasionally happen, he or she may be returned to the inpatient treatment format. Later, when additional progress has been made, the client may again return to an outpatient setting to complete the treatment program there.

An interesting variation on the two-by-four program is practiced by the Schick Shadel chain of hospitals, which operates facilities in California, Texas, and Washington. The individual patient is admitted for 10 days of inpatient treatment, followed by 2 additional inpatient "reinforcement" days 1 month after discharge, and another 2 days of inpatient treatment 2 months following the initial admission.

Although there is no long-term follow-up data for this treatment approach, it does seem to offer some advantages over more traditional two-by-four programs. Berg and Dubin (1990) found that if an alcoholic is admitted to an inpatient program for even a short period of time, he or she is unlikely to follow through with outpatient treatment following discharge from the hospital. The authors found that of those alcoholics who were briefly hospitalized for detoxification and stabilization of outstanding medical problems and then were referred to an intensive outpatient treatment program for their alcoholism, fully 60% failed to follow through by entering the outpatient program. The treatment format practiced by the Schick Shadel hospital chain might offer one means by which these high dropout rates might be avoided.

Day hospitalization The day hospitalization is also known as partial day hospitalization. As Lewis et al. (1988) point out, this rehabilitation format combines elements of inpatient treatment with the opportunities for growth that come from living at home. After detoxification has been achieved, the client is allowed to spend the evening hours at home. He or she then returns to the treatment center during normal work hours to participate in the rehabilitation program.

Although Klar's (1987) work explores the advantages and disadvantages of partial hospital programs for psychiatric patients, his insights into the advantages of day hospitalization for chemical dependency patients are equally valid. In that the patient is living at home, Klar notes that

> the acute partial hospital program is akin to a full-time job, and is consequently less disruptive to social and family roles and is less stigmatizing. Partial hospitalization is a less regressive treatment modality than inpatient care, asks more of the patient, and actively attempts to mobilize the patient's adaptive skills and support network in the treatment. (p. 338)

An essential element of day hospitalization is that the client have a supportive, stable family. Obviously, if the client's spouse (or other family member) also has a drug-abuse problem, day hospitalization may not be a viable treatment option. If the client's spouse is severely codependent and continues to enable the client's chemical use, day hospitalization should not be the treatment of choice.

However, for the client with a stable home environment, day hospitalization offers the opportunity to combine the intensive programming possible through inpatient treatment programs with the opportunities for growth that home life offers. Such a program is of value for clients who need to rebuild family relationships after a protracted period of chemical use.

Halfway houses   The halfway house concept emerged in the 1950s in response to the need for an intermediate step between the inpatient treatment format and independent living (Miller & Hester, 1980). For those clients who lack a stable social support system, the period of time following treatment is often most difficult. Even if strongly motivated to remain sober, the client must struggle against the urge to return to chemical use without the social support that is sorely needed. The halfway house provides a transitional living facility for such a client.

Miller and Hester (1980) note several common characteristics of halfway houses, including (1) a small patient population (usually fewer than 25 individuals), (2) a brief patient stay, (3) emphasis on AA or a similar twelve-step philosophy, (4) minimal rules, and (5) a small number of professional staff members.

As noted, most halfway houses adopt a twelve-step philosophy. Many hold in-house self-help group meetings and some require a specified number of community self-help group meetings a week. Each individual is expected to find work within a given period of time (usually 2 to 3 weeks) or is assigned a job within the halfway house.

The degree of structure that characterizes the traditional halfway house setting is somewhere between that of an inpatient treatment program setting and a traditional household. This provides clients with enough support to function during the transitional period between treatment and self-sufficiency, but at the same time affords them the opportunity to make choices about their lives. As Miller and Hester (1980) point out, halfway houses usually have fewer rules than inpatient treatment centers. Halfway house participation is usually time-limited, generally from 3 to 6 months, after which clients are ready to assume their responsibilities again.

Surprisingly, there is little evidence to support the halfway house concept, according to Miller and Hester (1980). They report that research has failed to uncover significantly greater improvement in patients admitted to halfway houses following treatment than in patients who are not admitted.

Adelman and Weiss (1989), however, report evidence of an inverse relationship between length of stay and rehospitalization in the first 6 months following treatment. In other words, those patients who elect to enter a halfway house following inpatient treatment are less likely to be hospitalized for relapse than those who do not. Finney, Moos, and Chan (1975) also examined the relationship between length of stay in a halfway house setting following treatment and treatment outcome. According to their findings, for some subgroups of patients length of stay correlates with successful treatment outcomes.

SUMMARY

There is significant evidence that outpatient treatment is an option that should be considered by treatment professionals, at least for some addicted individuals. For those with the proper social support and for whom there is no coexisting psychiatric illness or need for inpatient hospitalization, outpatient therapy for drug addiction may offer the chance to participate in treatment and still live at home. This avoids the need for a reorientation period following treatment.

Outpatient treatment also allows for long-term therapeutic support that is often not available from inpatient programs. Within an outpatient program, random urine toxicology screening may be used to check on medication compliance and to identify those individuals who have engaged in illicit drug use.

Research evidence suggests that outpatient drug-addiction treatment is as effective as inpatient treatment for many clients. There is a significant dropout rate from outpatient treatment programs, however, and there remains much to be learned about how to make outpatient addiction treatment more effective.

Inpatient treatment is often viewed as a drastic step. Yet, such a drastic step may be necessary for some clients if they are ever to regain control of their lives. The inpatient rehabilitation program has many advantages over less restrictive treatment options, including a depth of support services unavailable in outpatient treatment. For many of those in the advanced stages of addiction, inpatient treatment offers the only realistic hope of recovery.

In recent years, questions have been raised concerning the need for inpatient treatment programs or halfway house placement following treatment. It has been suggested that inpatient treatment does not offer any advantage over outpatient treatment and that a longer length of stay is not necessarily more effective than short-term treatment (Miller & Hester, 1980). However, Adelman and Weiss (1989) note that length of stay is inversely related to the probability of relapse following treatment. They also contend that halfway house placement is appropriate for some clients following inpatient treatment.

PHARMACOLOGICAL INTERVENTION TACTICS AND SUBSTANCE ABUSE

In a very real sense, the pharmacological treatment of substance abuse is a logical extension of the medical model. It is based on the premise that the individual's substance use can be controlled, or totally eliminated, through the administration of various biochemicals. The specific components of treatment may vary from one program to another. But whether it is detoxification from alcohol, the prevention of relapse for the chronic drinker, or the control of the "craving" for cocaine that many addicts report in the early stages of recovery, all forms of pharmacological intervention center on the use of selected chemicals to combat substance abuse.

THE PHARMACOLOGICAL TREATMENT OF ALCOHOLISM

In their summation of addiction treatment, Frances and Miller (1991) strike a rather pessimistic note:

> At this writing there is no proven biological treatment for alcoholism. Each promising drug that has been tested in the hope it would reduce relapse by intervening in the basic disease process has failed. (p. 13)

However, Frances and Miller do point out that Antabuse continues to provide one avenue for the symptomatic treatment of alcoholism. In this section, we will first discuss Antabuse and then some of the other medications used to treat chronic alcoholism.

Antabuse

The theory behind Antabuse (disulfiram) is that while the exact cause(s) of the individual's alcohol use are unknown, it is possible to use various chemical agents to interfere with the reward value of alcohol. Perhaps the most common

Note: The pharmacological support of alcohol or drug withdrawal, or pharmacological intervention as part of the treatment of an ongoing drug-abuse problem, should be supervised by a licensed physician who is skilled and experienced in working with drug-abuse cases. The information provided in this chapter is in no way intended to encourage self-treatment of drug-abuse problems, nor should it be interpreted as a standard of care for patients who are addicted to chemicals.

pharmacological treatment for alcoholism is disulfiram. This is a potentially dangerous drug, which should not be used with patients who have serious medical disorders (Schuckit, 1989). However, for those patients who *can* use it, disulfiram often provides time for the "second thought" desperately needed by the alcoholic who is tempted to drink.

In brief, disulfiram does not decrease the alcoholic's desire to drink. However, it does interfere with the metabolism of alcohol after it enters the individual's body. This will cause a number of unpleasant—*possibly fatal*—effects for the individual who mixes alcohol with disulfiram. When small amounts of alcohol are ingested by the individual who is on disulfiram, the interaction between these two chemicals will bring about facial flushing, heart palpitations and a rapid heart rate, difficulty in breathing, nausea, vomiting, and possibily a serious drop in blood pressure (Schuckit, 1989). The patient is warned about these effects when the medication is prescribed.

The strength of these side-effects depends on how much alcohol has been ingested, the amount of disulfiram being used each day, and the time lapse since the last dose of disulfiram was ingested. It take 3 to 12 hours after the first dose before disulfiram will begin to interfere with the metabolism of alcohol, and alcohol–disulfiram interactions have been reported for up to 2 weeks after the last dose was ingested.

Some treatment centers advocate a learning process in which the patient takes disulfiram for a short period of time (usually a few days) and then is allowed to drink a small amount of alcohol under controlled conditions. This is done so that alcoholics can themselves experience, under controlled conditions, the negative consequences of mixing these chemicals. In such a demonstration, the treatment staff has access to emergency medical support to help clients recover from the experiment. By allowing them to experience the negative consequences under controlled conditions, after drinking only a small amount of alcohol, it is hoped that they will not attempt to drink a large amount of alcohol on their own, outside of the treatment center.

On occasion, treatment professionals have encountered the situation where a codependent spouse will inquire about the possibility of obtaining disulfiram to teach the husband or wife a lesson. The spouse usually wants the sample of disulfiram in order to put it in the alcoholic's coffee, or "eye-opener." Then, the next time the alcoholic drinks, he or she will experience the alcohol–disulfiram interaction without expecting it. Needless to say, *disulfiram should **never** be given to an individual without the user's knowledge and consent.* The interaction between disulfiram and alcohol is *potentially serious*, and *may require emergency hospitalization for observation and treatment.* Death *is* possible from the mixture of alcohol and disulfiram.

A serious drawback of disulfiram is that it takes about 30 minutes for the individual to begin to experience discomfort from the alcohol–disulfiram reaction (Schuckit, 1989). This delay makes disulfiram of little value in aversion conditioning. Aversion conditioning requires *immediate* consequences paired to undesired behavior in order to be effective. Theoretically, effective alcohol-aversion therapy would involve an immediate aversive event following the ingestion of alcohol. In this manner, the person learns to associate drinking behavior with the aversive event, and, in theory, will gradually discontinue the undesired behavior.

The 30-minute delay between the ingestion of alcohol and the disulfiram–alcohol reaction is far too long for the reaction to serve as an *immediate* consequence for the drinker. Thus, it is difficult for the person to associate the use of alcohol with the delayed discomfort caused by the alcohol–disulfiram reaction.

A third problem with disulfiram is that its full effects last only for about 24 to 48 hours. The individual must take the drug every day, or perhaps every other day, for optimal effectiveness. Between doses, the disulfiram will gradually be eliminated from the body by the liver. Thus, it is up to the individual to take the medication according to the schedule worked out with a physician to ensure that there is an adequate amount of the drug in the body at all times.

A further drawback is that disulfiram interacts with even the small amounts of alcohol found in many over-the-counter cough syrups, aftershaves, and a wide range of other products. The individual on disulfiram should be warned by his or her physician to avoid certain products so that an unintentional reaction will not occur. Most treatment centers and physicians who use disulfiram have lists of such products and foods, and will provide a copy to patients for whom disulfiram has been prescribed.

Further, research has suggested that disulfiram interacts with the neurotransmitter serotonin to boost brain levels of a byproduct of serotonin known as 5-hydroxytryptophol (5-HTOL) (Cowen, 1990). Animal research suggests that increased levels of 5-HTOL results in greater alcohol consumption. While research with human subjects has yet to be completed, preliminary data suggest that alcoholics should avoid "serotonin-rich" foods, such as bananas and walnuts, to avoid increasing the craving for alcohol many recovering alcoholics experience.

Disulfiram is *not* recommended for individuals with a history of cardiovascular disease, cerebrovascular disease, kidney failure, depression, seizure disorders, liver disease, or for those who might be pregnant (Fuller, 1989). Drug interactions between disulfiram and phenytoin (sold under the brand name Dilantin), warfarin, isoniazid (used in the treatment of tuberculosis), diazepam (Valium), chlordiazepoxide (Librium), and several commonly used antidepressants have been reported (Fuller, 1989). Thus, patients on any of these medications should not take disulfiram except under a doctor's supervision.

In spite of these disadvantages, alcoholism treatment programs that include the use of disulfiram as a part of the overall treatment program have a lower relapse rate than programs that do not (Adelman & Weiss, 1989). What disulfiram does, once clients have taken their scheduled dose, is to provide them with the knowledge that they will be unable to drink for that day, or perhaps for as long as 2 weeks afterwards—at least not without becoming very sick.

Admittedly, some alcoholics will drink in spite of the disulfiram in their system, which is known as trying to "drink through" the disulfiram. Further, many alcoholics believe they know how to neutralize the drug while it is in their body. In spite of these notions, for the majority of those who choose Antabuse, the drug provides an extra bit of support during a weak moment.

Lithium

Recently, the use of lithium in the treatment of alcoholism has received a great deal of attention. Lithium is an element that has been found to be useful in the treatment of bipolar affective disorders (formerly called manic–depressive disorders). Surprisingly, lithium has also been found to apparently reduce the number of relapses that chronic alcholics experience, reduce their apparent level of intoxication, and reduce their desire to drink (Judd & Huey, 1984; Miller et al., 1989).

Unfortunately, research findings as to the effectiveness of lithium in the treatment of chronic alcoholism are not conclusive, and there is no indication that lithium is useful in the treatment of *every* chronic alcoholic (Miller et al., 1989). However, research into what subtypes of alcoholics might benefit from the use of lithium, and under what circumstances lithium might be useful, continues at this time.

Other Pharmacological Treatments for Chronic Alcoholism

Other medications, such as Flagyl (metronidazole), also cause discomfort when mixed with alcohol. According to Graedon (1980), when mixed with alcohol, Flagyl causes nausea, vomiting, flushing, and headache. One physician, when faced with a patient who was allergic to Antabuse, elected to use metronidazole as a short-term substitute, although this practice is not currently recommended by the Food and Drug Administration.

However, in this case, the physician was able to provide pharmacological support for an alcoholic who needed some external constraint during the initial period of sobriety, when relapse commonly occurs. This is not to say that metronidazole should be routinely administered to alcoholics who require pharmacological support. There is evidence to suggest that metronidazole has a significant potential for causing cancer (Graedon, 1980). Metronidazole should be used only when the benefits clearly outweigh the risks.

A different treatment approach to the problem of rehabilitation of the alcoholic has been suggested by Blum and Trachtenberg (1988). They suggest that alcohol craving might be influenced by the neurochemicals available in the brain; thus, they advocate the use of "neurotransmitter precursor loading" (p. 5). According to Blum and Trachtenberg, the proper nutritional supplements will

> improve brain nutrition, improve the balance of the neurotransmitters, reduce the craving, and help the alcoholic respond more favorably to supportive treatment such as that provided by treatment centers, counselors, and alcoholics anonymous. (p. 35)

Blum and Trachtenberg offer a patented combination of vitamins, amino acids, and minerals for use in the rehabilitation of alcoholics. This approach has the advantage of using nonaddictive substances to restore the balance of neurotransmitters found in the otherwise healthy brain. However, Peele (1991) notes that research has failed to uncover any positive effects from this approach.

It has recently been discovered that a drug normally used in the treatment of narcotics addiction, *naltrexone hydrochloride* (to be discussed next), may also be useful in the treatment of alcoholism. Early research findings suggest that naltrexone may actually block the pleasurable effects of alcohol, thus reducing its reward value (Holloway, 1991). Further research into the possible use of naltrexone hydrochloride in the treatment of alcoholism is currently being conducted.

THE PHARMACOLOGICAL TREATMENT OF NARCOTICS ADDICTION

Naltrexone hydroxide (sold under the brand name Trexan) has recently been found to block the euphoric effects of injected opiates for up to 72 hours, depending on the dose used. The theory behind the use of Trexan is that if the person does not experience any feelings of euphoria from opiates while on Trexan, he or she will be less likely to use them again.

Naltrexone should be used *only after the person is* **completely** *detoxified from opiates*, in order to avoid an undesired withdrawal syndrome in the addict. Callahan (1980) notes that few addicts attempt to use narcotics even once while on a narcotics blocker. However, when the medication is discontinued, the opiate addict will begin to reexperience a craving for narcotics. Thus, there is no extinction of the craving for the drug during the period that the addict is being maintained on the blocker.

Jenike (1989) reports that a 50-mg dose of naltrexone will block the euphoria of an injection of narcotics for 24 hours and that a 100-mg dose will work for about 48 hours. Further, a 150-mg dose of naltrexone will block the euphoria from injected narcotics for 72 hours. According to Jenike, the usual dosage schedule is three times per week, with 100 mg being administered on Monday and Wednesday, and 150 mg being administered on Friday to provide a longer term dose for the weekend.

To date, there is no research that demonstrates an *unequivocal* benefit from naltrexone, according to the *1991 Physician's Desk Reference* (Medical Economics Company, 1991). Indeed, research has discovered that a major drawback of naltrexone is that so many addicts discontinue it on their own (Youngstrom, 1990a). In one study exploring the application of naltrexone in the treatment of narcotics addiction, only 2% of the original sample continued to take the drug for 9 months (Youngstrom, 1990a). Holloway (1991) suggests that naltrexone is most useful for the narcotics addict who is "motivated to stay drug free" (p. 100). Thus, while naltrexone does seem to offer pharmacological support during the initial period after detoxification, when an addict is most vulnerable to relapse, its usefulness in the long-term treatment of narcotics addiction is still unclear.

Withdrawal from Narcotics

Programs that specialize in the treatment of opiate addiction often offer controlled withdrawal programs. As mentioned previously, hospitals will occasionally offer these programs even if they do not provide long-term treatment for addicts.

Methadone is currently the drug of choice for opiate withdrawal (Jenike, 1989). Methadone is a synthetic narcotic, first developed by German chemists during World War II. The drug was developed as a substitute for morphine, which the Germans were unable to obtain because of the war. Methadone is taken orally and has the additional advantage of a duration of action between 24 and 36 hours (Mirin et al., 1991). A daily dosage level of between 10 and 40 mg/day of methadone is usually sufficient to prevent withdrawal symptoms in narcotic addicts, according to Mirin et al.

The methadone withdrawal program begins with an initial dose of 10 mg. The patient receives an additional dose of 10 mg each hour, until the withdrawal symptoms are brought under control. The total amount of methadone received by the patient is then calculated, and this dose becomes the starting point for the withdrawal program. On the second day of the withdrawal program, the patient receives the same amount of methadone as the day before, but as a single dose administered in the morning.

To illustrate this process, let us assume that on the first day a hypothetical patient required a total of five hourly 10-mg doses of methadone before the withdrawal symptoms were controlled. On the second day, that patient would receive a single 50-mg dose of methadone in the morning. Then, on each subsequent day, the dosage level of methadone would be reduced by 5 mg, until the patient was completely detoxified from opiates (Mirin et al., 1991).

The usual detoxification program lasts between 3 and 21 days. If a detoxification program lasts longer than 3 weeks, it must be licensed by the government as a methadone maintenance project (Jenike, 1989). Surprisingly, in spite of the length of the program, detoxification programs suffer from a significant dropout rate (Baekeland & Lundwall, 1975). Mirin et al. (1991) note that as the daily dosage levels drop to the 15- or 20-mg/day range, the individual will experience a return of withdrawal symptoms. Indeed, opiate addicts going through withdrawal should be reminded *not to expect a symptom-free withdrawal.*

Some treatment programs view methadone withdrawal as inappropriate. Narcotic addicts have been known to report that methadone withdrawal, is in their opinion, worse than going "cold turkey." As we noted in Chapter 10 on narcotics, withdrawal from opiates is not life-threatening, and many addicts have reported that, if truth be told, this withdrawal is no worse than a bad cold or the flu.

Some programs offer pharmacological support during withdrawal in the form of benzodiazepines to help the addict relax and sleep, but do not use narcotics. Indeed, Charney, Heninger, and Kleber (1986) outline a treatment program in which two different drugs—an antihypertensive, Catapres (clonidine hydrochloride), and an opiate antagonist, Narcan (naloxone)—are used to bring about an opiate withdrawal lasting from 4 to 5 days rather than the more extended withdrawal sequence often found in traditional methadone withdrawal programs.

The clonidine hydrochloride is used to control the individual's craving for narcotics, while the antagonist blocks the drug-receptor sites in the brain and counteracts the effects of the narcotics. Charney et al. found that over 90% of their sample population were completely withdrawn from narcotics at the end of 5 days, without having experienced significant distress. They go on to recommend this drug program as part of an opiate addiction treatment program. Unfortunately, some addicts have learned to combine clonidine with methadone, alcohol, benzodiazpeines, or other drugs to produce a sense of euphoria (Jenike, 1989).

Methadone maintenance programs   The concept of methadone maintenance was advanced by Dole and Nyswander (1965). The theory behind methadone maintenance is that when a sufficiently high dosage of methadone is used orally, it will block the majority of the euphoric effects of injected narcotics. It is hoped that this will ultimately result in an extinction of the intraveneous narcotics use (National Acadcemy of Sciences, 1990).

The goal of methadone maintenance is to provide medically supervised doses of methadone to eliminate the drug craving in the "otherwise intractable" addicts (Dole, 1989, p. 1880). The methadone maintenance program allows addicts to function without the need to obtain drugs illegally to support their habit. The usual dosage level is between 40 and 120 mg of methadone each day.

It has been estimated that, at any given time, between an eighth and a fifth of narcotics addicts in the United States are involved in methadone maintenance programs (National Academy of Sciences, 1990). However, the concept of methadone maintenance rests on the unproven assumption that the use of opiates brings about permanent changes in brain function at the cellular level (Dole, 1988; Dole & Nyswander, 1965). According to this theory, when the narcotics are removed from the body, the individual will experience a craving for narcotics that may last for months, or even years. This drug craving then makes it more likely that the individual will ultimately return to the use of narcotics in order to feel "normal" again.

The initial results of methadone maintenance are quite promising (Callahan, 1980), although subsequent research has uncovered a number of weaknesses with the concept. First, while addicts may not crave narcotics, and may even be unable to experience the euphoria of injected narcotics while on methadone, this does not prevent them from abusing cocaine, alcohol, marijuana, benzodiazepines, and so forth. Indeed, the incidence of illicit drug use among patients in methadone maintenance programs is high (Calsyn, Saxon, & Barndt).

Mirin et al. (1991) report that at least 20% of addicts in a methadone maintenance program could be expected to abuse other chemicals besides narcotics. Even Dole (1989) acknowledges that methadone is "highly specific for the treatment of opiate addiction" (p. 1880) and that it will not block the euphoric effects of other drugs of abuse. Moreover, there is no similar pharmacological therapy for nonopiate addictions.

Secondly, many physicians challenge the concept of methadone maintenance on moral grounds. A significant number of physicians question the morality of physicians knowingly administering methadone, an addictive substance, to people who are known to suffer from addictive disorders (D'Amico, 1990). Further, as Baekeland and Lundwall (1975) note, despite the supposed advantages of this treatment approach, methadone maintenance programs suffer from a significant dropout rate. This would argue that they are not the final answer to the problem of narcotics addiction.

Dole (1988), one of the major proponents of the methadone maintenance concept, states that methadone maintenance is "corrective, but not curative" (p. 3025) for a suspected, but as yet unproven, neurological dysfunction that brings about the compulsive use of narcotics. Originally, Dole and Nyswander (1965) advanced a theory that *even a single dose* of narcotics would bring about a change in the structure of the brain of the addict-to-be, forever altering the way that his or her brain functioned. Only through the use of further narcotics would the brain function be restored to its normal state, according to Dole and Nyswander. Theoretically, when the neurological function that was disrupted by the use of narcotics is restored,

> the ex-addict, supported by counseling and social services, can begin the long process of social rehabilitation. (Dole, 1988, p. 3025)

Thus, simply providing a sufficient supply of methadone to the addict is not the final answer. There remains a need for the individual to participate in a formal rehabilitation program. Unfortunately, as Callahan (1980) points out, many methadone maintenance clinics have become little more than "warehouses in which methadone [is] doled out to a great number of people each day" (p. 148). Indeed, all too often methadone maintenance clinics serve only as drug-administration centers, with little effort at rehabilitation in evidence (*The Addiction Letter*, 1989a).

As envisioned, methadone maintenance assumes that the addict is not just using the program as a guaranteed source of narcotics to avoid withdrawal. Careful screening of clients and strict contingency contracting (in which addicts are informed at the outset that they will be withdrawn from the program if their urine tests positive for drugs other than methadone) have been found useful in helping addicts use methadone maintenance as it was intended (Callahan, 1980).

It is interesting to note that the National Academy of Sciences (1990), after reviewing the literature on methadone maintenance programs, states that these programs are able to pay for themselves through reduced criminal activity on the part of the participants. Thus, while there is little evidence to support the theory of Dole and Nyswander's (1965) original theory, the concept of methadone maintenance does seem to have a role to play in the treatment of chronic opiate addiction.

Experimental forms of pharmacological intervention in narcotics addiction Recently, a synthetic narcotic agent developed in the 1960s, *buprenorphine,* has been found to have a potential to actually block the euphoric effects of intraveneously administered narcotics (Horgan, 1989; Rosen & Kosten, 1991). Experimental data suggest that this agent, sold under the brand name Buprenex (Conlan, 1990), binds to the same opiate receptor sites in the brain that are utilized by morphine, providing an analgesic effect. At high dosage levels, it will block the euphoric effects of heroin, although at the same dosage level it might increase the craving for cocaine (Holloway, 1991).

However, when administered orally at low dosage levels, buprenorphine does not bring about a sense of euphoria (Holloway, 1991). Further, it appears to be at least as effective as methadone in blocking the euphoria experienced when a narcotics addict injects an opiate-based drug. Another advantage is that withdrawal from buprenorphine lasts only a few days (Horgan, 1989), whereas the withdrawal from methadone may last up to 2 weeks. Further, withdrawal from buprenorphine does not seem to be as uncomfortable as withdrawal from methadone (Rosen & Kosten, 1991). As we will discuss shortly, there is experimental evidence suggesting that buprenorphine also may block some of the effects of cocaine, in addition to those of narcotics.

However, buprenorphine is not a "magic bullet." Orally administered, it has no euphoric value; *intravenously administered,* it has a significant abuse potential (Horgan, 1989). Thus, while buprenorphine may prove to be a valuable tool in working with narcotic addicts, it is not the ultimate answer to the problem of opiate addiction.

THE PHARMACOLOGICAL TREATMENT OF COCAINE ADDICTION

In recent years, as the mechanism by which cocaine impacts on the brain has become more clear, researchers have attempted to find an agent or agents that will control the "craving" or "hunger" for cocaine that many addicts experience in the early stages of recovery. Two antidepressants—imipramine (Wilbur, 1986) and desipramine hydrochloride (Gawin et al., 1989; Jenike, 1989)—have proven effective in curbing the postwithdrawal craving for cocaine, when used at therapeutic dosage levels.

Unfortunately, there is some debate over whether or not it is safe to use antidepressants to curb postcocaine craving. Decker et al. (1987) state:

> Little attention has been given to the possible cardiac risks of using antidepressants to prevent cocaine intoxication or to treat "crashes" or withdrawal symptoms. (p. 465)

In research conducted by Margolin, Kosten, Petrakis, Avants, and Kosten (1991), the attempt was made to avoid possible cardiac complications through the use of a "second generation antidepressant"—*bupropion*. While this research suggests that bupropion might offer some promise in controlling the craving associated with abstinence from cocaine, it must be noted that the sample population consisted of only 6 subjects. According to Margolin et al., 5 of them completed the experiment, while 1 was dropped for medical reasons. Of these 5 individuals, 4 subjects had stopped the use of cocaine after a period of 4 weeks, and were still cocaine-free after 3 months.

A significant problem with the use of tricyclic antidepressants to control the craving for cocaine is that it typically takes 7 to 14 days for the antidepressant to *begin* to reduce the craving (Gawin, Allen, & Humblestone, 1989). Many addicts are unable or unwilling to tolerate the severe craving that they experience during this period, and so they drop out of treatment.

As a possible solution to this problem, Gawin et al. have experimented with the drug *flupenthixol* as a means to control cocaine craving. Flupenthixol is currently available in Europe, the Far East, and the Caribbean, but not in the United States. This drug would seem to be quite effective in the control of postcocaine craving, according to Gawin et al. They recommend further research into its use in the treatment of cocaine addicts. According to Holloway (1991), some cocaine addicts on flupenthixol report that their craving for cocaine is "manageable but is not eliminated" (p. 100). Thus, while flupenthixol shows some promise, other possible solutions to cocaine craving need to be explored.

Still another drug that has demonstrated some promise in controlling cocaine craving, at least in experimental settings, is *bromocriptine* (sold in the United States under the brand name Parlodel). When administered in a single dose of 1.25 mg, bromocriptine was found to decrease cocaine withdrawal craving, according to DiGregorio (1990), while 0.625 mg taken orally four time a day was found to reduce psychiatric symptoms associated with cocaine withdrawal.

Unfortunately, bromocriptine's side-effects include headaches, sedation, muscle tremor, and dry mouth, which may make the user so uncomfortable as to discontinue use of this drug. Further, the possibility that bromocriptine is itself addictive has been suggested. Holloway (1991) reports that early clinical trials with bromocriptine have failed to yield any positive results, suggesting that this medication will ultimately prove of little value in the treatment of cocaine addiction.

Surprisingly, another agent that may prove valuable in the treatment of cocaine withdrawal craving is buprenorphine. In addition to its effectiveness in laboratory studies with narcotic addicts, buprenorphine has also been shown to have an effect on postcocaine craving (*The Economist*, 1989; Holloway, 1991; Rosen & Kosten, 1991; Youngstrom, 1990a). At low doses, oral buprenorphine seems to reduce the craving for cocaine, although the exact mechanism by which this is accomplished remains unknown (Holloway, 1991; Rosen & Kosten, 1991).

Trachtenberg and Blum (1988) suggest that the effects of cocaine are brought about, at least in part, by activation of both dopamine and opioid peptide neurotransmitter systems. They point out, for example, that naloxone hydrochloride, which is normally used to block the effects of narcotics in the brain, actually potentiates the stimulation and euphoria of cocaine. If this is true, then it would suggest that the reward mechanism for both cocaine and the narcotics seems to involve activation of the same neurotransmission systems. It would also seem to make sense that a drug such as buprenorphine could prove of value in controlling the craving for both narcotics and cocaine.

According to Trachtenberg and Blum (1988), cocaine addiction, as well as alcoholism, may be influenced by the neurochemicals available in the brain. In an extension of the neurotransmitter precursor loading system used in their treatment of alcoholism, they advocate the use of "nutritional neurochemical support" (p. 326) to aid in the treatment of cocaine addiction.

Trachtenberg and Blum advocate the use of a combination of amino acids, selected minerals, and vitamins to stimulate the formation of the neurotransmitters depleted by chronic cocaine use. They refer to a ninefold reduction in dropout rates for patients in an experimental group who received a patented formulation of this "neuronutrient" (p. 315) over those who did not receive it in one research study. This evidence suggests a need to explore this approach more fully to determine whether it might prove of value in the treatment of cocaine withdrawal.

Surprisingly, on the basis of their investigation into the cocaine withdrawal process, Satel et al. (1991) challenge the need for routine pharmacological support of recovering cocaine addicts. They report that their subjects attested to a craving for cocaine following the initiation of abstinence, but that the strength and frequency of this craving decreased markedly over the first three weeks of recovery without pharmacological support. This finding would indicate that pharmacological support may not be necessary for the recovering cocaine addict in all cases.

SUMMARY

The pharmacological treatment of substance abuse involves the use of selected chemicals to aid recovering addicts in their attempt to maintain sobriety. To this end, a number of different chemicals have been investigated as experimental agents in the hope that one or more would prove useful in controlling either the withdrawal symptoms experienced in the early stages of sobriety or in controlling the craving that may last for months, or even years.

Chapter 30

ALCOHOLICS ANONYMOUS AND NARCOTICS ANONYMOUS

THE TWELVE STEPS OF ALCOHOLICS ANONYMOUS

STEP ONE:	*We admitted that we were powerless over alcohol—that our lives had become unmanageable.*
STEP TWO:	*Came to believe that a Power greater than ourselves could restore us to sanity.*
STEP THREE:	*Made a decision to turn our will and our lives over to the care of God* **as we understood Him.**
STEP FOUR:	*Made a searching and fearless moral inventory of ourselves.*
STEP FIVE:	*Admitted to God, to ourselves, and to another human being the exact nature of our wrongs.*
STEP SIX:	*Were entirely ready to have God remove all these defects of character.*
STEP SEVEN:	*Humbly asked Him to remove our shortcomings.*
STEP EIGHT:	*Made a list of all persons we had harmed and became willing to make amends to them all.*
STEP NINE:	*Made direct amends to such people wherever possible, except when to do so would injure them or others.*
STEP TEN:	*Continued to take personal inventory and when we were wrong, promptly admitted it.*
STEP ELEVEN:	*Sought through prayer and meditation to improve our conscious contact with God* **as we understood Him**, *praying only for knowledge of His will for us, and the power to carry that out.*
STEP TWELVE:	*Having had a spiritual awakening as the result of these steps, we tried to carry this message to alcoholics, and to practice these principles in all our affairs.*[1]

Note: The opinions stated in this chapter are those of the author, and not those of Alcoholics Anonymous or Narcotics Anonymous.

[1]The Twelve Steps are reprinted by permission of Alcoholics Anonymous World Services, Inc.

A BRIEF HISTORY OF ALCOHOLICS ANONYMOUS

The diverse factors that played a part in the formation of Alcoholics Anonymous include the American temperance movement of the late 1800s (Peele, 1984; 1989); a nondenominational religious organization known as the Oxford Group, which was popular in the 1930s (Nace, 1987); and the psychoanalysis of an American alcoholic by Carl Jung in the year 1931 (Edmeades, 1987). Over the years, the cofounders of Alcoholics Anonymous were both hospitalized, mistakes were made, questions were asked, and the early pioneers of AA embarked on a struggle for sobriety that transcended individual members.

Historically, AA is thought to have been founded on June 10, 1935, the day an alcoholic physician, Dr. Robert Holbrook Smith, had his last drink (Nace, 1987). But the foundation of AA was set down earlier, during a meeting between Dr. Smith and William Griffith Wilson, an out-of-town stockbroker on a business trip who was struggling to protect his new-found sobriety. After making several telephone calls in an attempt to find support in his struggle, Wilson was asked to talk to Dr. Smith, who was drinking at the time Wilson called. Rather than looking out for his own needs, Wilson chose a different approach. He carried a message of sobriety to another alcoholic.

The self-help philosophy of AA was born in that moment. In the half-century since then, it has grown to a fellowship of 50,000 "clubs," or AA groups, including chapters in 114 countries. Its total membership is estimated at more than a million people (*Alcoholics Anonymous*, 1976; Edmeades, 1987).

During its early years, AA struggled to find a method that would support its members in their struggle to both achieve and maintain sobriety. Within 3 years of its founding, three different AA groups were in existence, but even with three groups "it was hard to find twoscore of sure recoveries" (*Twelve Steps and Twelve Traditions*, 1981, p. 17). Nace (1987) reports that by the fourth year following its inception, there were about 100 members in the isolated AA groups.

The early members wrote of their struggle to achieve sobriety, and published the first edition of the book *Alcoholics Anonymous* in 1939. The organization took its name from the title of the book, *Alcoholics Anonymous* (*Twelve Steps and Twelve Traditions*, 1981), which has since come to be known as the "Big Book" of AA.

ELEMENTS OF ALCOHOLICS ANONYMOUS

Peele (1984) notes that many of the features of AA are "peculiarly American" (p. 1338), including public confession, contrition, and salvation through spirituality. *Twelve Steps and Twelve Traditions* (1981) notes that AA freely borrowed from the fields of medicine and religion to establish a program that worked.

A Breakdown of the Twelve Steps

The book *Al-Anon's Twelve Steps and Twelve Traditions*, which has borrowed the Twelve Steps of AA for use with families, divides the steps into three groups. The first three steps are viewed as necessary for the acceptance of one's limitations. Through these first three steps, the individual is able to come to accept that his or her own resources are not sufficient to solve life's problems, especially the problems inherent in living with an addicted person. In the AA twelve-step program, these steps serve to help the alcoholic accept that his or her resources are insufficient for dealing with the problems of life, especially the problem of addiction.

Steps four through nine are a series of change-oriented activities. These steps are designed to help the individual identify, confront, and ultimately overcome character shortcomings that are so much a part of the addicted life-style. Through these steps, one may work through the guilt associated with past behaviors and learn to recognize the limits of personal responsibility. These steps allow the person to learn the tools of nondrug-centered living, something that at first is often alien to both addicts and their families.

Finally, steps ten through twelve challenge the addict to continue to build on the foundation established in steps four through nine. The individual is asked to continue to search out personal shortcomings and to confront them. The person also is challenged to continue the spiritual growth initiated during the earlier steps, and to carry the message of hope to others.

It has been suggested (Alibrandi, 1978; Peck, 1991) that AA functions as a form of "folk psychotherapy." Alibrandi (1978) suggests that the AA therapy program involves five different phases. The first phase starts on the first day of membership, and lasts for 1 week. During this phase, the addict's goal is simply to stay away from the first drink or chemical use.

The second phase of recovery, according to Alibrandi, starts at the end of the first week, and lasts until the end of the second month of AA membership. In this part of the recovery process, the addict learns to accept the concept of addiction and to "let go and let God." During this phase, the individual struggles to replace old drug-centered behavioral habits with new sobriety-oriented habits.

The third stage of recovery spans the interval from the second through the sixth month of sobriety, according to Alibrandi. During this stage, the individual is to use the Twelve Steps as a guide and to try and let go of old ideas. Guilt feelings about past chemical use are to be replaced with gratitude for sobriety, and the member is to stand available for service to other addicts.

The fourth stage begins at around the sixth month of sobriety and lasts until the first year of sobriety has been reached. During the fourth stage, the addict is encouraged to take a searching and fearless moral inventory of "self," and to share this with another person. At the same time, if the addict is still "shaky," he or she is encouraged to work with another addict. Emphasis during this phase of recovery is on accepting responsibility and resolving the anger and resentments on which addiction is so often based.

Finally, after the first year of sobriety, the recovery process has reached what S. Brown (1985) terms "ongoing sobriety." Alibrandi (1978) identifies the goal during this phase of recovery as the maintenance of a "spiritual condition." The person is warned not to dwell on the shortcomings of others, to suspend judgment of self and others, and to beware of the false pride that could lead to a return to chemical use.

In speaking of the process of spiritual growth, which is a central component of the AA program, Dyer (1989) states:

> Once you start to make the transformational awakening journey, there is no going back. You develop a knowledge that is so powerful that you will wonder how you could have lived any other way. The awakened life begins to own you, and then you simply know within that you are on the right path. (p. 17)

Although Dr. Dyer was not speaking directly of the Twelve Steps, his description of spiritual growth would seem to fit the goal of the founders of AA. Alcoholics Anonymous appears to offer its members a program for living that moves them toward lifelong behavioral change. There are those who believe that a personality transformation is possible through the Twelve Steps. Others view them as a series of successive approximations toward the goal of sobriety. While the steps are not required for AA membership, they are a proven method of behavioral change that offers addicts a change to rebuild their lives. There are many who believe that these steps have been instrumental in saving their lives.

ALCOHOLICS ANONYMOUS AND RELIGION

Alcoholics Anonymous distinguishes between spirituality and religion (Berenson, 1987). It identifies with no single religious group or religious doctrine, but rather is a spiritual recovery program.

Jensen (1987b) notes that Step Three "doesn't demand an immediate conversion experience . . . but . . . does call for a decision" (p. 22). This decision is for addicts to make a conscious decision to turn their will over to their God. In addressing the issue of religion, Jensen notes that "Step Three simply assumes that there is a God to understand and that we each have a God of our own understanding" (p. 23).

In this manner, AA sidesteps the question of religion while still addressing the spiritual disease that it views as existing within addiction. In turning one's will over to a higher power, the addict comes to accept that his or her own will is not enough to maintain sobriety. Thus, AA offers a spiritual program that ties the individual's will to that of a higher power without offering a specific religious dogma.

ONE "A" IS FOR ANONYMOUS

Anonymity is central to both the AA and the NA programs (*Understanding Anonymity*, 1981). This is a major reason why most meetings are "closed."

During a closed meeting, which is limited only to members, discussion will center on "personal problems or interpretations of the Twelve Steps or the Twelve Traditions" (Lewis et al., 1988, p. 151). In open meetings, one or two volunteers will speak to the audience, and visitors are encouraged to ask questions about AA and how it works.

The anonymity that is central to AA both protects the identities of members and ensures that no identified spokesperson emerges as a representative for AA (*Understanding Anonymity*, 1981). Through this policy, the members of AA strive for humility, each knowing that he or she is equal to the other members. The concept of anonymity is so important that it has been described as "the spiritual foundation of the Fellowship" (*Understanding Anonymity*, 1981, p. 5).

The concept of the equality of its members underlies the AA tradition that no "directors" are nominated or voted upon. Rather, "service boards" or special committees are created from the membership, as needed. These boards always remain responsible to the group *as a whole*, and must answer to the entire AA or NA membership. As is noted in Tradition Two of AA: "Our leaders are but trusted servants; they do not govern" (*Twelve Steps and Twelve Traditions*, 1981, p. 10).

ALCOHOLICS ANONYMOUS AND OUTSIDE ORGANIZATIONS

The AA organization is both self-supporting and not-for-profit. Each individual group is autonomous and must rely on the contributions of its members to support itself. Outside donations are discouraged to avoid the problem of having to decide how to deal with them. Outside commitments are also discouraged for AA group members. As stated in *Twelve Steps and Twelve Traditions* (1981), AA groups will not

> endorse, finance, or lend the A.A. name to any related facility or outside enterprise, lest problems of money, property and prestige divert us from our primary purpose. (p. 11)

Relations between the various autonomous AA groups and between these groups and other organizations are governed by the Twelve Traditions of AA. The Traditions provide guidelines for interaction between groups and for the work of AA as a whole. The Twelve Traditions will not be reviewed in this chapter, but interested readers may wish to read *Twelve Steps and Twelve Traditions* (1981) to learn more about them.

THE PRIMARY PURPOSE OF ALCOHOLICS ANONYMOUS

This "primary purpose" of AA is twofold. First, the members strive to "carry the message to the addict who still suffers" (*The Group*, 1976, p. 1). Secondly, AA seeks to provide its members with a program for living without chemicals.

This is not done by preaching, but rather by presenting a simple, truthful, realistic picture of the disease of addiction.

To accomplish this twofold purpose, it is necessary to confront addicts with the facts of their addiction, in plain language that they can understand. The manner in which this is carried out differs somewhat from the usual methods of confrontation. In AA, speakers share their own life stories—a public confession of sorts. Each individual tells of the lies, distortions, self-deceptions, and denial that supported his or her chemical use. In so doing, the speaker hopes to break through the defensiveness of the addict by showing that others have walked the same road, yet found a way to sobriety. Thus, helping others is a central theme of AA:

> Even the newest of newcomers finds undreamed rewards as he tries to help his brother alcoholic, the one who is even blinder than he. . . . And then he discovers that by the divine paradox of this kind of giving he has found his own reward, whether his brother has yet received anything or not. (*Twelve Steps and Twelve Traditions*, 1981, p. 109)

Yet, here we find a therapeutic paradox. In helping others, speakers seek first of all to help themselves through the public admission of their powerlessness over chemicals. Through the public admission of weakness, speakers seek to gain strength. By owning the reality of their own addiction, they are saying, "This is what *my* life was like, and by having shared it with you I am reminded again of the reason why I will never return to drugs."

This process reflects the methods pioneered by Bill Wilson in his first meeting with Bob Smith. In that meeting, Wilson spoke at length of his own addiction to alcohol—of his own pain and suffering and the pain he had caused others in the service of his addiction. He did not preach, but simply shared with Dr. Smith the history of his own alcoholism. Wilson concluded with the statement: "So thanks a lot for hearing me out. I know now that I'm not going to take a drink, and I'm grateful to you" (Kurtz, 1979, p. 29).

Earlier, it was noted that the methods of AA present a paradox: By helping others the speaker comes to receive help for his or her own addiction. In effect, the speaker is saying to the new member, "I am a mirror of yourself, and just as you cannot look into a mirror without seeing your own image, you can not look at me without seeing yourself.") In this way, the speaker seeks to cary the message to others.

As we have mentioned, AA is a spiritual program, but one that is not religious. According to McCrady and Irvine (1989), AA defines drinking as a symptom of spiritual illness:

> The central spiritual "defect" of alcoholics is described as an excessive preoccupation with self. . . . Treatment of the preoccupation with self is at the core of A.A.'s approach. (p. 153)

In place of the disease of the spirit on which addiction rests, AA offers a program for living. Lewis et al. (1988) point out that the Twelve Steps are usually introduced with the words: "Here are the steps we took, which are suggested as a program for recovery" (p. 149).

We have noted that individuals are not required to follow the Twelve Steps to participate in AA. Jensen (1987a) observes that *"the program* does not issue orders: it merely *suggests* Twelve Steps to recovery" (p. 15). Thus, the individual is offered a choice between the way of life that preceded AA or acceptance of a program used by others to achieve and maintain their sobriety.

The Twelve Steps offer the promise and the tools necessary for daily sobriety. But, it is up to the individual to put the tools to use. Members are not encouraged to look for the "cause" of their addiction; rather, their addiction is accepted as a given: "It is not so much *how* you came to this place, as what you are going to do now that you are here," as one member said to a newcomer.

Neither is the member admonished for being unable to live without chemicals. Members of AA know from bitter experience that relapse is possible and common (McCrady & Irvine, 1989). Chemical addiction is assumed in membership: "If chemicals were not a problem for you, you wouldn't be here!" In place of the drug-centered way of life, the new member is offered a step-by-step program for living that enables addicts to achieve and maintain sobriety.

To take advantage of this program, the member need only accept *the program*. Admittedly, in so doing, the individual is asked to accept yet another therapeutic paradox—that of Step One. Step One asks that addicts first of all accept that they are powerless over chemicals. They are asked to do so not on the most superficial of levels necessary to speak the words "I am powerless over chemicals," but on the deepest levels of their beings.

Many addicts have found that conformity, at least to the point of saying the phrase "I am addicted to chemicals" is enough to help them escape the consequences of their addiction. But it is easy to say the words, even if one does not believe them to be true. To accept *the program*, addicts must look within themselves and totally accept that they are *addicted* to chemicals and *totally powerless* over them.

William Springborn (1987) describes how he reacts when he confronts the rationalization that chemicals alone are the bane of addicts and that addicts are helpless victims. He emphasizes that

> it is we ourselves, not the pills or alcohol, who cause most of our problems. Chemicals will not bring destruction upon a person until that person learns how to justify continual use and abuse of those chemicals. (p. 8)

When addicts accept the painful, bitter, frightening reality that their lives are no longer their own but are spent in the service of their addiction, and when they come to understand that there is *nothing* that they can do that will allow them to control their chemical use, they have "hit bottom." It is at this point that they are able to turn to another person, and say, "My way does not work for me. I need help." At this moment, they are taking the first step (the ultimate admission of powerlessness) and opening themselves up to try new ways of dealing with their addiction, other than using drugs.

OF AA AND RECOVERY

Alcoholics Anonymous does not speak of a "cure" for the disease of alcoholism. The members of AA do not speak of themselves as having "recovered." Although they believe that addiction is a disease whose progress can be arrested, they acknowledge that alcoholism can never be cured. Thus, they speak of themselves as *recovering* alcoholics, not as having *recovered.*

Members of AA recognize that a recovering addict is only a moment away from the next "slip." Even the 25-year veteran may relapse in a weak moment. No matter how strong the motivation to remain sober, recovering alcoholics can only strive to be sober for a day at a time. If "today" is too long a period to consider, the addict is encouraged to think about saying sober for the next hour, or the next minute, or just the next second.

Jensen (1987a) states:

> We may not have freely chosen to go to A.A. or perhaps treatment. We may have been pressured by an employer, a spouse, or other family members, a medical doctor, or even a court. We may not have a sincere desire to quit drinking or using and are proceeding with *the program* only because it appears to be better than the consequences of not complying. (p. 24)

But once addicts accept *the program*, they find a way of living that provides support 24 hours a day for the rest of their lives. In accepting the program, they may discover the second chance that they thought was forever lost.

SPONSORSHIP OF ALCOHOLICS ANONYMOUS

To help new members embark on the spiritual odyssey that will result in their sobriety, they are encouraged to find a "sponsor." Sponsors have worked their way through the twelve-step program and have achieved a basic understanding of their own addiction. The sponsor acts as a spiritual guide, confronting the new member and also offering insight and support.

It is the duty of the sponsor to take an interest in the newcomer's progress, but *not to take responsibility for it* (Alibrandi, 1978; McCrady & Irvine, 1989). The responsibility for recovery is placed on the individual. Thus, the sponsor gives the message, "I can be concerned for you, but I am not responsible for you." In today's terminology, the sponsor is a living example of "tough love." Peck (1991) views the sponsor's role as similar to that of a psychotherapist.

The sponsor should not try to control the newcomer's life, and ideally should recognize the newcomer's limitations. Many of the characteristics of the healthy human-services professional identified by Rogers (1961) apply to the AA sponsor as well. The sponsor, acting as an extension of AA, is a means to achieve sobriety. But it is up to the newcomer to use this means. The newcomer must assume the responsibility for reaching out and taking advantage of the tools that are offered.

Sponsorship is essentially an expression of the second mission of AA—that of carrying the message to other addicts who are still actively using chemicals. This is a reflection of Step Twelve, and one will often hear the sponsor speak of having participated in a twelfth-step visit or of having been involved in twelfth-step work. In a sense, the sponsor is a guide, friend, peer-counselor, fellow traveler, conscience, and devil's advocate, all rolled into one.

ALCOHOLICS ANONYMOUS AND PSYCHOLOGICAL THEORY

M. Scott Peck (1991) advance the theory that AA offers a form of folk psychotherapy. However, AA and NA twelve-step programs are different from other therapeutic programs that the addict may have been exposed to. The Twelve Steps are "reports of action taken rather than rules not to be broken" (Alibrandi, 1978, p. 166). Each step, then, is a public (or private) demonstration of action taken in the struggle to achieve and maintain sobriety, rather than a rule that might be broken.

S. Brown (1985) speaks of another purpose the AA Twelve Steps serve. They keep recovering addicts focused on their addiction. Alcohol was the "axis" on which the addict's life revolved while drinking; through the Twelve Steps, the addict continues to center his or her life around alcohol, but in a different way—a way without chemicals.

WHAT MAKES ALCOHOLICS ANONYMOUS EFFECTIVE?

Charles Bufe (1988) offers three reasons why AA is effective "at least for some people" (p. 55). First of all, AA is a social outlet for its members. "Loneliness," Bufe observes, "is a terrible problem in our society, and people will flock to almost *anything* that relieves it—even AA meetings" (p. 55).

Secondly, Bufe suggests that AA shows its members that their problems are not unique. This point is also noted by Alibrandi (1978). Nace (1987) notes that through AA participation, the individual member is able to restore identity and self-esteem through the unconditional acceptance of the group. Each member of AA has walked the same roads and experienced the same trials. Thus, each member feels a kinship with the others.

Finally, according to Bufe, AA offers a proven path to follow. Such a path has great appeal "when your world has turned upside down and you no longer have your best friend—alcohol—to lean on" (p. 55).

Herman (1988) states that twelve-step programs such as AA offer at least one more feature to the recovering addict—predictability. Consistency is one of the characteristics identified by Rogers (1961) as being of value in the helping relationship, and one must wonder if the predictability of AA is not one of the curative forces of this self-help group. However, research in this area is lacking, and this remains only a hypothesis.

According to Berenson (1987), the AA twelve-step program provides a format for "a planned spontaneous remission . . . designed so that a person can stop drinking by either education, therapeutic change, or transformation" (p. 30). As part of the therapeutic transformation inherent in AA participation, Berenson also speculates that people will "bond to the group and use it as a social support and as a refuge to explore and release their suppressed and repressed feelings" (p. 30).

Alcoholics Anonymous meetings, as noted by Nace (1987) "are generally characterized by warmth, openness, honesty, and humor" (p. 242). As such, they may promote personal growth. For active alcoholics, AA is thought to be "the treatment of choice" (Berenson, 1987), yet there has been surprisingly little research into what factors make AA so effective, or what types of people might benefit from it the most (Galanter, Castaneda, & Franco, 1991; Ogborne & Glaser, 1985).

Outcome Studies on the Effectiveness of Alcoholics Anonymous

Although AA is viewed by many treatment professionals as the single most important component of an addict's recovery program, others are more cautious in their appraisal (Ogborne & Glaser, 1985). For example, Lewis et al. (1988) warn that AA "should be used only as a supportive adjunct to treatment" (p. 151), and not considered as "treatment" by itself. Questions have even been raised as to whether AA is needed at all (Peele, 1989; Peele et al., 1991). However, even its critics seem to accept the fact that AA may be helpful to some people who have a problem with chemicals (Ogborne & Glaser, 1985).

It has been pointed out that those people who join AA and who remain members are not a representative sample of alcoholics (Galanter et al., 1991). The very fact that these people have elected to join and remain in AA of their own free will distinguishes them from those alcoholics who choose not to join AA and from those who join, but do not remain as active members.[2]

According to the National Institute on Alcohol Abuse and Alcoholism (1989),

> there is evidence that approximately 90 percent of alcoholics are likely to experience at least one relapse over the 4-year period following treatment. (p. 1)

Are these statistics true for the AA membership as well? Although the data are not as clear as those of the National Institute on Alcohol Abuse and Alcoholism, they do suggest that membership in AA is not a guarantee of sobriety. For example, Alibrandi (1978) reports that at least half of the newcomers to AA relapse during their first year of membership. Nace (1987) reports that 70% of those who stay sober for one year will be sober at the end of their second year and that 90% of those who are sober at the end of their

[2]Yet, as the reader will recall, it was upon data obtained from members of AA that Jellinek (1960) based his model of alcoholism.

second year will still be sober at the end of their third year. While these figures do not refer to the percentage of those who relapse, they do suggest that a significant percentage of those who join AA do relapse within the first 3 years.

Only a limited number of research studies have attempted to measure the effectiveness of AA (McCrady & Irvine, 1989). Indeed, although there is a need for further research, it would appear that AA may not be effective for some people with alcohol problems (Ogborne & Glaser, 1985). Further, it would appear that AA is most effective with a subset of problem drinkers—socially stable white males over 40 years of age, who are physically dependent on alcohol and prone to guilt, and who are the first born or only child. However the evidence supporting the discriminatory power of these character-istics was found to be quite weak, and thus they should not be relied on to predict successful AA membership, according to Ogborne and Glaser.

Alcoholics Anonymous certainly does *not* seem to be effective with those who are coerced into attending meetings by the courts (Glaser & Ogborne, 1982; Peele, 1989; Peele et al., 1991). Indeed, individuals who are sen-tenced to jail or placed on probation for driving while intoxicated have better subsequent driving records (fewer accidents or further arrests) than those "sentenced" to treatment in which AA often plays a part (Peele, 1989; Peele et al., 1991).

Peele (1989) is quite critical of AA as it exists today, partly on the grounds that current AA philosophy has been accepted as established fact in the absence of confirming evidence. As support for this criticism, he cites the fallacy that alcoholism will *always* grow worse without treatment and that individuals cannot cut back or quit drinking on their own. Indeed, research has shown that alcoholics follow the downward spiral thought to be inescap-able by AA only infrequently. Moreover, they often control or discontinue drinking without formal intervention (Peele, 1989; Vaillant, 1983).

It has been suggested that the issue of whether or not AA is effective is far too complex to be measured by a single research study (Glaser & Ogborne, 1982). There is a need for a series of well-controlled research studies to identify all the variables that might influence the outcome of AA participation (McCrady & Irvine, 1989). Thus, the question of the effectiveness of AA has yet to be settled.

It could be argued that the very nature of the question, Is AA effective? makes it unanswerable. Would the chronic alcoholic who stopped continual drinking as a result of participation in AA, but who then entered into a pattern of binge drinking with month-long periods of sobriety in between be measured as a successful outcome? Would the chronic alcoholic who entered AA and stopped drinking, but who died 6 weeks later as a result of the effects of many years of chronic alcohol use be measured as an unsuccessful outcome?

The thrust of Ogborne and Glaser's (1985) work is that the simplistic question of whether AA is effective is unlikely to generate a meaningful answer. Rather, to better understand the strengths of AA, one must consider which factors make it effective for a particular subgroup of people.

NARCOTICS ANONYMOUS

In 1953, another self-help group patterned after AA was founded—a group that goes by the name of Narcotics Anonymous (NA). Although this group honors its debt to AA, its members state:

> We follow the same path with only a single exception. Our identification as addicts is all-inclusive in respect to any mood-changing, mind-altering substance. "Alcoholism" is too limited a term for us; our problem is not a specific substance, it is a disease called "addiction" (*Narcotics Anonymous*, 1982, p. x).

The major differences between AA and NA seems to be one of scope. Whereas AA addresses only alcoholism, NA addresses addiction to a wide range of chemicals. The growth of NA has been phenomenal, with a 600% increase in the number of NA groups from 1983 through 1988 (Coleman, 1989). Currently, more than 14,000 NA meetings are held in the United States each week, according to Coleman.

Although AA and NA are not affiliated with each other, there is an element of cooperation between them. Both follow essentially the same twelve-step program that offers the addict a day-by-day program for recovery. The question arises: Which group works best for the individual? Some people feel quite comfortable going to AA for their addiction to alcohol. Others feel that NA offers them what they need to deal with their addiction, be it to alcohol or other drugs. In the final analysis, the name of the group does not matter so much as the fact that it offers the support and understanding the recovering addict needs to remain sober for today.

AL-ANON AND ALATEEN

The book *Al-Anon's Twelve Steps and Twelve Traditions* provides a short history of Al-Anon in its introduction. According to this history, while their husbands were at the early AA meetings, the wives would often meet. As they waited for their husbands, they would often talk over their problems. At some point, they decided to try to apply the same twelve steps that their husbands had found so helpful to their own lives. Thus, Al-Anon was born.

At first, each isolated group changed whatever it felt was necessary in the Twelve Steps. However, by 1948 the wife of one of the cofounders of AA became involved in the growing organization, and in time a uniform family support program emerged. This program, known as the Al-Anon Family Group, modified the AA Twelve Steps and Twelve Traditions according to the needs of families of alcoholics.

By 1957, in response to the recognition that teenagers presented special needs and concerns, Al-Anon itself gave birth to a modified Al-Anon group for teens known as Alateen. Alateen members follow the same twelve steps outlined in the Al-Anon program. The goal of the Alateen program, however, is to provide the opportunity for teenagers to come together to share experiences, discuss problems, and learn how to cope more effectively with their various concerns, and provide encouragement to each other (*Facts about Alateen*, 1969).

Through Alateen, teenagers learn that alcoholism is a disease. They are helped to detach emotionally from the alcoholic's behavior, at the same time still loving the individual. The goal of Alateen is also to help teenagers learn that they did not "cause" the alcoholic to drink, and to see that they can build a rewarding life despite the alcoholic's continued drinking (*Facts about Alateen*, 1969).

SUMMARY

The self-help group Alcoholics Anonymous has emerged as one of the predominant forces in the field of drug-abuse treatment. Drawing on the experience and knowledge of its members, AA has developed a program for living that is spiritual without being religious and confrontational without using confrontation in the traditional sense. Alcoholics Anonymous relies on no outside support and is believed by many to be effective in helping addicts stay sober on a daily basis.

The program for living established by AA is based on those factors that early members believed were important to their own sobriety. This program for living is known as the Twelve Steps. These steps are suggested as a guide to new members. Because the equality of all members is considered fundamental, there is no board of directors within the AA group.

Questions have emerged as to whether or not AA is effective. Researchers agree that it seems to be effective for some people, but not for all of those who join. The question of how to measure the effectiveness of AA is quite complex. A series of well-designed research studies to identify the multitude of factors that make AA effective for certain subpopulations is required.

Despite limited research regarding the effectiveness of AA, it has served as a model for many other self-help groups, including Narcotics Anonymous. Narcotics Anonymous holds that the alcohol focus of AA is too narrow for those who have become addicted to other chemicals, either alone or in combination with alcohol. Narcotics Anonymous expounds the belief that addiction is a common disease that may express itself through many different forms of drug dependency. Its twelve-step program is based on the Twelve Steps offered by AA, and it draws heavily from the AA philosophy.

Other self-help groups that have emerged as a result of the AA experience include Al-Anon and Alateen. Al-Anon emerged from informal encounters between the spouses of early AA members. It strives to provide an avenue for helping the families of those who are addicted to alcohol. Alateen emerged from Al-Anon, in response to the recognition that adolescents have special needs. Both groups strive to help their members be supportive without being dependent on the alcoholic and to detach from the alcoholic and his or her behavior.

Chapter 31

Drugs and Crime

Much has been written about the complex relationship between chemical abuse and crime. Substance abuse is one of the factors associated with violent crime (Lewis, 1989), and fully a quarter of property crime, such as car theft and burglary, is also thought to be connected with chemical use (National Academy of Sciences, 1990). But, is crime a natural consequence of substance abuse? Do these two social problems go hand in hand, or are they entirely separate? The answer to these questions is a matter of considerable debate.

PROBLEMS ASSOCIATED WITH THE STUDY OF DRUG USE AND CRIMINAL ACTIVITY

As we have noted, the possible relationship between drug use and criminal activity is extremely complex. One factor that complicates research in this area is the tendency for those who are arrested for criminal activity to attribute their crime to their use of drugs. These offenders hope that such a claim will reduce the severity of their sentence.

Thus, alcohol or substance abuse is often used as an excuse for socially unacceptable behavior. As Newland (1989) points out,

> [the crimes] we commit, under the influence, are the only crimes we can generally elude punishment for by utilizing an escape into the recovery process established by our medical society. (p. 18)

It is not unusual for prosecutors and defense lawyers to negotiate a reduced sentence based on the claim that the defendant abuses chemicals (M. Graham, 1989). While drug use in itself is not an excuse for criminal behavior, extreme drug use often derails the legal system, which is unable to address the issue of whether or not the individual actually *intended* to commit a crime while under the influence of chemicals. Indeed, it is for this reason that "as of 1986, 15 states had . . . created a 'diminished capacity' defense as a legal way station between innocence and full criminal responsibility" for cases in which alcohol or drugs were involved (M. Graham, 1989, p. 21).

Although it is not uncommon for individuals who are facing possible prosecution for criminal behavior to try to escape full responsibility by claiming to have been under the influence of chemicals, this does not necessarily mean that they are addicted to chemicals, or even that they were actually under the influence of drugs at the time the crime was committed. They merely have claimed to have a substance abuse problem, which may or may not be the case.

One must view the criminal's claims to have been under the influence of chemicals at the time that the crime was committed with some degree of skepticism. Law-enforcement officials often do not have the opportunity to test individuals for the use of alcohol or drugs at the time of the crime. Many people are arrested for crimes committed hours, days, or even weeks earlier. By then, any traces of the drug supposedly used at the time of the crime have been eliminated from the body. In such cases, it is not possible to obtain objective data as to whether the individual had indeed used chemicals prior to committing the crime.

A second problem in exploring the relationship between chemical use and crime is that many researchers assume that virtually *any* crime committed under the influence of drugs is drug-related. In Western culture, it is generally assumed that, if a crime is committed under the influence of chemicals, the *drugs* were responsible for the criminal's behavior. As the National Commission on Marihuana and Drug Abuse (1973) states:

> Perceived correlation between the use of a drug and the unwanted consequences is attributed to the drug, removing the individual from any and all responsibility. (p. 4)

Peele (1989) suggests that this is an extension of the "demon rum" philosophy of the late 1800s. It was felt that once a person had ingested even one drink, the alcohol totally overwhelmed his or her self-control, making the person unable to control his or her behavior. The modern version of this belief holds that responsibility for crimes committed by those under the influence of chemicals is attributable not to the person, but to the drug. The individual's role in the commission of the crime is not considered. Rather, he or she is viewed as a helpless victim of circumstance; that is, a victim of the drug's effects. Unfortunately, the relationship between chemical use and criminal activity is not that simple. In the eyes of the law, the individual remains responsible for his or her behavior, even when he or she is intoxicated by chemicals.

Even though there is a statistical relationship between drug use and crime, it must be kept in mind that statistical relationships do *not* imply causality—a concept that college statistics instructors struggle to help their students understand. Criminal activity and substance abuse are independent but overlapping problems. Not all criminal activity is carried out under the influence of drugs or in their service. And not all drug users commit crimes (except in the sense that the use of illicit drugs does constitute breaking the law).

Thus, in exploring the meaning of the statistical relationship between drug use and criminal activity, the following possibility must be taken into account:

> Some users commit crimes more frequently than non-users not because they use . . . but because they happen to be the kinds of people who would be expected to have a higher crime rate. (*National Commission on Marihuana and Drug Abuse.* 1972, p. 77)

That is to say that those individuals who are predisposed to crime also seem to be attracted to the use of alcohol and drugs (Peele, 1989; Ray & Ksir, 1987). According to this line of reasoning, drugs do not so much *cause* criminal activity as attract those who are predisposed to commit crimes. The fact that the crimes are now being committed to support a drug addiction only serves to obscure the fact that these same individuals tend to commit crimes *before* their addiction develops. For example, more than half of the heroin addicts in the United States have a legal history *prior to their first use of narcotics* (Jaffe, 1989).

The relationship between chemical use and crime involves numerous factors. For example, cultural factors may favor or inhibit an individual's decision to turn to criminal activity. Socioeconomic factors also may play a role in whether or not an individual is drawn to criminal activity. One socioeconomic factor that seems to relate to a tendency toward both criminal acts and chemical use is membership in a gang (which itself is a result of a number of interacting factors).

As we discussed in Chapter 4, alcohol is frequently involved in such antisocial acts as rape and murder. Does the alcohol *cause* one individual to rape or murder another? Or, as it has been suggested, does alcohol attract those individuals who are predisposed to commit antisocial acts? There is no simple answer to these questions.

Such drugs as PCP, cocaine, steroids, and the amphetamines have been documented to be linked to violent acts. But it is difficult to say that these substances cause the violence. It is equally difficult to ignore the relationship between substance abuse and criminal activity. Consider this hypothetical example: A 27-year-old male is arrested for the stabbing death of his girlfriend, with whom he had been living. At the time of his arrest, he claimed to have been using cocaine for several days and that he had not known what he was doing at the time of the assault.

Urine toxicology screening confirmed that the suspect had been using cocaine. However, he had been arrested twice in the past 4 years for domestic assault, without evidence of alcohol or drug use being presented at the time of these earlier arrests. He had been arrested once for an assault that took place in a "bar fight," during which he attempted to stab another individual. Several years prior to the fatal attack on his girlfriend, while he was a juvenile, he had also been arrested for having participated in a gang fight, in which he used a baseball bat as a weapon.

The question that must be answered at this time is, *What role did the suspect's cocaine use play in the fatal assault?* There are several ways of looking at this. First, one could build a case for the suspect being prone to aggressive behaviors. The girlfriend's death was a consequence of his violent tendencies. After all, the suspect had a history of violent behaviors that predated his attack on his girlfriend.

A second viewpoint is that this individual did indeed have violent tendencies, but that his drug use contributed to the fatal stabbing by interfering with his self-control. That is, the suspect may not have gone to the extreme of stabbing his girlfriend had he not been using cocaine. (This is not to say, however, that he would not have harmed her in other ways even if he had not been using cocaine.)

It is also possible that the suspect became physically aggressive as a result of having used cocaine, and ultimately killed his girlfriend. This possibility would be a direct outcome of cocaine's known effects on the user. (See Chapter 8 for more information on this aspect of cocaine use.)

Such determinations are not easily achieved. The whole issue of criminal responsibility is quite complex. When the suspect has been using chemicals, and that chemical use may having a bearing on the case, it becomes *extremely* complex (M. Graham, 1989). Ultimately, the determination of whether the substance use was (a) causal, (b) one of a number of factors associated with the crime, or (c) totally unrelated to the crime must be made on a case-by-case basis.

THE DRUG UNDERWORLD AND CRIME

With the exception of alcohol and tobacco, the drugs of abuse are not sold in a "free-market" economy. Rather, because these substances are illegal, their production, distribution, and sale are carried out through illegal channels. In a very real sense, the drugs of abuse are sold through a monopoly that controls the cost of the product being sold.

Addicts must find some way to obtain the money to buy their drugs at the inflated prices at which they are sold. All too often, they will do so through criminal acts. Addicts have been known to rob, burglarize, or prostitute themselves to obtain the money that they need to support their habit. Engaging in drug sales (itself a criminal act) to support one's own addiction is also not uncommon.

It has been estimated that the typical heroin addict in an average city would have to steal some $200,000 worth of goods annually in order to support his or her drug habit (Thomason & Dilts, 1991). Such criminal activity forms a backdrop against which life in a major city goes on. For example, it was reported in the *Chicago Sun-Times* (1989) that 254 youths in Dade County, Florida, had committed an average of 880 crimes *each* in the preceding year. Thus, these 254 youths were responsible for a total of approximately 223,000 crimes, most of which were committed to support their addiction to crack cocaine.

Drug use or criminal activity. Which came first? There are those who argue that it is not drugs that bring about criminal activity, but rather legal sanctions against drugs. Legal sanctions, they contend, help to create a drug "underworld," which in turn leads to a high crime rate (Nadelmann, 1989).

Proponents of this position argue that crime is not a natural consequence of drug use or abuse. Rather, it is the attempt to control access to and distribution of chemicals through the legal justice system that breeds criminal behaviors. The criminal activities of the pre-Prohibition era need only be contrasted with the criminal activities of the Prohibition era to prove this point.[1]

Indeed, in discussing the relationship between narcotics abuse and crime, Jaffe (1989) states:

> The association between opioid use and crime emerges primarily in countries such as the United States, that have tried to restrict the use of opioids to legitimate medical indications, but have been unable to eliminate illicit opioid traffic. (p. 656)

The attempt to control recreational drug use through the criminal justice system rests on the efforts of law-enforcement officials to interdict supplies of illicit chemicals and on the criminal prosecution of individuals proven to be in possession of illegal drugs. However, it has been suggested that many of the evils related to recreational chemical use, such as criminal activities, are actually a *byproduct* of efforts to control that drug use through the criminal justice system (Nadelmann, 1989; Nadelmann et al., 1990).

Further, there is some question as to whether the efforts of law enforcement agencies to interdict the flow of illegal chemicals has really been very effective. For example, the theory has even been advanced that the interdiction efforts against marijuana may have contributed to the switch from marijuana to cocaine by international drug dealers. Cocaine is "less bulky, less smelly, more compact, and more lucrative" to smuggle than marijuana (Nadelman et al., 1990). If this theory is true, then the efforts of law-enforcement officials to deal with the marijuana problem through interdiction may have contributed to the later growth of cocaine abuse in the United States.

DRUG USE AND VIOLENCE: THE UNSEEN CONNECTION

The drug user is vulnerable for a number of reasons. Drug pushers have been known to attack customers simply to steal their money, or in retaliation for unpaid drug debts. Indeed, addicts who fail to pay drug debts on time are often murdered. Goldstein (1990) concludes that 18% of all the homicides committed in the state of New York in 1986 were the result of drug-related debts. Further, there are those who prey on known addicts, armed with the knowledge that the addicts will be unlikely to report a robbery to the police. Those who engage in illegal acts avoid the police as much as possible, even to the extent of not reporting having been victimized by other criminals.

[1]During Prohibition, for example, the Chicago gang leader Al "Scarface" Capone made most of his money through gambling and prostitution operations, rather than through illegal alcohol sales, according to Shenkman (1991).

On occasion, drug pushers themselves are shot, then dropped in front of a hospital emergency room, or they are simply left to die where they fall. Sometimes, these crimes are committed by other drug pushers in order to scare off competition over "territory." On other occasions, the murder is carried out by others associated with the drug trade because of unpaid drug debts, or for other drug-related reasons.

Obviously, there is a relationship between addiction and violence. In a study conducted in St. Louis, 35% of the addicts reported having been shot or stabbed at some point during their drug-using careers (Jaffe, 1990). It has been speculated that one in every five homicide victims in the United States may have been using cocaine shortly before being killed (Bays, 1990). Although estimates of the risk of death for a narcotics addict vary, urban narcotics addicts are reported to have a death rate of approximately 1% per year. The leading causes of death for narcotics addicts are thought to be suicide, homicide, accidents, and disease (Jenike, 1989; Mirin et al., 1991; Schuckit, 1989). Heyward and Curran (1988) report that AIDS is now the leading cause of death in intravenous drug users.

Jaffe (1989) suggests that the death rate from all causes—illness, accidents, suicide, and interpersonal violence—may be as high as 1% to 1.5% per year for narcotics addicts. The mortality figures associated with other forms of substance abuse have not been calculated. Although substance abuse is a known factor in suicide and homicide, the exact number of victims attributed to each form of drug of abuse has not been computed.

Substance Abuse and Sexual Crimes

At first glance, there *does* appear to be a strong relationship between chemical use and sexual abuse (rape, child molestation, and so forth). However, as Finkelhor (1986) points out, the relationship between alcohol use and sexual assault is quite complex:

> Alcohol plays a role in the commission of offenses by some groups of sex abusers. Alcohol may act as a direct physiologic disinhibitor or it may have some social meaning that allows a person to disregard the taboos against child molestation. (pp. 115–116)

According to Finkelhor, between 30% and 40% of cases involving some form of sexual assault are alcohol-related. The role of the alcohol differs from one abuser to another, however. For one individual, the alcohol disinhibition effect may play a role in the sexual assault; for another, alcohol may serve as an antianxiety agent to steady the attacker's nerves *after* the decision is made to carry out the assault.

UNSEEN VICTIMS OF STREET-DRUG CHEMISTRY

Product integrity is hardly a hallmark of today's clandestine, illegal drug laboratories. But even during the Prohibition era, the "bathtub gin" or "homebrew" sometimes included a form of alcohol that could blind people, or even kill them. Indeed, it is estimated by Nadelmann et al. (1990) that "tens of thousands" became blind or died from illicitly produced alcohol during Prohibition. This was one reason why smuggling alcohol was so popular during Prohibition. People could be sure that a legitimate alcoholic beverage would not blind or kill them.

Simple mistakes in the production of drugs in an illegal laboratory can produce lethal chemical combinations. As would often happen with alcohol during the Prohibition era, contaminated or impure drugs are simply sold on the streets today (Gallagher, 1986; Kirsch, 1986). Shafer (1985) explored the impact of many of these "mistakes" that were sold on California streets in the late 1970s under the guise of "new heroin." They are reported to have included chemical impurities capable of literally "burning out" parts of the brain. Some addicts developed a drug-induced Parkinson's disease after having used a drug sold as "synthetic heroin" (Kirsch, 1986). No one knows how many addicts died as a result of mistakes in the manufacture of "synthetic heroin," but it is known that some loss of life did occur.

Addicts still are being poisoned because of mistakes made in the production of street drugs. Parras, Patier, and Ezpeleta (1988), for example, report a case in which a heroin addict developed lead poisoning as a result of lead-contaminated heroin. Cases have also been reported in which users of methamphetamine have developed lead poisoning as a result of impurities in street drugs (Allcott, Barnhart, & Mooney, 1987; Centers for Disease Control, 1990).

Lombard, Levin, and Weiner (1989) describe a case in which a cocaine abuser developed arsenic poisoning as a result of his drug use. When the individual was told of the cause of his nausea, vomiting, and diarrhea, he was reportedly quite unimpressed with the medical detective work that had uncovered the source of his illness. The addict informed the physicians that everyone knew that cocaine might be mixed with compounds that contained arsenic. Lombard et al. warned that similar cases might be encountered by other physicians as the cocaine epidemic spread.

The problem of contaminated drugs is not limited to narcotics or cocaine. As Haynor and McKinney (1986) state,

> substances intended for popular recreational use are most often produced in clandestine laboratories with little or no quality control, so generally speaking users cannot be sure of the purity of what they are ingesting. (p. 341)

Indeed, it should be pointed out that "misrepresentation is the rule with illicit drugs" (Brown & Braden, 1987, p. 341). A capsule might be sold on the street as "THC," but actually contain PCP—a very different chemical. Without a detailed chemical analysis, a buyer cannot be sure what the substance purchased actually is, whether or not it is contaminated, or how potent it might be.

In a study by Scaros et al. (1990), only 60% of the street-purchased amphetamine samples tested actually contained amphetamines. It is not uncommon for "amphetamines" sold on the street to actually be nothing more than caffeine tablets.

Street Drugs and Adulterants

According to Scaros et al. (1990), the purity of cocaine purchased on the street ranges from just 14% to 75%, with an average purity of 49%. This means that, on average, more than half of each gram of cocaine purchased on the street is actually some other substance. These foreign substances, known as "adulterants," fall into one of five categories: sugars, stimulants, local anesthetics, toxins, and inert compounds.

Cocaine is most commonly adulterated with the various sugars:

> Lactose, sucrose and mannitol are frequently added . . . and have little clinical toxicity. Stimulants are the second most common adulterants, and include caffeine, ephedrine, phenylpropanolamine, amphetamine, or methamphetamine. . . . The local anesthetics are the third most frequent adulterants, and include lidocaine, benzocaine, procaine, and tetracaine. . . . The two most common [lethal toxins] are quinine and strychnine. (Scaros et al., 1990, p. 24)

It is also quite common for narcotics to be mixed with adulterants. Indeed, many of the compounds used to adulterate cocaine are also mixed with street narcotics. Other common adulterants found in narcotics include food coloring, talcum powder, starch, powdered milk, baking soda, brown sugar, or sometimes even dog manure (Scaros et al., 1990).

Street marijuana is still another frequently adulterated drug. It is not uncommon for up to half of the "marijuana" purchased on the street to be seeds and woody stems, which must be removed before the marijuana can be smoked. Further, the marijuana may be laced with other compounds, including PCP, cocaine paste, opium, or such toxic compounds as "Raid" insect spray (Scaros et al., 1990). Marijuana samples have also been found to have been adulterated with dried shredded cow manure (which may expose the user to salmonella bacteria), as well as with herbicide sprays such as paraquat (Jenike, 1989).

All of these chemicals gain admission into the user's body when the adulterated marijuana is smoked, and medical researchers have little understanding of their effects on the human body. The same thing happens when a drug user injects or ingests a drug that has been adulterated in some manner. The adulterants gain admission to the body, with consequences that are not well understood.

This is one reason why "pharmaceuticals" (drugs produced by legal pharmaceutical manufacturers) that have been diverted to the streets are so highly prized among addicts. Such chemicals are of a known quality and potency and are unlikely to be contaminated. However, pharmaceuticals are difficult to obtain, with rare exceptions. The majority of addicts must resort to chemicals produced in illegal laboratories, which may have been adulterated time and time again.

DRUG ANALOGS: THE "DESIGNER" DRUGS

The process by which drugs are identified, be they legal or illegal, is highly specific. A drug's chemical structure is examined, and the exact location of each atom in relation to every other atom in its chemical chain is noted. The chemical structure for the specific drug is then registered with the federal government and used for purposes of identifying the drug.

The identification and regulation of new pharmaceuticals is a complex and difficult task, the description of which lies outside the scope of this chapter. To simplify matters, our discussion will be limited to illegal drugs only. In this context, consider the simplified drug molecule shown in Figure 31-1, which has been outlawed as an illegal hallucinogen.

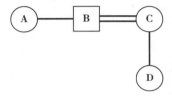

FIGURE 31-1

The exact location of every atom in the drug molecule has been noted, and the molecule has been described in specific detail to allow for its easy identification. However, a drug with the chemical structure shown in Figure 31-2 would technically be a "different" drug, since its molecular structure is not *exactly* the same as the first drug's. The molecule in Figure 31-2 is called a drug "analog" of the parent drug.

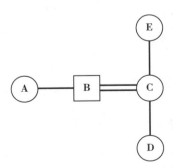

FIGURE 31-2

There is an obvious difference in the chemical structures shown in Figures 31-1 and 31-2. The new atom that was added in Figure 31-2 might not do anything to the potency of the drug, but it does change the chemical structure of that drug just enough so that it is not covered by the law that made the parent drug illegal.

For this analog to be declared illegal, researchers would have to identify the location of every atom in its chemical chain and the nature of the chemical bond that held that atom in place. Then, law-enforcement officials would have to present their findings to the appropriate agency for the drug analog to be outlawed. This is a process that might take months, or even longer. When this happens, it would be a simple matter to again change the chemical structure a little bit to build a new "analog," as shown, for example, in Figure 31-3.

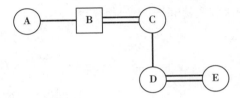

FIGURE 31-3

Notice that there is a very subtle difference in the chemical structure of the last two hypothetical drug molecules. In each case, however, in the eyes of the law, they are "different" drugs. Technically, the structure shown in Figure 31-3 would again be that of a new "drug," not covered by the law that prohibited the parent drug. If *this* drug molecule were to be outlawed, the street chemist might again change the drug, as shown in Figure 31-4.

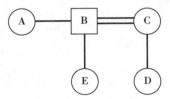

FIGURE 31-4

The drug molecule used in the preceding example was a very simple one, with only five atoms. However, even with this example, it was possible to produce several different "analogs" of the original parent molecule. When you stop to consider that many of the psychoactive drugs have drug molecules that contain dozens or even hundreds of atoms, the number of potential combinations is impressive.

Drug analogs vary both in terms of potency and safety. When they are produced by underground laboratories, they are called "designer" drugs. Their regulation by the courts is extremely difficult if only because it is so easy to alter the chemical structure of a drug to produce a new drug that is not covered by existing laws and because it is so hard for chemists to identify the chemical structure of a drug.

Drug Analogs Currently on the Street

It should come as no surprise that street chemists have been manipulating the chemical structure of known drugs of abuse for some time in the attempt to come up with new drugs that have not yet been outlawed. Some analogs of the amphetamine family of drugs include 2,5-dimetoxy-4-methylamphetamine, or the hallucinogenic DOM (Scaros et al., 1990). MDMA, also known as "ecstasy," is another drug analog of the amphetamines. As we noted in Chapter 13 on the hallucinogens, research evidence suggests that MDMA is capable of selectively destroying certain neurons in the brain.

The drug 3,4-methylenedioxyamphetamine, or MEDA, is still another drug analog of the amphetamine family. When MDMA was classified as a controlled substance in 1985, "street" chemists started to produce MEDA, whose chemical structure is very similar to that of MDMA. This substance, often sold under the name "Eve," has not been classified as a controlled substance as of July, 1991. According to Mirin et al., its effects are very similar to those of MDMA, although the long-term effects of this substance are still unknown.

Street chemists have also produced at least five drug analogs to the hallucinogen PCP, each of which has an effect similar to that of PCP (Scaros et al., 1990). These are the drugs N-ethyl-1-phenylcyclohexylamine, also known as PCE; (1-(1-2-thienylcyclohexyl) piperidine), or TCP; (1-(1-phenylcyclohexyl) pyrrolidine), or PHP; (1-piperidinocyclohexanecarbonitrile), or PCC; and Eu4ia (pronounced "euphoria"), an amphetaminelike drug synthesized from legally purchased over-the-counter drugs.

Another drug that is occasionally produced in illicit laboratories is (2-o-chorophenyl)-2-methylamine cyclohexanone), or ketamine. Ketamine, surprisingly, is a legitimate pharmaceutical agent that is used as a surgical anesthetic. When it is abused, ketamine is said to have effects similar to those of heroin (*The Economist*, 1989); for this reason, it is often produced illegally.

In the early 1980s, there was a series of fatal overdoses in California, as street chemists started to produce various designer drugs that were similar to the analgesic fentanyl (Hibbs, Perper, & Winek, 1991). Kirsch (1986) lists nine different drug analogs to fentanyl that are known or suspected to have been sold on the streets. These drug analogs range from 1/10th as potent as morphine for the fentanyl analog benzylfentanyl to between 1,000 times (Hibbs et al., 1991) and 3,000 times (Kirsch, 1986) more potent than morphine for 3-methylfentanyl.

The drug 3-methyfentanyl is also known to chemists as TMF. This analog of fentanyl has been identified as the cause of narcotic overdoses in the area around Pittsburgh, Pennsylvania (Hibbs et al., 1991), and also in New York City (*Newsweek*, 1991). Hibbs et al. conducted a retrospective analysis to determine how serious a problem TMF-induced overdoses were for the Allegheny County region surrounding Pittsburgh. Surprisingly, they found that fully 27% of the drug-overdose deaths in Allegheny County in 1988 were caused by TME. This would suggest that designer narcotics are a significant part of the narcotics problem in the United States.

THE ARTIFICIALLY INFLATED PRICE OF STREET DRUGS

As we have noted, the drugs produced in clandestine laboratories, or imported through illegal means, are not sold in a free-market economy. Rather, they are sold in a controlled environment—a monopoly—where prices may be artificially inflated many times over. Lessard (1989) contends that the drug market is "a grotesque, over-heated form of capitalism" (p. 70). Indeed, some pushers earn upward of $400 or $500 a day (Collier, 1989).

Mixing drugs with adulterants is one way by which prices are inflated. Also, the fact that the drugs are often produced in illicit laboratories inflates the price on the street. For example, Brecher (1972) notes that the amphetamines are relatively cheap, with a thousand tablets costing a pharmaceutical company only 75¢ to manufacture in the late 1960s. They are also easily transported and require no specialized training in chemistry to manufacture. This makes amphetamine manufacture especially tempting in college chemistry classes, a fact not unknown to faculty and law-enforcement officials.

The financial rewards for the illegal manufacture of amphetamines are quite high. For example, an investment of $1,000 to buy the materials necessary to produce amphetamines will eventually yield a return of as much as $40,000 for methamphetamine (Peluso & Peluso, 1988), or the form of methamphetamine known as ice (*Playboy*, 1990b). The illicit manufacture of amphetamines is thought to be centered in Texas and California, and is estimated to be a $3 billion a year industry by Cho (1990).

The phenomenon of overpricing is not limited to illicit amphetamines. Byrne (1989b) reports, for example, that raw cocaine leaves are sold for $2 a kilogram by the farmer in South America. The coca paste that is produced from the leaves is then sold for $200 a kilogram, while the cocaine base that is isolated from the coca paste sells for about $1,500 a kilogram. The cocaine hydrochloride that is obtained from the base is sold for up to $3,000 a kilogram, which then is sold at wholesale for upwards of $20,000 a kilogram. When packaged for sale on the streets in 1-gram lots, this same kilogram sells for between $80,000 and $192,000.

At each step in the distribution process, the cocaine is mixed with adulterants, reducing the purity of the resulting mixture while increasing the amount of the "drug" to be sold. Cocaine and narcotics are adulterated to increase the profit from the sale of these drugs. The raw opium necessary to produce a kilogram of heroin costs only a few hundred dollars. This same kilogram of heroin will ultimately sell on the street for between $1 million and $5 million after it is "cut" over and over again.

According to Lingeman (1974), heroin may be cut between four and seven times before it is sold on the street. At each stage, the potency of the heroin may be reduced by half, or even more. When it is finally sold on the street, a single kilogram of heroin will be sold in powder form in small "bags," or sometimes condoms. These bags or condoms will sell for between $5 (a "nickel bag") and $10 (a "dime bag") each. A typical "bag" of heroin may contain only 1% to 5% heroin. The rest is composed of various adulterants that have been added along the way.

A further complicating factor is that drugs are prohibited. The fact that drug use is illegal contributes to the high cost of the drugs. Drug dealers use the fact that their product is illegal as an excuse to keep the price at an artificially inflated level.

At the same time, the illegal status of drug use may actually serve to *increase* its appeal to adolescents and young adults. Access to chemicals of abuse is available only through a *criminal* market, where prices are artificially inflated and quality control is limited (*Health News*, 1990; Lessard, 1989). The illegal status of many drugs of abuse makes their use attractive to many who are going through a stage of rebellion against society's norms.

Another consequence of the prohibition against chemical use is that addicts must use their drugs of choice under conditions that are hazardous. For example, it has been suggested that narcotic addicts inject drugs only because this is the most efficient method to administer the limited amount of the drug available. When allowed access to unlimited supplies, the preferred method of administration is by smoking, as was done in turn-of-the-century opium dens.

Lingeman (1974) speaks of how heroin addicts live on the fringes of the criminal underworld. He describes how heroin addicts often die as a result of overdoses, infections brought on by unsterile needles, malnutrition, accidents, and violence. In her report on the impact of crack on one city hospital, Gross (1989) found that on any given night at least half of the patients in the emergency room were drug users. On some nights, every patient seen was addicted to chemicals. In at least one major trauma center, 65% of all patients test positive for drugs (*Alcoholism & Drug Abuse Week*, 1990).

SHOULD DRUGS BE LEGALIZED?

The current social climate surrounding substance use/abuse is one of repression, with legal sanctions and incarcaration imposed on those who are convicted of a drug-related criminal offense. Nadelmann et al. (1990) estimate that approximately 40% of those incarcerated in federal penitentiaries are there because of drug-related convictions. It has been estimated that the incarceration of all those arrested for drug-related crimes would create a need for 1,800 new prison cells each week (*Playboy*, 1990a).

There are more than a million people incarcerated in various federal and state prisons. If one assumes that it costs $25,000 per inmate per year to have a person incarcerated (a rather low estimate), this means that $10 billion per year is being spent just to keep already convicted drug offenders incarcerated. This does not include an estimated $10 billion to $20 billion that must be spent to enforce existing laws against drug abuse (Nadelmann et al. 1990). One must ask how long society can afford these costs.

Syndicated columnist Mike Royko (1990) put forth the argument that individuals who want to use drugs are going to do so whether or not it is legal, and that the legalization of drugs would serve to avoid "the gun battles, the corruption and the wasted money and effort trying to save the brains and noses of those who don't want them saved" (p. 46). He suggests that by legalizing drugs some measure of control could be gained over who had access to them and at what age people might be allowed to use them, in much the manner that access to alcohol is restricted by law.

On the other hand, Frances (1991) argues against the legalization of drugs, in part because their increased availability would result in more widespread use. The number of cocaine users would triple, for example, if cocaine were ever to be legalized. Further, Frances points out that when drugs were legal during the past century, society was swept by a wave of addiction the likes of which had never been seen before and has not been seen since. If drugs were to be legalized now the black market would be destroyed, but the price of chemicals of abuse would fall so drastically that prices would come "within reach of lunch money for elementary school children" (p. 120). Frances's prediction is a frightening one.

Lessard (1989) suggests an alternative to a free-market legalization program such as that fearfully envisioned by Frances. Rather than to have drugs freely available in the marketplace, Lessard recommends that the drugs be made available through a physician's prescription. In this way, access to the drugs could be limited, while the profit incentive for criminals would be removed. In other words, Lessard advocates that the problem of drug abuse be approached from a health perspective, as it is in Holland.

The Dutch Experience

The social experiment that currently is under way in Holland would tend to support the arguments of those who believe that the American response to the drug problem has created more problems than it has solved (Peele, 1989; Scheer, 1990; Szaz, 1988). In 1976 the Dutch revised their antidrug laws, making possession of less than 1 ounce of marijuana a misdemeanor. Furthermore, the decision was made not to enforce the strict antidrug laws already on the books. To do so, government officials reasoned, would be to drive what was essentially a health problem underground, turning it into a legal problem.

In Holland, although the possession of heroin or cocaine for personal use is discouraged, it is also tolerated by authorities as long as the individual does not engage in illegal activities such as burglary and the like (*The Economist*, 1990b; Lewis, 1989). Surprisingly, in spite of this tolerance for drug use, the number of heroin addicts has dropped by approximately a third (*The Economist*, 1990b; Scheer, 1990).

Small amounts of marijuana and hashish are sold openly in Dutch coffee houses, and users may purchase up to 13 grams of marijuana legally. The price of marijuana is quite low—approximately $1.50 per gram. Since this policy went into effect, the percentage of the Dutch population addicted to chemicals remained stable throughout the 1980s, and recent evidence suggests that it is even dropping (*The Economist*, 1990b; Lewis, 1989).

Substance abuse has never been a significant problem in Holland, at least in the sense that it has been in this country. Gay (1991), for example, reports that only 5% of high school graduates admit to having experimented with drugs as compared to some 18% of American high school graduates. Whereas a third of American teenagers have at least tried marijuana, only a quarter of Dutch adolescents have done so. Further, evidence would suggest that a relaxed drug policy has resulted in Dutch heroin addicts living longer, although the exact reason for this is not yet clear (*The Economist*, 1990b).

SUMMARY

The relationship between substance abuse and criminal activity is a very complex one. Although it would appear on the surface that drug use *causes* crime, a deeper exploration reveals that this conclusion does not fit known facts. Indeed, an in-depth exploration of the relationship between chemical use and criminal activity reveals that these two social problems are so intertwined that it is difficult to determine how they contribute to one another. Even now, after a century of study, professionals are still unclear as to the true relationship between chemical use and crime.

The "American model" of drug intradiction and criminal prosecution is not universally accepted. Indeed, Holland's attempt to approach the problem differently has met with some success. This social experiment casts doubt as to the utility of antidrug laws, which can be enforced only at a tremendous cost to society.

Sample Assessment: A Case of Alcohol Abuse

HISTORY AND IDENTIFYING INFORMATION

Mr. John D____ is a 35-year-old married white male from ____ County, Missouri. He is employed as an electrical engineer for XYZ Company, where he has worked for the past 3 years. Prior to this, Mr. D____ was in the United States Navy, where he served for 4 years. He was discharged under honorable conditions and reported that he only had "a few" minor rules infractions. According to his account, he was never brought before a court-martial.

CIRCUMSTANCES OF REFERRAL

Mr. D____ was seen after having been arrested on the charge of driving while under the influence of alcohol. He reported that he had been drinking with co-workers to celebrate a promotion at work. His measured blood alcohol level (or BAL) was .150—well above the legal limit necessary for a charge of driving while under the influence. Mr. D____ reported that he had had "seven or eight" mixed drinks in approximately a 2-hour time span. By his report, he had been arrested within 15 minutes after having left the bar.

After his initial court appearance, Mr. D____ was referred to this evaluator by the court to determine whether or not he had a chemical dependency problem.

DRUG AND ALCOHOL USE HISTORY

Mr. D____ reported that he first began to drink at the age of 15, when he and a friend would steal beer from his father's supply in the basement. He would drink an occasional beer from time to time after that, and first became intoxicated when he was 17.

1

Note: This case is entirely fictitious. No similarity between any person, living or dead, is intended or should be inferred.

When he was 18, Mr. D___ enlisted in the United States Navy, and after basic training he was stationed in the San Diego area. Mr. D___ reported that he was first exposed to chemicals while he was stationed in San Diego, and that he tried both marijuana and cocaine while on weekend liberty. Mr. D___ reported that he did not like the effects of cocaine, and that he only used this chemical once or twice. He did like the effects of marijuana either, and reported that he would smoke one or two marijuana cigarettes obtained from friends perhaps once a month.

According to Mr. D___'s report, he would drink about twice a weekend, when on liberty. The amount he would drink ranged from "a couple of beers" up to 12 or 18 beers. Mr. D___ reported that his first alcohol-related blackout occurred while he was in the navy and stated that he "should have been arrested" for driving on base while under the influence of alcohol on several different occasions but was never stopped by the Shore Patrol.

Following his honorable discharge from the navy, at the age of 22, Mr. D___ enrolled in college. His chemical use declined to the weekend use of alcohol, usually in moderation, but Mr. D___ reported that he did drink to the point of an alcohol-related blackout "once or twice" in the 4 years that he was in college. There was no other chemical use following his discharge from the navy, and Mr. D___ reports that he has not used other chemicals since the age of 20 or 21.

Upon graduation at the age of 26, Mr. D___ began to work for XYZ Company, where he is now employed. He met his wife shortly after he began work, and they were married after a courtship of 1 year. Mr. D___'s wife, Pat, does not use chemicals other than an "occasional" social drink. Upon further questioning, it was revealed that Mrs. D___ will drink a glass of wine with a meal about twice a month. She denied other chemical use.

Mrs. D___ reported that her husband does not usually drink more than one or two beers, and that he will drink only on weekends. She reported that the night he was arrested was "unusual" for him, in the sense that he is not a drinker. His employer was not contacted, but court records failed to reveal any other arrest records for Mr. D___.

Mr. D___ admitted to several alcohol-related blackouts, but none since he was in college. He denied seizures, DT's, or alcohol-related tremor. There was no evidence of ulcers, gastritis, or cardiac problems. His last physical was "normal" according to information provided by his personal physician. There were no abnormal blood chemistry findings, nor did his physician find any evidence suggesting alcoholism. Mr. D___ denied ever having been hospitalized for an alcohol-related injury, and there was no evidence suggesting that he has been involved in fights.

2

On the Michigan Alcoholism Screening Test, Mr. D____'s score of four (4) points would not suggest alcoholism. This information was reviewed in the presence of his wife, who did not suggest that there was any misrepresentation on his test scores. On this administration of the MMPI, there was no evidence of psychopathology noted. Mr. D____'s MacAndrew Alcoholism Scale score fell in the normal range, failing to suggest an addictive disorder.

PSYCHIATRIC HISTORY
Mr. D____ denied psychiatric treatment of any kind. He did admit that he had seen a marriage counselor "on one occasion" shortly after he married, but he added that overall he and his wife were happy together. Apparently, they had a problem that was cleared up after one visit, which took place after 3 or 4 years of marriage.

SUMMARY AND CONCLUSIONS
At this point, there is little evidence to suggest an ongoing alcohol problem. Mr. D____ would seem to be a well-adjusted young man who drank to the point of excess after having been offered a long-desired promotion at work. Excessive drinking would seem to be unusual for Mr. D____, who generally limits his drinking to one or two beers on the weekends. There was no evidence of alcohol-related injuries, accidents, or legal problems noted in Mr. D____'s records.

RECOMMENDATIONS
A light sentence, possibly a fine, limited probation, with no restrictions on license. It is also recommended that Mr. D____ attend "DWI School" for 8 weeks to learn more about the effects of alcohol on driving.

Appendix 2

SAMPLE ASSESSMENT: A CASE OF CHEMICAL DEPENDENCY

HISTORY AND IDENTIFYING FEATURES

Mr. Michael S⎯is a 35-year-old divorced white male who is self-employed. He has been a resident of ⎯⎯⎯ County, Kansas, for the past 3 months. Prior to this, he apparently was living in ⎯⎯⎯ County, New York, according to his account. On the night of June 6th of this year, Mr. S⎯ was arrested on the charge of possession of a controlled substance. Specifically, Mr. S⎯ was found to be in possession of two grams of cocaine, according to police records. This is his first arrest for a drug-related charge in Kansas, although he has been arrested on two other occasions for similar charges in New York State. A copy of his police record is attached to this report.

CIRCUMSTANCES OF REFERRAL

Mr. S⎯ was referred to the undersigned for a chemical dependency evaluation, which will be part of his presentence investigation (PSI) for the charge of felony possession of a controlled substance and the charge of sale of a controlled substance.

DRUG AND ALCOHOL USE HISTORY

Mr. S⎯ reported that he began to use alcohol when he was 13 years of age and that by the age of 14 he was drinking on a regular basis. Further questioning revealed that by the time he was about to turn 15, Mr. S⎯ was drinking on "weekends," with friends. He reported that he first became intoxicated on his 15th birthday, but projected responsibility for this onto his friends, who

1

by his report "kept on pouring more and more into the glass until I was drunk."

By the age of 16, Mr. S____ was using alcohol "four or five nights a week" and was also using marijuana and hallucinogenics perhaps two or three times a week. He projected responsibility for his expanded chemical use onto his environment, noting that "everybody was selling the stuff—you couldn't walk down the street without people stopping you to ask if you wanted to buy some."

Also, by the age of 16, Mr. S____ was supporting his chemical use through burglaries, which he commited with his friends. He was never caught, but volunteered this information commenting that since the statute of limitations had expired, he did not have to fear being charged for these crimes.

By the age of 21, Mr. S____ was using cocaine "once or twice a week." He was arrested for possession of cocaine for the first time when he was about 22. This was when he was living in the state of _____. After being tried in court, he was convicted of felony possession of cocaine, and placed on probation for 5 years. When asked if he had used chemicals while he was on probation, Mr. S____ responded, "I don't have to answer that."

Mr. S____ reported that he first entered treatment for chemical dependency when he was 27 years of age. At that time, he was found to be addicted to a number of drugs, including alcohol, cocaine, and "downers." Although in treatment for 2 months at the chemical dependency unit of _____ Hospital, Mr. S____ stated, "I left as addicted as when I arrived." He reported with some degree of pride that he had found a way to use chemicals even while in treatment. His chemical use apparently was the reason for his ultimate discharge from this program. While Mr. S____ was somewhat vague about why he was discharged, he did report that the treatment staff "did not like how I was doing."

Since his discharge from _____ Hospital, Mr. S____ has been using cocaine, alcohol, various drugs obtained from a series of physicians, and opiates. Mr. S____ was quite vague as to how he supported his chemical use, but noted, "There are ways of getting money, if you really want some."

Mr. S____ reported that he has been using cocaine "four or five times a week" over the past year, although he did admit to having used cocaine "for a whole week straight" on occasion. He admitted that he shared needles with other cocaine users from time to time, but added, "I am careful." By his account, however, he was diagnosed as having hepatitis B in the past year. He also reported that he had overdosed on cocaine "once or twice," but that he treated this overdose himself with benzodiazepines and alcohol.

In addition to the possible cocaine overdoses, Mr. S____

2

admitted that he had experienced chest pain while using cocaine on at least two occasions and that he regularly used alcohol or tranquilizers to combat the side-effects of cocaine. He admitted to frequently using tranquilizers or alcohol to help him sleep after using cocaine for extended periods of time. He also admitted that he had spent money on drugs that was meant to meet other expenses (loan payments, and the like) and by his report he has had at least one automobile repossessed for failure to make payments on the loan.

Mr. S____ has been unemployed for at least the past 2 years, but is rather vague as to how he supports himself. He apparently was engaged in selling cocaine at the time of his arrest, this being one of the charges brought against him by the police.

Prior to his arrest, Mr. S____ had not seen a physician for several years. The undersigned noted, however, that he had scars strongly suggestive of intravenous needle use on both arms. When asked about these marks, he referred to them as "tracks"—a street term for drug needle scars. This would suggest long-term intravenous drug use on Mr. S____'s part. He denied the intravenous use of opiates, but a urine toxicology screen detected narcotics. This would suggest that Mr. S____ has not been very open about his narcotic drug use.

On this administration of the Michigan Alcoholism Screening Test (MAST) Mr. S____ achieved a score of 17 points—a score strongly suggestive of alcoholism. He reported that the longest period he was able to go without using chemicals in the past 5 years was only "hours." His profile on this administration of the Minnesota Multiphasic Personality Inventory (MMPI) was suggestive of a very impulsive, immature individual who was likely to have a chemical dependency problem.

PSYCHIATRIC HISTORY

Mr. S____ reported that he was hospitalized for psychiatric reasons "only once." This hospitalization took place several years ago, while Mr. S____ was living in _____. Apparently, he was hospitalized for observation following a suicide attempt in which he slit his wrists with a razor blade. Mr. S____ was unable to recall whether or not he had been using cocaine prior to this suicide attempt, but he mentioned that it was "quite possible" that he had experienced a cocaine-induced depression.

MEDICAL HISTORY

As noted above, Mr. S____ had not seen a physician for several years prior to his arrest. Since the time of his arrest, however, he has undergone a medical examination for a cough that he has had for some time. The physician (report enclosed) concluded that Mr.

3

S___ is "seropositive" for HIV and classified him as falling into category CDC_1. While it is not possible to determine whether Mr. S___ contracted HIV through sharing needles, this is at least a possibility.

SUMMARY AND CONCLUSIONS
Overall, it is quite apparent that Mr. S___ has a long-standing chemical dependency problem. In spite of his evasiveness and denial, there is strong evidence of significant chemical dependency problems. Mr. S___ seems to support his drug and alcohol use through criminal activity, although he is rather vague about this. He was convicted of drug-related charges in the state of ___ and was on probation following this conviction. It could be assumed that Mr. S___'s motivation for treatment is quite low at this time, given that he expressed the belief that his attorney would "make a deal" for him, whereby he would not have to spend time in prison.

RECOMMENDATIONS
1.   Given the fact that Mr. S___ has contracted HIV and hepatitis B, most likely from infected needles, it is strongly recommended that he be referred to the appropriate medical facility for treatment.

2.   It is the opinion of this reviewer that Mr. S___'s motivation for treatment is low at this time. If he is referred to treatment, it is recommended that this be made part of his sentencing agreement with the court. If he is incarcerated, chemical dependency treatment might be made part of his treatment plan in prison.

3.   Referral to a therapeutic community should be considered for Mr. S___ for long-term residual treatment.

Signed/s/

4

Appendix 3

Acquired Immune Deficiency Syndrome (AIDS) and Hepatitis B

A ddicts who inject drugs and who fail to use proper sterile techniques run the risk of local and systemic infections. Addicts who share intravenous needles, a very common practice, risk exposing themselves to infections of previous users. Some of the infections commonly found in intravenous drug addicts who fail to use proper sterile techniques or who share needles include peripheral cellulitis, skin abscesses, viral hepatitis, infection of the heart valves (endocarditis), pneumonia, lung abscesses, tetanus, and malaria (Wetli, 1987).

Thus, an individual runs the risk of contracting a number of bacteriological or viral infections by sharing an intravenous needle with someone who is infected. Of the four different types of viral hepatitis identified by medical researchers, one of them—hepatitis B—may be passed from one individual to another by sharing of needles. Another viral infection commonly encountered in addicts who share needles is acquired immune deficiency syndrome (AIDS).

ACQUIRED IMMUNE DEFICIENCY SYNDROME

It is surprising how many people speak of AIDS as if it were a disease in itself. AIDS is not a disease, it is a *syndrome*—the end stage of a viral infection thought to be caused by a virus known as human immunodeficiency virus (also known as HIV, or HTLV-3) (Koop, 1986; McCutchan, 1990). The process through which HIV is able to infect and ultimately kill a victim is based on a remarkable chain of events involving the human immune system.

How Does AIDS Kill?

The normal function of the immune system is quite complex, and lies beyond the scope of this text. In brief, however, every species of bacteria, virus, or fungus has a characteristic pattern of proteins within its cell wall. Antibodies, found principally in blood serum, learn to recognize these patterns and

Note: The author would like to express his appreciation to John P. Doweiko, M.D. for his assistance with the portions of this appendix dealing with AIDS.

distinguish between the protein pattern of an invading organism and that of the body's own cells. Thus, the body learns to protect itself from invading organisms by building antibodies, the so-called white blood cells, which recognize foreign cells and attack them. Each antibody is tailor-made for each species of bacteria, fungus, or virus encountered by the body over the years.

This is why a person who once had an infection might become "immune" to that disease. He or she has a number of white blood cells from the previous exposure to the invader that can isolate and destroy the invading organism this time around. In the case of an infection to which the individual has not been exposed previously, the process of producing the specific antibody necessary to fight it off may take hours, days, weeks, or even years.

In the case of those infected with HIV, antibodies against the invading virus may not be produced for up to 6 months following initial exposure to the virus (McCutchan, 1990). However, even though a person's immune system has not yet started to produce antibodies against HIV, the infected individual still remains capable of passing the virus on to others through his or her blood or through sexual contact. At this point, the infected individual would exhibit no outward signs of the infection.

Unfortunately, one characteristic of a virus infection is that the virus is able to work its way into body tissues (Radetsky, 1990). This allows the virus to hide from the body's defenses while it reproduces. In the case of the AIDS virus, it will infect various components of the immune system, especially the antibodies. Thus, in the infected individual, one will often find the virus hiding in the antibodies, many of which were produced by the body to attempt to fight off the HIV infection.

HEPATITIS B

Hepatitis B is one of four different viral diseases that infects the liver. It is known to be *extremely contagious*—perhaps 100 times as contagious as HIV. Whereas the HIV is quite fragile and requires direct exposure to the infected individual's blood, hepatitis B may be contracted simply by sharing a toothbrush or razor with an infected person, or just by kissing someone who is infected (Brody, 1991).

How Does Hepatitis B Kill?

There are several mechanisms through which the hepatitis B virus may kill the infected person, either directly or indirectly. First, the virus infects the liver, causing damage to that organ. If the liver damage is great enough, hepatitis B might kill the individual through simple liver failure. This is a rare, but not unknown, result of hepatitis B infection.

However, hepatitis B may also kill indirectly. For reasons that are not known at this time, the person who has been infected with the hepatitis B virus is 200 times as likely to develop liver cancer as a noninfected person (Brody, 1991). Liver cancer is quite difficult to detect and treat, and it is often fatal.

THE TRANSMISSION OF HIV AND HEPATITIS B

HIV is a fragile virus that is not easily transmitted from one person to another (Koop, 1986; Langone, 1989). There is no evidence to date that it is possible to catch the virus through saliva, tears, or toilet seats (Koop, 1986). The virus must be passed directly from one individual to another. According to *Consumer Reports* (1989), the modes of HIV transmission are limited to sexual intercourse with an infected person, direct mixing of one's blood with infected fluids, passage of the virus from the mother to the fetus, or transmission through the mother's milk to the suckling baby (Glasner & Kaslow, 1990; Redfield & Burk, 1988).

Addicts who share needles and other drug paraphernalia are at risk for becoming infected with HIV (Redfield & Burk, 1988) and hepatitis B. In some communities, from 60% (Glasner & Kaslow, 1990) to 80% (Michelson, Carroll, McLane, & Robin, 1988) of intravenous drug users are "seropositive," which is to say that blood samples from these individuals contain antibodies against HIV. Blood samples also would suggest that between 75% and 98% of intraveneous drug users have been exposed to the hepatitis B virus at some time in their lives (Michelson et al., 1988).

When an individual with AIDS uses an intravenous needle, he or she leaves a reservoir of infected blood in the syringe, infecting those who use the intravenous "rig" next. In the past 5 years, AIDS has become the leading cause of death for intravenous drug users (Heyward & Curran, 1988; Pope & Morin, 1990).

The virus is also found in the semen of all infected men and may be passed on to others through the semen. People involved in sexual relationships with addicts are at risk for contracting AIDS or hepatitis B if the addict is infected with either virus. Further, people involved in sexual relationships with homosexual or bisexual males are also considered to be at risk for these (or other) infections because of the known association between male homosexual activity and AIDS/hepatitis B.

Those who engage in promiscuous sexual activity, which is to say those individuals who have intercourse with prostitutes or who have multiple sexual partners, are also thought to be at risk. The greater the number of sexual partners any one individual has, the greater his or her chances of being exposed to HIV or hepatitis B. Each new partner must be considered in light of his or her previous partners, and the partners of those individuals, and so on. Thus, each new partner dramatically increases the population pool from which the virus may be transmitted to the individual in question.

Because of the high probability that drug addicts, promiscuous individuals, prostitutes, and bisexual or homosexual males are infected and are thus able to transmit either AIDS or hepatitis B on to their partners, it is advised that sexual contact with such people be avoided. The tendency for the addict to resort to prostitution as a way of obtaining money for chemicals has contributed to a significant rise in sexually transmitted diseases such as syphilis, hepatitis B, and HIV (*The Nation's Health*, 1990).

Chemicals may *indirectly* contribute to hepatitis B or HIV infection. In a study by Schleifer et al. (1990), for example, almost 5% of the alcoholics tested were seropositive for HIV. This is an infection rate several times higher than that found in the general population, a finding that Schleifer et al. attribute to the disinhibiting effects of alcohol. In other words, because alcohol lowers inhibitions, it may indirectly contribute to promiscuous behavior, exposing the individual to a partner who is infected with AIDS.

At one point, the two groups with the greatest risk of contracting AIDS were thought to be homosexual males and intravenous drug users. These are still high-risk groups. In the San Francisco area, perhaps as many as half of the homosexual or bisexual males are infected with AIDS (Pope & Morin, 1990). It is primarily through intravenous drug users, however, that the virus has been transmitted to the heterosexual population and to children (Langone, 1989; Valdiserri, Hartl, & Chambliss, 1988).

THE SCOPE OF THE PROBLEM

It has been estimated that some 1.4 million Americans, and perhaps as many as 10 million people worldwide, have already contracted AIDS (Langone, 1989; Slim, 1990). Of those infected, approximately 23% have contracted this virus through the use of contaminated needles (Thompson, 1990).

As for hepatitis B, it is difficult to obtain a true picture of the infection pattern, if only because there are no symptoms of infection in up to half of those who have acquired this virus in one way or another (Brody, 1991). It was estimated that in 1990 300,000 new cases of hepatitis B were added to those already infected.

Until recently, it was thought that perhaps only about a third of those who tested positive for HIV would go on to develop AIDS in 5 years. According to Patlak (1988), however, recent research suggests that "nearly all those infected will develop the disease within a mean period of 7.8 years" (p. 26). No vaccine to prevent the infection is available at this time, although there is evidence to suggest that such a vaccine may be possible (Radetsky, 1990).

At this time, AIDS victims are predominantly male, at least in the United States. In over 88% of the reported cases of AIDS in the United States the victim has been male (Pope & Morin, 1990). Consequently, virtually all the research on the manifestations and treatment of AIDS has involved male victims (Squires, 1989). Very little is known about the evolution of AIDS in females or whether current treatment programs need to be modified for female AIDS victims.

As reported in *Medical Aspects of Human Sexuality* (1990), of the documented cases of AIDS in women in the United States, the majority (just over half) are found in intravenous drug users. Approximately a third of the women infected with the virus contracted it through sexual contact with an infected man, while approximately 10% contracted it from a contaminated blood transfusion. With the advent of new blood tests, however, the incidence of infection through blood transfusions is now quite rare. Homosexual transmission of AIDS in women is thought to be very rare.

THE STAGES OF AIDS

There is a long latency period between the initial exposure to the HIV virus and the development of the full AIDS syndrome. Because of this, the number of new AIDS cases will continue to increase for several years (Heyward & Curren, 1988). In working with AIDS victims, the CDC (Centers for Disease Control) has adopted a classification system to identify those who are infected and the stage of each individual's infection.

AIDS is detected through a series of blood tests. Pope and Morin (1990) describe these tests in the following manner:

> Generally, the initial tests screen blood samples of antibodies to the virus; such tests are termed ELISA (enzyme-linked immunosorbent assay). If the individual reacts positively to ELISA tests, a more difficult, expensive, and supposedly accurate test such as the Western Blot (which searches for antibodies against specific protein molecules) or radioimmunoprecipitation or radioimmunofluorescence assay is carried out. (p. 47)

The individual who does not test positive on the ELISA tests would be classified as being CDC_0 (Antoni et al., 1990). This means one of two things: (a) the individual in question has never been exposed to the AIDS virus or (b) the individual has not had sufficient time to develop antibodies to the AIDS virus. In either case, the individual should be tested again at a later date, usually 6 to 10 months after the initial blood test or last high-risk behavior to rule out the second possibility.

Assuming that the individual has been exposed to the virus, then during the next few months, the infected person's body will begin to develop antibodies in an attempt to fight off the AIDS virus. Unfortunately, the virus that causes AIDS may rapidly change its outer shell—a trait that may help it escape the body's immune system (Patlak, 1989). As many as 200 different strains of HIV have been identified, each with subtle genetic variations.

However, the body will attempt to produce antibodies to fight as many different strains of the invading virus as possible. This person, when tested, will be "antibody positive," or "seropositive." Individuals whose blood does not have the antibodies for the AIDS virus will be said to be "seronegative," or "antibody negative." The individual who has antibodies in his or her blood for HIV, but who has not developed other symptoms of the disease, would be classified as CDC_1 (Antoni et al., 1990). It has been estimated that 1 in 75

American men and 1 in 700 American women carry HIV, many of whom are unaware that they are infected (CDC *AIDS Weekly*, 1992).

During this stage of the disease, individuals will have no significant symptoms other than a positive antibody response on a blood test. But they are still infected, and the infection will progress. Research findings by Jacobsen, Perry, and Hirsch (1990) suggest that 75% of those individuals who "convert" from seronegative to seropositive will develop symptoms of AIDS within 6 years of the time that they first test positive for the infection. However, it is possible for an individual to be asymptomatic for 10 to 15 years before going on to the next stage of the infection (Antoni et al., 1990). During this period, the individual remains capable of passing the infection on to others in the ways previously discussed.

When one AIDS virus cell has successfully invaded one antibody, it will reproduce hundreds or thousands of times. When it is ready, the duplicates of the original virus will burst from the cell, killing the antibody and releasing all of the duplicates into the bloodstream (Antoni et al., 1990). Many of the duplicate virus cells will then infect other antibodies. As the infection progresses, the body's immune system will be impaired, but it will still be functional at a reduced level of efficiency. This is the stage known as "aids related complex," or ARC. The body's impaired immune system can now be easily detected through blood tests (McCutchan, 1990).

The person in this stage of the disease process would be classified as falling into the category of CDC_3 (Antony et al., 1990). Some of the symptoms of ARC include loss of appetite, weight loss, fever, night sweats, skin rashes, diarrhea, tiredness, lack of resistance to infections, and swollen lymph glands (Koop, 1986). It should be noted, however, that these conditions are also symptoms of other, often treatable, diseases.

Over time, this viral infection brings about the immune system dysfunction formally known as acquired immune deficiency syndrome, or AIDS (Redfield & Burke, 1988). This final phase of the infection is known as CDC_4 (Antoni et al., 1990). By this time, the body's weakened immune system is no longer able to fight off infection by organisms that previously were easily contained (Glasner & Kaslow, 1990; McCutchan, 1990). The individual will then develop one or more "opportunistic infections" that are the hallmark of AIDS.

As time progresses, death will follow from these opportunistic infections. Thus, in a technical sense, the destruction of the body's immune system is only one stage (the final stage) of the infection caused by HIV (Glasner & Kaslow, 1990).

AIDS and Kaposi's Sarcoma

There was a time when a rare form of cancer, *Kaposi's sarcoma*, was thought to be one of the opportunistic infections that indicated that an individual had AIDS. Recent research, however, has suggested that Kaposi's sarcoma may be caused by a *different* infectious agent, possibly also a virus. By coincidence, this virus seems to have been introduced into the United States at about the same time the AIDS virus was introduced (Oliwenstein, 1990). Both Kaposi's sarcoma and HIV are sexually transmitted diseases (STDs). Because of the similarities in the mode of transmission, both infections are commonly found in homosexual or bisexual males. This led to the mistaken conclusion that Kaposi's sarcoma was a manifestation of AIDS.

Current thought is that Kaposi's sarcoma is transmitted through sexual contact with an infected individual, as is the case with HIV. Unlike HIV, however, Kaposi's sarcoma apparently cannot be transmitted through contact with infected blood (Oliwenstein, 1990). Indeed, in rare cases it is possible for an individual to develop Kaposi's sarcoma without ever having been exposed to the AIDS virus, providing further evidence that the two are actually separate disorders.

THE TREATMENT OF AIDS

Although there is no cure for AIDS once the infection has been transmitted, researchers hope to develop treatment methods that will *arrest the progression* of the disease once the individual has been infected (Gallo & Montagner, 1988; Heaton, 1990). If researchers are successful in finding a drug or drugs that arrest the progression of AIDS, it will be a significant step forward. However, unless there is a unprecedented breakthrough in the treatment of AIDS,

> the combined effects of antiretroviral agents and drugs to prevent specific infectious diseases are likely to produce incremental gains in survival, rather than a dramatic cure. (McCutchan, 1990, p. 11)

Current research is aimed at developing a treatment program that will slow or completely arrest the progression of AIDS. However, this will not be a cure, just as insulin is not a cure for diabetes mellitus. Injections of insulin serve as a substitute for the body's own insulin, slowing or even arresting the progression of diabetes mellitus. However, the insulin is not a cure for the diabetes. At this time, then, the ultimate "treatment" for AIDS lies in prevention.

AIDS and Suicide

Indirectly, AIDS may kill through a mechanism other than opportunistic infections. Pope and Morin (1990) report that individuals who are aware that they are infected with HIV have a suicide rate over 30 times higher than that of individuals who are not infected. Thus, there is a significantly higher risk of suicidal behavior in those individuals who have learned that they are infected with HIV, posing legal and ethical dilemmas for the human-services professional.

THE TREATMENT OF HEPATITIS B

At this point in time, there is no effective treatment for the hepatitis B virus once it has been acquired. However, there is a vaccine that is quite effective in preventing the development of the infection, if the individual is vaccinated prior to exposure to the virus (Brody, 1991). The Centers for Disease Control now recommends that children routinely be vaccinated against hepatitis B along with the other "preventable" diseases, and that adults who engage in activities that might expose them to hepatitis B also be vaccinated.

A CLOSING NOTE

Despite the risk of AIDS and hepatitis B, addicts continue to share contaminated needles, syringes, or both—often simply because they do not want to wait until a clean needle or syringe is available. Although rinsing the needle and syringe with bleach will often destroy the AIDS virus, many addicts do not engage in this practice because it takes too much time. Some addicts have been known to stand in line to use another person's needle and syringe, even though they have a new needle and syringe at home.

Individuals also continue to engage in high-risk sexual behavior, either heterosexual or homosexual, in spite of the known association between such behavior and AIDS. It is important, then, for chemical dependency professionals to have a working knowledge of infections such as AIDS and hepatitis B so as to better help their clients understand and come to terms with these diseases.

Appendix 4

Drugs and Sexuality

Students are often surprised to learn that sexual arousal is a multiphasic process that involves the neurological, vascular, muscular, and hormonal systems of the human body (Kaplan, 1974). Because many drugs of abuse have their greatest impact on these body systems, drug abusers and addicts frequently experience some form of sexual dysfunction. In this chapter, we will consider the interaction between the drugs of abuse and sexual dysfunction.

THE EFFECTS OF DRUGS ON SEXUAL AROUSAL

There are several problems associated with the assessment of how drugs impact the sexual arousal process. Numerous factors must be considered, including (a) the specific drug(s) present in the individual's body, (b) the specific amount of each drug in the body, (c) the specific amount of each drug already in the bloodstream, and (d) the specific amount of each drug that will potentially reach the blood. Finally, potential interactions between the drugs present in the individual's body must be taken into account.

To complicate matters still further, the same drug may have different effects on the sexual arousal process as a result of still other factors. According to Kaplan (1974), additional factors include the individual's physical health, prescription and nonprescription medications being used by the individual, and the individual's emotional health (which includes his or her expectations for the drug or drugs being used).

Gold (1988) postulated that there are three elements to normal sexual function: (a) desire, (b) performance, and (c) satisfaction. The various drugs of abuse may impact each of these elements. To assess the impact of drugs on sexual arousal, one must understand how they disrupt sexual desire, interfere with sexual performance, and in many cases block sexual satisfaction.

Expectations and Sexual Arousal

In their study of peoples' preconceptions about the effects of alcohol, Brown et al. (1980) found that subjects anticipated enhancement of both social and

401

physical pleasure, including enhancement of sexual performance. Subjects also thought that moderate alcohol use would increase social aggressiveness, increase assertiveness, and reduce tension.

Kaplan (1974) points out that although research findings suggest that LSD is either nonstimulating or possibly even a drug that depresses sexual desire, expectations for the drug still may play a role in how its effects are perceived by the individual. Thus, in certain circumstances a person under the influence of LSD may report an "unusually intense sexual encounter" despite the drug's known physiological effects.

Chemicals and Intimacy Dysfunction

Intimacy might be thought of as an element of sexual desire or emotional health. The emotionally secure individual will desire both sexual and nonsexual intimacy without feeling anxious or ashamed. Unfortunately, many people do not accept the desire for sexual intimacy as totally normal. Often, they believe that they must be under the influence of alcohol or drugs in order to express sexual feelings.

According to Masters and Johnson (1986), the belief that alcohol increases sexual desire in both men and women is a common one. Sometimes alcohol is used as an "excuse" for expressing normal sexual desires and possibly acting on them. One danger, however, is that as the chemicals reduce the individual's inhibitions, he or she may choose a sexual partner who may be infected with AIDS.

Covington (1987) defines alcoholism as an intimacy disorder; in his words, "a love affair with alcohol" (p. 21). He suggests that feelings of shame, guilt, and pain associated with a history of physical, sexual, or emotional abuse set the stage for drug use as a way of dealing with the anxiety the individual experiences when offered the opportunity for intimacy. The history of abuse inhibits the development of trust. Trust, in Covington's view, enables surrender—an element of the sexual experience.

According to Coleman (1988a, 1988b), chemical dependency itself may be the result of a lack of adequate intimacy skills. Many people may initially turn to drugs as a way of dealing with this problem. By substituting chemicals for the desired intimacy skills, the individual is ultimately faced with an even more painful awareness of continued isolation.

This sets the stage for a cycle of continued drug use. As noted by Gold (1988) chemical use may, in itself, bring about sexual dysfunction—the discovery of which may cause the individual to avoid further opportunities for intimacy. This results in a renewed sense of loneliness and shame, which may then be self-medicated through further drug or alcohol use.

Often, the newly recovering alcoholic must learn how to be sexual without using drugs (Coleman, 1988a). Covington (1987) notes that the media often bombard women with the message that in order to be sexually appealing they must be drinkers. This message makes if difficult for the recovering female alcoholic to separate her sexuality from continued alcohol use.

Marital counseling or therapy with a qualified sex therapist is often a necessary component of recovery programs (Coleman, 1988a; Miller & Foy, 1981). Marital counseling or sex therapy helps struggling addicts develop the intimacy skills they often lack. Most addictions specialists are not trained in marital counseling or sex therapy; thus, individuals who need these services should be referred to the appropriate professional.

THE IMPACT OF SPECIFIC CHEMICALS ON SEXUAL PERFORMANCE

An *aphrodisiac* is a substance that enhances sexual pleasure and/or performance. Although empirical research has consistently demonstrated that chemical use is likely to interfere with sexual performance rather than enhance it, the belief persists that one drug or another can make for better sex (Kolodny, 1985). First one drug will be rumored to be the long-awaited aphrodisiac, only to have clinical research ultimately disprove the rumors. Then another drug will be touted as an aphrodisiac, and this, too, will turn out to be false.

Alcohol

Alcohol has long been thought to be an effective aphrodisiac. In recent years, however, Shakespeare's observation that alcohol "provokes the desire but . . . takes away the performance" (*Macbeth*, act 2, scene 3) has been found to be quite accurate. In a study by Gold (1987), for example, even at blood alcohol levels below that of legal intoxication, male college students experienced a significant decrease in the erectile response while viewing erotic films.

Under certain conditions, however, alcohol actually may enhance sexual excitement through the disinhibition effect. Low doses of alcohol depress the action of that portion of the brain involved in anxiety and fear responses (Flatto, 1990; Kaplan 1974). This allows alcohol to lower the individual's anxiety level, making it easier for him or her to engage in sexual activities.

However, in moderate to high doses or in cases of chronic use, alcohol disrupts sexual desire, performance, and satisfaction (Gold, 1988; Lieberman, 1988). Blood tests taken before, during, and after the use of alcohol have revealed that serum testosterone levels decrease as blood alcohol levels increase (Gold, 1987). The chronic use of alcohol will result in abnormally low serum testosterone levels—a condition that ultimately decreases sexual desire. This condition may be permanent, if significant liver or testicular damage has occurred (Flatto, 1990; Gold, 1988; Lieberman, 1988).

Moderate to high doses of alcohol or chronic use of alcohol may also inhibit sexual arousal through a disruption of the spinal cord nerves involved in penile erections (Gold, 1988; Flatto, 1990; Galbraith, 1991; Lieberman, 1988). Up to 80% of male alcoholics are thought to have developed alcohol-related sexual dysfunctions of one kind or another (Flatto, 1990). Surgical intervention may be necessary in cases of permanent alcohol-related impotence (Lieberman, 1988).

Women who drink will experience lowered levels of vaginal vasocongestion at higher levels of intoxication, inhibiting sexual desire and possibly performance. Even low doses of alcohol may reduce sexual responsiveness in women (Flatto, 1990). This information could explain why Gold (1987) found that 55% of his female subjects who drank reported experiencing a decrease in sexual pleasure.

In their study of human sexuality, Masters and Johnson (1966) report that excessive use of alcohol is the most frequently encountered cause of impotence in middle-aged men. They note that after first experiencing alcohol-induced impotence, the men will often fear further sexual failures. This fear may cause them to avoid sexual activity, which in turn will establish the groundwork for sexual adjustment problems in their relationships.

According to Masters et al. (1986), alcohol may decrease the intensity and pleasure of orgasm in males. In females, even a moderate level of intoxication makes it more difficult to achieve orgasm. In many cases, for the chronic alcoholic, sexual desire will disappear altogether (Masters & Johnson, 1966). Geller (1991) reports that between 31% and 58% of chronic male alcoholics will experience a lack of sexual desire; for chronic female alcoholics, 64% will experience this same problem.

As we discussed in Chapter 4, the chronic use of alcohol may bring about nerve damage in the extremities, a condition known as *peripheral neuropathy*. The nerves in the penis are also affected, according to Geller (1991). Although abstinence from further alcohol use and a regimen of dietary supplements and thiamine replacement therapy may reverse some of the peripheral neuropathy experienced by chronic male alcoholics, "a certain degree of permanent impairment may remain" (p. 62).

Further, the chronic use of alcohol will contribute to the atrophy of the testicles in men. Indeed, Geller (1991) states that between 70% and 80% of chronic male alcoholics will experience this complication from their drinking. Also, in part because of alcohol-induced liver disease, the ratio of androgen/estrogen is altered in the male alcoholic, resulting in a loss of secondary sex characteristics according to Geller.

The chronic female alcoholic may experience menstrual disturbances, infertility, and a loss of secondary sexual characteristics (Geller, 1991). In some cases, these problems may reverse after abstinence has been achieved. However, Geller notes that in many cases the problems persist for life.

In both men and women, sobriety may bring with it shame over past alcohol-related sexual behavior, a loss of desire, and fear over sexuality without the use of alcohol. According to Geller (1991), "newly sober alcoholics having sex without alcohol for the first time may find the experience strange, awkward, and anxiety provoking" (p. 63). Further, if the newly abstinent individual was the victim of a sexual assault, he or she might reexperience memories of the assault after achieving sobriety. There might be a need for couples' therapy as an aid to helping individuals deal with the problems brought on, or covered up, by the chronic use of alcohol.

Narcotics

The narcotic family of drugs impairs sexual desire, performance, and satisfaction (Galbraith, 1991; Gold, 1988). Obviously, this will nor present a problem for those taking narcotics for medical reasons. Few people for whom narcotics have been prescribed to control severe pain will be motivated to engage in sexual activity.

Males who abuse narcotics or who are addicted to them will experience diminished erections and orgasms (Gold, 1988) and possibly retarded ejaculation (Galbraith, 1991; Lieberman, 1988). Chronic use of narcotics will also reduce sexual desire (Lieberman, 1988; Masters et al., 1986) and inhibit the individual's ability to experience orgasm (Kaplan, 1979). The need to resort to prostitution to support their habit also decreases sexual desire for many women (Masters et al., 1986).

Research findings indicate both a lowered testosterone level and lowered libido in male narcotic addicts (Kolodny, 1985; Lieberman, 1988). Kolodny (1985) reports lowered libido in the majority of the female narcotic addicts he studied. Lieberman (1988) reports lowered fertility for both male and female narcotic addicts. Both lowered libido and infertility will usually resolve themselves in the first 60 to 90 days of abstinence.

Masters et al. (1986) postulate that decreased sexual desire in chronic narcotic addicts could be the result of the malnutrition and history of infections inherent in the life-style of the addict. Illness and malnutrition are factors known to reduce sexual desire and performance; thus, it is not surprising that narcotic addicts often experience sexual problems.

Kolodny (1985) notes that male narcotic addicts, like male alcoholics, may withdraw from further sexual activities after first discovering that their drug of choice has impaired their ability to achieve or maintain an erection. This withdrawal represents an attempt to avoid further injury to their self-esteem.

It is often difficult to determine which came first—the sexual dysfunction or the opiate addiction. For some individuals, addiction is a response to sexual dysfunction (Masters et al., 1986). According to Kaplan and Moodie (1982), drug addiction must be addressed first when working with addicts who are sexually dysfunctional.

Amphetamines and Cocaine

According to Kolodny (1985), there is little reliable research data on the effects of the CNS stimulants on sexual performance or satisfaction. However, both the amphetamines and cocaine have been touted as aphrodisiacs at various times (Kolodny, 1985; Washton, 1989).

Both Masters et al. (1986) and Kaplan (1979) are in agreement that the

CNS stimulants may increase sexual responsiveness when used at low doses, a factor that may have contributed to their reputation as aphrodisiacs. Gold (1988) states that the drug-naive male (a male with little or no drug-use experience) *might* experience a sustained erection and delay in orgasm at low dosage levels of amphetamines or cocaine.

Kolodny (1985) suggests that the CNS stimulants may have been regarded as aphrodisiacs because they produce physiological changes in the body similar to those associated with sexual excitement (increased blood pressure, increased heart rate, and an increase in blood flow to the genitals). They also bring about a feeling of well being. However, at high dosage levels, or when used for extended periods of time, the CNS stimulants have a negative impact on sexual performance and satisfaction (Galbraith, 1991).

There is a possibility that the amphetamines might reinforce a tendency toward compulsive sexual behaviors, such as compulsive masturbation, sadism, exhibitionism, and possibly mutilation of the penis (Lieberman, 1988). Washton (1989) estimates that perhaps as many as 60% of cocaine addicts engage in compulsive sexual behaviors. Because of its effects on the brain's reward system,

> cocaine can provoke or intensify sexual thoughts, feelings and fantasies that ignite compulsive sexual behaviors of all kinds. Many users experience increased sexual desire, prolonged sexual endurance, and markedly reduced inhibitions while high on cocaine. (Washton, 1989, p. 34)

Both the amphetamines and cocaine may inhibit orgasm, a condition known as *anorgasmia* (Galbraith, 1991). Kaplan (1979) and Lieberman (1988) suggest that this effect is most pronounced in female users. Kolodny (1985) agrees with this assessment, noting that about a third of the women who frequently use cocaine freebase will have problems experiencing orgasm. Washton (1989) also agrees, but points out that while male and female cocaine addicts might be unable to perform sexually, they still retain sexual feelings and fantasies.

As noted by Inciardi, Lockwood, and Pottieger (1991), a new trend—sex in exchange for crack cocaine—has emerged in recent years. They refer to "a strong association between crack use and apparent hypersexual behavior" (p. 26), with female addicts engaging in sex-for-drugs transactions on a scale never before seen in the drug world. They also warn that this promiscuous sexual behavior places the addict at high risk for contracting and spreading AIDS and other sexually transmitted diseases.

Gold (1988) states that moderate to high dosage levels of the amphetamines may result in male impotence and difficulty in achieving orgasm. In an earlier study, Gold (1987) notes that 14 of 39 males on cocaine (36% of the sample population) experienced some difficulty in achieving or maintaining an erection. In this same study, it was found that some men experience *priapism*—a pathological condition characterized by persistent erection of the penis that may require surgical intervention. Louie (1990) reports that individuals who use cocaine may experience panic episodes during sexual activity—a complication of their cocaine use that would interfere with sexual desire, performance, and satisfaction.

Masters et al. (1986) note that some women (or their partners) engage in the practice of rubbing a little cocaine powder onto the clitoris prior to intercourse. This is done on the theory that the cocaine will enhance the woman's sexual arousal and responsiveness. Cocaine is sometimes placed on the tip of the penis for the opposite reason: to reduce responsiveness so that the male may engage in intercourse for a longer period of time. According to Lieberman (1988), some women use cocaine for vaginal douching in the belief that this will cause the muscles in the vagina to contract, gripping the penis more tightly. Further, some of the cocaine will be absorbed through the walls of the vagina, resulting in feelings of euphoria, according to Lieberman.

As we discussed in Chapter 8, cocaine is a local anesthetic, and it is difficult to understand how the use of a local anesthetic on the clitoris could enhance sexual arousal and responsiveness. Both Masters et al. (1986) and Gold (1987) conclude that an individual's expectations for cocaine often exert influence on how the combination of cocaine and the sexual encounter are perceived by the couple who engage in this practice.

The amphetamines and cocaine are drugs with significant potential for harm and injury. The practice of placing a little cocaine powder on the tip of the penis immediately prior to intercourse is actually quite dangerous. As noted, this is done to prolong the male's ability to engage in intercourse, since the nerves at the tip of the penis are quite sensitive under normal conditions. The cocaine's local anesthetic effects help to lower the male's responsiveness, allowing him to engage in intercourse for a longer period of time.

Unfortunately, some of the contaminants of street cocaine are quite irritating to tissues of the body. Local irritation may break the skin, leading to the development of infections. On occasion, these infections have allowed for the development of gangrene, requiring amputation of the infected organ. Further, cocaine acts as a vasoconstrictor. This action, when combined with the constriction of blood vessels in the penis to achieve erection, may cause damage to the very blood vessels necessary for erection. This may result in long-term erectile problems in the male.

Marijuana

Marijuana's reputed effects on users during sexual encounters are somewhat at variance with its known physiological properties. Masters et al. (1986) report that research has demonstrated that marijuana either has no impact on tactile perception, or that it actually lessens touch perception. Yet, over 80% of some 1,000 subjects examined by Masters et al. claimed that the use of marijuana prior to intercourse led to heightened awareness of being touched by their partner all over their bodies.

As was discussed in Chapter 9, marijuana alters an individual's perceptions through an unknown mechanism. It has been postulated that an individual's *subjective perception* of marijuana's effects on the sexual experience is of greater consequence than actual physiological effects. (Masters, Johnson, & Kolodny, 1986). For example, Masters et al. point out that when one partner is under the effects of marijuana but the other is not, the sexual encounter is unlikely to be reported as being quite so pleasurable. Kaplan (1974) advances an alternative theory, suggesting that marijuana's disinhibiting effects help individuals release sexual feelings normally inhibited by the cortex of the brain.

Masters et al. (1986) also note that research has shown that 20% of the men who use marijuana on a daily basis will experience erectile problems. No corresponding problem has been found for the women who use marijuana daily, according to Masters et al. However, Galbraith (1991) reports that marijuana may contribute to a lower level of sexual desire and interfere with sexual satisfaction for both male and female users.

According to Kolodny (1985), some women who use marijuana report vaginal dryness during intercourse, which may be accompanied by pain. However, Kolodny does concede that marijuana users seem to report enhanced sexual awareness when both partners are under the influence of the drug. Marijuana has also been found to lower the testosterone levels of regular users, which is one factor associated with a loss of sexual desire (Kaplan, 1979; Lieberman, 1988). There is also research evidence to suggest that the regular use of marijuana will disrupt normal sperm production in men (Kolodny, 1985). These changes seem to reverse over time, after the individual discontinues further use of the drug.

Hallucinogens

A number of hallucinogens have been regarded as aphrodisiacs at one time or another. Masters et al. (1986) note that there has been little research on the effects of these drugs on sexual functioning; they suggest that because these drugs affect perception, the individual might be distracted by mental imagery during sexual activities.

Kolodny (1985) also points to a scarcity of research on the effects of the hallucinogens on sexual performance, but he does note that professionals have encountered sexual performance problems in users of these drugs. In a study by Kaplan (1979), LSD had little measurable impact on sexual performance, although it was noted that some individuals reported altered perceptions as a result of LSD use.

CNS Depressants

The effects of such CNS depressants as the barbiturates and the benzodiazepines on sexuality have not been studied in detail. Gold (1988) states that alcohol, the barbiturates, and the benzodiazepines decrease the strength of the spinal reflexes necessary for erection in the male and the orgasm response for both sexes. Women who use CNS depressants might experience decreased vaginal secretions before and during intercourse (Gold, 1988). Lieberman

(1988) notes that some women experience a reduction in libido and difficulty achieving orgasm after taking as little as 10 mg of the benzodiazepine diazepam.

Over 50% of those addicted to barbituates experience some form of sexual dysfunction (Kolodny, 1985). Indeed, in a study by Lieberman (1988), 16% of 155 patients who were taking phenobarbital as prescribed for the control of epilepsy complained of a decrease in sex drive, or, for males, impotence. The possibility that phenobarbital might at least partially block the effects of oral contraceptives was also suggested by Lieberman.

According to Masters et al. (1986), although some people may find the antianxiety effects of some CNS depressants helpful in achieving a state of sexual excitement, these medications could cause erectile dysfunctions in males, loss of sexual desire, and difficulty in achieving orgasm. Kaplan (1979) warns that when used at high dosage levels, the CNS depressants could cause impotence in males. Lieberman (1988) suggests that the CNS depressants could contribute to inhibited orgasm in women and inhibited ejaculation in men.

Over-the-Counter Analgesics and Other Drugs

Ibuprofen, which is often prescribed for the discomfort of menstruation, has been found to delay the onset of menstruation in some women by as much as 14 days (Lieberman, 1988).

The drug amyl nitrate, a prescription drug in most states, is used to relieve the pain of angina pectoris. However, amyl nitrite or butyl nitrite may also be used by some to prolong the moment of orgasm (Masters et al. 1986), possibly by altering one's sense of time (Lieberman, 1988). The use of amyl nitrite for this purpose is especially common among homosexual men, according to Masters et al. Amyl nitrite and similar agents are quick acting, taking effect in less than 30 seconds in some cases. These drugs will cause the blood vessels leading to the heart to dilate for a brief period of time, usually less than 5 minutes.

These effects are achieved at a cost of such possible side-effects as nausea, vomiting, headaches, and a loss of consciousness. Perhaps 10% of the men who use amyl nitrite will experience a temporary loss of erection, and those who overuse amyl nitrite or butyl nitrite run the risk of developing nitrite poisoning (Lieberman, 1988).

Galbraith (1991) suggests that when disulfiram (see Chapter 29 on pharmacological intervention tactics) is taken by male alcoholics, impotence may result.

SUMMARY

Human sexuality, as a field of study, has received little attention from addiction specialists (Gold, 1987). This is surprising, since each class of commonly abused drugs has been found to produce a wide range of effects on sexual desire, performance, and sexual satisfaction. Further, there is evidence to suggest that, for some, initial drug use is a response to a lack of adequate intimacy skills.

The final determination of a given drug's effects on any individual is based on the individual's state of health, his or her drug-use history, and the expectations (if any) the individual might have for the drug. Although little research has been conducted on the effects of many drugs of abuse on sexual desire, performance, and satisfaction, the limited research that is available strongly suggests that each class of these drugs has the potential to detract from an individual's ability to enter into, or enjoy, normal sexual relations.

BIBLIOGRAPHY

ABEL, E. L. (1982). *Drugs and Behavior: A Primer in Neuropsychopharmacology.* Malabar, FL: Robert E. Krieger.

ABRAMS, R. C., & ALEXOPOULOS, G. (1987). Substance abuse in the elderly: Alcohol and prescription drugs. *Hospital & Community Psychiatry, 38,* 1285–1288.

ACKERMAN, R. J. (1983). *Children of Alcoholics: A Guidebook for Educators, Therapists, and Parents.* Holmes Beach, FL: Learning Publications, Inc.

ADAMS, J. K. (1988). Setting free chemical dependency. *Alcoholism & Addiction,* 8(4), 20–21.

Addiction Letter, The. (1989a). Methadone centers ineffective in treating heroin addicts—GAO, 6(5),5.

Addiction Letter, The. (1989b). Therapeutic community research yields interesting results, 5(1),2.

ADELMAN, S. A., & WEISS, R. D. (1989). What is therapeutic about inpatient alcoholism treatment? *Hospital & Community Psychiatry, 40*(5),515–519.

AIDS Alert. (1989). Research on nitrites suggests drug plays role in AIDS epidemic, 4(9),153–156.

Al-Anon's Twelve Steps & Twelve Traditions. (1985). New York: Al-Anon Family Group Headquarters, Inc.

Alcoholics Anonymous. (1976). New York: Alcoholics Anonymous World Services, Inc.

Alcoholism & Drug Abuse Week. (1990a). ONDCP gives rundown on treatment approaches, 2(26),3–5.

Alcoholism & Drug Abuse Week. (1990b). House panel considers impact of drugs on emergency rooms, 3(38),4–5.

Alcoholism & Drug Abuse Week. (1991a). DAWN: Emergency rooms seeing fewer drug cases, 3(6),1.

Alcoholism & Drug Abuse Week. (1991b). ONDCP says Americans spent $41 billion on drugs in 1990, 3(24),3.

Alcoholism & Drug Abuse Week. (1991c). Mixed signals on possible upsurge in heroin use, 3(24),4–5.

ALEXANDER, B. (1991). Alcohol abuse in adolescents. *American Family Physician,* 43(2),527–532.

ALIBRANDI, L. A. (1978). The folk psychotherapy of Alcoholics Anonymous. In *Practical Approaches to Alcoholism Psychotherapy* (Zimberg, S., Wallace, J., & Blume, S., eds.). New York: Plenum.

ALLCOTT, J. V., BARNHART, R. A., & MOONEY, L. A. (1987). Acute lead poisoning in two users of illicit methamphetamine. *Journal of the American Medical Association, 258,*510–511.

ALLGULANDER, C., BORG, S., & VIKANDER, B. (1984). A 4–6 year follow-up of 50 patients with primary dependence on sedative and hypnotic drugs. *American Journal of Psychiatry, 141,*1580–1582.

ALMADORI, G., PALUDETTI, G., CERULLO, M., OTTAVINI, F., & D'ALATRI, L. (1990) Marijuana smoking as a possible cause of tongue carcinoma in young patients. *Journal of Laryngology and Otology, 104*(11),896–899.

ALTERMAN, A. I., ERDLEN, D. I., LAPORTE, D. J., & ERDLEN, F. R. (1982). Effects of illicit drug use in an inpatient psychiatric population. *Addictive Behaviors, 7,*231–242.

AMERICAN ACADEMY OF FAMILY PHYSICIANS. (1989). Screening for alcohol and other drug abuse. *American Family Physician, 40*(1),137–147.

AMERICAN ACADEMY OF FAMILY PHYSICIANS. (1990a). Marijuana use and memory loss. *American Family Physician, 41*(3),930–932.

AMERICAN ACADEMY OF FAMILY PHYSICIANS. (1990b). Effects of fetal exposure to cocaine and heroin. *American Family Physican, 41*(5),1595–1597.

AMERICAN CANCER SOCIETY. (1990). Data bank. *Breakthroughs, 1*(2),12.

American Druggist. (1989). The top 200 drugs, *199*(2),38–48.

American Druggist. (1990). The top 200 drugs, *201*(2),27–31.

AMERICAN PSYCHIATRIC ASSOCIATION. (1987). *Diagnostic and Statistical Manual of Mental Disorders* (3rd ed., revised). Washington, DC: The Association.

AMERICAN PSYCHIATRIC ASSOCIATION. (1991). *DSM-IV Options Book: Work in Progress.* Washington, DC: The Association.

ANANTH, J., VANDEWATER, S., KAMAL, M., BRODSKY, A., GAMAL, R., & MILLER, M. (1989). Missed diagnosis of substance abuse in psychiatric patients. *Hospital & Community Psychiatry, 40,*297–299.

ANDERSON, D. J. (1989a). Inhalant abusers risk death, permanent injury. *Minneapolis Star-Tribune, VIII* (165), 4ex.

ANDERSON, D. J. (1989b). An alcoholic is never too old for treatment. *Minneapolis Star-Tribune, VIII* (200), 7ex.

ANDERSON, D. J. (1990). Job success can follow addiction. *Minneapolis Star-Tribune IX* (104),8E.

ANDERSON, D. J. (1991). Alcohol abuse takes a toll in head injuries. *Minneapolis Star-Tribune, X* (152),7E.

ANDREASEN, N. C. (1984). *The Broken Brain.* New York: Harper & Row.

ANGIER, N. (1990). Storming the wall. *Discover, 11*(5),67–72.

ANSEVICS, N. L., & DOWEIKO, H. E. (1983). A conceptual framework for intervention with the antisocial personality. *Psychotherapy in Private Practice, 1*(3),43–52.

ANTONI, M. H., SCHNEIDERMAN, H., FLETCHER, M. A., GOLDSTEIN, D. A., IRONSON, G., & LAPERRIERE, A. (1990). Psychoneuroimmunology and HIV-1. *Journal of Consulting and Clinical Psychology, 58,*38–49.

APPLEBAUM, P. S. (1992). Controlling prescription of benzodiazepines. *Hospital & Community Psychiatry, 43,* 12–13.

ARONOFF, G. M., WAGNER, J. M., & SPANGLER, A. S. (1986). Chemical interventions for pain. *Journal of Consulting and Clinical Psychology, 54,*769–775.

ASSOCIATED PRESS. (1991a). Smoking catches up: Deaths top 400,000 in '88. *Minneapolis Star-Tribune, IX* (303), 7A.

ASSOCIATED PRESS. (1991b). Second-hand smoke kills 53,000 annually, says unreleased report for EPA. *Minneapolis Star-Tribune, X* (77), 7A.

ASSOCIATED PRESS. (1991c). Americans' illegal drug tab last year was over $40 billion. *Minneapolis Star-Tribune, X* (56), 1.

ASSOCIATED PRESS. (1991d). Study: Daily alcohol use cuts heart attack risk. *Minneapolis Star-Tribune, X* (141), 1A, 22A.

ASTRACHAN, B. M., & TISCHLER, G. L. (1984). Normality from a health systems perspective. In *Normality and the Life Cycle* (Offer, D., & Sabshin, M., eds.). New York: Basic Books.

AUSABEL, D. P. (1983). Methadone maintenance treatment: The other side of the coin. *International Journal of the Addictions, 18,*851–862.

BAEKELAND, F., & LUNDWALL, L. (1975). Dropping out of treatment: A critical review. *Psychological Bulletin, 82,*738–783.

BAHRKE, M. S. (1990). Psychological research, methodological problems, and relevant issues. Paper presented at the 1990 meeting of the America Psychological Association, Boston, MA.

BALES, J. (1988). Legalized drugs: Idea flawed, debate healthy. *APA Monitor, 19*(8),22.

BANERJEE, S. (1990). Newest wrinkle for smokers is on their faces. *Minneapolis Star-Tribune, VIII*(341). 1Ex,5Ex.

BARDEN, J. C. (1991). In depth. *Minneapolis Star-Tribune, X*(153), 4A,6A.

BARNHILL, J. G., CIRAULO, A. M., CIRAULO, D. A. (1989). Interactions of importance in chemical dependence. In *Drug Interactions in Psychiatry* (Ciraulo, D. A., Shader, R. I., Greenblatt, D. J., & Creelman, W., eds.). Baltimore: Williams & Wilkins.

BARNES, D. (1988). New data intensify the agony over Ecstacy. *Science, 139,*864–866.

BAUMAN, J. L. (1988). Acute heroin withdrawal. *Hospital Therapy, 13,*60–66.

BAUMAN, J. L. (1989). Alcohol withdrawal syndrome. *Hospital Therapy, 14*(7),47–51.

BAYS, J. (1990). Substance abuse and child abuse. *Pediatric Clinics of North America, 37,*881–903.

BEAN-BAYOG, M. (1988). Alcohol and drug abuse: Alcoholism as a cause of psychopathology. *Hospital & Community Psychiatry, 30,*352–354.

BEASLEY, J. D. (1987). *Wrong Diagnosis: Wrong Treatment: The Plight of the Alcoholic in America.* New York: Creative Infomatics, Inc.

BEATTIE, M. (1987). *Codependent No More.* New York: Harper & Row.

BEATTIE, M. (1989). *Beyond Codependency.* New York: Harper & Row.

BEAUVAIS, F., & OETTING, E. R. (1988). Inhalant abuse by young children. In *Epidemiology of Inhalant Abuse: An Update.* Washington, DC: National Institute on Drug Abuse.

BERENSON, D. (1987). Alcoholics Anonymous: From surrender to transformation. *The Family Therapy Networker, 11*(4),25–31.

BERG, B. J., & DUBIN, W. R. (1990). Economic grand rounds: Why 28 days? An alternative approach to alcoholism treatment. *Hospital and Community Psychiatry, 41,*1175–1178.

BERG, R., FRANZEN, M. M., & WEDDING, D. (1987). *Screening for Brain Impairment: A Manual for Mental Health Practice.* New York: Springer.

BERGER, P. A., & DUNN, M. J. (1982). Substance induced and substance use disorders. In *Treatment of Mental Disorders* (Griest, J. H., Jefferson, J. W., & Spitzer, R. L., eds.). New York: Oxford University Press.

BERKOWITZ, A., & PERKINS, H. W. (1988). Personality characteristics of children of alcoholics. *Journal of Consulting and Clincial Psychology, 56,* 206–209.

BERTONE, R. J., GOMEZ, M., JACQUES, M. A., & MATTIKO, M. J. (1988). Comprehensive nicotine treatment. *Alcoholism & Addiction, 9*(2),14–17.

BLACK, C. (1987). How different is recovery for a COA? *Alcoholism & Addiction, 8*(6), insert.

BLAKE, R. (1990). Mental health counseling and older problem drinkers. *Journal of Mental Health Counseling, 12*(3),354–367.

BLAU, M. (1990). Toxic parents, perennial kids: Is it time for adult children to grow up? *Utne Reader, 42,*60–65.

BLEIDT, B. A., & MOSS, J. T. (1989). Age-related changes in drug distribution. U.S. Pharmacist, 14(8),24–32.

BLISS, R. E., GARVEY, A. J., HEINOLD, J. W., & HITCHCOCK, J. L. (1989). The influence of situation and coping on relapse crisis outcomes after smoking cessation. *Journal of Consulting and Clinical Psychology, 57,*443–449.

BLOODWORTH, R. C. (1987). Major problems associated with marijuana abuse. *Psychiatric Medicine, 3*(3),173–184.

BLUM, K. (1984). *Handbook of Abusable Drugs.* New York: Gardner Press.

BLUM, K. (1988). The disease process in alcoholism. *Alcoholism & Addiction, 8*(5),5–8.

BLUM, K. NOBLE, E. P., SHERIDAN, P. J., MONTGOMERY, A., RITCHIE, T., JAGADEESWARAN, P., NOGAMI, H., BRIGGS, A. H., & COHEN, J. B. (1999). Allelic association of human dopamine D_2 receptor gene in alcoholism. *Journal of the American Medical Association, 263*(15),2055–2060.

BLUM, K., & PAYNE, J. E. (1991). *Alcohol and the Addictive Brain.* New York: The Free Press.

BLUM, K., & TRACHTENBERG, M. C. (1988). Neurochemistry and alcohol craving. *California Society for the Treatment of Alcoholism and Other Drug Dependencies News, 13*(2),1–7.

BLUME, S. (1985). Women and alcohol. In *Alcoholism and Substance Abuse: Strategies for Clinical Intervention* (Bratter, T. E., & Forrest, G. G., eds.). New York: The Free Press.

BLUME, S. (1989). Dual diagnosis: Psychoactive substance dependence and the personality disorders. *Journal of Psychoactive Drugs, 21*(2),139–144.

BOARD OF TRUSTEES. (1991). Drug abuse in the United States. *Journal of the American Medical Association, 256,*2102–2107.

BOLOS, A. M., DEAN, M., LUCAS-DERSE, A., RAMSBURG, M., BROWN, G. L., & GOLDMAN, D. (1991). Population and pedigree studies reveal a lack of association between the dopamine D_2 receptor gene and alcoholism. *Journal of the American Medical Association, 264,*3156–3160.

BOODMAN, S. G. (1990). Like Marion Barry, many who seek help are addicted to more than one substance. *Minneapolis Star-Tribune, VIII*(307), 1E, 8E.

BOND, W. S. (1989). Smoking's effects on medications. *American Druggist, 200*(1), 24–25.

BONSTEDT, T., ULRICH, D. A., DOLINAR, L. J., & JOHNSON, J. J. (1984). When and where should we hospitalize alcoholics? *Hospital & Community Psychiatry, 35,*1038–1040.

BOWEN, M. (1985). *Family Therapy in Clinical Practice.* Northvale, NJ: Jason Aronson.

BOWER, B. (1991). Pumped up and strung out. *Science News, 140*(2),30–31.

BRADSHAW, J. (1988a). Compulsivity: The black plague of our day. *Lear's Magazine, 42,*89–90.

BRADSHAW, J. (1988b). *Bradshaw on: The Family.* Deerfield Beach, FL: Health Communications, Inc.

BRANT, J., & BUTTERS, N. (1986). The alcoholic Wernicke-Korsakoff syndrome and its relationship to long-term alcohol use. In *Neuropsychological Assessment of Neuropsychiatric Disorders* (Grant, I., & Adams, K. M., eds.). New York: Oxford University Press.

BRECKER, E. M. (1972). *Licit and Illicit Drugs.* Boston: Little, Brown.

BRENT, D. A., KUPFER, D. J., BROMET, E. J., & DEW, M. A. (1988). The assessment and treatment of patients at risk for suicide. In *American Psychiatric Association Annual Review (Vol 7)* (Frances, A. J., & Hales, R. E., eds.). Washington, DC: American Psychiatric Association Press.

BREO, D. L. (1990). Of MD's and muscles—Lessons from two "retired steroid doctors." *Journal of the American Medical Association, 263,* 1697–1705.

BRESLIN, J. (1988). Crack. *Playboy, 35*(12), 109–110, 210, 212–213, 215.

BRIGGS, G. G., FREEMAN, R. K., & YAFFE, S. J. (1986). *Drugs in Pregnancy and Lactation* (2nd ed.). Baltimore: Williams & Wilkins.

BRODY, J. (1991). Hepatitis B still spreading. *Minneapolis Star-Tribune, X*(269), 4E.

BROPHY, J. J. (1990). *Psychiatric disorders.* In *Current Medical Diagnosis and Treatment* (Schroeder, S. A., Krupp, M. A., Tierney, L. M., & McPhee, S. J., eds.). Norwalk, CT: Appleton & Lange.

BROWER, K. J., BLOW, F. C., YOUNG, J. P., & HILL, E. M. (1991) Symptoms and correlates of anabolic-androgenic steroid dependence. *British Journal of Addiction, 86,* 759–768.

BROWER, K. J., CATLIN, D. H., BLOW, F. C., ELIOPULOS, G. A., & BERESFORD, T. P. (1991). Clinical assessment and urine testing for anabolic-androgenic steroid abuse and dependence. *American Journal of Drug and Alcohol Abuse, 17,*(2), 161–172.

BROWN, R. T., & BRADEN, N. J. (1987). Hallucinogens. *Pediatric Clinics of North America, 34*(2), 341–347.

BROWN, S. (1985). *Treating the Alcoholic: A Developmental Model of Recovery.* New York: Wiley.

BROWN, S. A., CREAMER, V. A., & STETSON, B. A. (1987). Adolescent alcohol expectancies in relation to personal and parental drinking patterns. *Journal of Abnormal Psychology, 96,* 117–121.

BROWN, S. A. (1990). Adolescent alcohol expectancies and risk for alcohol abuse. *Addiction & Recovery, 10*(5/6), 16–19.

BROWN, S. J. (1987). Morphine: The benefits are worth the risks. *RN, 50*(3), 20–26.

BROWN, S. A., GOLDMAN, M. S., INN, A., & ANDERSON, L. R. (1980). Expectations of reinforcement from alcohol: Their domain and relation to drinking patterns. *Journal of Consulting and Clinical Psychology, 48,* 419–426.

BROWN, V. B., RIDGELY, M. S., PEPPER, B., LEVINE, I. S., & RYGLEWICZ, H. (1989). The dual crisis: Mental illness and substance abuse. *American Psychologist, 44,* 565–569.

BROWNING, C., REYNOLDS, A. L., DWORKIN, S. H. (1991). Affirmative psychotherapy for lesbian women. *The Counseling Psychologist, 19,* 177–196.

BRUNSWICK, M. (1989). More kids turning to inhalant abuse. *Minneapolis Star-Tribune, VII*(356), 1A, 6A.

BUBER, M. (1970). *I and Thou*. New York: Charles Scribner's Sons.

BUFE, C. (1988). A. A.: Guilt and god for the gullible. *Utne Reader, 30*, 54–55.

BURDEN, L. L., & ROGERS, J. C. (1988). Endocarditis: When bacteria invade the heart. *RN, 51*,(2), 38–43.

BURNAM, M. A., STEIN, J. A., GOLDING, J. M., SIEGEL, J. M., SORENSEN, S. B., FORSYTHE, A. B., & TELLES, C. A. (1989). Sexual assault and mental disorders in a community population. *Journal of Consulting and Clinical Psychology, 56*(6), 843–850.

BUTCHER, J. N. Introduction to the special series. (1988). *Journal of Consulting and Clinical Psychology, 56*, 171.

BYCK, R. (1987). Cocaine use and research: Three histories. In *Cocaine: Clinical and Behavioral Aspects* (Fisher, S., Rashkin, A., & Unlenhuth, E. H., eds.). New York: Oxford University Press.

BYRNE, C. (1989a). Pregnancy and crack: Trying to heal horror. *Minneapolis Star-Tribune, VIII*(89), 1, 4A.

BYRNE, C. (1989b). Cocaine alley. *Minneapolis Star-Tribune, VIII*(215), 29a–32a.

CALLAHAN, E. J. (1980). Alternative strategies in the treatment of narcotic addiction: A review. In *The Addictive Behaviors* (Miller, W. R., ed.). New York: Pergamon Press.

CALLAHAN, E. J., & PECSOK, E. H. (1988). Heroin addiction. In *Assessment of Addictive Behaviors* (Donovan, D. M., & Marlatt, G. A., eds.). New York: The Guilford Press.

CALSYN, D. A., SAXON, A. J., & BARNDT, D. C. (1991). Urine screening practices in methadone maintenance clinics: A survey of how the results are used. *Journal of Nervous and Mental Disease, 179*(4), 222–228.

CALSYN, R. J., & MORSE, G. A. (1991). Correlates of problem drinking among homeless men. *Hospital and Community Psychiatry, 42*, 721–724.

CAMERON, N. (1963). *Personality Development and Psychopathology: A Dynamic Approach*. Boston: Houghton Mifflin.

CARDONI, A. A. (1990). Focus on *adinasolam:* A benzodiazepine with antidepressant activity. *Hospital Formulary, 25*, 155–158.

CAREY, K. B. (1989). Emerging treatment guidelines for mentally ill chemical abusers. *Hospital and Community Psychiatry, 40*, 341–342, 349.

CARLSON, J. L., STROM, B. L., MORSE, L., WEST, S. L., SOPER, K. A., STOLLEY, P. D., & JONES, J. K. (1987). The relative gastrointestinal toxicity of the nonsteroidal anti-inflammatory drugs. *Archives of Internal Medicine, 147*, 1054–1059.

CATON, C. L. M., GRALNICK, A., BENDER, S., & SIMON, R. (1989). Young chronic patients and substance abuse. *Hospital and Community Psychiatry, 40*, 1037–1040.

CDC *AIDS Weekly*. (1992). Update on global AIDS situation. August 13, 1992, 2–4.

CENTERS FOR DISEASE CONTROL. (1990). Lead poisoning associated with intraveneous methamphetamine use—Oregon, 1988. *Journal of the American Medical Association, 263*, 797.

CHARNESS, M. E., SIMON, R. P., & GREENBERG, D. A. (1989). Ethanol and the nervous system. *New England Journal of Medicine, 321*(7), 442–454.

CHARNEY, D. S., HENINGER, G. R., & KLEBER, H. D. (1986). The combined use of clonidine and naltrexone as a rapid, safe, and effective treatment of abrupt withdrawal from methadone. *American Journal of Psychiatry, 143*, 831–837.

CHASNOFF, I. J. (1988). Drug use in pregnancy: Parameters of risk. *Pediatric Clinics of North America, 35*(6), 1403–1412.

CHASNOFF, I. J. (1991). Drugs, alcohol, pregnancy, and the neonate. *Journal of the American Medical Association, 266*, 1567–1568.

CHASNOFF, I. J., & SCHNOLL, S. H. (1987). Consequences of cocaine and other drug use in pregnancy. In *Cocaine: A Clinician's Handbook* (Washton, A. M., & Gold, M. S., eds.). New York: The Guilford Press.

CHAVEZ, G. F., MULINARE, J., & CORDERO, J. E. (1989). Maternal cocaine use during early pregnancy as a risk factor for congenital urogenital anomalies. *Journal of the American Medical Association, 262*(6), 795–798.

CHEREK, D. R. (1990). Laboratory studies on aggression and drugs: Variations in behavioral effects. Symposium presented at the annual meeting of the 1990 American Psychological Association, Boston, MA.

CHIAUZZI, E. (1990). Breaking the patterns that lead to relapse. *Psychology Today, 23*(12), 18–19.

Chicago Sun-Times. (1989). Scarey statistics on cocaine, 43,(159), 36.

CHO, A. K. (1990). Ice: A new dosage form of an old drug. *Science, 249*, 631–634.

CLIMKO, R. P., ROEHRICH, H., SWEENEY, D. R., & AL-RAZI, J. (1987). Ecstacy: A review of MDMA and MDA. *International Journal of Psychiatry in Medicine, 16*(4), 359–372.

CLONINGER, C. R., GOHMAN, M., & SIGVARDSSON, S. (1981). Inheritance of alcohol abuse: Cross fostering analysis of adopted men. *Archives of General Psychiatry, 38*, 861–868.

COHEN, L. S. (1989). Psychotropic drug use in pregnancy. *Hospital and Community Psychiatry, 40*(6), 566–567.

COHEN, N. L., & MARCOS, L. R. (1989). The bad–mad dilemma for public psychiatry. *Hospital and Community Psychiatry, 40*, 677.

COHEN, S. (1977). Inhalant abuse: An overview of the problem. In *Review of Inhalants: Euphoria to Dysfunction* (Sharp, C. W., & Brehm, M. L., eds.). Washington, DC: U.S. Government Printing Office.

COHEN, S. (1984). Cocaine: Acute medical and psychiatric complications. *Psychiatric Annuals, 14*, 747–749.

COHEN, S., LICHTENSTEIN, E., PROCHASKA, J. O., ROSSI, J. S., GRITZ, E. G., CARR, C. R., ORLEANS, C. T., SCHOENBACH, V. J., BIENER, L., ABRAMS, D., DICLEMENTE, C., CURRY, S., MARLATT, G. A., CUMMINGS, K. M., EMONT, S. L., GIOVINO, G., & OSSIP-KLEIN, D. (1989). Debunking myths about self-quitting. *American Psychologist, 44*, 1355–1365.

COLEMAN, E. (1988a). Chemical dependency and intimacy dysfunction: Inextricably bound. In *Chemical Dependency and Intimacy Dysfunction* (Coleman, E., ed.). New York: The Haworth Press.

COLEMAN, E. (1988b). Child physical and sexual abuse among chemically dependent individuals. In *Chemical Dependency and Intimacy Dysfunction* (Coleman, E. ed.). New York: The Haworth Press.

COLEMAN, P. (1989). Letter to the editor. *Journal of the American Medical Association, 261*(13), 1879–1880.

COLLETTE, L. (1988). Step by step: A skeptic's encounter. *Utne Reader, 30*, 69–76.

COLLETTE, L. (1990). After the anger, what then? *Networker, 14*(1), 22–31.

COLLIER, A. (1989). To deal and die in L.A. *Ebony, 44*(10), 106–108.

COLLINS, J. J., & ALISON, M. (1983). Legal coercion and retention in drug abuse treatment. *Hospital & Community Psychiatry, 34*, 1145–1150.

COLQUITT, M., FIELDING, L. P., & CRONAN, J. E. (1987). Drunk drivers and medical and social injury. *New England Journal of Medicine, 317*, 1262–1266.

CONLAN, M. F. (1990). Research and development plan proposed for pharmacotherapy. *Drug Topics, 134*(1), 50.

CONRAD, S., HUGHES, P., BALDWIN, D. C., ACHENBACK, K. E., & SHEEHAN, D. V. (1989). Cocaine use by senior medical students. *American Journal of Psychiatry, 146*, 382–382.

Consumer Reports. (1989). *The New Medicine Show.* Mt. Vernon, NY: Author.

CORDERO, J. F. (1990). Effect of environmental agents on pregnancy outcomes: Disturbances of prenatal growth and development. *Medical Clinics of North America, 72*(2), 279–290.

COTTON, P. (1990). Medium isn't accurate "ice age" message. *Journal of the American Medical Association, 263*, 2717.

COUNCIL ON SCIENTIFIC AFFAIRS. (1990a). The worldwide smoking epidemic. *Journal of the American Medical Association, 263*, 3312–3318.

COUNCIL ON SCIENTIFIC AFFAIRS. (1990b). Medical and nonmedical uses of anabolic-androgenic steroids. *Journal of the American Medical Association, 264*, 2923–2927.

COUSINS, N. (1989). *Head First: The Biology of Hope.* New York: E. P. Dutton.

COVINGTON, S. S. (1987). Alcohol and female sexuality. *Alcoholism & Addiction, 7*(5), 21.

COWEN, R. (1990). Alcoholism treatment under scrutiny. *Science News, 137*, 254.

CRAWSHAW, J. P. (1985). Recognizing anabolic steroid abuse. *Patient Case, 19*, 28.

CREELMAN, W., CIRAULO, D. A., & Shader, R. I. (1989). Lithium drug interactions. In *Drug Interactions in Psychiatry* (Ciraulo, D. A., Shader, R. I., Greenblatt, D. J., & Creelman, W., eds.). Baltimore: Williams & Wilkins.

CREELMAN, W., SANDS, B. F., CIRAULO, D. A., GREENBLATT, D. J., & SHADER, R. I. (1989). Benzodiazepines. In *Drug Interactions in Psychiatry* (Ciraulo, D. A., Shader, R. I., Greenblatt, D. J., & Creelman, W., eds.). Baltimore: Williams and Wilkins.

CRITCHLOW, B. (1986). The powers of John Barleycorn: Beliefs about the effects of alcohol on social behavior. *American Psychologist, 41*, 751–764.

CROWLEY, T. J. (1988). Substance abuse treatment and policy: Contributions of behavioral pharmacology. Paper presented at the 1988 meeting of the American Psychological Association, Atlanta, GA.

CRUMLEY, F. E. (1990). Substance abuse and adolescent suicidal behavior. *Journal of the American Medical Association, 263*, 3051–3056.

CUMMINGS, C., GORDON, J. R., & MARLATT, G. A. (1980). Relapse: Prevention and prediction. In *The Addictive Behaviors* (Miller, W. R., ed.). New York: Pergamon Press.

CUNNIEN, A. J. (1988). Psychiatric and medical syndromes associated with deception. In *Clinical Assessment of Malingering and Deception* (Rogers, R., ed.). New York: The Guilford Press.

DAIGLE, R. D. (1990). Anabolic steroids. *Journal of Psychoactive Drugs, 22*(1), 77–80.

D'AMICO, P. M. (1990). Letter to the editor. *Journal of the American Medical Association, 263*(5), 658.

DAVIS, J. M., & BRESNAHAN, D. B. (1987). Psychopharmacology in clinical psychiatry. In *American Psychiatric Association Annual Review (Vol 6).* Washington, DC: American Psychiatric Association Press.

DEANGELIS, T. (1989). Behavior is included in report on smoking. *AFA Monitor, 20*(3), 1, 4.

DECKER, S., FINS, J., & FRANCES, R. (1987). Cocaine and chest pain. *Hospital & Community Psychiatry, 33,* 464–466.

DELEON, G. (1989). Psychopathology and substance abuse: What is being learned from research in therapeutic communities. *Journal of Psychoactive Drugs, 21*(2), 177–188.

DEPARTMENT OF HEALTH AND HUMAN SERVICES. (1990). *National Household Survey on Drug Abuse: Population Estimates 1990.* Rockville, MD: U.S. Government Printing Office.

DIETCH, J. (1983). The nature and extent of benzodiazepine abuse: An overview of recent literature. *Hospital & Community Psychiatry, 34,* 1139–1144.

DIFRANZA, J. R, & TYE, J. B. (1990). Who profits from tobacco sales to children? *Journal of the American Medical Association, 263,* 2784–2787.

DIFRANZA, J. R., RICHARDS, J. W., PAULMAN, P. M., WOLF-GILLESPIE, N., FLETCHER, C., JAFFE, R. D., & MURRAY, D. (1991). RJR Nabisco's cartoon camel promotes Camel cigarettes to children. *Journal of the American Medical Association, 266,* 3149–3153.

DIGREGORIO, G. J. (1990). Cocaine update: Abuse and therapy. *American Family Physician, 41*(1), 247–251.

DOGHRAMI, K. (1989). Sleep disorders: A selective update. *Hospital and Community Psychiatry, 40,* 29–40.

DOLE, V. P. (1988). Implications of methadone maintenance for theories of narcotic addiction. *Journal of the American Medical Association, 260,* 3025–3029.

DOLE, V. P. (1989). Letter to the editor. *Journal of the American Medical Association, 261*(13), 1880.

DOLE, V. P., & NYSWANDER, M. A. (1965). Medical treatment for diacetyl morphine (heroin) addiction. *Journal of the American Medical Association, 193,* 645–656.

DOMINGUEZ, R., VILA-CORO, A. A., AGUIRRE, V. C., SLIPIS, J. M., & BOHAN, T. P. (1991). Brain and ocular abnormalities in infants in utero exposure to cocaine and other street drugs. *American Journal of Diseases of Children, 145,* 688–694.

DONOVAN, D. M. (1988). Assessment of addictive behaviors: Implications of an emerging biopsychosocial model. In *Assessment of Addictive Behaviors* (Donovan, D. M., & Marlatt, G. A., eds.). New York: The Guilford Press.

DONOVAN, D. M. (1992). The assessment process in addictive behaviors. *The Behavior Therapist, 15*(1), 18.

Dorland's Illustrated Medical Dictionary (27th ed.). (1988). Philadelphia, PA: W. B. Saunders.

DOWEIKO, H. (1979). Identifying the street names of drugs. *Journal of Emergency Nursing, 5*(6), 44–47.

DOWNING, C. (1990). The wounded healers. *Addiction & Recovery, 10*(3), 21–24.

DRAKE, R. E., OSHER, F. C., & WALLACH, M. A. (1989). Alcohol use and abuse in schizophrenia. *Journal of Nervous and Mental Disease, 177,* 408–414.

DRAKE, R. E., & WALLACH, M. A. (1989). Substance abuse among the chronic mentally ill. *Hospital and Community Psychiatry, 40,* 1041–1046.

DRAPER, N., & HAGA, C. (1989). Two recent surveys suggest that drug use is declining nationally. *Minneapolis Star-Tribune, VIII* (170), 1A, 7A.

DREIGER, R. M. (1986). Does anyone really believe that alcoholism is a disease? *American Psychologist, 37,* 322.

DREYFUSS, I. (1989). Federal agency to prove anabolic steroid abuse. *The Physician and Sports Medicine. 17*(7), 16.

DULFANO, C. (1978). Family therapy of alcoholism. In *Practical Approaches to Alcoholism Psychotherapy* (Zimberg, S., Wallace, J., & Blume, S., eds.). New York: Plenum.

DUNLOP, J., MANGHELLI, D., & TOLSON, R. (1989). Senior alcohol and drug coalition statement of treatment philosophy for the elderly. *Professional Counselor*, 4(2), 39–42.

DUPONT, R. L. (1987). Cocaine in the workplace: The ticking time bomb. In *Cocaine: A Clinician's Handbook* (Washton, A. M., & Gold, M. S., eds.). New York: The Guilford Press.

DYER, W. W. (1989). *You'll See It When You Believe It.* New York: William Morrow.

Economist, The. (1989). Ice overdose, *313*(7631), 29–31.

Economist, The. (1990a). Just say buprenorphine, *313*(7626), 95.

Economist, The. (1990b). War by other means, *314*(7641), 50.

EDMEADES, B. (1987). Alcoholics Anonymous celebrates its 50th year. In *Drugs, Society and Behavior* (Rucker, W. B., & Rucker, M. E. eds.). Guilford, CN: Dushkin Publishing Group.

EFRAN, J. S., HEFFNER, K. P., & LUKENS, R. T. (1987). Alcoholism as an opinion. *Family Networker, 11*(4), 43–46.

EHLERT, B. (1989). Alcoholism among the elderly. *Minneapolis Star-Tribune Sunday Magazine, VII*(363), 6–14.

EHRENREICH, B. (1992). Stamping out a dread scourge. *Time, 137*(7), 88.

EISON, A. S., & TEMPLE, D. L. (1987). Buspirone: Review of its pharmacology and current perspectives on its mechanism of action. *American Journal of Medicine, 80*(Supplement 3B), 1–9.

ELLIS, A., MCINERNEY, J. F., DIGIUSEPPE, R., & YEAGER, R. J. (1988). *Rational Emotive Therapy with Alcoholics and Substance Abusers.* New York: Pergamon Press.

ENGELMAN, R. (1989). Researcher says quest for intoxication is common throughout animal kingdom. *Minneapolis Star-Tribune, VIII*(173), 12E.

ERIKSON, E. H. (1963). *Childhood and Society.* New York: W. W. Norton & Co.

ESTROFF, T. W. (1987). Medical and biological consequences of cocaine abuse. In *Cocaine: A Clinician's Handbook* (Washton, A. M., & Gold, M. S., eds.). New York: The Guilford Press.

EVANS, K., & SULLIVAN, J. M. (1990). *Dual Diagnosis.* New York: The Guilford Press.

FABIAN, M. S., & PARSONS, O. A. (1983). Differential improvement of cognitive functions in recovering alcoholic women. *Journal of Abnormal Psychology, 92*, 87–95.

Facts about Alateen. (1969). New York: Al-Anon Family Group Headquarters.

FARIELLO, D., & SCHEIDT, S. (1989). Clinical case management of the dually diagnosed patient. *Hospital and Community Psychiatry, 40*, 1065–1067.

FARROW, J. A. (1990). Adolescent chemical dependency. *Medical Clinics of North America, 74*, 1265–1274.

FASSINGER, R. E. The hidden minority: Issues and challenges in working with lesbian women and gay men. *The Counseling Psychologist, 19*, 157–176.

FEIGHNER, J. P. (1987). Impact of anxiety therapy on patients' quality of life. *American Journal of Medicine, 32*(Supplement A), 14–19.

FINGARETTE, H. (1988). Alcoholism: The mythical disease. *Utne Reader, 30*, 64–69.

FINKELHOR, D. (1986). *A Sourcebook on Child Sexual Abuse.* Beverly Hills; Sage.

FINNEY, J. W., MOOS, R. H., & CHAN, D. A. (1975). Length of stay and program component effects in the treatment of alcoholism. *Journal of Studies on Alcohol, 36,* 88–108.

FIORE, M. C., NOVOTNY, T. E., PIERCE, J. P., GIOVINO, G. A., HATZIAN-DREU, E. J., NEWCOMB, P. A., SURAWICZ, T. S., & DAVIS, R. M. (1990). Methods used to quit smoking in the United States. *Journal of the American Medical Association, 263,* 2760–2765.

FISCHER, R. G. (1989). Clinical use of nonsteroidal anti-inflammatory drugs. *Pharmacy Times, 55*(8), 31–35.

FISS, H. (1979). Current dream research: A psychobiological perspective. In *Handbook of Dreams* (Wolman, B. B., ed.). New York: Van Nostrand Reinhold Co.

FLATTO, E. (1990). Alcohol and impotence from the doctor's casebook. *Nutrition Health Review, 53,* 19.

FOA, P. P. (1989). Letters to the editor. *Smithsonian, 20*(6), 18.

FORNAZZAZRI, L. (1988). Clinical recognition and management of solvent abusers. *Internal Medicine for the Specialist, 9*(6), 99–108.

FORWARD, S., & BUCK, C. (1989). *Toxic Parents.* New York: Bantam Books.

FOSSUM, M. A., & MASON, M. J. (1986). *Facing Shame: Families in Recovery.* New York: W. W. Norton & Co.

FOULKES, D. (1979). Children's dreams. In *Handbook of Dreams* (Wolman, B. B., ed.). New York: Van Nostrand Reinhold Co.

FRANCES, R. J. (1991). Should drugs be legalized? Implications of the debate for the mental health field. *Hospital and Community Psychiatry, 42,* 119–120, 125.

FRANCES, R. J., & MILLER, S. I. (1991). Addiction treatment: The widening scope. In *Clinical Textbook of Addictive Disorders* (Frances, R. J., & Miller, S. I., eds.). New York: The Guilford Press.

FRANKL, V. E. (1978). *The Unheard Cry for Meaning.* New York: Touchstone Books.

FRANKLIN, J. (1987). *Molecules of the Mind.* New York: Dell.

FRANKLIN, J. E. (1989). Alcoholism among blacks. *Hospital and Community Psychiatry, 40,* 1120–1122, 1127.

FRANKS, P., HARP, J., & BELL, B. (1989). Randomized, controlled trial of clonidine for smoking cessation in a primary care setting. *New England Journal of Medicine, 321,* 3011–3013.

FREDERICKSON, P. A., RICHARDSON, J. W., ESTHER, M. S., & LIN, S. (1990). Sleep disorders in psychiatric practice. *Mayo Clinic Procedures, 65,* 861–868.

FREIBERG, P. (1991). Panel hears of families victimized by alcoholism. *APA Monitor, 22*(4), 30.

FREZZA, M., DI PADOVA, C., POZZATO, G., TERPIN, M., BARONA, E., LIEBER, C. S. (1990). High blood alcohol levels in women. *New England Journal of Medicine, 322,* 95–99.

FRIEDMAN, D. (1987). Toxic effects of marijuana. *Alcoholism & Addiction, 7*(6), 47.

FROMM, E. (1956). *The Art of Loving.* New York: Harper & Row.

FROMM, E. (1968). *The Revolution of Hope.* New York: Harper & Row.

FULLER, R. K. (1989). Antidipsotropic medications. In *Handbook of Alcoholism Treatment Approaches* (Hester, R. K., & Miller, W. R., eds.). New York: Pergamon Press.

FULTZ, O. (1991). Roid rage. *American Health, X*(4), 60–64.

GALANTER, M. (1986). Treating substance abusers: Why therapists fail. *Hospital and Community Psychiatry, 37,* 769.

GALANTER, M., CASTANEDA, R., & FERMAN, J. (1988). Substance abuse among general psychiatric patients: Place of presentation, diagnosis, and treatment. *American Journal of Drug and Alcohol Abuse, 14*(2), 211–235.

GALANTER, M., CASTANEDA, R., & FRANCO, H. (1991). Group therapy and self-help groups. In *Clinical Textbook of Addictive Disorders* (Frances, R. J., & Miller, S. I., eds.). New York: The Guilford Press.

GALBRAITH, R. A. (1991). Sexual side effects of drugs. *Drug Therapy, 23*(3), 38–40, 46.

GALLAGHER, W. (1986). The looming menace of designer drugs. *Designer, 7*(8), 24–35.

GALLO, R. C., & MONTAGNIER, L. (1988). Aids in 1988. *Scientific American, 259*(4), 41–48.

GANNON, K. (1989). Pharmacists need to caution athletes about steroid use. *Drug Topics, 133*(12), 25.

GAWIN, F. H., ALLEN, D., & HUMBLESTONE, B. (1989). Outpatient treatment of "crack" cocaine smoking with flupenthixol deconate: A preliminary report. *Archives of General Psychiatry, 46*, 122–126.

GAWIN, F. H., & ELLINWOOD, E. H. (1988). Cocaine and other stimulants: Actions, abuse, and treatment. *New England Journal of Medicine, 318*, 1173–1182.

GAWIN, F. H., & KLEBER, H. D. (1986). Abstinence symptomology and psychiatric diagnosis in cocaine abusers. *Archives of General Psychiatry, 43*, 107–113.

GAWIN, F. H., KLEBER, H. D., BYCK, R., ROUNSAVILLE, B. J., KOSTEN, T. R., JATLOW, P. I., & MORGAN, C. (1989). Desipramine facilitation of initial cocaine abstinence. *Archives of General Psychiatry, 46*, 117–121.

GAY, G. R. (1990). Another side effects of NSAIDs. *Journal of the American Medical Association, 164*, 2677–2678.

GAY, L. (1991). In Amsterdam, drug war is fought by example, not crackdowns. *Minneapolis Star-Tribune, IX*(285), 11A.

GAZZANIGA, M. S. (1988). *Mind Matters.* Boston: Houghton Mifflin.

GELLER, A. (1991). Sexual problems of the recovering alcoholic. *Medical Aspects of Human Sexuality, 25*(3), 60–63.

GELLES, R. J., & STRAUS, M. A. (1988). *Intimate Violence: The Definitive Study of the Causes and Consequences of Abuse in the American Family.* New York: Simon & Schuster.

GELMAN, D., UNDERWOOD, A., KING, P., HAGER, M., & GORDON, J. (1990). Some things work! *Newsweek, CXVI*(13), 78–81.

GIACONA, N. S., DAHL, S. L., & HARE, B. D. (1987). The role of nonsteroidal antiinflammatory drugs and non-narcotics in analgesia. *Hospital Formulary, 22*, 723–733.

GIBBONS, B. (1992). Alcohol, the legal drug. *National Geographic, 181*(2), 2–35.

GILLIN, J. C. (1991). The long and the short of sleeping pills. *New England Journal of Medicine, 324*, 1735–1736.

GLASER, F. B., & OGBORNE, A. C. (1982). Does A.A. really work? *British Journal of the Addictions, 77*, 88–92.

GLASER, P. D., & KASLOW, R. A. (1990). The epidemiology of human immunodeficiency virus infection. *Journal of Clinical and Consulting Psychology, 58*, 13–21.

GLASSMAN, A. H., STETNER, F., WALSH, T., RAIZMAN, P. S., FLEISS, J. L., COOPER, T. B., & COVEY, L. S. (1988). Heavy smokers, smoking cessation and clonidine. *Journal of the American Medical Association, 259*, 2863–2866.

GLOWA, J. R. 1986). *Inhalants: The Toxic Fumes.* New York: Chelsea House Publishers.

GOLD, M. S. (1987). Sexual dysfunction challenges today's addictions clinicians. *Alcoholism & Addiction, 7*(6), 11.

GOLD, M. S. (1988). Alcohol, drugs, and sexual dysfunction. *Alcoholism & Addiction, 9*(2), 13.

GOLD, M. S. (1989a). Opiates. In *Drugs of Abuse* (Giannini, A. J., & Slaby, A. E., eds.). Oradell, NJ: Medical Economics Books.

GOLD, M. S. (1989b). Medical implications of cocaine intoxication. *Alcoholism & Addiction, 9*(3), 16.

GOLD, M.S . (1990). Weekend warriors and addicts. *Alcoholism & Addiction, 10*(3), 12.

GOLD, M. S., & PALUMBO, J. M. (1991). The future treatment of cocaine addiction. *Alcoholism & Addiction, 11*(3), 35–37.

GOLD, M. S., & VEREBEY, K. (1984) The psychopharmacology of cocaine. *Psychiatric Annuals, 14,* 714–723.

GOLD, S., & SHERRY, L. (1984). Hyperactivity, learning disabilities, and alcohol. *Journal of Learning Disabilities, 17*(1), 3–6.

GOLDSTEIN, P. (1990). Drugs and violence. Paper presented at the 1990 meeting of the American Psychological Association, Boston, MA.

GONDOLF, E. W., & FOSTER, R. A. (1991). Wife assault among VA alcohol rehabilitation patients. *Hospital and Community Psychiatry, 42,* 74–79.

GONZALES, L. (1985). Cocaine: A special report. *Playboy, 30*(3), 13–14, 148, 194–202.

GOODWIN, D. W. (1989). Alcoholism. In *Comprehensive Textbook of Psychiatry/V.* Baltimore: Williams & Wilkins.

GOODWIN, D. W., SCHULSINGER, F., & HERMANSEN, L. (1973). Alcohol problems in adoptees raised apart from alcoholic biological parents. *Archives of General Psychiatry, 28,* 238–243.

GOODWIN, D. W., & WARNOCK, J. K. (1991). Alcoholism: A family disease. In *Clinical Textbook of Addictive Disorders* (Frances, R. J., & Miller, S. I., eds.). New York: The Guilford Press.

GOODWIN, F. K. (1989). From the alcohol, drug abuse, and mental health administration. *Journal of the American Medical Association, 261,* 3517.

GOTTLIEB, A. M., KILLEN, J. D., MARLATT, G. A., & TAYLOR, C. B. (1987). Psychological and pharmacological influences in cigarette smoking withdrawal: Effects of nicotine gum and expectancy on smoking withdrawal symptoms and relapse. *Journal of Clinical and Consulting Psychology, 55,* 606–608.

GOVONI, L. E., & HAYES, J. E. (1988). *Drugs and Nursing Implications* (6th ed.). Norwalk, CT: Appleton & Lange.

GRAEDON, J. (1980). *The People's Pharmacy-2.* New York: Avon Books.

GRAHAM, B. (1988). The abuse of alcohol: Disease or disgrace? *Alcoholism & Addiction. 8*(4), 14–15.

GRAHAM, J. R. (1990). *MMPI-2 Assessing Personality and Psychopathology.* New York: Oxford University Press.

GRAHAM, M. (1989). One toke over the line. *The New Republic, 200*(16),20–22.

GRANT, I. (1987). Alcohol and the brain: Neuropsychological correlates. *Journal of Clinical and Consulting Psychology, 55,* 310–324.

GRANT, P. D., & HEATON, R. K. (1990). Human immunodeficiency virus-type 1 (HIV-1) and the brain. *Journal of Clinical and Consulting Psychology, 58,* 22–30.

GREENBLATT, D. J., & SHADER, R. I. (1975). Treatment of the alcohol withdrawal syndrome. In *Manual of Psychiatric Therapeutics* (Shader, R. I., ed.). Boston: Little, Brown.

GRIFFIN, M. L., WEISS, R. D., MIRIN, S. M., & LANG, U. (1989). A comparison of male and female cocaine abusers. *Archives of General Psychiatry, 46,* 122–126.

GRINSPOON, L., & BAKALAR, J. B. (1985). Drug dependence: Nonnarcotic agents. In *The Pharmacological Basis of Therapeutics* (7th ed.) (Gilman, A. G., Goodman, L. S., Rall, T. W., & Murad, F., eds.). New York: Macmillan.

GRINSPOON, L., & BAKALAR, J. B. (1990). What is phencyclidine? *Harvard Medical School Mental Health Letter, 6*(7), 8.

GROB, L. H., BRAVO, G. WALSH, R. (1990). Second thoughts on 3,4-methylenedioxymethamphetamine (MDMA) neurotoxicity. *Archives of General Psychiatry, 47,* 288.

GROUP FOR THE ADVANCEMENT OF PSYCHIATRY. (1991). Substance abuse disorders: A psychiatric priority. *American Journal of Psychiatry, 148,* 1291–1300.

Group, The. (1976). Narcotics Anonymous World Service Office, Inc.

HALL, S. M., HAVASSY, B. E., & WASSERMAN, D. A. (1991). Effects of commitment to abstinence, positive moods, stress and coping on relapse to cocaine use. *Journal of Consulting and Clinical Psychology, 59,* 526–532.

HALLER, D. L. (1991). Recovery for two: Pregnancy and addiction. *Alcoholism & Addiction, 11*(4), 14–18.

HAMMER, S., & HAZELTON, L. (1984). Cocaine and the chemical brain. *Science Digest, 92*(10), 58–62, 100–103.

HAND, R. P. (1989). Taking another look at triazolam—Is this drug safe? *Focus on Pharmacology: Theory and Practice. 11*(6), 1–3.

HARRIS, M., & BACHRACH, L. L. (1990). Perspectives on homeless mentally ill women. *Hospital & Community Psychiatry, 41,* 253–254.

Harvard Medical School Mental Health Letter. (1988). Sleeping pills and antianxiety drugs, *5*(6), 1–4.

Harvard Medical School Mental Health Letter. (1990). Amphetamines, *6*(10), 1–4.

HARVEY, S. C. (1985). Hypnotics and sedatives. In *The Pharmacological Basis of Therapeutics* (7th ed.) (Gilman, A. G., Goodman, L. S., Rall, T. W., & Murad, F., eds.). New York: Macmillan.

HATFIELD, A. B. (1989). Patients' accounts of stress and coping in schizophrenia. *Hospital and Community Psychiatry, 40,* 1141–1145.

HAYNER, G. N., & McKINNEY, H. (1986). MDMA: The dark side of Ecstacy. *Journal of Psychoactive Drugs, 18*(4), 341–347.

Health News. (1990). Drug problems in perspective, 8(3), 1–10.

HEATON, R. K. (1990). Introduction to the special series on acquired immune deficiency syndrome (AIDS). *Journal of Consulting and Clinical Psychology, 58,* 3–4.

HEIMEL, C. (1990). It's now, it's trendy, it's codependency. *Playboy,* 37(5), 43.

HEIMEL, C. (1991). Sickos "R" Us. *Playboy, 38*(9), 42.

HELLMAN, R. E., STANTON, M., LEE, J., TYTUN, A., & VACHON, R. (1989). Treatment of homosexual alcoholics in government-funded agencies: Provider training and attitudes. *Hospital and Community Psychiatry, 40,* 1163–1168.

HELZER, J. E. (1987). Epidemiology of alcoholism. *Journal of Consulting and Clinical Psychology, 55*(3), 284–292.

HELZER, J. E., ROBINS, L. N., TAYLOR, J. R., CAREY, K., MILLER, R. H., COMBS-ORME, T., & FARMER, A. (1985). The extent of long-term moderate drinking among alcoholics discharged from medical and psychiatric treatment facilities. *New England Journal of Medicine, 312*, 1678–1682.

HENNINGFIELD, J. E., & NEMETH-COSLETT, R. (1988). Nicotine dependence. *Chest, 93*(2), 37s–55s.

HERMAN, E. (1988). The twelve step program: Cure or cover? *Utne Reader, 30*, 52–53.

HESTER, R. K., & MILLER, W. R. (1989). Self-control training. In *Handbook of Alcoholism Treatment Approaches* (Hester, R. K., & Miller, W. R., eds.). New York: Pergamon Press.

HEYWARD, W. L., & CURRAN, J. W. (1988). The epidemiology of AIDS in the U.S. *Scientific American, 259*(4), 72–81.

HIBBS, J., PERPER, J., & WINEK, C. L. (1991). An outbreak of designer-drug-related deaths in Pennsylvania. *Journal of the American Medical Association, 265*, 1011–1013.

HIRSCHFIELD, R. M. A., & DAVIDSON, L. (1988). Risk factors for suicide. In *Review of Psychiatry, (Vol 7)* (Frances, A. J., & Hales, R. E., eds.). Washington, DC: American Psychiatic Association Press.

HOARD, P. S. (1988). Premenstrual syndrome can trigger relapse. *Alcoholism & Addiction, 8*(6), 41–42.

HOBSON, J. A. (1989). Dream theory: A new view of the brain-mind. *Harvard Medical School Mental Health Letter, 5*(8), 3–5.

HOFFMANN, H., LOPER, R. G., & KAMMEIER, M. L. (1974). Identifying future alcoholics with MMPI alcohol scales. *Quarterly Journal of Studies on Alcohol, 35*, 490–498.

HOFFMANN, N. G., BELILLE, C. A., & HARRISON, P. A. (1987). Adequate resources for a complex population? *Alcoholism & Addiction, 7*(5), 17.

HOLLAND, W. W., & FITZSIMONS, B. (1991). Smoking in children. *Archives of Disease in Childhood, 66*, 1269–1270.

HOLLOWAY, M. (1991). Rx for addiction. *Scientific American, 264* (3), 94–103.

HONG, R., MATSUYAMA, E., & NUR, K. (1991). Cardiomyopathy associated with smoking of crystal methamphetamine. *Journal of the American Medical Association, 265*, 1152–1154.

HONIGFELD, G., & HOWARD A. (1978). *Psychiatric Drugs: A Desk Reference* (2nd ed.). New York: Academic Press.

HORGAN, J. (1989). Lukewarm turkey: Drug firms balk at pursuing a heroin-addiction treatment. *Scientific American, 260*(3), 32.

HORNEY, K. (1964). *The Neurotic Personality of Our Time*. New York: W. W. Norton & Co.

HOUGH, D. O., & KOVAN, J. R. (1990). Is your patient a steroid abuser? *Medical Aspects of Human Sexuality, 24*(11), 24–32.

HOUSE, M. A. (1990). Cocaine. *American Journal of Nursing, 90*(4), 40–45.

HOWLAND, R. H. (1990). Barriers to community treatment of patients with dual diagnoses. *Hospital & Community Psychiatry, 41* 1136–1138.

HUGHES, J. R., GUST, S. W., & PECHACEK, T. F. (1987). Prevalence of tobacco dependence and withdrawal. *American Journal of Psychatry, 144*, 205–208.

HUGHES, J. R., GUST, S. W., SKOOG, K., KEENAN, R. M., & FENWICH, J. W. (1991). Symptoms of tobacco withdrawal. *Archives of General Psychiatry, 48*, 52–59.

HUNTER, M., & KELLOGG, T. (1989). Redefining ACA characteristics. *Alcoholism & Addiction, 9*(3), 28–29.

HURT, R. D., FINLAYSON, R. E., MORSE, R. M., & DAVIS, L. J. (1988). Alcoholism in elderly persons: Medical aspects and prognosis of 216 inpatients. *Mayo Clinic Proceedings, 63,* 753–760.

HUSSAR, D. A. (1990). Update 90: New drugs. *Nursing 90, 20*(12), 41–51.

HUTCHINSON, B. M., & HOOK, E. W. (1990). Syphilis in adults. *Medical Clinics of North America, 74,* 1389–1416.

HYDE, G. L. (1989). Management of the impaired person in the O.R. *Bulletin of the American College of Surgeons, 74*(11), 6–9.

HYMAN, S. E. (1988). *Manual of Psychiatric Emergencies* (2nd ed.). Boston: Little, Brown.

IGGERS, J. (1990). The addiction industry. *Minneapolis Star-Tribune, IX*(102), 1E, 4E, 10E.

INCIARDI, J. A., LOCKWOOD, D., & POTTIEGER, A. E. (1991). Crack-dependent women and sexuality: Implications for STD acquisition and transmission. *Addiction & Recovery, 11*(4), 25–28.

Internal Medicine Alert. (1989). Aspirin reduces the risk of heart attack—the physician's health study data. *11*(15), 57–58.

ISNER, J. M., & CHOKSHI, S. K. (1989). Cocaine and vasospasm. *New England Journal of Medicine, 321,* 1604–1606.

JACOBSEN, P. B., PERRY, S., & HIRSCH, D. A. (1990). Behavioral and psychological responses to HIV antibody testing. *Journal of Consulting and Clinical Psychology, 58,* 31–37.

JAFFE, J. H. (1986). Opioids. In *American Psychiatric Association Annual Review (Vol 5).* Washington, DC: American Psychiatric Association.

JAFFE, J. H. (1989). Drug dependence: Opioids, nonnarcotics, nicotine (tobacco) and caffeine. In *Comprehensive Textbook of Psychiatry/V* (Kaplan, H. I., & Sadock, B. J., eds.). Baltimore: Williams & Wilkins.

JAFFE, J. H. (1990). Drug addiction and drug abuse. In *The Pharmacological Basis of Therapeutics* (8th ed.) (Gilman, A. G., Goodman, L. S., Rall, T. W., Murad, F., eds.). New York: Macmillan.

JAFFE, J. H., & MARTIN, W. R. (1985). Opioid analgesics and antagonists. In *The Pharmacological Basis of Therapeutics* (7th ed.) (Gilman, A. G., Goodman L.S., Rall, T. W., & Murad, F., eds.). New York: Macmillan.

JAPENGA, A. (1991). You're tougher than you think! *Self, 13*(4), 174–175, 187.

JAY, S. M., ELLIOTT, C., & VARNI, J. W. (1986). Acute and chronic pain in adults and children with cancer. *Journal of Consulting and Clinical Psychology, 54,* 601–607.

JELLINEK, E. M. (1952). Phases of alcohol addiction. *Quarterly Journal of Studies on Alcohol, 13,* 673–674.

JELLINEK, E. M. (1960). *The Disease Concept of Alcoholism.* New Haven, CT: College and University Press.

JENIKE, M. A. (1989). Drug abuse. In *Scientific American Medicine* (Rubenstein, E., & Federman, D. D., eds.). New York: Scientific American Press.

JENSEN, J. G. (1987a). Step Two: A promise of hope. In *The Twelve Steps of Alcoholics Anonymous.* New York: Harper & Row.

JENSEN, J. G. (1987b). Step Three: Turning it over. In *The Twelve Steps of Alcoholics Anonymous.* New York: Harper & Row.

JOHNSON INSTITUTE. (1987). *The Family Enablers.* Minneapolis: The Institute.

JOHNSON, L. D., O'MALLEY, P. M., & BACHMAN, J. G. (1988). *Drug Use, Drinking and Smoking: National Survey Results from High School, College and*

Young Adults Populations 1975–1988. Rockville: MD: U.S. Department of Health and Human Services.

JOHNSON, L. D., O'MALLEY, P. M., & BACHMAN, J. G. (1989). *1989 National High School Senior Drug Abuse Survey*. Rockville: MD: U.S. Department of Health and Human Services.

JOHNSON, M. D. (1990). Anabolic steroid use in adolescent athletes. *The Pediatric Clinics of North America, 37*, 1111–1123.

JOHNSON, V. E. (1980). *I'll Quit Tomorrow*. San Francisco: Harper & Row.

JONES, R. L. (1990). Evaluation of drug use in the adolescent. In *Clinical Management of Poisoning and Drug Overdoses* (2nd ed.) (Haddad, L. M., & Winchester, J. F., eds.) Philadelphia, PA: W. B. Saunders.

JONES, R. T. (1987). Psychopharmacology of cocaine. In *Cocaine: A Clinician's Handbook* (Washton, A. G., & Gold, M. S., eds.) New York: The Guilford Press.

JOSHI, N. P., & SCOTT, M. (1988). Drug use, depression, and adolescents. *Pediatric Clinics of North America, 35*(6), 1349–1364.

JOYCE, C. (1989). The woman alcoholic. *American Journal of Nursing, 89*, 1314–1316.

JUDD, L. L., & HUEY, L. Y. (1984). Lithium antagonizes ethanol intoxication in alcoholics. *American Journal of Psychiatry, 141*, 1517–1521.

JUERGENS, S. M., & MORSE, R. M. (1988). Alprazolam dependence in seven patients. *American Journal of Psychiatry, 145*, 625–627.

JULIEN, R. M. (1988). *A Primer of of Drug Action* (5th ed.). New York: W. H. Freeman & Co.

KAMBACK, M. C. (1978). Animal models of addictive behavior. In *Basic Psychopathology, Vol. III*. (Balis, G. U., editor in chief). Boston: Butterworth.

KAMINER, Y. (1991). Adolescent substance abuse. In *Clinical Textbook of Addictive Disorders* (Frances, R. J., & Miller, S. I., eds.). New York: The Guilford Press.

KAMINER, Y., & FRANCES, R. J. (1991). Inpatient treatment of adolescents with psychiatric and substance abuse disorders. *Hospital and Community Psychiatry, 42*, 894–896.

KANDEL, D. B., & RAVEIS, V. H. (1989). Cessation of illicit drug use in young adulthood. *Archives of General Psychiatry, 46*, 109–116.

KANWISCHER, R. W., & HUNDLEY, J. (1990). Screening for substance abuse in hospitalized psychiatric patients. *Hospital & Community Psychiatry, 41*, 795–797.

KAPLAN, H. I., & SADOCK, B. J. (1988). *Synopsis of Psychiatry* (5th ed.). Baltimore: Williams & Wilkins.

KAPLAN, H. I., & SADOCK, B. J. (1990). *Pocket Handbook of Clinical Psychiatry*. Baltimore: Williams & Wilkins.

KAPLAN, H. S. (1974). *The New Sex Therapy*. New York: Brunner/Mazel.

KAPLAN, H. S. (1979). *Disorders of Sexual Desire*. New York: Brunner/Mazel.

KAPLAN, H. S., & MOODIE, J. L. (1982). Psychosexual dysfunctions. In *Treatment of Mental Disorders* (Greise, J. H., Jefferson, J. W., & Spitzer, R. L., eds.). New York: Oxford University Press.

KASHKIN, K. B., & KLEBER, H. D. (1989). Hooked on hormones? An anabolic steroid addiction hypothesis. *Journal of the American Medical Association, 262*, 3166–3172.

KAUFMAN, G. (1989). *The Psychology of Shame*. New York: Springer.

KAY, S. R., KALATHARA, M., & MEINZER, A. E. (1989). Diagnostic and behavioral characteristics of psychiatric patients who abuse substances. *Hospital and Community Psychiatry, 40,* 1062–1065.

KERR, M. S. (1988). Chronic anxiety and defining a self. *Atlantic Monthly, 262*(3), 35–45.

KHANTZIAN, E. J. (1985). The self-medication hypothesis of addictive disorders: Focus on heroin and cocaine dependence. *American Journal of Psychiatry, 142,* 1259–1264.

KHANTZIAN, E. J. (1986). A contemporary psychodynamic approach to drug abuse treatment. *American Journal of Drug and Alcohol Abuse, 12*(3), 213–222.

KHURI, E. T. (1989). Narcotic poisoning. In *Conn's Current Therapy.* Philadelphia, PA: W. B. Saunders.

KILPATRICK, C. (1990). Violence as a precursor of women's substance abuse: The rest of the drugs-violence story. Paper presented at the 1990 meeting of the American Psychological Association, Boston, MA.

KIMMAGE, P. (1990). Drugs and cycling: The inside story. *Bicycling, XXXI* (6), 48–52.

KIRN, T. F. (1989). Studies of adolescents indicate just how complex the situation is for this age group. *Journal of the American Medical Association, 261,* 3362.

KIRSCH, M. M. (1986). *Designer Drugs.* Minneapolis: CompCare Publications.

KISSIN, B. (1985). Alcohol abuse and alcohol-related illness. In *Cecil Textbook of Medicine* (17th ed.) (Wyngaarden, J. B., & Smith, L. H., eds.). Philadelphia, PA: W. B. Saunders.

KIVLAHAN, D. R., HEIMAN, J. R., WRIGHT, R. C., MUNDT, J. W., & SHUPE, J. A. (1991). Treatment cost and rehospitalization rate in schizophrenic outpatients with a history of substance abuse. *Hospital and Community Psychiatry, 42,* 609–614.

KLAG, M. J., & WHELTON, P. K. (1987). Risk of stroke in male cigarette smokers. *New England Journal of Medicine, 316,* 628.

KLAR, H. (1987). The setting for psychiatric treatment. In *American Psychiatric Association Annual Review (Vol 6).* Washington, DC: American Psychiatric Association Press.

KLASS, P. (1989). Vital signs. *Discover, 10* (1), 12–14.

KLEBER, H. D. (1991). Tracking the cocaine epidemic. *Journal of the American Medical Association, 266,* 2272–2273.

KLEIN, J. M., & MILLER, S. I. (1986). Three approaches to the treatment of drug addiction. *Hospital & Community Psychiatry, 37,* 1083–1085.

KLEIN, M. The emperor's new addiction. *Playboy, 37*(3), 41.

KOFOED, L., KANIA, J., WALSH, T., & ATKINSON, R. M. (1986). Outpatient treatment of patients with substance abuse and coexisting psychiatric disorders. *American Journal of Psychiatry, 143,* 867–872.

KOFOED, L., & KEYS, A. (1988). Using group therapy to persuade dual-diagnosis patients to seek substance abuse treatment. *Hospital & Community Psychiatry, 39,* 1209–1211.

KOHR, J. (1988). Grandchildren of alcoholics. *Alcoholism & Addiction, 9*(1), 44.

KOLODNY, R. C. (1985). The clinical management of sexual problems in substance abusers. In *Alcoholism and Substance Abuse: Strategies for Clinical Intervention* (Bratter, T. E., & Forrest, G. G., eds.). New York: The Free Press.

KOOP, C. E. (1986). *Surgeon General's Report on Acquired Immune Deficiency Syndrome.* Washington, DC: U.S. Department of Health and Human Services.

KORNETSKY, C., & BAIN, G. (1987). Neuronal bases for hedonic effects of cocaine and opiates. In *Cocaine: Clinical and Biobehavioral Aspects* (Fisher, S., Rashkin, A., & Uhlenhuth, E. H., eds.). New York: Oxford University Press.

KOZLOWSKI, L. T., WILKINSON, A., SKINNER, W., KENT, W., FRANKLIN, T., & POPE, M. (1989). Comparing tobacco cigarette dependence with other drug dependencies. *Journal of the American Medical Association, 261*, 898–901.

KRUZICKI, J. (1987). Dispelling a myth: The facts about female alcoholics. *Corrections Today, 49*, 110–115.

KUNITZ, S. J., & LEVY J. E. (1974). Changing ideas of alcohol use among Navaho Indians. *Quarterly Journal of Studies on Alcohol, 46*, 953–960.

KURTZ, E. (1979). *Not God: A history of Alcoholics Anonymous.* Center City, MN: Hazelden.

LADER, M. (1987). Assessing the potential for buspirone dependence or abuse and effects of its withdrawal. *American Journal of Medicine, 82* (Supplement 5A), 20–26.

LAMAR, J. V., RILEY, M., SMGHABADI, R. (1986). Crack: A cheap and deadly cocaine is spreading menace. *Time, 128*, 16–18.

Lancet, The. (1991). The smoking epidemic. *338*, 1387.

LAND, W., PINSKY, D., & SALZMAN, C. (1991). Abuse and misuse of anticholinergic medications. *Hospital and Community Psychiatry, 42*, 580–581.

LANDRY, G. L., & PRIMOS, W. A. (1990). Anabolic steroid abuse. *Advances in Pediatrics, 37*, 185–205.

LANGE, R. A., CIGARROA, R. G., YANCY, C. W., WILLARD, J. E., POPMA, J. J., SILLS, M. N., McBRIDE, W., KIM, A. S., & HILLIS, L. D. (1989). Cocaine induced coronary artery vasoconstiction. *New England Journal of Medicine, 321*, 1557–1562.

LANGEVIN, R. (1988). Defensiveness in sex offenders. In *Clinical Assessment of Malingering and Deception* (Rogers, R., ed.). New York: The Guilford Press.

LANGONE, J. (1989). Hot to block a killer's path. *Time, 133*(5), 60–62.

LARSON, K. K. (1982). Birthplace of "The Minnesota Model." *Alcoholism, 3*(2), 34–35.

LAYNE, G. S. (1990). Schizophrenia and substance abuse. In *Managing the Dually Diagnosed Patient.* (O'Connell, D. F., ed.). New York: The Haworth Press.

LEDERBERG, M. S., & HOLLAND, J. C. Psycho-oncology. In *Comprehensive Textbook of Psychiatry/V* (Kaplan, H. I., & Sadock, B. J., eds.). Baltimore: Williams & Wilkins.

LEHMAN, A. F., MYERS, C. P., & CORTY, E. (1989) Assessment and classification of patients with psychiatric and substance abuse syndromes. *Hospital and Community Psychiatry, 40*, 1019–1025.

LEIGH, G. (1985) Psychosocial factors in the etiology of substance abuse. In *Alcoholism and Substance Abuse: Strategies for Clinical Intervention* (Bratter, T. E., & Forrest, G. G., eds.). New York: The Free Press.

LENDER, M. E. (1981). The disease concept of alcoholism in the United States: Was Jellinek first? *Digest of Alcoholism Theory and Application, 1*(1), 25–31.

LEO, J. (1990). The it's-not-my-fault syndrome. *U.S. News & World Report, 109*(12), 16.

LESSARD. S. (1989). Bursting our mental blocks on drugs and crime. *Washington Monthly, 21*(1), 70.

LEVERS, L. L., & HAWES, A. R. (1990). Drugs and gender: A woman's recovery program. *Journal of Mental Health Counseling, 12*, 527–531.

LEWIS, D. O. (1989). Adult antisocial behavior and criminality. In *Comprehensive*

Textbook of Psychiatry/V (Kaplan, H. I., & Sadock, B. J., eds.). New York: Williams & Wilkins.

LEWIS, J. A., DANA, R. Q., & BLEVINS, G. A. (1988). *Substance Abuse Counseling.* Pacific Grove, CA: Brooks/Cole.

LEWIS, K. D., BENNET, B., SCHMEDER, N. H. (1989). The care of infants menaced by cocaine abuse. *American Journal of Maternal/Child Nursing, 14,* 324–329.

LEWIS, R. (1989). Drug tolerance apparently works in Holland. *Minneapolis Star-Tribune, VIII*(173), 15A.

LICHTENSTEIN, E., & BROWN, R. A. (1980). Smoking cessation methods: Review and recommendations. In *Addictive Behaviors* (Miller, W. R., ed.). New York: Pergamon Press.

LIEBERMAN, M. L. (1988). *The Sexual Pharmacy.* New York: New American Library.

LIEVELD, P. E., & ARUNA, A. (1991). Diagnosis and management of the alcohol withdrawal syndrome. *U.S. Pharmacist, 16*(1), H1–H11.

LINGEMAN, R. R. (1974). *Drugs from A to Z: A Dictionary.* New York: McGraw-Hill.

LINN, L., SPIEGEL, J. S., MATHEWS, W. C., LEAKE, B., LIEN, R., & BROOKS, S. (1989). Recent sexual behaviors among homosexual men seeking primary medical care. *Archives of Internal Medicine, 149,* 2685–2691.

LINNOILA, M., DeJONG, J., & VIRKKUNEN, M. (1989). Family history of alcoholism in violent offenders and impulsive fire setters. *Archives of General Psychiatry, 46,* 613–616.

LIPKIN, M. (1989). Psychiatry and medicine. In *Comprehensive Textbook of Psychiatry/V* (Kaplan, H. I., & Sadock, B. J., eds.). Baltimore: Williams & Wilkins.

LIPSCOMB, J. W. (1989). What pharmacists should know about home poisonings. *Drug Topics, 133*(15), 72–80.

LITTLE, R. E., ANDERSON, K. W., ERVIN, C. H., WORTHINGTON-ROBERTS, B., & CLARREN, S. K. (1989). Maternal alcohol use during breast-feeding and infant mental and motor development at one year. *New England Journal of Medicine, 321,* 425–430.

LØBERG, T. (1986). Neuropsychological findings in the early and middle phases of alcoholism. In *Neuropsychological Assessment of Neuropsychiatric Disorders* (Grant, I., & Adams, K. M., eds.). New York: Oxford University Press.

LOMBARD, J., LEVIN, I. H., & WEINER, W. J. (1989). Arsenic intoxication in a cocaine abuser. *New England Journal of Medicine, 320,* 869.

LOPER, R. G., KAMMEIER, M. L., & HOFFMAN, H. (1973). MMPI characteristics of college freshman males who later become alcoholics. *Journal of Abnormal Psychology, 82,* 159–162.

LORANGER, A. W., & TULIX, E. H. (1985). Family history of alcoholism in borderline personality disorder. *Archives of General Psychiatry, 42,* 153–157.

Los Angeles Times. (1990). Teen steroid use is rising in U.S., study indicates. *Minneapolis Star-Tribune, IX* (157), 7A.

LOUIE, A. K. (1990). Panic attacks—When cocaine is the cause. *Medical Aspects of Human Sexuality, 24*(12), 44–46.

LOURWOOD, D. L., & RIEDLINGER, J. E. (1989). The use of drugs in the breast feeding mother. *Drug Topics, 133*(21), 77–85.

LYONS, J. S., & McGOVERN, M. P. (1989). Use of mental health services by dually diagnosed persons. *Hospital & Community Psychiatry, 40,* 1067–1069.

MAAS, E. F., ASHE, J., SPIEGEL, P., ZEE, D. S., & LEIGH, R. J. (1991). Acquired pendular nystagmus in toluene addiction. *Neurology, 41*, 282–286.

MADDUX, J. F., DESMOND, D. P., & COSTELLO, R. (1987). Depression in opioid users varies with substance use status. *American Journal of Drug & Alcohol Abuse, 13*(4), 375–378.

MAGUIRE, J. (1990). *Care and Feeding of the Brain*. New York: Doubleday.

MAISTO, S. A., & CONNORS, G. J. (1988). Assessment of treatment outcome. In *Assessment of Addictive Disorders* (Donovan, D. M., & Marlatt, G. A., eds.). New York: The Guilford Press.

MANFREDI, R. L., KALES, A., VGONTZAS, A. N., BIXLER, E. O., ISAAC, M. A., & FALCONE, C. M. (1991). Buspirone: Sedative or stimulant effect? *American Journal of Psychiatry 148*, 1213–1217.

MANLEY, M., EPPS, R. P., HUSTEN, C., GLYNN, T., SHOPLAND, D. (1991). Clinical interventions in tobacco control. *Journal of the American Medical Association, 266*, 3172–3173.

MANN, C. C., & PLUMMER, M. L. (1991). *The Aspirin Wars*. New York: Knopf.

MARANTO, G. (1985). Coke: The random killer. *Discover, 12*(3), 16–21.

MARGOLIN, A., KOSTEN, T., PETRAKIS, I., AVANTS, S. K., & KOSTEN, T. (1991). Bupropion reduces cocaine abuse in methadone-maintained patients. *Archives of General Psychiatry, 48*, 87.

MASTERS, W. H., & JOHNSON, V. E. (1966). *Human Sexual Response*. Boston: Little, Brown.

MASTERS, W. H., JOHNSON, V. E., & KOLODNY, R. C. (1986). *Sex and Human Loving*. Boston: Little, Brown.

MATSUDA, L. A., LOLAIT, S. J., BROWNSTEIN, M. J., YOUNG, A. C., & BONNER, T. I. (1990). Structure of a cannabinoid receptor and functional expression of the cloned cDNA. *Nature, 346*, 561–564.

MATUSCHKA, E. (1985). Treatment, outcomes and clinical evaluation. In *Alcoholism and Substance Abuse: Strategies for Clinical Intervention* (Bratter, T. E., & Forrest, G. G., eds.). New York: The Free Press.

MATUSCHKA, P. R. (1985). The psychopharmacology of addiction. In *Alcoholism and Substance Abuse: Strategies for Clinical Intervention* (Bratter, T. E., & Forrest, G. G., eds.). New York: The Free Press.

MAY, G. G. (1988). *Addiction & Grace*. New York: Harper & Row.

MAY, R. (1975). *The Courage to Create*. New York: W. W. Norton & Co.

MAYES, L. C., GRANGER, R. H., BORNSTEIN, M. H., & ZUCKERMAN, B. (1992). The problem of prenatal cocaine exposure. *Journal of the American Medical Association, 267*, 406–408.

Mayo Clinic Health Letter. (1989). America's drug crisis. Rochester, MN: Mayo Foundation for Medical Education and Research.

McCARTHY, J. J., & BORDERS, O. T. (1985). Limit setting on drug abuse in methadone maintenance patients. *American Journal of Psychiatry, 142*, 1419–1423.

McCARTY, D., ARGERIOU, M., HUEBNER, R. B., & LUBRAN, B. (1991). Alcoholism, drug abuse, and the homeless. *American Psychologist, 46*, 1139–1148.

McCRADY, B. S., & IRVINE, S. (1989). Self-help groups. In *Handbook of Alcoholism Treatment Approaches* (Hester, R. K., & Miller, W. R., eds.). New York: Pergamon Press.

McCUTCHAN, J. A. (1990). Virology, immunology, and clinical course of HIV infection. *Journal of Clinical and Consulting Psychology, 58*, 5–12.

McENROE, P. (1990). Hawaii is fighting losing battle against the popularity of drug "ice." *Minneapolis Star-Tribune, IX*,(44), 1, 20A.

McGUIRE, L. (1990). The power of non-narcotic pain relievers. *RN, 53*(4), 28–35.

McHUGH, M. J. (1987). The abuse of volatile substances. *Pediatric Clinics of North America, 34*(2), 333–340.

Medical Aspects of Human Sexuality. (1990). Women with AIDS: The growing threat, *24*,(10), 68–69.

MEDICAL ECONOMICS COMPANY. (1991). *1991 Physician's Desk Reference* (45th ed.). Oradell, NJ: Author.

MEDICAL ECONOMICS COMPANY. (1989). Anabolic steroid abuse and primary care. *Patient Care, 23*(8), 12.

Medical Letter, The. (1989). Aspirin for prevention of myocardial infarction and stroke, *31*(799), 77–79.

MEER, J. (1986). Marijuana in the air: Delayed buzz bomb. *Psychology Today, 20,* 68.

MELZACK, R. (1990). The tragedy of needless pain. *Scientific American, 262*(2), 27–33.

MENDELSOHN, R. S., & ARTHUR, P. B. Drug use among athletes. (1989). *Doctor's People Newsletter, 2*(8), 4–7.

MERTON, T. (1961). *New Seeds of Contemplation.* New York: New Directions Publishing.

MERTON, T. (1978). *No Man Is an Island.* New York: New Directions Publishing.

MEYER, R. (1988). Intervention: Opportunity for healing. *Alcoholism & Addiction, 9*(1), 7.

MEYER, R. E. (1989a). Who can say no to illicit drug use. *Archives of General Psychiatry, 46,* 189–190.

MEYER, R. E. (1989b). What characterizes addiction? *Alcohol Health & Research World, 13*(4), 316–321.

MICHELSON, J. B., CARROLL, D., McLANE, N. J., & ROBIN, H. S. (1988). Drug abuse and ocular disease. In *Surgical Treatment of Ocular Inflammatory Disease* (Michelson, J. B., & Nozik, R. A., eds.). New York: J. B. Lippincott.

MIKKELSEN, E. (1985). Substance abuse in adolescents and children. In *Psychiatry* (Michels, R., Cavenar, J. O., Brodie, H. K. H., Cooper, A. M., Guze, S. B., Judd, S. B., Klerman, G., & Solnit, A. J., eds.). New York: Basic Books.

MILLER, A. (1988). *The Enabler.* Claremont, CA: Hunter House.

MILLER, F. T., & TANENBAUM, J. H. (1989). Drug abuse in schizophrenia. *Hospital and Community Psychiatry, 40,* 847–849.

MILLER, N. S., & GOLD, M. S. (1991). Organic solvent and aerosol abuse. *American Family Physician, 44,* 183–190.

MILLER, P. M., & FOY, D. W. (1981). Substance abuse. In *Handbook of Clinical Behavior Therapy* (Turner, S. M., Calhoun, K. S., & Adams, H. E., eds.). New York: Wiley.

MILLER, R. R. (1990). Athletes and steroids: Playing a deadly game. *Journal of Chiropratic, 27*(2), 35–38.

MILLER, S. I., FRANCES, R. J., & HOLMES, D. J. (1988). Use of psychotropic drugs in alcoholism treatment: A summary. *Hospital & Community Psychiatry, 39,* 1251–1252.

MILLER, S. I., FRANCES, R. J., & HOLMES, D. J. (1989). Psychotropic medications. In *Handbook of Alcoholism Treatment Approaches* (Hester, R. K., & Miller, W. R., eds.). New York: Pergamon Press.

MILLER, W. R. (1976). Alcoholism scales and objective measures. *Psychological Bulletin, 83,* 649–674.

MILLER, W. R., (1980). The addictive behaviors. In *The Addictive Behaviors* (Miller, W. R., ed.). New York: Pergamon Press.

MILLER, W. R. (1989). Increasing motivation for change. In *Handbook of Alcoholism Treatment Approaches* (Hester, R. K., & Miller, W. R., eds.). New York: Pergamon Press.

MILLER, W. R. (1992). Client/treatment matching in addictive behaviors. *The Behavior Therapist, 15*(1), 7–8.

MILLER, W. R., & HESTER, R. K. (1980). Treating the problem drinker: Modern approaches. In *The Addictive Behaviors* (Miller, W. R., ed.). New York: Pergamon Press.

MILLER, W. R., & HESTER, R. K. (1986). Inpatient alcoholism treatment. *American Psychologist, 41*(7), 794–806.

MILLER, W. R., & HESTER, R. K. (1989). Treating alcohol problems: Toward an informed eclectism. In *Handbook of Alcoholism Treatment Approaches* (Hester, R, K., & Miller, W. R., eds.). New York: Pergamon Press.

MILLON, T. (1981). *Disorders of Personality.* New York: Wiley.

MINER, B. (1989). LSD's return piques teens' interest. *Milwaukee Journal, 108*(4), 1B, 10B.

MINKOFF, K. (1989). An integrated treatment model for dual diagnosis of psychosis and addiction. *Hospital and Community Psychiatry, 40,* 1031–1036.

Minneapolis Star-Tribune. (1989a). Study finds "casual" use of drugs down 37% since '85. *VIII*(199), 1, 7a.

Minneapolis Star-Tribune. (1989b). New drug "ice" grips Hawaii, threatens mainland. *VIII* (150), 12a.

MIRIN, S. M., WEISS, R. D., & GREENFIELD, S. F. (1991). Psychoactive substance use disorders. In *The Practitioner's Guide to Psychoactive Drugs* (3rd ed.) (Galenberg, A. J., Bassuk, E. L., & Schoonover, S. C., eds.). New York: Plenum Medical Book Co.

MITCHELL, J. R. (1988). Acetaminophen toxicity. *New England Journal of Medicine, 319,* (1601–1602).

MONCHER, M. S., HOLDEN, G. W., & TRIMBLE, J. E. Substance abuse among native-American youth. *Journal of Consulting and Clinical Psychology, 58,* 408–415.

MORGENROTH, L. (1989). High-risk pain pills. *Atlantic, 264*(6), 36–42.

MORRISON, M. A. (1990). Addiction in adolescents. *Western Journal of Medicine, 152,* 543–547.

MORTENSEN, M. E., & RENNEBOHM, R. M. (1989). Clinical pharmacology and use of non-steroidal anti-inflammatory drugs. *Pediatric Clinics of North America, 36,* 1113–1139.

MORTON, H. G. (1987). Occurrence and treatment of solvent abuse in children and adolescents. *Pharmacological therapy, 33,* 449–469.

MORTON, W. A., & SANTOS, A, (1989). New indications for benzodiazepines in the treatment of major psychiatric disorders. *Hospital Formulary, 24,* 274–278.

MOYER, T. P., & ELLEFSON, P. J. (1987). Marijuana testing—How good is it? *Mayo Clinic Procedures, 62,* 413–417.

MOYLAN, D. W. (1990). Court intervention. *Adolescent Counselor, 2*(5), 23–27.

MUESER, K. T., YARNOLD, P. R., & BELLACK, A. S. (1992). Diagnostic and demographic correlates of substance abuse in schizophrenia and major affective disorder. *Acta Psychiatrica Scandinavica, 85,* 48–55.

MURPHY, S. M., OWEN, R., TYRER, P. (1989). Comparative assessment of efficacy and withdrawal symptoms after 6 and 12 weeks' treatment with diazepam or buspirone. *British Journal of Psychiatry*, 154, 529–534.

MURRAY, R. M., CLIFFORD, C. A., AND GURLING, H. M. D. (1983). Twin and adoption studies: How good is the evidence for a genetic role? In *Recent Developments in Alcoholism, Vol 1.* (Galanter, M., ed.). New York: Plenum.

MUSTO, D. F. (1991). Opium, cocaine and marijuana in American history. *Scientific American, 265*(1), 40–47.

NACE, E. P. (1987). *The Treatment of Alcoholism.* New York: Brunner/Mazel.

NACE, E. P., & ISBELL, P. G. (1991). Alcohol. In *Clinical Textbook of Addictive Disorders* (Frances, R. J., & Miller, S. I., eds.). New York: The Guilford Press.

NADELMANN, E. A. (1989). Drug prohibition in the United States: Costs, consequences, and alternatives. *Science, 245*, 939–946.

NADELMANN, E. A., KLEIMAN, M. A. R., & EARLS, F. J. (1990). Should some illegal drugs be legalized? *Issues in Science and Technology, VI*(4), 43–49.

NAHAS, G. G. (1986). Cannabis: Toxicological properties and epidemiological aspects. *Medical Journal of Australia, 145*, 82–87.

Narcotics Anonymous. (1982). Van Nuys, CA: Narcotics Anonymous World Service Office, Inc.

NATHAN, P. E. (1980). Etiology and process in the addictive behaviors. In *The Addictive Behaviors* (Miller, W. R., ed.). New York: Pergamon Press.

NATHAN, P. E. (1988). The addictive personality *is* the behavior of the addict. *Journal of Consulting and Clinical Psychology, 56*, 183–188.

NATHAN, P. E. (1991). Substance use disorders in the *DSV-IV, Journal of Abnormal Psychology, 100*, 356–361.

NATIONAL COMMISSION ON MARIJUANA AND DRUG ABUSE. (1972). *Marihuana: A Signal of Misunderstanding.* Washington, DC: U.S. Government Printing Office.

NATIONAL COMMISSION ON MARIJUANA AND DRUG ABUSE. (1973). *Drug Use in America: Problem in Perspective.* Washington, DC: U.S. Government Printing Office.

NATIONAL INSTITUTE ON ALCOHOL ABUSE AND ALCOHOLISM. (1989). Relapse and craving. *Alcohol Alert (#6).* Washington, DC: U.S. Department of Health and Human Services.

Nation's Health, The. (1990). Sex-for-drugs pushes US syphilis rates up, *20*(1), 17.

NATIONAL ACADEMY OF SCIENCES. (1990). *Treating Drug Problems (Vol 1).* Washington, DC: National Academy Press.

NELIPOVICH, M., & BUSS, E. (1991). Investigating alcohol abuse among persons who are blind. *Journal of Visual Impairment & Blindness, 85*, 343–345.

NELSON, D. J. Group helps smokers break addictive cycle. (1989). *Minneapolis Star-Tribune, VIII* (53), 8Ex.

NEWCOMB, M. G., & BENTLER, P. M. (1989). Substance use and abuse among children and teen agers. *American Psychologist, 44*, 242–248.

NEWELL, T., & COSGROVE, J. (1988). Recovery of neuropsychological functions during reduction of PCP use. Paper presented at the 1988 annual meeting of the American Psychological Association, Atlanta, GA.

NEWLAND, D. (1989). Alcohol and drug addiction—A disease or a crime? *Supervision, 50*(6), 16–19.

NEWSWEEK. (1991). A new market for a lethal drug, *CXVII* (7), 58.

NEWTON, R. E., MARUNYCZ, J. D., ALDERDICE, M. C., & NAPOLIELLO, M.

J. (1986). Review of the side effects of buspirone. *American Journal of Medicine*, *80* (Supplement 3B).

NEY, J. A., DOOLEY, S. L., KEITH, L. G., CHASNOFF, I. J., & SOCOL, M. L. (1990). The prevalence of substance abuse in patients with suspected preterm labor. *American Journal of Obstetrics and Gynecology*, *162*, 1562–1568.

NIAURA, R. S., ROHSENOW, D. J., BINKOFF, J. A., MONTI, P. M., PEDRAZA, M., & ABRAMS, D. B. (1988). Relevance of cue reactivity to understanding alcohol and smoking relapse. *Journal of Abnormal Psychology*, *97*(2), 133–153.

NICASTRO, N. (1989). Visual disturbances associated with over-the-counter ibuprofen in three patients. *Annals of Ophthalmology*, 21, 447–450.

NOBEL, E. P., BLUM, K., RITCHIE, T., MONTGOMERY, A. & SHERIDAN (1991). Allelic association of the D_2 dopamine receptor gene with receptor-binding characteristics in alcoholism. *Archives of General Psychiatry*, *48*, 648–654.

NOLAN, K. (1990). No more honeymooners. *Playboy*, *37*(8), 41.

NUNN-THOMPSON, C. L., & SIMON, P. A. (1989). Pharmacotherapy for smoking cessation. *Clinical Pharmacology*, *8*, 710–720.

O'DONNELL, M. (1986). The executive ailment: "Curable only by death." *International Management*. *41*(7), 64.

OETTING, E. R., & BEAUVAIS, F. (1990). Adolescent drug use: Findings of national and local surveys. *Journal of Consulting and Clinical Psychology*, *58*, 385–394.

OGBORNE, A. C., & GLASER, F. B. (1985). Evaluating Alcoholics Anonymous. In *Alcoholism and Substance Abuse: Strategies for Clinical Intervention* (Bratter, T. E., & Forrest, G. G., eds.). New York: The Free Press.

OLIWENSTEIN, L. (1988). The perils of pot. *Discover*, *9*(6), 18.

OLIWENSTEIN, L. (1990). The Kaposi's connection. *Discover*, *11*(8), 28.

OLSON, S. (1988). Following aspirin's trail. In *The Day that Lightning Chased the Housewife . . . and Other Mysteries of Science*. New York: Madison Books.

OSHER, F. C., & KOFOED, L. L. (1989). Treating patients with psychiatric and psychoactive substance abuse disorders. *Hospital and Community Psychiatry*, *40*, 1025–1030.

OTTO, R. K., LANG, A. R., MEGARGEE, E. I., & ROSENBLATT, A. I. (1989). Ability of alcoholics to escape detection by the MMPI. *Critical Items*, *4*(2), 2, 7–8.

OWINGS-WEST, M., & PRINZ, R. J. (1987). Parental alcoholism and child psychopathology. *Psychological Bulletin*, *102*(2), 204–281.

PAPE, P. A. (1988). EAP's and chemically dependent women. *Alcoholism & Addiction*, *8*(6), 43–44.

PAPPAS, N. (1990). Dangerous liasons: When food and drugs don't mix. *In Health*, *4*(4), 22–24.

PARRAS, F., PATIER, J. L., & EZPELETA, C. (1988). Lead contaminated heroin as a source of inorganic lead intoxication. *The Staff*, *316*, 755.

PARSIAN, A., & CLONINGER, C. R. (1991). Genetics of high-risk populations. *Addiction & Recovery*, *11*(6), 9–11.

PARSIAN, A., TODD, R. D., DEVOR, E. J., O'MALLEY, K. L., SUAREZ, B. K., REICH, T., & CLONINGER, C. R. (1991). Alcoholism and alleles of the human D_2 dopanine receptor locus: Studies of association and linkage. *Archives of General Psychiatry*, *48*, 655–663.

PATLAK, M. (1988). The treatment dilemma. *Discover*, *9*(10), 26–27.

PATLAK, M. (1989). The fickle virus. *Discover*, *10*(2), 24–25.

PECK, M. S. (1978). *The Road Less Traveled.* New York: Simon & Schuster.

PECK, M. S. (1991). Playboy interview. *Playboy, 38*(3), 43–62.

Pediatrics for parents. (1990). Marijuana and breast feeding, *11* (10), 1.

PEELE, S. (1984). The cultural context of psychological approaches to alcoholism. *American Psychologist, 39,* 1337–1351.

PEELE, S. (1985). *The Meaning of Addiction.* Lexington, MA: D.C. Heath.

PEELE, S. (1988). On the diseasing of America. *Utne Reader, 30,* 67.

PEELE, S. (1989). *Diseasing of America,* Lexington, MA: D C. Heath.

PEELE, S. (1991). What we now know about treating alcoholism and other addictions. *Harvard Mental Health Letter, 8*(6), 5–7.

PEELE, S., BRODSKY, A, & ARNOLD, M. (1991). *The Truth about Addiction and Recovery.* New York: Simon & Schuster.

PELUSO, E., & PELUSO, L. S. (1988). *Women & Drugs.* Minneapolis: CompCare Publishers.

PELUSO, E., & PELUSO, L. S. (1989). Alcohol and the elderly. *Professional Counselor, 4*(2), 44–46.

PENICK, E. C., NICKEL, E. J., CANTRELL, P. F., POWELL, B. J., READ, M. R., & THOMAS, M. M. (1990). The emerging concept of dual diagnosis: An overview and implications. In *Managing the Dually Diagnosed Patient* (O'Connell, D. F., ed.). New York: The Haworth Press.

PENTZ, M. A., DWYER, J. H., MacKINNON, D. P., FLAY, B. R., HANDEN, W. B., WANG, E. Y. I., & JOHNSON, A. (1989). A multicommunity trial for primary prevention of adolescent drug abuse. *Journal of the American Medical Association, 261*(2), 3259–3266.

PEROUTKA, S. J. (1989). "Ecstacy": A human neurotoxin? *Archives of General Psychiatry, 46,* 191.

PERRIN, P., & COLEMAN, W. (1988). Is addiction actually a misguided move to wholeness? *Utne Reader, 30,* 58–59.

PERRY, J. C., & COOPER, S. H. (1989). An empirical study of defense mechanisms. *Archives of General Psychiatry, 46,* 444–452.

PETERS, H., & THEORELL, C. J. (1991). Fetal and neonatal effects of maternal cocaine use. *Journal of Obstetric, Gynecologic, and Neonatal Nursing, 20*(2), 121–126.

PETTINE, K. A. (1991). Association of anabolic steroids and avascular necrosis of femoral heads. *American Journal of Sports Medicine, 19*(1), 96–98.

PEYSER, H. S. (1989). Alcohol and drug abuse: Underrecognized and untreated. *Hospital and Community Psychiatry, 40*(3), 221.

PHIBBS, C. S., BATEMAN, D. A., & SCHWARTZ, R. M. (1991). The neonatal costs of maternal cocaine use. *Journal of the American Medical Association, 266,* 1521–1526.

PHILLIPS, D. A. (1979). The alcoholic man—Too much/too little. *CAFC News, 2*(2), 5–8.

PICKENS, R. W., SVIKIS, D. S., McGUE, M., LYKKEN, D. T., HESTON, L. L., & CLAYTON, P. J. (1991). Heterogeneity in the inheritance of alcoholism: a study of male and female twins. *Archives of General Psychiatry, 48,* 19–28.

PIERCE, J. P., GILPIN, E., BURNS, D. M., WHALEN, E., ROSBROOK, B., SHOPLAND, D., & JOHNSON, M. (1991). Does tobacco advertising target young people to start smoking? *Journal of the American Medical Association, 266,* 3154–3158.

PINKNEY, D. S. (1990). Substance abusers seen shifting to "kitchen lab" drugs. *American Medical News, 33*(16), 5–7.

PLASKY, P., MARCUS, L., & SALZMAN, C. (1988). Effects of psychotropic drugs on memory: Part 2. *Hospital & Community Psychiatry, 39*, 501–502.

Playboy. (1988). Forum newsfront, *35*(4), 51.

Playboy. (1990a). Forum, *37*(1), 47.

Playboy. (1990b). Raw data, *37*(1), 16.

Playboy. (1991). Forum, *38*(1), 52.

POPE, H. G., & KATZ, D. L. (1987). Bodybuilder's psychosis. *Lancet, 334,* 863.

POPE, H. G., & KATZ, D. L. (1988). Affective and psychotic symptoms associated with anabolic steroid use. *American Journal of Psychiatry, 145,* 487–490.

POPE, H. G., & KATZ, D. L. (1990). Homicide and near-homicide by anabolic steroid users. *Journal of Clinical Psychiatry, 51*(1), 28–31.

POPE, H. G., & KATZ, D. L. (1991). What are the psychiatric risks of anabolic steroids? *Harvard Mental Health Letter, 7*(10), 8.

POPE, H. G., KATZ, D. L., & CHAMPOUX, R. (1986). Anabolic-androgenic steroid use among 1,010 college men. *The Physician and Sports Medicine, 17*(7), 75–81.

POPE, K. S., & MORIN, S. F. (1990). AIDS and HIV infection update: New research, ethical responsibilities, evolving legal frameworks, and published sources. *Independent Practitioner, 10*(4), 43–53.

PORTERFIELD, L. M. (1991). Steroid abuse. *Advancing Clinical Care, 6*(2), 44.

POST, R. M., WEISS, S. R. B., PERT, A., & UHDE, T. W. (1987). Chronic cocaine administration: Sensitization and kindling effects. In *Cocaine: Clinical and Behavioral Aspects* (Fisher, S., Rashkin, A., & Unlenhuth, E. H., eds.). New York: Oxford University Press.

POTTER, W. Z., RUDORFER, M. V., & GOODWIN, F. K. (1987). Biological findings in bipolar disorders. In *American Psychiatric Association Annual Review (Vol 6).* Washington, DC: American Psychiatric Association Press.

POWELL, B. J., READ, M. R., PENICK, E. C., MILLER, N. S., & BINGHAM, S. F. (1987). Primary and secondary depression in alcoholic men: An important distinction. *Journal of Clinical Psychiatry, 48,* 98–101.

PRATT, C. T. (1990). Addiction treatment for health care professionals. *Addiction & Recovery, 10*(3), 17–19, 38–41.

PRICE, L. H., RICAURTE, G. A., KRYSTAL, J. H., & HENINGER, G. R. (1989). Neuroendocrine and mood responses to intravenous L-tryptophan in 3,4-methylenedioxymethamphetamine (MDMA) users. *Archives of General Psychiatry, 46,* 20–22.

PRICE, L. H., RICAURTE, G. A., KRYSTAL, J. H., & HENINGER, G. R. (1990). In reply. *Archives of General Psychiatry, 47,* 289.

PRISTACH, C. A., & SMITH, C. M. (1990). Medication compliance and substance abuse among schizophrenic patients. *Hospital and Community Psychiatry, 41,* 1345–1348.

Psychiatry Drug Alerts. (1989). Aspirin in the prevention of cardiovascular disease, *III*(8), 64.

Psychotherapy Today. (1991). Addiction treatment field becoming more competitive, *2*(7), 8.

PUIG-ANTICH, J., GOETS, D., DAVIES, M., KAPLAN, T., DAVIES, S., OSTROW, L., ASNIS, L., TOWMEY, J., IYENGAR, S., & RYAN, N. D. (1989). A controlled family history of prepubertal major depressive disorder. *Archives of General Psychiatry, 46,* 406–418.

PURSCH, J. A. (1987). Mental illness and addiction. *Alcoholism & Addiction, 7*(6), 42.

PUTNAM, F. W. (1989). *Diagnosis and treatment of multiple personality disorder.* New York: The Guilford Press.

RADETSKY, P. (1990). Closing in on an AIDS vaccine. *Discover, 11*(9), 71–77.

RADO, T. (1988). The client with a dual diagnosis—A personal perspective. *Alcohol Quarterly, 1*(1), 5–7.

RAINS, V. S. (1990). Alcoholism in the elderly—The hidden addiction. *Medical Aspects of Human Sexuality, 24*(10), 40–42, 43.

RAPOPORT, J. L. (1989). *The Boy Who Couldn't Stop Washing.* New York: E. P. Dutton.

RAPPORT, D. J., & COVINGTON, E. D. (1989). Motor phenomena in benzodiazepine withdrawal. *Hospital & Community Psychiatry, 40,* 1277–1280.

RAVEL, R. (1989). *Clinical Laboratory Medicine: Clinical Application of Laboratory Data* (5th ed.). Chicago: Yearbook Medical Publishers.

RAY, O. S., & KSIR, C. (1987). *Drugs, Society and Human Behavior* (4th ed.). St. Louis: C. V. Mosby.

REDFIELD, R. R., & BURK, D. S. (1988). HIV infection: The clinical picture. *Scientific American, 259*(4), 90–98.

REDMAN, G. L. (1990). Adolescents and anabolics. *American Fitness, 8*(3), 30–33.

REGIER, D. A., FARMER, M. E., RAE, D. S., LOCKE, B. Z., KIETH, S. J., JUDD, L. L., & GOODWIN, F. K. (1990). Comorbidity of mental disorders with alcohol and other drug abuse. *Journal of the American Medical Association, 264,* 2511–2518.

REISER, M. F. (1984). *Mind, Brain, Body.* New York: Basic Books.

REISS, B. S., & MELICK, M. E. (1984). *Pharmacological Aspects of Nursing Care.* Albany: Delmar.

RERUCHA, M. A. (1986). Alcohol dependence syndrome in women: Perspectives on disability and rehabilitation. *Journal of Rehabilitation, 52,* 67–70.

RESTAK, R. (1984). *The Brain.* New York: Bantam Books.

RESTAK, R. (1991). *The Brain Has a Mind of Its Own.* New York: Harmony Books.

REULER, J. B., GIRARD, D. E., & COONEY, T. G. (1985). Wernicke's encephalopathy. *New England Journal of Medicine, 316,* 1035–1039.

REVKIN, A. C. (1989). Crack in the cradle. *Discover, 10*(9), 63–69.

RHODES, J. E., & JASON, L. A. (1990). A social stress model of substance abuse. *Journal of Consulting and Clinical Psychology, 58,* 395–401.

RICHARDSON, M. A., CRAIG, T. J., & HOUGHLAND, G. (1985). Treatment patterns of young chronic schizophrenic patients in the era of deinstitutionalization. *Psychiatric Quarterly, 57*(2), 104–109.

RICKELS, L. K., GIESECKE, M. A., & GELLER, A. (1987). Differential effects of the anxiolytic drugs, diazepam and buspirone on memory function. *British Journal of Clinical Pharmacology, 23,* 207–211.

RICKELS, K., SCHWEIZER, E., & LUCKI, I. (1987). Benzodiazepine side effects. In *American Psychiatric Association Annual Review (Vol 6)* (Hales, R. E., & Frances, A. J., eds.). Washington, DC: American Psychiatric Association Press.

RICKELS, K., SCHWEIZER, E., CASE, W. G., GREENBLATT, D. J. (1990). Long-term therapeutic use of benzodiazepines: I. Effects of abrupt discontinuation. *Archives of General Psychiatry, 47,* 899–907.

RICKELS, K., SCHWEIZER, E., CSANALOSI, I., CASE, W. G., & CHUNG, H. (1988). Long-term treatment of anxiety and risk of withdrawal. *Archives of General Psychiatry, 45,* 444–450.

RIES, R. K., & ELLINGSON, T. (1990). A pilot assessment at one month of 17 dual diagnosis patients. *Hospital and Community Psychiatry, 41,* 1230–1233.

ROBERTS, M. (1986). MDMA: "Madness, not ecstacy." *Psychology Today, 20,* 14–16.

RODRIGUES, C. (1990). Drug market runs on a cycle of poverty and greed. *Minneapolis Star-Tribune, IX* (155), 21A.

ROFFMAN, R. A., & GEORGE, W. H. (1988). Cannabis abuse. In *Assessment of Addictive Behaviors* (Donovan, D. M., & Marlatt, G. A., eds.). New York: The Guilford Press.

ROGERS, C. R. (1961). *On Becoming a Person.* Boston: Houghton Mifflin.

ROGERS, P. D., HARRIS, J., & JARMUSKEWICZ, J. (1987). Alcohol and adolescence. *Pediatric Clinics of North America, 34*(2), 289–303.

ROHSENOW, D. J., & BACHOROWSKI, J. (1984). Effects of alcohol and expectancies on verbal aggression in men and women. *Journal of Abnormal Psychology, 93,* 418–432.

ROINE, R., GENTRY, T., HERNANDEZ-MUNDOZ, R., BARAONA, E., & LIEBER, C. S. (1990). Aspirin increases blood alcohol concentrations in humans after ingestion of alcohol. *Journal of the American Medical Association, 264,* 2406–2408.

ROME, H. P. (1984). Psychobotanica revisted. *Psychiatric Annuals,* 14, 711–712.

ROPER, W. L. (1991). Making smoking prevention a reality. *Journal of the American Medical Association, 266,* 3188–3189.

ROSE, K. J., (1988). *The Body in Time.* New York: J. Wiley.

ROSEN, M. I., & KOSTEN, T. R. (1991). Buprenorphine: Beyond methadone? *Hospital and Community Psychiatry, 42,* 347–349.

ROSENBAUM, J. F. (1990). Switching patients from alprazolam to clonazepam. *Hospital and Community Psychiatry, 41,* 1302.

ROSENBAUM, J. F., AND GELENBERG, A. J. (1991). Anxiety. In *The Practitioner's Guide to Psychoactive Drugs* (3rd ed.) (Gelenberg, A. J., Bassuk, E. L., & Schoonover, S. C., eds.). New York: Plenum.

ROSENBERG, N. (1989). Nervous systems effects of toluene and other organic solvents. *Western Journal of Medicine,* 150, 571–573.

ROSENTHAL, E. Bad fix. *Discover, 13*(2), 82–84.

ROSS, A. (1991). Poland's dark harvest. *In Health, 5*(4), 66–70.

ROTHENBERG, L. (1988). The ethics of intervention. *Alcoholism & Addiction, 9*(1), 22–24

ROUNSAVILLE, B. J., ANTON, S. F., CARROLL, K., BUDDE, D., PRUSOFF, B. A., & GAWIN, F. (1991). Psychiatric diagnosis of treatment-seeking cocaine abusers. *Archives of General Psychiatry, 48,* 43–51.

ROYKO, M. (1990). Drug war's over: Guess who won. *Playboy. 37*(1), 46.

RUBINSTEIN, L., CAMPBELL, F., & DALEY, D. (1990). Four perspectives on dual diagnosis: An overview of treatment issues. In *Managing the Dually Diagnosed Patient* (O'Connell, D. F., ed.). New York: The Haworth Press.

RUSTIN, T. (1988). Treating nicotine addiction. *Alcoholism & Addiction, 9*(2), 18–19.

SACKS, O. (1970). *The Man Who Mistook His Wife for a Hat.* New York: Harper & Row.

SAGAR, S. M. (1991). Toxic and metabolic disorders. In *Manual of Neurology* (Samuels, M. A., ed.). Boston: Little, Brown.

SAGAR, S. M., & McGUIRE, D. (1991). Infectious diseases. In *Manual of Neurology* (Samuels, M. A., ed.). Boston: Little, Brown.

SALLOWAY, S., SOUTHWICK, S., & SADOWSKY, M. (1990). Opiate withdrawal presenting as posttraumatic stress disorder. *Hospital & Community Psychiatry, 41,* 666–667.

SALZMAN, C. (1990). What are the uses and dangers of the controversial drug halcion? *Harvard Medical School Mental Health Letter, 6*(9), 8.

SANDERS, S. R. (1990). Under the influence. *Networker, 14*(1), 32–37.

SATEL, S. L., & EDELL, W. S. (1991). Cocaine-induced paranoia and psychosis proneness. *American Journal of Psychiatry, 148,* 1708–1711.

SATEL, S. L., PRICE, L. H., PALUMBO, J. M., McDOUGLE, C. J., KRYSTAL, J. H., GAWIN, F., CHARNEY, D. S., HENINGER, G. R., & KLEBER, H. D. (1991). Clinical phenomenology and neurobiology of cocaine abstinence: A prospective inpatient study. *American Journal of Psychiatry, 148,* 1712–1716.

SBRIGLIO, R., & MILLMAN, R. B. (1987). Emergency treatment of acute cocaine reactions. In *Cocaine: A Clinician's Handbook* (Washton, A. M., & Gold, M. S., eds.). New York: The Guilford Press.

SCARF, M. (1980). *Unfinished Business.* New York: Ballantine Books.

SCAROS, L. P., WESTRA, S., & BARONE, J. A. (1990). Illegal use of drugs: A current review. *U.S. Pharmacist, 15*(5), 17–39.

SCHAEFER, S., & EVANS, S. (1988). Women, sexuality and the process of recovery. In *Chemical Dependency and Intimacy Dysfunction* (Coleman, E., ed.). New York: The Haworth Press.

SCHAFER, J., & BROWN, S. A. (1991). Marijuana and cocaine effect expectancies and drug use patterns. *Journal of Consulting and Clinical Psychology, 59,* 558–565.

SCHEER, R. (1990). Drugs: Another wrong war. *Playboy, 37*(1), 51–52.

SCHENKER, S., & SPEEG, K. V. (1990). The risk of alcohol intake in men and women. *New England Journal of Medicine, 322,* 127–129.

SCHLEIFER, S. J., KELLER, S. E., FRANKLIN, J. E., LaFARGE, S., & MILLER, S. I. (1990). HIV seropositivity in inner-city alcoholics.

SCHMITZ, J., DeJONG, J., ROY, A., GARNETT, D., MOORE, V., LAMPARSKI, D., WAXMAN, R., & LINNOILA, M. (1991). Substance abuse among subjects seeking treatment for alcoholism. *Archives of General Psychiatry, 48,* 182–183.

SCHUCKIT, M. A. (1983). Alcoholic patients with secondary depression. *American Journal of Psychiatry, 140,* 711–714.

SCHUCKIT, M. A. (1986). Primary men alcoholics with histories of suicide attempts. *Journal of Studies on Alcohol, 47,* 78–81.

SCHUCKIT, M. A. (1987). Biological vulnerability to alcoholism. *Journal of Consulting and Clinical Psychology, 55,* 301–309.

SCHUCKIT, M. A. (1989). *Drug and Alcohol Abuse: A Clinical Guide to Diagnosis and Treatment* (3rd ed.). New York: Plenum.

SCHUCKIT, M. A., ZISOOK, S., & MORTOLA, J. (1985). Clinical implications of DSM-III diagnoses of alcohol abuse and alcohol dependence. *American Journal of Psychiatry, 142,* 1403–1408.

SCHWARTZ, R. H. (1987). Marijuana: An overview. *The Pediatric Clinics of North America, 34*(2), 305–317.

SCHWARTZ, R. H. (1988). Urine testing in the detection of drugs of abuse. *Archives of Internal Medicine, 148,* 2407–2412.

SCHWARTZ, R. H. (1989). When to suspect inhalant abuse. *Patient Care, 23*(10), 39–50.

SCHWEIZER, E., RICKELS, K., CASE, W. G., & GREENBLATT, D. J. Long term therapeutic use of benzodiazepines: II. Effects of gradual taper. *Archives of General Psychiatry, 47,* 908–916.

Science Digest. (1989). Nightcap dangers, *2*(5), 90.

SCOTT, M. J., & SCOTT, M. J., Jr. (1989). HIV infection associated with injections of anabolic steroids. *Journal of the American Medical Association, 262*, (2), 207–208.

SCOTT, N. (1987). Dealing with nicotine addiction. *Alcoholism & Addiction, 7*(6), 24.

SEGAL, R., & SISSON, B. V. (1985). Medical complications association with alcohol use and the assessment of risk of physical damage. In *Alcoholism and Substance Abuse: Strategies for Clinical Intervention* (Bratter, T. E., & Forrest, G. G., eds.). New York: The Free Press.

SELZER, M. (1971). The Michigan Alcoholism Screening Test: The quest for a new diagnostic instrument. *American Journal of Psychiatry, 127*, 1653–1658.

SEYMORE, R. A., & RAWLINS, M. D. (1982). The efficacy and pharmokinetics of aspirin in post-operative dental pain. *British Journal of Clinical Pharmacology, 13*, 807–810.

SHAFER, J. (1985). Designer drugs. *Science '85, 12*(3), 60–67.

SHAPIRO, D. (1981). *Autonomy and Rigid Character.* New York: Basic Books.

SHARP, C. W., & BREHM, M. L. (1977). Review of inhalants: Euphoria to dysfunction. NIDA Research Monograph 15. Washington, DC: U.S. Government Printing Office.

SHEDLER, J., & BLOCK, J. (1990). Adolescent drug use and psychological health. *American Psychologist, 45*, 612–630.

SHENKMAN, R. (1991). *I Love Paul Revere, Whether He Rode or Not.* New York: Harper Collins.

SHEPHERD, C. (1990). News of the weird. *Minneapolis Star-Tribune, VIII*, 327, 2Ex.

SHER, K. J., WALITZER, K. S., WOOD, P. K., & BRENT, E. E. (1991). Characteristics of children of alcoholics: Putative risk factors, substance use and abuse, and psychopathology. *Journal of Abnormal Psychology, 100*, 427–448.

SHERIDAN, E., PATTERSON, H. R., & GUSTAFSON, E. A. (1982). *Falconer's The Drug, the Nurse, the Patient* (7th ed.). Philadelphia, PA: W. B. Saunders.

SHIFFMAN, L. B., FISCHER, L. B., ZETTLER-SEGAL, M., & BENOWITZ, N. L. (1990). Nicotine exposure among nondependent smokers. *Archives of General Psychiatry, 47*, 333–340.

SHIFFMAN, S. (1992). Relapse process and relapse prevention in addictive behaviors. *The Behavior Therapist, 15*(1), 99–11.

SIEGEL, B. S. (1986). *Love, Medicine & Miracles.* New York: Harper & Row.

SIEGEL, B. S. (1989). *Peace, Love & Healing.* New York: Harper & Row.

SIEGEL, L. (1989). Want to take the risks? It should be your choice. *Playboy, 36*,(1), 59.

SIEGEL, R. L. (1986). Jungle revelers: When beasts take drugs to race or relax, things get zooey. *Omni, 8*(6), 70–74, 100.

SIEGEL, R. K. (1982). Cocaine smoking disorders: Diagnosis and treatment. *Psychiatric Annuals, 14*, 728–732.

SIEGEL, R. K. (1991). Crystal meth or speed or crank. *Lear's, 3*(1), 72–73.

SIERLES, F. S. (1984). Correlates of malingering. *Behavioral Sciences and the Law, 2*(1), 113–118.

SILVERMAN, M. M. (1989). Children of psychiatrically ill parents: A prevention perspective. *Hospital & Community Psychiatry, 40*, 1257–1265.

SILVERS, J. (1990). Wounded country. *Playboy, 37*(8), 76–77, 80, 147–150.

SIMMONS, A. L. (1991). A peculiar dialect in the land of 10,000 treatment centers. *Minneapolis Star-Tribune, X*(24), 23A.

SIMPSON, D. D., CRANDALL, R. L., SAVAGE, J., & PAVA-KRUEGER, E. (1981). Leisure of opiate addicts at posttreatment follow-up. *Journal of Counseling Psychology, 28,* 36–39.

SKYELBRED, P. (1984). The effects of acetylsalicyclic acid on swelling, pain, and other events after surgery. *British Journal of Clinical Pharmacology, 17,* 379–384.

SLABY, A. E., LIEB, J., & TANCREDI, L. R. (1981). *Handbook of Psychiatric Emergencies* (2nd ed.). Garden City, NY: Medical Examination Publishing Co.

SLIM, J. (1990). AIDS News. *Medical Aspects of Human Sexuality, 29*(9), 69–71.

SMITH, B. D., & SALZMAN, C. (1991). Do benzodiazepines cause depression? *Hospital and Community Psychiatry, 42,* 1101–1102.

SMITH, R. (1990). Psychopathology and substance abuse: A psychoanalytic perspective. In *Managing the Dually Diagnosed Patient* (O'Connell, D.F., ed.). New York: The Haworth Press.

Smithsonian. (1989). Letters to the editor, *20* (6), 18.

SNYDER, S. H. (1977). Opiate receptors and internal opiates. *Scientific American, 260,* (3), 44–56.

SNYDER, S. H. (1986). *Drugs and the Brain.* New York: Scientific American Books.

SPARADEO, F. R., & GILL, D. (1989). Effects of prior alcohol use on head injury recovery. *Journal of Head Trauma Rehabilitation, 4* (1), 75–82.

SPRINGBORN, W. (1987). Step one: The foundation of recovery. In *The Twelve Steps of Alcoholics Anonymous.* New York: Harper & Row.

SQUIRES, S. (1989). Studies slight women's medical problems. *Minneapolis Star-Tribute, VIII* (257), 6Ex.

SQUIRES, S. (1990). Popular painkiller ibuprofen is linked to kidney damage. *Minneapolis Star-Tribune, VIII* (315), 1E, 4E.

STEENLAND, K. (1992). Passive smoking and the risk of heart disease. *Journal of the American Medical Association, 267,* 94–99.

STEVENS, V. J., & HOLLIS, J. F. (1989). Preventing smoking relapse, using an individually tailored skills-training technique. *Journal of Consulting and Clinical Psychology, 57,* 420–424.

STOCKWELL, T., & TOWN, C. (1989). Anxiety and stress management. In *Handbook of Alcoholism Treatment Approaches* (Hester, H. K., & Miller, W. R., eds.). New York: Pergamon Press.

STOFFELMAYR, B. E., BENISHEK, L. A., HUMPHREYS, K., LEE, J. A., & MAVIS, B. E. (1989). Substance abuse prognosis with an additional psychiatric diagnosis: Understanding the relationship. *Journal of Psychoactive drugs, 21*(2), 145–152.

STONE, J. (1991). Light elements. *Discover, 12*(1), 12–16.

STREISSGUTH, A. P., AASE, J. M., CLARREN, S. K., RANDELS, S. P., LA DUE, R. A., & SMITH, D. F. (1991). Fetal alcohol syndrome in adolescents and adults. *Journal of the American Medical Association, 265,* 1961–1967.

STUART, R. B. (1980). *Helping Couples Change.* New York: The Guilford Press.

SUPERNAW, R. B. (1991). Phazrmacotherapeutic management of acute pain. *U.S. Pharmacist, 16*(2), H1–H14.

SUSSMAN, N. (1988). Diagnosis and drug treatment of anxiety in the elderly. *Geriatric Medicine Today, 7*(10), 1–8.

SVANUM, S., & McADOO, W. G. (1989). Predicting rapid relapse following treatment for chemical dependence: A matched-subjects design. *Journal of Consulting and Clinical Psychology, 34,* 1027–1030.

SWAIM, R. C., OETTING, R. W., EDWARDS, R. W., & BEAUVAIS, F. (1989).

Links from emotional distress to adolescent drug use: A path model. *Journal of Consulting and Clinical Psychology*, 57,227–231.

SWANSON, L., & BIAGGIO, M. K. (1985). Therapeutic perspectives on father-daughter incest. *American Journal of Psychiatry*, 142, 667–674.

SWINSON, R. P. (1980). Sex differences in the inheritance of alcoholism. In *Alcohol and Drug Problems in Women* (Kalant, O. J., ed.). New York: Plenum.

SZASZ, T. S. (1972). Bad habits are not diseases: A refutation of the claim that alcoholism is a disease. *Lancet, 2*, 83–84.

SZASZ, T. S. (1988). A plea for the cessation of the longest war of the twentieth century—the war on drugs. *The Humanistic Psychologist*, 16(2), 314–322.

SZASZ, T. S. (1991). Diagnoses are not diseases. *Lancet, 338*, 1574–1576.

SZUSTER, R. R., SCHANBACHER, B. L., & McCANN, S. C. (1990). Characteristics of psychiatric emergency room patients with alcohol- or drug-induced disorders. *Hospital and Community Psychiatry, 41*, 1342–1345.

TARTER, R. E. (1988). Are there inherited behavioral traits that predispose to substance abuse? *Journal of Consulting and Clinical Psychology*, 56, 189–197.

TARTER, R. E., OTT, P. J., & MEZZICH, A. C. (1991). Psychometric assessment. In *Clinical Textbook of Addictive Disorders* (Frances, R. J., & Miller, S. I., eds.). New York: The Guilford Press.

TATE, C. (1989). In the 1800's, antismoking was a burning issue. *Smithsonian, 20*(4), 107–117.

TAVRIS, C. (1990). One more guilt trip for women. *Minneapolis Star-Tribune, VIII*, (341), 21A.

TAYLOR, W. A., & GOLD, M. S. (1990). Pharmacologic approaches to the treatment of cocaine dependence. *Western Journal of Medicine*, 152, 573–578.

TEST, M. A., KNOEDLER, W. H., ALLNESS, D. J., & BURKE, S. S. (1985). Characteristics of young adults with schizophrenic disorders treated in the community. *Hospital and Community Psychiatry*, 36(8), 853–858.

TEST, M. A., WALLISCH, L. S., ALLNESS, D. J., & RIPP, K. (1990). Substance use in young adults with schizophrenic disorders. *Schizophrenia Bulletin, 15*, 465–476.

THACKER, W., & TREMAINE, L. (1989). Systems issues in serving the mentally ill substance abuser: Virginia's experience. *Hospital and Community Psychiatry, 40*, 1046–1049.

THOMASON, H. H., & DILTS, S. L. (1991). Opioids. In *Clinical Textbook of Addictive Disorders* (Frances, R. J., & Miller, S. I., eds.). New York: The Guilford Press.

THOMPSON, D. (1990). A losing battle with AIDS. *Time, 136*(1), 42–43.

THORNTON, J. (1990). Pharm aid: 10 new medicines you should know about. *Men's Health, 5*(4), 73–78.

THUN, M. J., NAMBOODIRI, M. M., & HEATH, C. W. (1991). Aspirin use and reduced risk of fatal colon cancer. *New England Journal of Medicine, 325*, 1593–1596.

TRACHTENBERG, M. C., & BLUM, K. (1987). Alcohol and opioid peptides: Neuropharmacological rationale for physical craving of alcohol. *American Journal of Drug and Alcohol Abuse, 13*(3), 365–372.

TRACHTENBERG, M. C., & BLUM, K. (1988). Improvement of cocaine-induced neuromodulator deficits by the neuronutrient Tropamine. *Journal of Psychoactive Drugs, 20*(3), 315–331.

TREADWAY, D. (1987). The ties that bind. *Family Therapy Networker, 11*(4), 17–23.

TREADWAY, D. (1990). Codependency: Disease, metaphor, or fad? *Family Therapy Networker, 14*(1), 39–43.

Triangle of Self-Obsession, The. New York: Narcotics Anonymous World Service Office.

TUCKER, J. A., & SOBELL, L. C. (1992). Influences on help-seeking for drinking problems and on natural recovery without treatment. *The Behavior Therapist,* 15(1), 12–14.

TURBO, R. (1989). Drying out is just a start: Alcoholism. *Medical World News, 30*(3), 56–63.

Twelve Steps and Twelve Traditions. (1981). New York: Alcoholics Anonymous World Services, Inc.

TWERSKI, A. J., (1983). Early intervention in alcoholism: Confrontational techniques. *Hospital & Community Psychiatry, 34,* 1027–1030.

TWERSKI, A. J. (1989). Diagnosing and treating dual disorders. *Alcoholism & Addiction. 9*(3), 37–40.

Understanding Anonymity. (1981). New York: Alcoholics Anonymous World Services, Inc.

UNITED STATES PHARMACOPEIAL CONVENTION, INC. (1990a). *Drug Information for the Health Care Professional* (10th ed.). Rockville, MD: USPC Board of Trustees.

UNITED STATES PHARMACOPEIAL CONVENTION, INC. (1990b). *Advice for the Patient* (10th ed.). Rockville, MD: USPC Board of Trustees.

UNIVERSITY OF CALIFORNIA, BERKELEY. *The Wellness Letter.* (1990a). Codependency. 7(1), 7.

UNIVERSITY OF CALIFORNIA, BERKELEY. *The Wellness Letter.* (1990b). Marijuana: What we know. 6(6), 2–4.

UNIVERSITY OF CALIFORNIA, BERKELEY. *The Wellness Letter.* (1990c). Women's magazines: Whose side are they on? 7(3), 7.

UNIVERSITY OF CALIFORNIA, BERKELEY. *The Wellness Letter.* (1990d). Is there an addictive personality? 6(9), 1–2.

UNIVERSITY OF CALIFORNIA, BERKELEY. *The Wellness Letter.* (1991). The changing face of AIDS. 7(8), 6.

UPJOHN COMPANY. (1989). Anxiety center. *Science Digest, 2*(1), 69–70.

U.S. News & World Report. (1991). The men who created crack. *111* (8), 44–53.

VAILLANT, G. E. (1983). *The Natural History of Alcoholism.* Cambridge, MA: Harvard University Press.

VAILLANT, G. E. (1990). We should retain the disease concept of alcoholism. *Harvard Medical School Mental Health Letter, 9*(6), 4–6.

VALDISERRI, E. V., HARTL, A., & CHAMBLISS, C. A. (1988). Practices reported by incarcerated drug abusers to reduce the risk of AIDS. *Hospital & Community Psychiatry, 39*(9), 966–972.

VANDEPUTTE, C. (1989). Why bother to treat older adults? The answer is compelling. *Professional Counselor, 4*(2), 34–38.

VEREBEY, K., & TURNER, C. E. (1991). Laboratory testing. In *Clinical Textbook of Addictive Disorders* (Frances, R. J., & Miller, S. I., eds.). New York: The Guilford Press.

WADE, R. (1988). Prescription drugs entwined with alcoholism. *Alcoholism & Addiction, 8*(3), 52.

WALKER, C. E., BONNER, B. L., and KAUFMAN, K. I. (1988). *The Physically and Sexually Abused Child.* New York: Pergamon Press.

WALLEN, M. C., & WEINER, H. D. (1989). Impediments to effective treatment of the dually diagnosed patient. *Journal of Psychoactive Drugs, 21,* 161–168.

WALSH, D. C., HINGSON, R. W., MERRIGAN, D. M., LEVENSON, S. M., CUPPLES, L. A., HEEREN, T., COFFMAN, G. A., BECKER, C. A., BARKER, T. A., HAMILTON, S. A., McGUIRE, T. G., & KELLY, C. A. (1991). A randomized trial of treatment options for alcohol-abusing workers. *New England Journal of Medicine, 325,* 775–782.

WARD, G. C., BURNS, R., & BURNS, K. (1990). *The Civil War.* New York: Knopf.

Washington Post. (1991). Britain bans widely prescribed sleeping pill. *St. Paul Pioneer Press, 143*(159), 5A.

WASHTON, A. M. (1989). Cocaine abuse and compulsive sexuality. *Medical Aspects of Human Sexuality, 23*(12), 32–39.

WASHTON, A. M. (1990). Crack and other substance abuse in the suburbs. *Medical Aspects of Human Sexuality, 24,*(5) 54–58.

WASHTON, A. M., STONE, N. S., & HENDRICKSON, E. C. (1988). Cocaine abuse. In *Assessment of Addictive Behaviors* (Donovan, D. M., & Marlatt, G. A., eds.). New York: The Guilford Press.

WATSON, J. M. (1984). Solvent abuse and adolescents. *The Practitioner, 228,* 487–490.

WAXMAN, H. (1991). Tobacco marketing. *Journal of the American Medical Association, 266,* 3186–3186.

WEBB, S. T. (1989). Some developmental issues of adolescent children of alcoholics. *Adolescent Counselor, 1*(6), 47–48, 67.

WEGSCHEIDER-CRUSE, S. (1985). *Choice-making.* Pompano Beach, FL: Health Communications, Inc.

WEGSCHEIDER-CRUSE, S., & CRUSE, J. R. (1990). *Understanding Co-dependency.* Pompano Beach, FL: Health Communications, Inc.

WEIL, A. (1986). *The Natural Mind.* Boston: Houghton Mifflin.

WEINER, N. (1985). Norepinephrine, epinephrine, and the sympathomimetic amines. In *The Pharmacological Basis of Therapeutics* (7th ed.) (Gilman, A. G., Goodman, L. S., Rall, T. W., & Murad, F., eds.). New York: Macmillan.

WEISS, R. D., & MIRIN, S. M. (1988). Intoxication and withdrawal syndromes. In *Handbook of Psychiatric Emergencies* (2nd ed.) (Hyman, S. E., ed.). Boston: Little, Brown.

WEISS, R. D., MIRIN, S. M., & FRANCES, R. J. (1992). The myth of the typical dual diagnosis patient. *Hospital and Community Psychiatry 43,* 107–108.

WEISS, R. D., MIRIN, S. M., GRIFFIN, M. L., & MICHAEL, J. L. (1988). Psychopathology in cocaine users: Changing trends. *Journal of Nervous and Mental Disease, 176,* 719–725.

WERNER, E. E. (1989). Children of the garden island. *Scientific American, 260*(4), 106–111.

WESTERMEYER, J. (1987). The psychiatrist and solvent-inhalent abuse: Recognition, assessment and treatment. *American Journal of Psychiatry, 144,* 903–907.

WETLI, C. V. (1987). Fatal reactions to cocaine. In *Cocaine: A Clinician's Handbook* (Washton, A. M., & Gold, M. S., eds.). New York: The Guilford Press.

WHEELER, K., & MALMQUIST, J. (1987). Treatment approaches in adolescent chemical dependency. *Pediatric Clinics of North America, 34,*(2), 437–447.

WHITE, P. T. (1989). Coca. *National Geographic, 175*(1), 3–47.

WHITMAN, D., FRIEDMAN, D., & THOMAS, L. The return of skid row. (1990). *U.S. News & World Report. 108,*(2), 27–30.

WILBUR, R. (1986). A drug to fight cocaine. *Science '86, 7*(2), 42–46.

WILFORD, J. N. (1991). 3500 B.C.: They have served no wine before this time. *Minneapolis Star-Tribune, X*(26), 7A.

WILLENBRING, M. L. (1986). Measurement of depression in alcoholics. *Journal of Studies on Alcohol, 47,* 367–372.

WILLIAMS, E. (1989). Strategies for intervention. *Nursing Clinics of North America, 24*(1), 95–107.

WILLIAMSON, D. F., MADANS, J., ANDA, R., KLEINMAN, J. C., GIOVINO, G. A., & BYERS, T. (1991). Smoking cessation and severity of weight gain in a national cohort. *New England Journal of Medicine, 324,* 739–745.

WILLOUGHBY, A. (1984). *The Alcohol Troubled Person: Known and Unknown.* Chicago: Nelson-Hall.

WILSNACK, S. C. (1991). Barriers to treatment for alcoholic women. *Addiction & Recovery, 11*(4), 10–12.

WOITITZ, J. G. (1983). *Adult Children of Alcoholics.* Pompano Beach, FL: Health Communications, Inc.

WOLF-REEVE, B. S. (1990). A guide to the assessment of psychiatric symptoms in the addictions treatment setting. In *Managing the Dually Diagnosed Patient* (O'Connell, D. F., ed.). New York: The Haworth Press.

WOLKOWITZ, O. M. (1990). Long-lasting behavioral changes following prednisone withdrawal. *Journal of the American Medical Association, 261,* 1731.

WOLKOWITZ, O. M., RUBINOW, D., DORAN, A. R., BREIER, A., BERRETTINI, W. H., KLING, M. A., & PICKAR, D. (1990). Prednisone effects on neurochemistry and behavior: Preliminary findings. *Archives of General Psychiatry, 47,* 963–968.

WOODS, J. H., KATZ, J. L., & WINGER, G. (1988). Use and abuse of benzodiazepines. *Journal of the American Medical Association, 260*(23), 3476–3480.

WOODS, J. H., WINGER, G. D., & FRANCE, C. P. (1987). Reinforcing and discriminative stimulus effects of cocaine: Analysis of pharmacological mechanisms. In *Cocaine: Clinical and Behavioral Aspects* (Fisher, S., Raskin, A., & Unlenhuth, E. H., eds.). New York: Oxford University Press.

WRAY, S. R., & MURTHY, N. V. A. (1987). Review of the effects of cannabis on mental and physiological functions. *West Indian Medical Journal, 36*(4), 197–201.

YABLONSKY, L. (1967). *Synanon: The Tunnel Back.* Baltimore: Penguin Books.

YALOM, I. D. (1985). *The Theory and Practice of Group Psychotherapy* (3rd ed.). New York: Basic Books.

YAZIGI, R. A., ODEM, R. R., & POLAKOSKI, K. L. (1991). Demonstration of specific binding of cocaine to human spermatozoa. *Journal of the American Medical Association, 266,* 1956–1959.

YOUCHA, G. A. (1978). *A Dangerous Pleasure.* New York: Hawthorn Books.

YOUNGSTROM, N. (1990a). The drugs used to treat drug abuse. *APA Monitor, 21*(10), 19.

YOUNGSTROM, N. (1990b). Debate rages on: In- or outpatient? *APA Monitor, 21*(10), 19.

YOUNGSTROM, N. (1991). Field, APA address drug abuse in society. *APA Monitor, 22,*(1), 14.

ZAREK, D., HAWKINS, D., & ROGERS, P. D. (1987). Risk factors for adolescent substance abuse. *Pediatric Clinics of North America, 34*(2), 481–493.

ZERWEKH, J., & MICHAELS, B. (1989). Co-dependency. *Nursing Clinics of North America, 24*(1), 109–120.

ZIMBERG, S. (1978). Psychosocial treatment of elderly alcoholics. In *Practical Approaches to Alcoholism Psychotherapy* (Zimberg, S., Wallace, J., & Blume, S. B., eds.). New York: Plenum.

ZUCKER, D. K., & BRANCHEY, L. (1985). Variables associated with alcoholic blackouts in men. *American Journal of Drug and Alcohol Abuse, 11* (3 & 4), 295–302.

ZUCKER, R. A., & GOMBERG, E. S. L. (1986). Etiology of alcoholism reconsidered: The case for a biopsychosocial process. *American Psychologist, 41*, 783–793.

ZUCKERMAN, B., & BRESNAHAN, K. (1991). Developmental and behavioral consequences of prenatal drug and alcohol exposure. *Pediatric Clinics of North America, 38*, 1387–1406.

INDEX

TO THE OWNER OF THIS BOOK:

I'd like to learn your reactions to using this textbook. Only through your comments and advice and the comments and advice of others can I hope to improve the next edition of *Concepts of Chemical Dependency*, 2nd edition.

School: _____

Your instructor's name: _____

_____

1. What did you like most about *Concepts of Chemical Dependency*? _____

_____

_____

2. What did you like least about the book? _____

_____

_____

3. Were all the chapters of the book assigned for you to read? _____

(If not, which ones weren't?) _____

4. In the space below or in a separate letter, please let me know what other comments about the book you'd like to make. (For example, were any chapters or concepts particularly difficult?) I'd be delighted to hear from you!

_____

_____

_____

_____

_____

_____

_____

_____

_____

Optional:

Your name: _____ Date: _____

May Brooks/Cole quote you, either in promotion for *Concepts of Chemical Dependency*, 2nd edition or in future publishing ventures?

Yes: _____ No: _____

Sincerely,

Harold Doweiko

- -

FOLD HERE

‖‖‖‖

NO POSTAGE
NECESSARY
IF MAILED
IN THE
UNITED STATES

BUSINESS REPLY MAIL
FIRST CLASS   PERMIT NO. 358   PACIFIC GROVE, CA

POSTAGE WILL BE PAID BY ADDRESSEE

ATT: *Dr. Harold Doweiko* _____

Brooks/Cole Publishing Company
511 Forest Lodge Road
Pacific Grove, California 93950-9968

|₁||₁₁₁₁||₁|₁|₁₁₁₁|₁|₁||₁₁₁₁|₁|₁||₁₁₁₁|₁|₁₁₁₁||₁|₁||₁|₁||

- -

FOLD HERE